SOME MATHEMATICAL
METHODS OF PHYSICS

SOME MATHEMATICAL METHODS OF PHYSICS

GERALD GOERTZEL

Technical Director
Nuclear Development Corporation of America
Formerly Associate Professor of Physics
New York University

NUNZIO TRALLI

Head, Theoretical Physics Section
Nuclear Development Corporation of America
Formerly Associate Professor of Physics
St John's University

McGRAW-HILL BOOK COMPANY, INC.

New York   Toronto   London   1960

SOME MATHEMATICAL METHODS OF PHYSICS

23647

Preface

A common set of mathematical techniques is useful as background for a variety of fields of theoretical and applied physics, such as quantum mechanics, acoustics, electromagnetic theory, and reactor physics. In an attempt to develop this background in one coherent manner, rather than have it appear in bits and pieces in various courses, one of us introduced and taught a graduate course, entitled Mathematical Methods of Theoretical Physics, at New York University. The prerequisites for the course included differential equations and a first course in theoretical physics. This book is an outgrowth of material developed in several years of teaching the course.

The book is not intended to cover the entire field of mathematical methods of physics but rather to give a well-rounded and thorough indication of the basic concepts involved in the study of linear systems, with emphasis on eigenvalues, eigenfunctions, and Green's functions. In Part One of the book, systems with a finite number of degrees of freedom (described by matrices) are considered and studied. In Part Two the concepts developed for discrete systems in Part One are extended to continuous systems. In addition, new concepts which are useful in the treatment of continuous systems are introduced. In Part Three, the reader is introduced to approximation methods (perturbation theory, variational methods, and numerical methods) needed in treating most of the problems of nature which confront the applied physicist. Certain background and supplementary material of use to the reader is included as appendix material. This was material omitted from the main text to provide a smoother flow of ideas and concepts.

The authors are indebted to Mrs. Purdy E. Brown for her assistance in preparing the manuscript. They are also indebted to many of their colleagues for encouragement and suggestions, in particular to Dr. Joan Brooks and Dr. Herbert Wilf.

The authors welcome any corrections or suggestions for improvement.

Gerald Goertzel
Nunzio Tralli

Contents

PART TWO.   SYSTEMS WITH AN INFINITE NUMBER OF DEGREES OF FREEDOM

PART THREE.   APPROXIMATE METHODS

References

Various useful sources of further information on the subject matter of the chapters of this book are listed following each chapter. In addition, we would like to call the attention of the reader to several general references which cover the field of mathematical methods of physics more completely than this book and serve to form the basis of a useful reference library. These are listed below in order of their difficulty.

Kármán, T. V., and M. A. Biot: "Mathematical Methods in Engineering," McGraw-Hill Book Company, Inc., New York, 1940.

Margenau, H., and G. M. Murphy: "The Mathematics of Physics and Chemistry," D. Van Nostrand Company, Inc., New York, 1943.

Courant, R., and D. Hilbert: "Methoden der Mathematischen Physik," Springer-Verlag OHG, Berlin, 1937.

Courant, R., and D. Hilbert: "Methods of Mathematical Physics," vol. 1, Interscience Publishers Inc., New York, 1953.

Morse, P. M., and H. Feshbach: "Methods of Theoretical Physics," McGraw-Hill Book Company, Inc., New York, 1953.

Jeffreys, H., and B. S. Jeffreys: "Mathematical Physics," Cambridge University Press, New York, 1946.

Whittaker, E. T., and G. N. Watson: "Modern Analysis," The Macmillan Company, New York, 1944.

Part One

SYSTEMS WITH A FINITE NUMBER OF DEGREES OF FREEDOM

CHAPTER 1

Formulation of the Problem and Development of Notation

1.1 Introduction

The equations of motion describing physical systems which are linear, have a finite number of degrees of freedom, and have properties independent of time are relatively simple in nature. (See also the last paragraph of Sec. 1.2.) These equations are linear differential equations with constant coefficients. There are a finite number of dependent variables (the coordinates of the physical system) and one independent variable (the time). Part One is concerned solely with the solution of such systems of equations for prescribed initial conditions.

Several physical problems and the equations of motion to which they lead will be considered in the remainder of this section. The simplest of these is that posed by the discharge of a capacitance C through a resistance R in the circuit of Fig. 1.1. It is supposed that prior to the closing of the key the capacitance has a voltage $E(0)$ across it. If the key is closed at the time $t = 0$, what is the voltage across the capacitance $E(t)$ at any time t after the key is closed? After the key is closed,[1] the equation of motion is

$$\dot{E} = \frac{-E}{RC} \tag{1.1}$$

The second example is that posed by the problem of determining the numbers of various radioactive species present in a decay chain, as a function of time, given the numbers present at the initial time $t = 0$. Thus, if species 1 with mean life T_1 decays into species 2, and species 2 has

---

[1] The notation $\dot{x} = dx/dt$ and $\ddot{x} = d^2x/dt^2$ will be used.

a mean life T_2 for decay into the stable species 3, the equations for the number of atoms of the various species present at any time are

$$\dot{N}_1 = \frac{-N_1}{T_1}$$

$$\dot{N}_2 = \frac{-N_2}{T_2} + \frac{N_1}{T_1} \tag{1.2}$$

$$\dot{N}_3 = \frac{N_2}{T_2}$$

As a third example, consider a mass on a spring. If m denotes the magnitude of the mass, k the spring constant of the spring, and x the displacement of the mass from its equilibrium position, the equation of motion of the system may be written as

$$m\ddot{x} + kx = 0 \tag{1.3}$$

A system which satisfies Eq. (1.3) is called a *harmonic oscillator*.

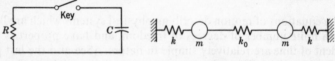

Figure 1.1   **Figure 1.2**

A somewhat more complicated system is that of two harmonic oscillators coupled to each other, diagramed in Fig. 1.2. The equations of motion are

$$m\ddot{x}_1 + kx_1 = k_0(x_2 - x_1)$$
$$m\ddot{x}_2 + kx_2 = k_0(x_1 - x_2) \tag{1.4}$$

While examples of this nature may be given indefinitely, those already presented will suffice to give a picture of the situation. It is of interest to note that some of the above examples contain only first derivatives with respect to the time, whereas others contain second derivatives. This does not constitute a fundamental distinction. Thus (1.3) may be replaced by the pair of equations below which contain only first time derivatives:

$$m\dot{x} = y$$
$$\dot{y} = -kx \tag{1.5}$$

Similarly, second time derivatives may be eliminated from Eqs. (1.4) by the introduction of the two new dependent variables x_3 and x_4.

$$m\dot{x}_1 = x_3$$
$$m\dot{x}_2 = x_4$$
$$\dot{x}_3 = k_0(x_2 - x_1) - kx_1$$
$$\dot{x}_4 = k_0(x_1 - x_2) - kx_2 \tag{1.6}$$

A more fundamental change in the form of the equations to be considered arises from the introduction of external forces. For example, one is often concerned with the problem of the motion of a mass on a spring, as induced by an external force $F(t)$ applied to the mass. In this case (1.5) becomes

$$\begin{aligned} m\dot{x} &= y \\ \dot{y} &= -kx + F(t) \end{aligned} \tag{1.7}$$

Similarly, if in the system sketched in Fig. 1.2 a force $F_1(t)$ is applied to mass 1 and a force $F_2(t)$ is applied to mass 2, the equations of motion become, in place of (1.4),

$$\begin{aligned} m\ddot{x}_1 + kx_1 &= k_0(x_2 - x_1) + F_1(t) \\ m\ddot{x}_2 + kx_2 &= k_0(x_1 - x_2) + F_2(t) \end{aligned} \tag{1.8}$$

If, in the problems indicated by (1.7) and (1.8), the forces F, F_1, and F_2 are independent of time, a simpler problem than that of solving the equations of motion suggests itself: What solutions exist in which the dependent variables do not change with time? To find this steady-state solution of (1.7) one sets $\dot{x} = \dot{y} = 0$ and thus has to solve

$$\begin{aligned} 0 &= y \\ kx &= F \end{aligned} \tag{1.9}$$

To find the steady-state solution of (1.8) one need merely solve

$$\begin{aligned} kx_1 &= k_0(x_2 - x_1) + F_1 \\ kx_2 &= k_0(x_1 - x_2) + F_2 \end{aligned} \tag{1.10}$$

1.2 Standardization of Notation

In order to focus attention on the form of the problems discussed in Sec. 1.1, it is desirable to introduce a uniform notation. A first step in this direction is carried out below. The problems discussed above may be divided into three categories: the time-dependent homogeneous problems of (1.1) to (1.6), the time-dependent inhomogeneous problems of (1.7) and (1.8), and the time-independent inhomogeneous (steady-state) problems of (1.9) and (1.10). For each of these categories, the corresponding equations have a definite form.

For the linear time-dependent homogeneous problems, the equations of motion may always be written in the form

$$\begin{aligned} \dot{x}_1 &= m_{11}x_1 + m_{12}x_2 + \cdots + m_{1,n-1}x_{n-1} + m_{1n}x_n \\ \dot{x}_2 &= m_{21}x_1 + m_{22}x_2 + \cdots + m_{2,n-1}x_{n-1} + m_{2n}x_n \\ & \cdots \cdots \cdots \cdots \cdots \cdots \cdots \cdots \cdots \cdots \cdots \cdots \\ \dot{x}_n &= m_{n1}x_1 + m_{n2}x_2 + \cdots + m_{n,n-1}x_{n-1} + m_{nn}x_n \end{aligned} \tag{1.11}$$

These equations are to be solved for prescribed values of the dependent variables at zero time. Equations (1.1), (1.2), (1.5), and (1.6), when written in the form of (1.11), become

$$\dot{E} = -\frac{1}{RC} E \qquad (1.12)$$

$$\dot{N}_1 = \frac{-1}{T_1} N_1 + 0N_2 + 0N_3$$
$$\dot{N}_2 = \frac{1}{T_1} N_1 + \left(\frac{-1}{T_2}\right) N_2 + 0N_3 \qquad (1.13)$$
$$\dot{N}_3 = 0N_1 + \frac{1}{T_2} N_2 + 0N_3$$

$$\dot{x} = 0x + \frac{1}{m} y$$
$$\dot{y} = (-k)x + 0y \qquad (1.14)$$

$$\dot{x}_1 = 0x_1 + 0x_2 + \frac{1}{m} x_3 + 0x_4$$
$$\dot{x}_2 = 0x_1 + 0x_2 + 0x_3 + \frac{1}{m} x_4 \qquad (1.15)$$
$$\dot{x}_3 = [-(k + k_0)]x_1 + k_0 x_2 + 0x_3 + 0x_4$$
$$\dot{x}_4 = k_0 x_1 + [-(k + k_0)]x_2 + 0x_3 + 0x_4$$

The usefulness of the notation of (1.11), as further exemplified by (1.12) through (1.15), arises from its display of the form of the problem. The problem to be solved is characterized by its form, as given in (1.11), by the number of dependent variables n, and by the n^2 numbers m_{ij}, i, and j taking on the n values $1, 2, \ldots, n - 1, n$ independently. As can be seen from the examples, many of the numbers m_{ij} may vanish.

The second category, that of time-dependent inhomogeneous problems, has equations of the form given by (1.16) below. It will be noted that setting $F_i(t) = 0$ reduces these to (1.11).

$$\dot{x}_1 = m_{11}x_1 + m_{12}x_2 + \cdots + m_{1n}x_n + F_1(t)$$
$$\dot{x}_2 = m_{21}x_1 + m_{22}x_2 + \cdots + m_{2n}x_n + F_2(t) \qquad (1.16)$$
$$\cdot \quad \cdot \quad \cdot \quad \cdot \quad \cdot \quad \cdot \quad \cdot \quad \cdot \quad \cdot \quad \cdot \quad \cdot \quad \cdot \quad \cdot \quad \cdot$$
$$\dot{x}_n = m_{n1}x_1 + m_{n2}x_2 + \cdots + m_{nn}x_n + F_n(t)$$

It is clear that a problem in this category is specified by stating the n functions $F_i(t)$ in addition to the n^2 numbers m_{ij}.

The form of the equations for the steady-state problem is obtained from (1.16) by setting all the $\dot{x}_i$ equal to zero and writing F_i in place of $F_i(t)$. These problems are again specified by n^2 quantities m_{ij}, but require in addition the n numbers F_i.

In the first sentence of Sec. 1.1 appear the words "are linear, have a finite number of degrees of freedom, and have properties independent of time." The limitations implied by these words are readily interpreted with the aid of Eqs. (1.16). *Linear* implies that each term in (1.16) contains at most one dependent variable x_i and that variable as a multiplicative factor. Terms containing $x_i x_j$, x_i^3, $x_i x_j$, etc., are not found in equations describing linear systems. The number of *degrees of freedom* is the number of dependent variables n, so that a finite number of degrees of freedom implies finite n. The phrase *properties independent of time* states that the quantities m_{ij} are constants.

1.3 Matrices

In each of the three categories of problems considered in Sec. 1.2, the set of n^2 numbers m_{ij} played a central role. This set of numbers is given a name as an assemblage. The assemblage is said to form a *matrix m*. The quantities m_{ij} are called the *elements* of the matrix m.

For the purpose of display of the matrix m one writes

$$m = \begin{pmatrix} m_{11} & m_{12} & m_{13} & \cdots & m_{1n} \\ m_{21} & m_{22} & m_{23} & \cdots & m_{2n} \\ m_{31} & m_{32} & m_{33} & \cdots & m_{3n} \\ \cdot & \cdot & \cdot & \cdot & \cdot & \cdot \\ m_{n1} & m_{n2} & m_{n3} & \cdots & m_{nn} \end{pmatrix} \quad (1.17)$$

To find the element m_{ij} one looks at the intersection of the ith row with the jth column.

The matrix m is a square matrix, having as many rows as columns. One may also define rectangular matrices. Thus, if q_{ij} is defined for all pairs of values i and j such that $i = 1, 2, 3, \ldots, p$, and $j = 1, 2, \ldots, n$, then the set of pn numbers q_{ij} is said to form a rectangular $p \times n$ matrix. Such a matrix may be displayed, following (1.17), by an array with p rows and n columns.

The elements m_{ii} ($= m_{11}, m_{22}, \ldots, m_{nn}$) lying on the principal diagonal of the matrix m are the *diagonal elements* of m; the remaining elements are the *off-diagonal* elements of m. A matrix all of whose off-diagonal elements are zeros is called a *diagonal matrix*.

Any matrix m for which $m_{ij} = m_{ji}$, $i \neq j$, is called a *symmetric matrix*. If $m_{ij} = -m_{ji}$, $m_{ii} = 0$, the matrix is said to be *antisymmetric* or *skew-symmetric*.

The n numbers x_i may be considered to form an $n \times 1$ matrix[1] or n column, so that one may write

$$x = \begin{pmatrix} x_1 \\ x_2 \\ x_3 \\ \cdot \\ \cdot \\ \cdot \\ x_n \end{pmatrix} \qquad \dot{x} = \begin{pmatrix} \dot{x}_1 \\ \dot{x}_2 \\ \dot{x}_3 \\ \cdot \\ \cdot \\ \cdot \\ \dot{x}_n \end{pmatrix} \qquad (1.18)$$

Similarly, the n quantities $F_i(t)$ appearing in (1.16) will be represented by the n-column $F(t)$.

It is clear that for the purposes of display the representations given in (1.17) and (1.18) might well be useful. On the other hand, this is scarcely sufficient advantage to justify strong interest. In order to make full use of the potentialities of the new symbols, it is necessary to define rules for their manipulation. Such rules will be presented in some detail in Sec. 1.4. These rules are so set up that, in terms of the matrix notation, Eqs. (1.11) and (1.16) become respectively

$$\dot{x} = mx \qquad (1.19)$$

$$\dot{x} = mx + F(t) \qquad (1.20)$$

At first glance it may seem that this apparent simplicity merely hides the truth. However, it will be found that the solution of (1.19) which would hold if x and m were 1×1 matrices (scalars) also holds if x and m are matrices. That is, the solution to Eq. (1.19) may be written as

$$x(t) = e^{mt}x(0) \qquad (1.21)$$

The interpretation of this result is, in fact, the main subject matter of this book. A similar procedure will be used to solve (1.20).

It may be argued that (1.21) is, in conjunction with (1.19), no more than a definition of e^{mt}. If this viewpoint be adopted, the methods of interpretation and evaluation of e^{mt} to be presented below will be found consistent with its definition. Alternately, if the definition of e^{mt} be taken as that given in Sec. 2.1, $x(t)$ as given by (1.21) will be found to satisfy (1.19).

[1] The x_i could just as well have been taken to form a $1 \times n$ matrix or n-row. Indeed, some authors prefer the alternate choice. With this alternate choice and the matrix multiplication rule of Sec. 1.4, the form of the various equations is slightly different. Thus, Eq. (1.20) would be written as $\dot{x} = xm + F(t)$.

To illustrate the method of writing the equations of motion suggested by the matrix notation, Eqs. (1.6) are rewritten below:

$$
\begin{pmatrix} \dot{x}_1 \\ \dot{x}_2 \\ \dot{x}_3 \\ \dot{x}_4 \end{pmatrix} = \begin{pmatrix} 0 & 0 & 1/m & 0 \\ 0 & 0 & 0 & 1/m \\ -k-k_0 & k_0 & 0 & 0 \\ k_0 & -k-k_0 & 0 & 0 \end{pmatrix} \begin{pmatrix} x_1 \\ x_2 \\ x_3 \\ x_4 \end{pmatrix} \tag{1.22}
$$

1.4 Elementary Arithmetic Operations with Matrices

In this section the equality of two matrices, the sum of two matrices, the product of two matrices, and the multiplication of a matrix with a constant will be defined. These definitions have been developed over many years. The reader of this book will note that the definitions are such as to assure that (1.19) is identical in meaning with (1.11) and that (1.20) contains the same information as (1.16).

Before entering into the main subject of this section, it is desirable to introduce a notation which enables one to write the required relations in concise and clear form. The new concept is the summation symbol Σ.

Let f_i, $i = 1, 2, \ldots, n$, be a set of n numbers (that is, f_i represents a function of the discrete variable i). The summation symbol Σ is defined by the equation

$$
\sum_{i=1}^{n} f_i = f_1 + f_2 + \cdots + f_n \tag{1.23}
$$

The power of this notation may be indicated by utilizing it for writing the set of Eqs. (1.16) in the abbreviated form

$$
\dot{x}_i = \sum_{j=1}^{n} m_{ij} x_j + F_i(t) \qquad i = 1, 2, \ldots, n \tag{1.24}
$$

The full notation $\sum_{i=1}^{n}$, which indicates both the variable of summation and its range, will rarely be used. Thus, if the range of the variable of summation is clear from context, one may write $\sum_{i}$. If the summation variable is clear but not the range of summation, one may write $\sum_{1}^{n}$. In many instances the unadorned symbol Σ suffices.

Just as the name of the variable of integration does not affect the value of a definite integral, so the symbol used as a summation index does not alter the value of a sum

$$
\sum_{i} m_{ji} x_i = \sum_{k} m_{jk} x_k \tag{1.25}
$$

The use of the same index for two summations occurring as factors in the same term of an equation will lead to confusion. Thus, suppose it is desired to evaluate Σz_i^2, where

$$z_i = \sum_j m_{ij} x_j$$

The result is obtained by the following processes:

$$\begin{aligned}
\sum z_i^2 &= \sum z_i z_i \\
&= \sum_i \left(\sum_j m_{ij} x_j \right) \left(\sum_k m_{ik} x_k \right) \\
&= \sum_{i,j,k} m_{ij} m_{ik} x_j x_k
\end{aligned}$$

It is to be noted that z_i was written once with j as the summation index and once with k as the summation index in order to obtain the final result. If this had not been done, the nonsensical result

$$\sum_{i,j,j} m_{ij} m_{ij} x_j x_j$$

might have been obtained.

The results of various arithmetic operations with matrices will now be defined. First, the *equality* of two matrices will be discussed. Two matrices may be equated only if each has the same number of columns and the same number of rows as the other. In this case, the matrices are equal if each element of one equals the corresponding element of the other. Thus, if m and p are matrices and x and y are columns (or rows),

$$\begin{aligned}
m = p \quad &\text{implies} \quad m_{ij} = p_{ij} \quad &&\text{all } i \text{ and } j \\
x = y \quad &\text{implies} \quad x_i = y_i \quad &&\text{all } i
\end{aligned} \tag{1.26}$$

To *multiply a matrix by a scalar* (number), multiply each element of the matrix by the scalar. To *add matrices*, one must start with matrices with equal numbers of rows and of columns. The result is then a matrix with the same number of rows and of columns as the summands. Each element of the sum matrix is obtained by adding the corresponding elements of the summand matrices. Both of these definitions may be summarized by the following rules (a and b are scalars):

$$\begin{aligned}
(am + bp)_{ji} &= am_{ji} + bp_{ji} \quad &&\text{all } i \text{ and } j \\
(ax + by)_i &= ax_i + by_i \quad &&\text{all } i
\end{aligned} \tag{1.27}$$

An immediate consequence of (1.27) is that the *derivative* of a matrix with time-dependent elements is obtained by replacing each element of the matrix with its time derivative. Thus

$$\left(\frac{dm}{dt}\right)_{ij} = \frac{dm_{ij}}{dt}$$

$$\left(\frac{dx}{dt}\right)_i = \frac{dx_i}{dt}$$.

(1.28)

The *product of two matrices* is a somewhat complicated concept which will be discussed further in Sec. 1.5. The definition will be given here. The product of two matrices is defined only if the number of columns in the matrix on the left is equal to the number of rows in the matrix on the right. The product is then defined by

$$(mp)_{ij} = \sum_k m_{ik} p_{kj}$$

$$(mx)_i = \sum_j m_{ij} x_j$$

(1.29)

As the reader will readily verify, the definition given above implies that the matrix product is associative

$$(mp)q = m(pq) = mpq \tag{1.30}$$

whence the product of any number of matrices written in a fixed order has a unique meaning. A further consequence of (1.29), together with (1.27), is the validity of the distributive law

$$(m + p)q = mq + pq \tag{1.31}$$

The section will be closed with the definition of two special kinds of matrices, the *zero* (or *null*) *matrices* and the *unit* (or *identity*) *matrices*. Any matrix all of whose elements are zero is a zero matrix. Zero matrices have the expected properties

$$0 + m = m$$

$$0m = m0 = 0$$

(1.32)

In (1.32) the symbol 0 must indicate a zero matrix with the appropriate number of rows and of columns so that the operations are defined. In particular, in the second line of (1.32), if m is not square, the symbol 0 must be interpreted differently in each term of the equations.

There also exists an $n \times n$ unit matrix for every positive integral value of n. This matrix satisfies the relations

$$Im = mI = m \tag{1.33}$$

It should be noted here that unless m is square, two distinct matrices I are involved in (1.33). The unit matrix I has the following form—all of its elements along the main diagonal (the elements I_{kk}) are unity and all others are zero. That is

$$I_{ij} = \delta_{ij} \tag{1.34}$$

where the symbol δ_{ij} is the Kronecker delta symbol and is defined by the following relations

$$\begin{aligned} \delta_{ii} &= 1 \\ \delta_{ij} &= 0 \qquad \text{for } i \neq j \end{aligned} \tag{1.35}$$

The importance of the Kronecker delta arises from (1.34) and from the corresponding property

$$\sum_j \delta_{ij} f_j = f_i \tag{1.36}$$

1.5   The Row-Column Rule

The definition of the product of two matrices, as given by Eqs. (1.29), is also the rule for the calculation of the product. To understand this rule, one might consider the result it gives for the product of a $1 \times n$ matrix (row) z with an $n \times 1$ matrix (column) x. The result is a 1×1 matrix zx given by

$$zx = \sum_{i=1}^{n} z_i x_i \tag{1.37}$$

In words the prescription becomes: To multiply the row z into the column x, multiply the leftmost element of z by the topmost element of x; then multiply the second element from the left of z by the second element from the top of x; continue until the rightmost element of z has been multiplied with the bottommost element of x, making n products in all; then sum these n products. The resultant number is the product zx. An example is given below in (1.38).

Using the above description of the process of multiplication of a row into a column, it is not difficult to describe the method of obtaining the ij element of the matrix product mp, where m and p are any two matrices such that the number of columns of m equals the number of rows of p. In fact, the ij element of mp is obtained by multiplying the ith row of m into the jth column of p:

$$(mp)_{ij} = (m_{i1}, m_{i2}, \ldots, m_{in}) \begin{pmatrix} p_{1j} \\ p_{2j} \\ \cdot \\ \cdot \\ \cdot \\ p_{nj} \end{pmatrix}$$

$$= m_{i1}p_{1j} + m_{i2}p_{2j} + \cdots + m_{in}p_{nj} \tag{1.38}$$

A question suggested in the above paragraph is the following: How does one designate the ith row of m? A convenient notation is to write $m_{i\cdot}$. Similarly, the ith column of m is written $m_{\cdot i}$. The period (.) is used to indicate the position of the index not specified relative to the position of the specified index (i in this case). Using this notation, one has as the rule for forming the product of two matrices

$$(mp)_{ij} = m_{i\cdot}p_{\cdot j} \qquad (1.39)$$

1.6 Warnings

The use of the same notation for matrix sums, products, etc., as is used when dealing with scalars has been deliberate. With this familiar symbolism, it will seem more plausible to consider functions of matrices,[1] power series involving matrices, and similar relations than it would if special notations were used when handling matrices. Before reaping this benefit from the notation, it is best to consider some of the dangers and corresponding precautions to be used. In this section a few of the ways in which matrices differ in their arithmetic properties from numbers will be considered. These differences all arise from the definition of the product of two matrices.

The first difference to be considered is the noncommutativity of matrix multiplication. That is, there are matrices p and m such that

$$mp \neq pm$$

In fact, an example of such a pair of matrices is given by

$$m = \begin{pmatrix} 1 & 0 \\ 0 & -1 \end{pmatrix} \qquad p = \begin{pmatrix} 0 & 1 \\ 1 & 0 \end{pmatrix}$$

This statement is, of course, best verified by calculating mp and pm and comparing.

The second difference between operations with matrices and with scalars is somewhat more profound and has many forms. Thus, in dealing with ordinary (real or complex) numbers, the following is true of all numbers except zero: the product of two nonzero numbers is not zero; the same factor may be canceled from both sides of an equation; every number (except zero) has an inverse. In the case of matrices, there is a class of matrices which are nonzero and yet have none of the three properties mentioned in the last sentence. These matrices are called singular matrices.[2] An example of such a matrix is the following:

$$q = \begin{pmatrix} 1 & 1 \\ 1 & 1 \end{pmatrix}$$

[1] Only square matrices are considered in Secs. 1.6 to 1.8.
[2] Or sometimes, divisors of zero.

Thus, if

$$p = \begin{pmatrix} 1 & -1 \\ -1 & 1 \end{pmatrix}$$

then neither p nor q is zero but $pq = 0$. Furthermore, in the following equation (that this is an equation may readily be verified by calculation of both sides), it is clear that the common factor q cannot be canceled.

$$\begin{pmatrix} 1 & 1 \\ 1 & 1 \end{pmatrix}\begin{pmatrix} 1 & -1 \\ 1 & 1 \end{pmatrix} = \begin{pmatrix} 1 & 1 \\ 1 & 1 \end{pmatrix}\begin{pmatrix} 1 & 3 \\ 1 & -3 \end{pmatrix}$$

A simple demonstration shows further that no matrix m exists such that $qm = I$ where I is the unit matrix. Thus, suppose that m exists. Then

$$pqm = p(qm) = pI = p$$
$$= (pq)m = 0m = 0$$

so that $p = 0$, which is clearly false. Thus, no such m exists.

A useful manner in which to define a singular matrix is as follows: A matrix is singular if and only if its determinant is zero. This definition yields also a test to tell when a matrix is singular—i.e., one need merely evaluate the determinant.

It will be seen in Sec. 1.8 that nonsingular matrices have the properties mentioned earlier in this section for nonzero numbers. Thus, the product of two nonsingular matrices is nonsingular (this is a stronger statement than that the product is nonzero). Further, the same nonsingular matrix may be canceled from both sides of an equation (provided it appears on the extreme left or on the extreme right on both sides of the equation). Also, every nonsingular matrix has an inverse.

Some of the properties of determinants which will be needed in Sec. 1.8 are summarized in Sec. 1.7.

1.7 Some Properties of Determinants

The determinant of a square matrix m is a number indicated as $|m|$, read "determinant of m." This determinant can be calculated, if the elements of m are known. Thus, if m is a 2×2 matrix,

$$|m| = m_{11}m_{22} - m_{12}m_{21} \tag{1.40}$$

whereas, if m is 3×3,

$$|m| = m_{11}m_{22}m_{33} + m_{12}m_{23}m_{31} + m_{13}m_{21}m_{32} - m_{11}m_{23}m_{32}$$
$$- m_{12}m_{21}m_{33} - m_{13}m_{22}m_{31} \tag{1.41}$$

The general definition of the determinant of m is given in Appendix 1A. Some properties of determinants as derived in Appendix 1A will be listed below.

1. The determinant of a matrix is equal to the determinant of the transpose of the matrix, where the transpose of a matrix m, written as m^T, is defined by $(m^T)_{ij} = m_{ji}$.

2. The necessary and sufficient condition that n simultaneous linear algebraic equations in n unknowns have a unique[1] solution is that the determinant of the matrix of coefficients is not zero.

3. A set of n homogeneous equations in n unknowns has a nontrivial solution if and only if the determinant of the matrix of coefficients is zero. A nontrivial solution is one in which not all the unknowns have the value zero.

4. The determinant of the product of two square matrices is equal to the product of the determinants; $|mp| = |m|\,|p|$.

5. The determinant of $zI - m$ is a polynomial of degree n in z, with leading term z^n, if m is an $n \times n$ square matrix, I the corresponding $n \times n$ unit matrix, and z a scalar.

An immediate consequence of property 5 is the existence of nonsingular matrices. Thus

$$f(z) = |zI - m|$$

as a polynomial of degree n in z can vanish for at most n values of z.

We may further deduce that $|I| = 1$. Thus, if m is a nonsingular matrix, since

$$mI = m$$

one has from property 4

$$|m|\,|I| = |m|$$

whence

$$|I| = 1$$

---

[1] The requirement that the solution be unique is a necessary part of the statement of this property, as is seen from the following example. The equations

$$\begin{pmatrix} 1 & 2 \\ 2 & 4 \end{pmatrix} x = \begin{pmatrix} 3 \\ 6 \end{pmatrix}$$

have the solutions

$$x = \begin{pmatrix} 1 + 2t \\ 1 - t \end{pmatrix}$$

for all values of t, despite the fact the determinant of the matrix of coefficients vanishes. This case is eliminated by requiring a *unique* solution.

1.8 Inverses

We now show that the product of two nonsingular matrices is non-singular. Let

$$pq = r$$

then

$$|p|\,|q| = |r|$$

whence if

$$|p| \neq 0$$

$$|q| \neq 0$$

then

$$|r| \neq 0$$

The following portions of this section will show (1) that if m has an inverse it is nonsingular, and (2) if m is nonsingular, it has a unique inverse.

Thus, suppose that there exist a pair of matrices p and m such that $pm = I$. Then, m is nonsingular; as the following shows

$$|pm| = |p|\,|m| = |I| = 1$$

so that

$$|m| \neq 0$$

Furthermore, it is clear that

$$mx = my$$

leads to the conclusion that $x = y$:

$$pmx = pmy$$

$$Ix = Iy$$

$$x = y$$

It is not difficult to show that if m is nonsingular (i.e., the determinant of m does not vanish) there exists a unique matrix, denoted by m^{-1}, such that $mm^{-1} = m^{-1}m = I$. Thus, it will first be shown that there exists a q such that $mq = I$, second that there exists a p such that $pm = I$, and third that $p = q$.

To find q such that $mq = I$, one need merely solve the equations for each of the n columns of q in turn. These are

$$mq_{.i} = \delta_{.i} \tag{1.42}$$

for the ith column of q. Written out, they become

$$\sum_k m_{jk} q_{ki} = \delta_{ji}$$

As follows directly from property 2, these equations have a unique solution for each column of q. Thus there exists a unique q.

To find the unique p one proceeds in a similar manner. The ith row of p satisfies

$$p_{i.}m = \delta_{i.} \tag{1.43}$$

or written out

$$\sum_k m_{kj}p_{ik} = \delta_{ij}$$

The matrix of coefficients is the matrix m^T, so that the existence of a unique solution for each row of p follows from properties 1 and 2 taken in conjunction with the nonvanishing of the determinant of m.

It has just been shown that p and q as required exist. To demonstrate their equality is trivial

$$pmq = (pm)q = Iq = q$$
$$= p(mq) = pI = p$$

Thus a matrix m has a unique inverse (denoted m^{-1}) if and only if the determinant of m does not vanish. This inverse may be written explicitly in usable form for 2×2 and 3×3 nonsingular matrices. Let D denote the determinant of m [as given in (1.40) or (1.41)]. For 2×2 matrices

$$m^{-1} = \frac{1}{D}\begin{pmatrix} m_{22} & -m_{12} \\ -m_{21} & m_{11} \end{pmatrix} \tag{1.44}$$

For 3×3 matrices

$$m^{-1} = \frac{1}{D}\begin{pmatrix} m_{22}m_{33} - m_{23}m_{32} & m_{13}m_{32} - m_{12}m_{33} & m_{12}m_{23} - m_{13}m_{22} \\ m_{23}m_{31} - m_{21}m_{33} & m_{11}m_{33} - m_{13}m_{31} & m_{13}m_{21} - m_{11}m_{23} \\ m_{21}m_{32} - m_{22}m_{31} & m_{12}m_{31} - m_{11}m_{32} & m_{11}m_{22} - m_{12}m_{21} \end{pmatrix} \tag{1.45}$$

The reader should have little difficulty verifying these relations.

1.9 Linear Independence

Up to now, square matrices have been separated into two categories, singular matrices and nonsingular matrices. It is further possible to define an index, the rank of a matrix, which indicates the degree of singularity. At the same time, one can obtain a better understanding of the problem of solving n equations in n unknowns. Thus, consider the equation

$$mx = y \tag{1.46}$$

For nonsingular m, a solution x exists for all y. For singular m, clearly a solution x exists for some y—i.e., for those y which may be written as a linear superposition of the columns of m

$$y = \sum m_{.i}x_i \tag{1.47}$$

A nonsingular matrix may be characterized by the statement that any column y can be written as a linear superposition of the columns of the matrix.

To proceed further, it is useful to introduce the concept of linear independence. A set of n columns is said to be linearly independent if there exists no linear combination of these columns which vanishes; that is, the k n-columns $m_{.i}$ are linearly independent if there exists no set of k numbers x_i not all zero such that

$$\sum_{i=1}^{k} m_{.i} x_i = 0 \tag{1.48}$$

The rank of a matrix may now be defined as the maximum number of linearly independent columns which the matrix has. A nonsingular matrix has rank n, since the nonvanishing of the determinant of m implies that the only solution of $mx = 0$ is $x = 0$ (see property 3). Furthermore, if m is an $n \times n$ matrix of rank n, it is nonsingular, as follows again from property 3, noting that m having rank n means that $mx = 0$ has no solution other than $x = 0$.

Any $n + 1$ n-columns are linearly dependent. Thus, call these $n + 1$ n-columns $m_{.i}$, $i = 1, 2, \ldots, n$, and y. If m is singular, there exists a non-zero x such that $mx = 0$, whence for this x the linear superposition $mx + 0y$ vanishes. If m is nonsingular, there exists an x such that $mx - y = 0$.

Exercises

1. Solve Eqs. (1.10) for x_1 and x_2.
2. Given the values f_i, g_i in the table, evaluate

$$\sum_{i=1}^{4} f_i \qquad \sum_{i=1}^{4} g_i \qquad \sum_{i=1}^{4} f_i^2 \qquad \sum_{i=1}^{4} g_i^2$$

$$\sum_{i=1}^{4} (f_i + g_i)^2 \qquad \sum_{i=1}^{4} f_i g_i \qquad \sum_{i=1}^{4} f_i g_{i+1} \qquad \sum_{i=1}^{4} f_{i+1} g_i$$

i	1	2	3	4	5
f_i	1	1.5	2.1	2.8	3.6
g_i	0.7	0.9	1.2	1.6	2.1

3. Let $\sigma_x = \begin{pmatrix} 0 & 1 \\ 1 & 0 \end{pmatrix} \qquad \sigma_y = \begin{pmatrix} 0 & i \\ -i & 0 \end{pmatrix} \qquad \sigma_z = \begin{pmatrix} -1 & 0 \\ 0 & 1 \end{pmatrix}$

Calculate $\sigma_x \cos \varphi + \sigma_y \sin \varphi$, σ_x^2, σ_y^2, σ_z^2, $\sigma_x \sigma_y$, $\sigma_y \sigma_x$, $\sigma_x \sigma_z$, $\sigma_z \sigma_x$, $\sigma_y \sigma_z$, $\sigma_z \sigma_y$.

4. For $M(t)$ given below, show that $\ddot{M}(t) = -\omega^2 M(t)$

$$M(t) = \begin{pmatrix} \cos \omega t & \sin \omega t \\ -\sin \omega t & \cos \omega t \end{pmatrix}$$

5. If

$$L_x = \begin{pmatrix} 0 & \sqrt{2}/2 & 0 \\ \sqrt{2}/2 & 0 & \sqrt{2}/2 \\ 0 & \sqrt{2}/2 & 0 \end{pmatrix}$$

$$L_y = \begin{pmatrix} 0 & i\sqrt{2}/2 & 0 \\ -i\sqrt{2}/2 & 0 & i\sqrt{2}/2 \\ 0 & -i\sqrt{2}/2 & 0 \end{pmatrix}$$

$$L_z = \begin{pmatrix} -1 & 0 & 0 \\ 0 & 0 & 0 \\ 0 & 0 & 1 \end{pmatrix}$$

Show that the following *commutation rules* hold:

$$L_x L_y - L_y L_x = iL_z$$
$$L_y L_z - L_z L_y = iL_x$$
$$L_z L_x - L_x L_z = iL_y$$
$$L_x^2 + L_y^2 + L_z^2 = 2$$

(Note this may be written in vector notation as $\mathbf{L} \times \mathbf{L} = i\mathbf{L}, \mathbf{L} \cdot \mathbf{L} = 2$.)

6. Given

$$A = \begin{pmatrix} 1 & 1 & 0 \\ 1 & 1 & 1 \\ 0 & 1 & 1 \end{pmatrix}$$

Find $|A|$, A^{-1}. Find three values of λ such that $A - \lambda I$ is singular.

7. Verify (1.45).

8. Let

$$\varepsilon = \begin{pmatrix} 0 & 0 & 0 \\ 1 & 0 & 0 \\ 0 & 1 & 0 \end{pmatrix}$$

Evaluate ε^2, ε^3, $e^{\varepsilon t}$.

9. Find the nth power of the square matrix M defined by

$$M = \begin{pmatrix} \alpha \\ \beta \\ \gamma \end{pmatrix} (abc)$$

10. Verify that $AB = BA$ if A and B are both diagonal matrices of the same order; i.e., show that diagonal matrices commute with one another.

11. Show that if a matrix A commutes with another matrix B, then A commutes with any matrix of the form

$$F(B) = \sum_n c_n B^n$$

where n is a positive integer and the c_n are numbers.

12. Show that if A is any square matrix and I is the unit matrix, then $IA = AI = A$.

13. Let M, N, and P be square matrices of the same order and show that $(MN)P = M(NP)$ where, for example, $(MN)P$ means that the product MN is first formed and then is multiplied by P from the right.

14. Verify the distributive law

$$(M + N)P = MP + NP$$

15. Verify that

$$(AB)^T = B^T A^T$$

16. Show that if $M = AA^T$, then $M = M^T$ and hence M is a symmetric matrix.

17. Show that a nonsquare matrix cannot have an inverse.

18. Verify that the elements of the inverse of a matrix M are given by

$$(M^{-1})_{ij} = \frac{M_{ji}}{|M|}$$

where M_{ji} is the cofactor of the element m_{ji} of M.

19. Show that

$$(AB)^{-1} = B^{-1} A^{-1}$$

20. Using the infinite series expressions for e^x, $\cos x$, and $\sin x$, show that

$$\exp \begin{pmatrix} 0 & 1 \\ -1 & 0 \end{pmatrix} t = \cos t + \begin{pmatrix} 0 & 1 \\ -1 & 0 \end{pmatrix} \sin t.$$

References

von Kármán, T., and M. A. Biot: "Mathematical Methods in Engineering," chap. 5, McGraw-Hill Book Company, Inc., New York, 1940.

Margenau, H., and G. M. Murphy: "The Mathematics of Physics and Chemistry," chap. 10, D. Van Nostrand Company, Inc., Princeton, N.J., 1943.

Jeffreys, H., and B. S. Jeffreys: "Mathematical Physics," chap. 4, Cambridge University Press, New York, 1946.

Frazer, R. A., W. J. Duncan, and A. R. Collar: "Elementary Matrices," Cambridge University Press, New York, 1947.

Aitken, A. C.: "Determinants and Matrices," 5th ed., Interscience Publishers, Inc., New York, 1948.

CHAPTER 2

Solution for Diagonalizable Matrices

2.1 Solution by Taylor Series

A standard method for the solution of the differential equation

$$\dot{u}(t) = Au(t) \tag{2.1}$$

yields the solution in the form of a power series in the independent variable t. Thus, as the reader will readily verify,

$$\frac{d^n u}{dt^n} = A^n u \tag{2.2}$$

whence, using the Taylor series expansion for $u(t)$ about $t = 0$, one obtains

$$u(t) = u(0) + \frac{t}{1!} \frac{du}{dt}\bigg|_{t=0} + \frac{t^2}{2!} \frac{d^2u}{dt^2}\bigg|_{t=0} + \cdots$$

$$= \left(1 + \frac{1}{1!} At + \frac{1}{2!} A^2 t^2 + \cdots\right) u(0) \tag{2.3}$$

or
$$u(t) = e^{At} u(0) \tag{2.4}$$

It is amazing that Eqs. (2.2) and (2.3) hold just as well when A is a matrix and u a column as they do when A and u are scalars, as is clear from the definition of the various matrix operations involved, at least in such cases as when the infinite series in (2.3) converges. The convergence of this series is demonstrated in Appendix 1B.

A comparison of (2.3) with (2.4) leads to a definition of e^{At} when A is a matrix. The power series not only defines this quantity but provides a means of evaluation. Such considerations as these further suggest the definition of the value of a function of a matrix. Thus, if $f(x)$ is a function of x with a power-series expansion

$$f(x) = \sum_{n=0}^{\infty} \frac{(x-a)^n}{n!} \frac{d^nf}{dx^n}\bigg|_{x=a} \tag{2.5}$$

then, provided merely that the series converge, $f(A)$ is defined as the matrix

$$f(A) = \sum_{n=0}^{\infty} \frac{(A-aI)^n}{n!} \frac{d^nf}{dx^n}\bigg|_{x=a} \tag{2.6}$$

It may be noted that the value of $f(A)$ occurring in (2.6) is independent of a, since the value of $f(x)$ given by (2.5) is independent of a.

In one sense, given (2.6), there remains no more to be done—the problem is solved. On the other hand, both for ease of calculation and for ease of understanding, a more satisfactory evaluation of e^{At} and $f(A)$ is to be desired. Such a method of evaluation will be determined in this chapter.

2.2 Eigenvalues and Eigencolumns

If there exist a number λ and a column u such that

$$Au = \lambda u \tag{2.7}$$

then λ is said to be an *eigenvalue* of A, u is said to be an *eigencolumn* of A, and the eigencolumn u and the eigenvalue λ are said to belong to each other. The immense importance of these definitions is suggested in the next paragraph.

A definition of $f(A)$ has been given in (2.6). As a brief calculation based on (2.7) will convince the reader, this definition yields the following result for $f(A)u$:

$$f(A)u = \sum_{n=0}^{\infty} \frac{1}{n!} \frac{d^nf}{dx^n}\bigg|_{x=a} (A-aI)^n u$$

$$= \sum \frac{1}{n!} \frac{d^nf}{dx^n}\bigg|_{x=a} (\lambda-a)^n u$$

From (2.5) it follows that

$$f(A)u = f(\lambda)u \tag{2.8}$$

The result given in (2.8), which holds for any u which is an eigencolumn of A [i.e., any u satisfying (2.7)], and for any f with convergent-power-series expansion, will be the basis of the work in the remainder of this chapter and in much of the remainder of this book. The result (2.8) which defines $f(A)$ as it acts on any eigencolumn of A may be applied to such f for which convergent power series do not exist, provided that the right side of (2.8) is meaningful.

2.3 Superposition

The problem under consideration is the evaluation of the solution (2.4) of the differential equation (2.1). If it so happens that $u(0)$ in (2.4) is an eigencolumn of A, then (2.8) yields immediately

$$u(t) = e^{At}u(0) = e^{\lambda t}u(0) \tag{2.9}$$

It should be noticed that the solution (2.9) is of very simple form. This simple form arises from the accident that the initial conditions as given by $u(0)$ were such that $Au(0) = \lambda u(0)$.

A circumstance such as that indicated in the last paragraph rarely arises. On the other hand, A will frequently have several eigencolumns such that $u(0)$ may be written as a linear combination (superposition) of these eigencolumns. In such a case, a solution almost as simple in form as that of (2.9) is obtained.

Thus, let the eigencolumns of A be denoted $s_{.i}$, so that

$$As_{.i} = \lambda_i s_{.i} \tag{2.10}$$

Further, suppose that there are enough such eigencolumns that one may write, for the specified initial conditions $u(0)$,

$$u(0) = s_{.1}a_1 + s_{.2}a_2 + \cdots = \sum_i s_{.i}a_i \tag{2.11}$$

In this case, the evaluation of $u(t)$ is straightforward.

$$\begin{aligned}
u(t) &= e^{At}u(0) \\
&= e^{At}s_{.1}a_1 + e^{At}s_{.2}a_2 + \cdots \\
&= e^{\lambda_1 t}s_{.1}a_1 + e^{\lambda_2 t}s_{.2}a_2 + \cdots \\
&= \sum_i e^{\lambda_i t}s_{.i}a_i
\end{aligned} \tag{2.12}$$

The meaning of the above formalism may become clearer upon study of its application to a simple illustration. As an example, consider

$$A = \begin{pmatrix} 1 & g \\ g & 1 \end{pmatrix} \qquad u(0) = \begin{pmatrix} c \\ d \end{pmatrix}$$

Then, as the reader will wish to verify,

$$A\begin{pmatrix} 1 \\ 1 \end{pmatrix} = (1 + g)\begin{pmatrix} 1 \\ 1 \end{pmatrix}$$

so that, following (2.10), one may write

$$s_{.1} = \begin{pmatrix} 1 \\ 1 \end{pmatrix} \qquad \lambda_1 = (1 + g)$$

Similarly, a second eigencolumn and eigenvalue are found to be

$$s_{.2} = \begin{pmatrix} 1 \\ -1 \end{pmatrix} \qquad \lambda_2 = (1 - g)$$

The initial conditions, as given by $u(0)$, may now be written in the form indicated in (2.11) as a linear superposition of eigencolumns of A:

$$u(0) = \frac{c+d}{2}\begin{pmatrix} 1 \\ 1 \end{pmatrix} + \frac{c-d}{2}\begin{pmatrix} 1 \\ -1 \end{pmatrix}$$

It follows immediately, as in (2.12), that

$$u(t) = e^{At}u(0) = \frac{c+d}{2} e^{(1+g)t}\begin{pmatrix} 1 \\ 1 \end{pmatrix} + \frac{c-d}{2} e^{(1-g)t}\begin{pmatrix} 1 \\ -1 \end{pmatrix}$$

In order to facilitate the verification of this result by substitution into the original equations, a person not yet familiar with matrix notation may wish to see things as they appear written out in detail. It has been found that the solution of the differential equations and initial conditions

$$\dot{u}_1 = u_1 + gu_2$$
$$\dot{u}_2 = gu_1 + u_2$$
$$u_1(0) = c \qquad u_2(0) = d$$

is given by

$$u_1(t) = \frac{c+d}{2} e^{(1+g)t} + \frac{c-d}{2} e^{(1-g)t}$$

$$u_2(t) = \frac{c+d}{2} e^{(1+g)t} - \frac{c-d}{2} e^{(1-g)t}$$

2.4   Completeness

The work of the preceding section shows that one may easily evaluate $f(A)u$ provided he can write u as a linear superposition of eigencolumns of the matrix A. Thus, it was found that if

$$As_{.i} = \lambda_i s_{.i}$$

and if

$$u = \sum_i s_{.i} a_i$$

then

$$f(A)u = \sum_i s_{.i} f(\lambda_i) a_i$$

It is clear that if $f(A)$ is a known matrix, the value of $f(A)u$ is known for arbitrary u, since the indicated multiplication can be carried out. Similarly, if the value of $f(A)u$ is known for arbitrary u, $f(A)$ may be considered a known matrix.[1]

As a result of these simple considerations, it is clear that the ability to write an arbitrary column u as a linear combination of the eigenvectors of A suffices to enable the evaluation of $f(A)$ and the solution of the initial value problems earlier considered.

It will now be shown that an arbitrary column u may be written as a linear combination of the eigencolumns of A if and only if A has n linearly independent eigencolumns. Thus, if A has less than n linearly independent eigencolumns, the resultant linear superposition will depend on less than n arbitrary constants, whereas an arbitrary column is specified by all n elements. If A does have n linearly independent eigencolumns, it is possible to solve specifically for u in terms of the eigencolumns (see the next paragraph), thus completing the proof of the theorem.

The problem is that of finding the quantities a_i such that

$$u = \sum s_{.i} a_i$$

This may be written as

$$u = sa \tag{2.13}$$

where s is the matrix of the eigencolumns of A. Note that s is nonsingular, since its columns are linearly independent. Then one may solve for the column a by multiplication of (2.13) on the left with the inverse of s to obtain

$$a = s^{-1}u \tag{2.14}$$

Thus, if A has n linearly independent eigencolumns, an arbitrary column may be written as a superposition of these eigencolumns. For this reason, the eigencolumns are said to form a *complete set*. As shall be seen later, not all matrices have a complete set of eigencolumns. This chapter shall consider only such matrices as do.

In the light of (2.14), the value of $f(A)u$ may be written concisely as

$$f(A)u = \sum_i s_{.i} f(\lambda_i)(s^{-1})_{i.} u \tag{2.15}$$

Since this equation is true for arbitrary u, it follows from the footnote at the beginning of this section that

$$f(A) = \sum_i s_{.i} f(\lambda_i)(s^{-1})_{i.} \tag{2.16}$$

---

[1] Thus, the identity matrix I may be written as $I = \Sigma \delta_{.i}\delta_{i.}$ whence $f(A) = f(A)I = \Sigma[f(A)\delta_{.i}]\delta_{i.}$. Since by hypothesis the quantities in the brackets are known, $f(A)$ has been explicitly determined, and is thus known.

Since the above two results are fundamental, it is desirable to consider them at some length.

Let the eigencolumns of A, belonging to the eigenvalues λ_i, be written as $s_{.i}$. Then, as follows from (2.8),

$$f(A)s_{.i} = s_{.i}f(\lambda_i) \tag{2.17}$$

To find $f(A)$ from (2.17) is a straightforward matter:

$$f(A) = f(A)I = f(A)\sum s_{.i}(s^{-1})_{i.} = \sum s_{.i}f(\lambda_i)(s^{-1})_{i.}$$

This result, derived from (2.17) in one line, is identical to (2.16).

These results may be written in even more elegant form if the definition of a function $f(\Lambda)$ of a diagonal matrix (with diagonal elements λ_i) is introduced as[1]

$$[f(\Lambda)]_{ij} = f(\lambda_i)\delta_{ij} \tag{2.18}$$

Then the definition of s becomes

$$As = s\Lambda \tag{2.19}$$

where Λ is specified to be diagonal. Further

$$f(A)s = sf(\Lambda) \tag{2.20}$$

replaces (2.17). To evaluate $f(A)$ one writes

$$f(A) = f(A)ss^{-1} = sf(\Lambda)s^{-1} \tag{2.21}$$

a result equivalent to (2.16).

If (2.21) is applied to the function $f(A) = A$, there results the remarkable relation

$$A = s\Lambda s^{-1} \tag{2.22}$$

in which A has been written in terms of the diagonal matrix of its eigenvalues.[2] Thus, A is said to be diagonalizable. This definition implies that the eigencolumns of a diagonalizable matrix form a complete set and vice versa.

It has been previously remarked that not all matrices are diagonalizable. Specifically, as the reader will verify, the matrix

$$\begin{pmatrix} 0 & 0 \\ 1 & 0 \end{pmatrix}$$

---

[1] This is clearly not a new definition but follows from the result (2.16) applied to a diagonal matrix. Thus, for a diagonal matrix one may take $s = I = s^{-1}$. With this value of s, (2.18) follows directly from (2.16).

[2] This is often called the *spectral representation* of A; the set of eigenvalues is called the *spectrum* of A.

cannot be diagonalized, nor do its eigenvectors form a complete set. It is clearly desirable to be able to tell when a matrix may be diagonalized. This question does not have a complete answer in terms of simple operations. However, as will be seen in Sec. 4.9, if

$$A^+ A = A A^+$$

where $$(A^+)_{ij} = \bar{A}_{ji}$$

then A is diagonalizable. (The bar denotes complex conjugate.) Another class of matrices for which diagonalizability is assured is determined by the following: If all the eigenvalues of A are distinct, so that A has n different eigenvalues, then A may be diagonalized. Since the eigenvalues of A must be determined in order to diagonalize A, this condition turns out to be useful. The diagonalization of matrices with n distinct eigenvalues is the subject of the next section.

2.5 Diagonalization of Nondegenerate Matrices

In the past few sections it has been indicated that a knowledge of the eigenvalues and eigencolumns of a matrix A enables the evaluation of arbitrary functions of the matrix A, provided only there be n distinct (linearly independent) eigencolumns. In this section, a method for determining the eigenvalues of A will be developed. As will be seen, each A has n eigenvalues. If two or more of these eigenvalues are equal (if A has less than n distinct eigenvalues) A is said to be degenerate. If A has indeed n distinct eigenvalues, A is nondegenerate. A further result, proven in this section, is that A has at least as many linearly independent eigencolumns as it has distinct eigenvalues, so that if A is nondegenerate it is certain that A may be diagonalized.

The best way to find the eigenvalues of A is by trying to find one of the eigencolumns of A. By definition, an eigencolumn u of A satisfies the equation

$$Au = \lambda u \qquad (2.23)$$

for some nonzero u and some number λ. But (cf. Sec. 1.7) the necessary and sufficient condition that (2.23) have a nontrivial solution u is that the determinant of coefficients vanish. Thus, it must be that

$$|\lambda I - A| = 0 \qquad (2.24)$$

Hence, before a solution to (2.23) can exist, it is necessary that the eigenvalue be so chosen as to satisfy (2.24). This determinantal equation is called the *characteristic equation* for the matrix A. Sometimes it is known as the *secular equation* for the problem $\dot{u} = Au$.

For given A, the characteristic equation equates a polynomial of degree n in λ, leading term λ^n (cf. Sec. 1.7) to zero. As such, the characteristic equation is satisfied by n values of λ, some of which may be multiple roots.

To summarize, the eigenvalues of an $n \times n$ square matrix A are found as the roots of the characteristic equation of A as given in (2.24). If the n roots of the characteristic equation are distinct, A is nondegenerate; otherwise A is degenerate. Corresponding to each distinct eigenvalue, there exists a nontrivial eigencolumn of A, found by solution of (2.23) after insertion for λ of the appropriate root of the characteristic equation.

It will now be shown that A has at least as many linearly independent eigencolumns as it has distinct eigenvalues. Thus, let these distinct eigenvalues be denoted λ_i, with i taking on a value for each distinct eigenvalue, and let the corresponding eigencolumns be denoted $s_{.i}$. It will be assumed that these eigencolumns are linearly dependent and it will be shown that this assumption leads to a contradiction.

If the eigencolumns are linearly dependent, there exists a set of numbers a_i, not all zero, such that

$$\sum s_{.i} a_i = 0 \tag{2.25}$$

The demonstration that this leads to an inconsistency is relatively straightforward. All that is necessary is to show that each a_i is zero, one after the other. The method will be applied by showing that a_1 vanishes. To do this, it is assumed that i runs from 1 to m. Then, to eliminate the term in the sum (2.25) which contains a_2, (2.25) is multiplied from the left by $A - \lambda_2$. This multiplies each term in the sum by $\lambda_i - \lambda_2$, causing the term proportional to a_2 to vanish. Next, the term proportional to a_3 is annihilated by multiplication with $A - \lambda_3$. This process is continued until all terms in the sum (2.25) have been annihilated except the first (the last factor needed is clearly $A - \lambda_m$). At this time, (2.25) has become

$$(\lambda_1 - \lambda_2)(\lambda_1 - \lambda_3)(\lambda_1 - \lambda_4) \cdots (\lambda_1 - \lambda_m)a_1 = 0 \tag{2.26}$$

Since, by hypothesis, the eigenvalues are all different, it is clear that a_1 has been shown to be equal to zero. A similar process shows that each a_i in turn must vanish. Thus the eigencolumns have been demonstrated to be linearly independent.

If A is nondegenerate, the above theorem shows that the matrix s has n linearly independent eigencolumns. Thus, s has an inverse and A may be diagonalized:

$$A = Ass^{-1} = s\Lambda s^{-1} \tag{2.27}$$

The reader should note that none of the above prohibits A from having a complete set of eigencolumns, even if A is degenerate.

2.6   Outline of Computation Procedure with Examples

The motivation of the considerations in the last sections was the evaluation of the solution of the equations of motion of a system, as written in the form

$$\dot{u} = Au$$

This solution was written formally as

$$u(t) = e^{At}u(0)$$

and a method for the evaluation of e^{At} has been indicated. In this section, the corresponding operations will be listed in sequence, and the procedure will be applied to two examples.

Step 1

Find the eigenvalues of A. That is, find the roots $\lambda_1, \lambda_2, \ldots, \lambda_n$ of the characteristic equation

$$|\lambda - A| = 0$$

Step 2

Find the eigencolumns of A. That is, solve the n sets of equations

$$(A - \lambda_i)s_{.i} = 0 \qquad i = 1, 2, \ldots, n$$

one set for each eigencolumn $s_{.i}$, belonging to the eigenvalue λ_i.

Step 3

Express the given $u(0)$ as a linear combination of the eigencolumns of A. That is, find x such that

$$u(0) = sx = \sum_{i=0}^{n} s_{.i}x_i$$

Step 4

Write down the answer:

$$u(t) = e^{At}u(0) = e^{At}sx$$

$$= se^{\Lambda t}x = \sum_{i=1}^{n} s_{.i}e^{\lambda_i t}x_i$$

A slightly different form for steps 3 and 4 is often useful:

Step 3a

Find r, the inverse of s, so that $sr = 1$. That is, solve the n sets of equations

$$\sum_i s_{.i}r_{ij} = \delta_{.j} \qquad j = 1, 2, \ldots, n$$

for the n columns of r.

Step 4a

Write down the answer:

$$e^{At} = e^{At}sr$$

$$= se^{\Lambda t}r = \sum_{i=1}^{n} s_{.i}e^{\lambda_i t}r_{i.}.$$

It may be noted that step 2 does not determine the matrix s uniquely, since each of the eigencolumns remains an eigencolumn when multiplied by any nonzero scalar. This implies, given any s, that the matrix sd is equally valid, provided that d is a nonsingular diagonal matrix. In step 3a, in place of $sr = 1$, one finds the matrix $d^{-1}r$ such that $sd\, d^{-1}r = 1$. The answer, as given in step 4a, becomes $sde^{\Lambda t}\, d^{-1}r$. But $e^{\Lambda t}$ is a diagonal matrix and all diagonal matrices commute with each other (two matrices p and q *commute* if $pq = qp$), so that this becomes $se^{\Lambda t}r$ as before. Thus, while s has not been uniquely determined, this lack of uniqueness does not affect the value of exp At.

The first illustration considers the problem solved in Sec. 2.3:

$$A = \begin{pmatrix} 1 & g \\ g & 1 \end{pmatrix} \qquad u(0) = \begin{pmatrix} c \\ d \end{pmatrix}$$

Step 1

$$|A - \lambda| = \begin{vmatrix} 1 - \lambda & g \\ g & 1 - \lambda \end{vmatrix} = (1 - \lambda)^2 - g^2 = 0$$

$$\lambda_1 = 1 + g$$
$$\lambda_2 = 1 - g$$

Step 2

$$(A - \lambda_1)s_{.1} = \begin{pmatrix} -g & g \\ g & -g \end{pmatrix}\begin{pmatrix} s_{11} \\ s_{21} \end{pmatrix} = 0$$

whence a solution is

$$s_{.1} = \begin{pmatrix} 1 \\ 1 \end{pmatrix}$$

Similarly
$$(A - \lambda_2)s_{.2} = \begin{pmatrix} g & g \\ g & g \end{pmatrix}\begin{pmatrix} s_{12} \\ s_{22} \end{pmatrix} = 0$$

whence
$$s_{.2} = \begin{pmatrix} 1 \\ -1 \end{pmatrix}$$

SOLUTION FOR DIAGONALIZABLE MATRICES

Step 3

$$sx = \begin{pmatrix} 1 & 1 \\ 1 & -1 \end{pmatrix} \begin{pmatrix} x_1 \\ x_2 \end{pmatrix} = u(0) = \begin{pmatrix} c \\ d \end{pmatrix}$$

whence

$$x = \tfrac{1}{2} \begin{pmatrix} c + d \\ c - d \end{pmatrix}$$

Step 4

$$u(t) = \sum_i s_{\cdot i} e^{\lambda_i t} x_i$$

$$= \begin{pmatrix} 1 \\ 1 \end{pmatrix} e^{(1+g)t} \tfrac{1}{2}(c + d) + \begin{pmatrix} 1 \\ -1 \end{pmatrix} e^{(1-g)t} \tfrac{1}{2}(c - d)$$

This is the result found in Sec. 2.3.

Alternately, steps 3*a* and 4*a* may be carried out.

Step 3*a*

$$sr_{\cdot 1} = \begin{pmatrix} 1 & 1 \\ 1 & -1 \end{pmatrix} \begin{pmatrix} r_{11} \\ r_{21} \end{pmatrix} = \delta_{\cdot 1} = \begin{pmatrix} 1 \\ 0 \end{pmatrix}$$

whence

$$r_{\cdot 1} = \begin{pmatrix} \tfrac{1}{2} \\ \tfrac{1}{2} \end{pmatrix}$$

Similarly

$$sr_{\cdot 2} = \begin{pmatrix} 1 & 1 \\ 1 & -1 \end{pmatrix} \begin{pmatrix} r_{12} \\ r_{22} \end{pmatrix} = \delta_{\cdot 2} = \begin{pmatrix} 0 \\ 1 \end{pmatrix}$$

whence

$$r_{\cdot 2} = \begin{pmatrix} \tfrac{1}{2} \\ -\tfrac{1}{2} \end{pmatrix} \qquad r = \begin{pmatrix} \tfrac{1}{2} & \tfrac{1}{2} \\ \tfrac{1}{2} & -\tfrac{1}{2} \end{pmatrix}$$

Step 4*a*

$$e^{At} = s_{\cdot 1} e^{(\lambda_1)t} r_{1\cdot} + s_{\cdot 2} e^{(\lambda_2)t} r_{2\cdot}$$

$$= \begin{pmatrix} 1 \\ 1 \end{pmatrix} e^{(1+g)t} (\tfrac{1}{2} \quad \tfrac{1}{2}) + \begin{pmatrix} 1 \\ -1 \end{pmatrix} e^{(1-g)t} (\tfrac{1}{2} \quad -\tfrac{1}{2})$$

$$= \begin{pmatrix} \tfrac{1}{2} & \tfrac{1}{2} \\ \tfrac{1}{2} & \tfrac{1}{2} \end{pmatrix} e^{(1+g)t} + \begin{pmatrix} \tfrac{1}{2} & -\tfrac{1}{2} \\ -\tfrac{1}{2} & \tfrac{1}{2} \end{pmatrix} e^{(1-g)t}$$

$$= e^t \begin{pmatrix} \cosh gt & \sinh gt \\ \sinh gt & \cosh gt \end{pmatrix}$$

As a second illustration, we carry out steps 1, 2, 3*a*, and 4*a* for

$$A = \begin{pmatrix} -15 & 12 \\ -24 & 19 \end{pmatrix}$$

Step 1

$$|A - \lambda| = \begin{pmatrix} -15 - \lambda & 12 \\ -24 & 19 - \lambda \end{pmatrix} = \lambda^2 - 4\lambda + 3 = 0$$

$$\lambda_1 = 1 \qquad \lambda_2 = 3$$

Step 2

$$\begin{pmatrix} -16 & 12 \\ -24 & 18 \end{pmatrix} \begin{pmatrix} s_{11} \\ s_{21} \end{pmatrix} = 0 \qquad s_{.1} = \begin{pmatrix} 3 \\ 4 \end{pmatrix}$$

$$\begin{pmatrix} -18 & 12 \\ -24 & 16 \end{pmatrix} \begin{pmatrix} s_{12} \\ s_{22} \end{pmatrix} = 0 \qquad s_{.2} = \begin{pmatrix} 2 \\ 3 \end{pmatrix}$$

Step 3a

$$\begin{pmatrix} 3 & 2 \\ 4 & 3 \end{pmatrix} \begin{pmatrix} r_{11} \\ r_{21} \end{pmatrix} = \begin{pmatrix} 1 \\ 0 \end{pmatrix} \qquad r_{.1} = \begin{pmatrix} 3 \\ -4 \end{pmatrix}$$

$$\begin{pmatrix} 3 & 2 \\ 4 & 3 \end{pmatrix} \begin{pmatrix} r_{12} \\ r_{22} \end{pmatrix} = \begin{pmatrix} 0 \\ 1 \end{pmatrix} \qquad r_{.2} = \begin{pmatrix} -2 \\ 3 \end{pmatrix}$$

$$r = \begin{pmatrix} 3 & -2 \\ -4 & 3 \end{pmatrix}$$

Step 4a

$$e^{At} = \begin{pmatrix} 3 \\ 4 \end{pmatrix} e^t (3 \quad -2) + \begin{pmatrix} 2 \\ 3 \end{pmatrix} e^{3t} (-4 \quad 3)$$

$$= \begin{pmatrix} 9 & -6 \\ 12 & -8 \end{pmatrix} e^t + \begin{pmatrix} -8 & 6 \\ -12 & 9 \end{pmatrix} e^{3t}$$

As a check, note that at $t = 0$, e^{At} becomes the identity matrix.

The carrying out of the above steps in practical numerical problems with n greater than 2 has been the subject of much study. See, for example, the first three references at the end of Chap. 1.

2.7 Change of Variable

The choice of the variables in terms of which a physical problem is written may strongly influence the difficulty of solution of the problem. One interpretation of the procedure of Sec. 2.6 is in terms of a change of variable in such a manner as to greatly simplify the solution of the problem at hand. The problem, written in terms of the new variables, is solved. The old variables are then calculated from their relation to the new.

To see how this works, consider diagonalizable A

$$A = S\Lambda R \qquad SR = RS = 1$$

and the initial value problem

$$\dot{u} = Au = S\Lambda Ru$$

This problem is much easier to handle in terms of the variable v where

$$v = Ru$$

Thus

$$\dot{v} = R\dot{u} = RS\Lambda v = \Lambda v$$

or

$$\dot{v}_i = \lambda_i v_i \qquad i = 1, 2, \ldots, n$$

Clearly

$$v_i(t) = v_i(0)e^{\lambda_i t}$$

This solution, in terms of the v_i, is easily related to a solution in terms of the u_i. Thus

$$v_i(0) = R_{i.}u(0)$$

and

$$u(t) = Sv(t) = \sum_i S_{.i}v_i(t)$$

The variables v_i are often called "normal coordinates." A solution in which all v_i but one are zero is called a normal mode. Thus, the jth normal mode is given by

$$u(t) = S_{.j}v_j(t)$$
$$= S_{.j}v_j(0)e^{\lambda_j t}$$

For the problem of Sec. 2.3, as just considered, the normal modes are

$$u(t) = \begin{pmatrix} 1 \\ 1 \end{pmatrix} e^{(1+g)t}$$

and

$$u(t) = \begin{pmatrix} 1 \\ -1 \end{pmatrix} e^{(1-g)t}$$

For the problem defined in Eq. (1.4), new coordinates which simplify the problem may be obtained by inspection. Thus, consider the new variables

$$y = x_1 - x_2$$
$$z = x_1 + x_2$$

which correspond to the masses of Fig. 1.2 moving together ($y = 0$ implies that $x_1 = x_2$) or oppositely ($z = 0$). Each of these motions may be expected to exist independently. (The first of the motions does not stretch the coupling spring, so that the two oscillators move at their equal uncoupled frequencies. The second motion corresponds to one-half the coupling spring being attached to each oscillator, so again the two oscillators have equal frequencies.) To obtain the equations satisfied by y and z, the two Eqs. (1.4) are added and subtracted to yield

$$m\ddot{z} + kz = 0$$
$$m\ddot{y} + (k - 2k_0)y = 0$$

2.8   The Steady-state Solution

As was seen in Sec. 1.1, one is sometimes concerned with the solution of

$$Au = f \qquad (2.28)$$

If A is nonsingular, this solution is immediately given by

$$u = A^{-1}f \qquad (2.29)$$

It is sometimes convenient to use the spectral representation of A to obtain A^{-1} or u. Thus, if

$$AS = S\Lambda \qquad A^{-1}S = S\Lambda^{-1}$$

so that

$$A^{-1} = A^{-1}SS^{-1} = S\Lambda^{-1}S^{-1}$$

and

$$u = A^{-1}SS^{-1}f = S\Lambda^{-1}S^{-1}f$$
$$= \sum_i S_{.i}\lambda_i^{-1}(S^{-1})_{i.}\, f \qquad (2.30)$$

Usually, it is easier to find A^{-1} directly than to calculate S, S^{-1}, and Λ.

If A is singular,[1] say because $\lambda_1 = 0$, then neither (2.29) nor (2.30) yields a solution to (2.28). Nevertheless, for certain f a solution exists. To determine the restrictions on f and the corresponding solutions, a simple procedure may be employed.

The new variables v are introduced by

$$u = Sv \qquad v = S^{-1}u$$

Then

$$Au = f = ASv = S\Lambda v$$

or

$$\Lambda v = S^{-1}f$$

If $\lambda_1 = 0$, then

$$0 = \lambda_1 v_1 = (S^{-1})_{1.}\, f$$

---

[1] If A is singular, there exists a nontrivial solution of $Ax = 0$, whence $Ax = 0x$, so that A has the eigenvalue zero.

so that a solution may exist only for such f that[1]

$$(S^{-1})_{1.}\,f = 0$$

v_1 is not determined.

The solution, in terms of u, may now be written:

$$u = Sv = \sum S_{.i} v_i$$

$$= S_{.1} v_1 + \sum_{i=2}^{n} S_{.i} \lambda_i^{-1} (S^{-1})_{i.}\,f$$

where v_1 is an arbitrary constant.

2.9 The Inhomogeneous Problem

A problem often of interest is to determine $u(t)$, given $u(0)$, when

$$\dot{u} = Au + F(t)$$

As may be verified by substitution, the solution is

$$u(t) = e^{At} u(0) + \int_0^t e^{A(t-s)} F(s)\,ds$$

when A is a matrix as well as when A is a scalar.

If A is diagonalizable

$$A = S\Lambda T \qquad ST = 1$$

then this solution may be written

$$u_i(t) = \sum_{k,j} S_{ik} e^{\lambda_k t} T_{kj} u_j(0) + \sum_{k,j} S_{ik} T_{kj} \int_0^t e^{\lambda_k(t-s)} F_j(s)\,ds$$

$$= \sum_k S_{ik} e^{\lambda_k t} \sum_j T_{kj} \left[u_j(0) + \int_0^t e^{-\lambda_k s} F_j(s)\,ds \right]$$

Exercises

1. Diagonalize the matrix

$$M = \begin{pmatrix} a & a-1 \\ b+1 & b \end{pmatrix}$$

where a and b are real numbers. Find the eigenvalues λ and eigencolumns x for which $Mx = \lambda x$. Under what conditions (on a and b) will the eigenvalues be real?

---

[1] This condition may be more easily derived. We have

$$Au = f \qquad S^{-1}A = \Lambda S^{-1}$$

or

$$(S^{-1})_{1.}\,A = \lambda_1 (S^{-1})_{1.} = 0$$

Thus

$$(S^{-1})_{1.}\,f = (S^{-1})_{1.}\,Au = 0$$

2. Find S and Λ such that

$$\begin{pmatrix} -5 & 6 \\ -4 & 5 \end{pmatrix} = S\Lambda S^{-1}$$

where Λ is a diagonal matrix.

3. Find

$$\begin{pmatrix} 1 & 3 \\ 3 & 1 \end{pmatrix}^{15}$$

4. Solve Eq. (1.13).
5. Solve Eq. (1.14).
6. Solve Eq. (1.15).
7. Let

$$M = \begin{pmatrix} 0 & 0 & 0 \\ 1 & 0 & 0 \\ 0 & 1 & 0 \end{pmatrix}$$

If $f(x)$ has a convergent power series about $x = 0$, show that

$$f(M) = f(0) + Mf'(0) + \frac{M^2}{2!} f''(0)$$

8. For M as defined above, find $\sqrt{I + M}$.
9. Find all 2×2 matrices M, such that

$$M^2 = \begin{pmatrix} 1 & 0 \\ 0 & 1 \end{pmatrix}$$

10. Find the eigenvalues and eigencolumns of the matrix

$$\begin{pmatrix} -2 & 1 & 0 & 0 & 0 \\ 1 & -2 & 1 & 0 & 0 \\ 0 & 1 & -2 & 1 & 0 \\ 0 & 0 & 1 & -2 & 1 \\ 0 & 0 & 0 & 1 & -2 \end{pmatrix}$$

Hint: Try as an eigencolumn

$$\begin{pmatrix} \sin \alpha \\ \sin 2\alpha \\ \sin 3\alpha \\ \sin 4\alpha \\ \sin 5\alpha \end{pmatrix}$$

and use the addition theorems for trigonometric functions:

$$\sin(n \pm 1)\alpha = \sin n\alpha \cos \alpha \pm \cos n\alpha \sin \alpha$$

11. For an $N \times N$ matrix M, let

$$|\lambda I - M| = \sum_{n=0}^{N} \alpha_n \lambda^n \qquad \text{(note that } \alpha_N = 1\text{)}$$

Show that for diagonalizable M

$$\sum_{n=0}^{N} \alpha_n M^n = 0$$

(This result is true for all M.)

12. Suppose

$$M = \alpha \begin{pmatrix} \tfrac{1}{2} \\ \tfrac{1}{2} \end{pmatrix}(1 \quad 1) + \beta \begin{pmatrix} \tfrac{1}{2} \\ -\tfrac{1}{2} \end{pmatrix}(1 \quad -1)$$

Show that $\qquad M^n = \alpha^n \begin{pmatrix} \tfrac{1}{2} \\ \tfrac{1}{2} \end{pmatrix}(1 \quad 1) + \beta^n \begin{pmatrix} \tfrac{1}{2} \\ -\tfrac{1}{2} \end{pmatrix}(1 \quad -1)$

13. Show that if $f(x) = \Sigma \alpha_n x^n$

$$f(M) = f(\alpha) \begin{pmatrix} \tfrac{1}{2} \\ \tfrac{1}{2} \end{pmatrix}(1 \quad 1) + f(\beta) \begin{pmatrix} \tfrac{1}{2} \\ \tfrac{1}{2} \end{pmatrix}(1 \quad -1)$$

14. Show that

$$\begin{pmatrix} \cos \delta & \sin \delta \\ -\sin \delta & \cos \delta \end{pmatrix}^n = \begin{pmatrix} \cos n\delta & \sin n\delta \\ -\sin n\delta & \cos n\delta \end{pmatrix}$$

15. Show that

$$\begin{pmatrix} \cosh x & \sinh x \\ \sinh x & \cosh x \end{pmatrix}^n = \begin{pmatrix} \cosh nx & \sinh nx \\ \sinh nx & \cosh nx \end{pmatrix}$$

16. Given

$$A = \begin{pmatrix} 3 & -4 \\ 1 & -1 \end{pmatrix}$$

show that when s is any integer

$$A^s = \begin{pmatrix} 1 + 2s & -4s \\ s & 1 - 2s \end{pmatrix}$$

CHAPTER 3

The Evaluation of a Function of a Matrix for an Arbitrary Matrix

3.1 Introduction

In Chap. 2 the evaluation of functions of matrices was based on the following relation:

If $AS = S\Lambda$ then $f(A)S = Sf(\Lambda)$

This method was then applied to any matrix A for which S^{-1} existed and indeed yielded

$$f(A) = Sf(\Lambda)S^{-1}$$

An alternate method of expressing $f(A)$ is by means of the Cauchy-integral formula from complex variable theory.[1]

$$f(A) = \frac{1}{2\pi i} \oint_C \frac{f(Z)}{Z - A} dZ \tag{3.1}$$

This formula may be applied to matrices[2] as well as to numbers, provided the contour C encloses all eigenvalues of A and no singularities of $f(Z)$. A proof is indicated in Sec. 3.3 for some special cases.

3.2 The Cauchy-integral Formula

The Cauchy-integral formula states that, if $f(Z)$ has no singularities within or on the contour of integration C and if the point a lies within C, then

$$f(a) = \frac{1}{2\pi i} \oint_C \frac{f(Z)}{Z - a} dZ \tag{3.2}$$

---

[1] It is assumed that the reader is acquainted with the elements of complex variable theory. A summary of some useful results is given in Appendix 1C.

[2] $Z - A$ is understood to mean $ZI - A$ where I and A are square matrices of the same order and Z is a scalar. This convention will be used in the following sections.

From (3.2) one may obtain

$$\frac{d^n}{da^n} f(a) = \frac{n!}{2\pi i} \oint_C \frac{f(Z)}{(Z-a)^{n+1}} \, dZ \qquad n \geq 0 \tag{3.3}$$

Further, for $n \geq 0$

$$0 = \frac{1}{2\pi i} \oint_C f(Z)(Z-a)^n \, dZ$$

since the integral is analytic within C.

3.3   Application to Matrices

The assertion made in (3.1) will now be discussed. Consider

$$\frac{1}{2\pi i} \oint_C \frac{f(Z)}{Z-A} \, dZ \tag{3.4}$$

where C encloses each zero of $|Z - A|$ and no singularity of $f(Z)$. It will be shown that (3.4) is $f(A)$ in the two cases where $f(A)$ has been otherwise defined. When $f(A)$ has not been otherwise defined, (3.4) will be used as the definition of $f(A)$.

The first case to be considered is that where A is diagonalizable. Then

$$A = S\Lambda T \qquad ST = 1$$

so that $\quad (Z-A)^{-1} = (Z-A)^{-1}ST = S(Z-\Lambda)^{-1}T = \sum_i S_{.i} \frac{1}{Z-\lambda_i} T_{i.}$

and

$$\frac{1}{2\pi i} \oint_C \frac{f(Z)}{Z-A} \, dZ = \sum_i S_{.i} \frac{1}{2\pi i} \oint \frac{f(Z)}{Z-\lambda_i} \, dZ \, T_{i.}$$

$$= \sum_i S_{.i} f(\lambda_i) T_{i.} = f(A)$$

The second case to be considered is that where a contour C exists enclosing each zero of $|Z - A|$ and such that

$$f(Z) = \sum_{n=0}^{\infty} a_n Z^n$$

on C. Then

$$\frac{1}{2\pi i} \oint_C \frac{f(Z)}{Z-A} \, dZ = \sum_{n=0}^{\infty} a_n \frac{1}{2\pi i} \oint_C \frac{Z^n}{Z-A} \, dZ$$

provided the series converges. But (as is seen below)

$$\frac{1}{2\pi i} \oint_C \frac{Z^n}{Z-A} \, dZ = A^n \tag{3.5}$$

so that, provided the series converges,

$$\frac{1}{2\pi i} \oint_C \frac{f(Z)}{Z - A}\, dZ = \sum_0^\infty a_n A^n = f(A)$$

It must still be shown that (3.5) holds. But, for sufficiently large Z (cf. Appendix 1B),

$$\frac{1}{Z - A} = \frac{1}{Z} + \frac{A}{Z^2} + \frac{A^2}{Z^3} + \cdots$$

whence, for a contour C' on each point of which the series converges,

$$\frac{1}{2\pi i} \oint_{C'} \frac{Z^n}{Z - A}\, dZ = \frac{1}{2\pi i} \oint_{C'} Z^n\left(\frac{1}{Z} + \frac{A}{Z^2} + \cdots\right) dZ = A^n$$

But

$$\oint_C = \oint_{C'}$$

Thus (3.5) is proved.

3.4 Evaluation of $f(A)$ with Illustrations

Let the matrix $(Z - A)^{-1}$ be represented by $q(Z)$. Then the formula (3.1) may be written

$$f(A) = \frac{1}{2\pi i} \oint f(Z) q(Z)\, dZ$$

and the evaluation of $f(A)$ carried out by the following procedure:

a. Find $q(Z) = (Z - A)^{-1}$ by solving the matrix equation

$$(Z - A)q(Z) = 1$$

b. Find $f_{ij}(A) = \dfrac{1}{2\pi i} \oint f(Z) q_{ij}(Z)\, dZ$, where $f_{ij}(A)$ and $q_{ij}(Z)$ are, respectively, the elements of the matrices $f(A)$ and $q(Z)$, by the use of the Cauchy-integral formula.

This procedure is illustrated by the following three examples:

Example 1

$$A = \begin{pmatrix} 1 & \epsilon \\ \epsilon & 1 \end{pmatrix}$$

According to step *a* in the procedure

$$(Z - A)q_{.i} = \begin{pmatrix} Z - 1 & -\epsilon \\ -\epsilon & Z - 1 \end{pmatrix} \begin{pmatrix} q_{11} \\ q_{21} \end{pmatrix} = \begin{pmatrix} 1 \\ 0 \end{pmatrix}$$

and

$$(Z - A)q_{.2} = \begin{pmatrix} Z - 1 & -\epsilon \\ -\epsilon & Z - 1 \end{pmatrix} \begin{pmatrix} q_{12} \\ q_{22} \end{pmatrix} = \begin{pmatrix} 0 \\ 1 \end{pmatrix}$$

A brief computation yields

$$q_{22} = q_{11} = \frac{Z - 1}{(Z - 1)^2 - \epsilon^2}$$

$$q_{12} = q_{21} = \frac{\epsilon}{(Z - 1)^2 - \epsilon^2}$$

One obtains, upon applying step b in the procedure,

$$(e^{At})_{11} = (e^{At})_{22} = \frac{1}{2\pi i} \oint \frac{Z - 1}{(Z - 1 - \epsilon)(Z - 1 + \epsilon)} e^{Zt} \, dZ$$

$$= \frac{1}{2} e^{(1 + \epsilon)t} + \frac{1}{2} e^{(1 - \epsilon)t}$$

and

$$(e^{At})_{12} = (e^{At})_{21} = \frac{1}{2\pi i} \oint \frac{\epsilon}{(Z - 1 - \epsilon)(Z - 1 + \epsilon)} e^{Zt} \, dZ$$

$$= \frac{1}{2} e^{(1 + \epsilon)t} - \frac{1}{2} e^{(1 - \epsilon)t}$$

These results have been obtained previously (cf. Sec. 2.6).

Another interesting calculation is

$$(A^{-1})_{11} = (A^{-1})_{22} = \frac{1}{2\pi i} \oint \frac{Z - 1}{(Z - 1 - \epsilon)(Z - 1 + \epsilon)} \frac{1}{Z} \, dZ$$

$$= \frac{1}{2} \left(\frac{1}{1 + \epsilon} + \frac{1}{1 - \epsilon} \right) = \frac{1}{1 - \epsilon^2}$$

$$(A^{-1})_{12} = (A^{-1})_{21} = \frac{1}{2\pi i} \oint \frac{\epsilon}{(Z - 1 - \epsilon)(Z - 1 + \epsilon)} \frac{1}{Z} \, dZ$$

$$= \frac{1}{2} \left(\frac{1}{1 + \epsilon} - \frac{1}{1 - \epsilon} \right) = -\frac{\epsilon}{1 - \epsilon^2}$$

It is to be noted that the contour of integration surrounded $1 + \epsilon$ and $1 - \epsilon$ but not 0 since $1/Z$ is not analytic at $Z = 0$.

As a second illustration consider Example 2.

Example 2

$$A = \begin{pmatrix} -15 & 12 \\ -24 & 19 \end{pmatrix}$$

From

$$(Z - A)q = 1$$

we obtain
$$q_{11} = \frac{Z - 19}{Z^2 - 4Z + 3}$$

$$q_{12} = \frac{12}{Z^2 - 4Z + 3}$$

$$q_{21} = \frac{-24}{Z^2 - 4Z + 3}$$

$$q_{22} = \frac{Z + 15}{Z^2 - 4Z + 3}$$

and from step b

$$(e^{At})_{11} = \frac{1}{2\pi i} \oint \frac{Z - 19}{(Z - 3)(Z - 1)} e^{Zt}\, dZ = 9e^t - 8e^{3t}$$

$$(e^{At})_{12} = -6e^t + 6e^{3t}$$
$$(e^{At})_{21} = 12e^t - 12e^{3t}$$
$$(e^{At})_{22} = -8e^t + 9e^{3t}$$

as before (cf. Sec. 2.6).
   Similarly,

$$(A^{-1})_{11} = \frac{1}{2\pi i} \oint \frac{Z - 19}{(Z - 1)(Z - 3)} \frac{1}{Z}\, dZ = 9 - \frac{8}{3} = \frac{19}{3}$$

$$(A^{-1})_{12} = -6 + 2 = -4$$
$$(A^{-1})_{21} = 12 - 4 = 8$$
$$(A^{-1})_{22} = -8 + 3 = -5$$

These examples have been the uninteresting ones—i.e., those where A is diagonalizable. The last illustration is that of a nondiagonalizable A. Thus consider

Example 3

$$A = \begin{pmatrix} 1 & 0 \\ 3 & 1 \end{pmatrix}$$

Then from

$$(Z - A)q = \begin{pmatrix} Z - 1 & 0 \\ -3 & Z - 1 \end{pmatrix} q = \begin{pmatrix} 1 & 0 \\ 0 & 1 \end{pmatrix}$$

there results

$$q_{11} = q_{22} = \frac{1}{Z - 1}$$

$$q_{12} = 0$$
$$q_{21} = \frac{3}{(Z - 1)^2}$$

Hence $(e^{At})_{11} = (e^{At})_{22} = \dfrac{1}{2\pi i} \oint \dfrac{1}{Z-1} e^{Zt} \, dZ = e^t$

$(e^{At})_{12} = 0$

$(e^{At})_{21} = \dfrac{1}{2\pi i} \oint \dfrac{3}{(Z-1)^2} e^{Zt} \, dZ = 3 \dfrac{d}{dZ} e^{Zt} \Big|_{Z=1} = 3te^t$

Therefore

$$e^{At} = \begin{pmatrix} e^t & 0 \\ 3te^t & e^t \end{pmatrix}$$

The point to be noted is the appearance of a term proportional to te^t. This cannot appear for diagonalizable matrices. Terms like $t^{m-1}e^{\lambda t}$ can appear for m-fold degenerate eigenvalues λ. As an illustration of this point the reader will verify that if

$$A = \begin{pmatrix} \lambda & 0 & 0 \\ \alpha & \lambda & 0 \\ \beta & \alpha & \lambda \end{pmatrix}$$

then $$e^{At} = \begin{pmatrix} 1 & 0 & 0 \\ \alpha t & 1 & 0 \\ \beta t + \tfrac{1}{2}\alpha^2 t^2 & \alpha t & 1 \end{pmatrix} e^{\lambda t}$$

3.5   The Inversion Formula

To evaluate e^{At} for given A, one may use the formula

$$e^{At} = \frac{1}{2\pi i} \oint e^{Zt} q(Z) \, dZ \qquad (3.6)$$

where $$q(Z) = (Z-A)^{-1} \qquad (3.7)$$

This yields e^{At}, given $q(Z)$.

The inverse problem, obtaining $q(Z)$ given e^{At}, is easily solved. Thus

$$\int_0^\infty e^{At} e^{-Zt} \, dt = \frac{1}{Z-A}\left(-\int_0^\infty \frac{d}{dt} e^{-(Z-A)t} \, dt\right) = q(Z) \qquad (3.8)$$

provided $\lim_{t\to\infty} e^{-(Z-A)t} = 0$. Consequently, if the real part of Z is large enough, $q(Z)$ may be obtained from (3.8). Analytic continuation takes care of other values of Z.

3.6 Laplace Transforms

According to (3.6) and (3.7), the solution of the equation

$$\dot{u} = Au \tag{3.9}$$

namely
$$u(t) = e^{At}u(0)$$

is given by

$$u(t) = \frac{1}{2\pi i} \oint e^{Zt} q(Z) u(0) \, dZ$$

or
$$u(t) = \frac{1}{2\pi i} \oint e^{Zt} U(Z) \, dZ \tag{3.10}$$

where $U(Z)$ satisfies

$$U(Z) = q(Z)u(0) = (Z - A)^{-1}u(0) \tag{3.11}$$

or
$$(Z - A)U(Z) = u(0) \tag{3.11a}$$

Substitution for $q(Z)$ in (3.11) by means of (3.8) yields

$$U(Z) = \int_0^\infty e^{At} e^{-Zt} u(0) \, dt = \int_0^\infty e^{-Zt} u(t) \, dt \tag{3.12}$$

The pair of relations

$$u(t) = \frac{1}{2\pi i} \oint e^{Zt} U(Z) \, dZ$$

$$U(Z) = \int_0^\infty e^{-Zt} u(t) \, dt$$

define an equivalence between $u(t)$ and $U(Z)$. $U(Z)$ is known as the Laplace transform of $u(t)$. It may be obtained by solving Eq. (3.11a).

The main reason for the introduction of the Laplace transform $U(Z)$ is that Eq. (3.11a) for $U(Z)$ is often easier to solve than is Eq. (3.9) for $u(t)$. In such cases the Laplace transform may be used to solve the equation

$$\dot{u} = Au \tag{3.13}$$

by means of the following procedures:

a. Define $U(Z)$ by the relation

$$U(Z) = \int_0^\infty e^{-Zt} u(t) \, dt \tag{3.14}$$

b. Multiply Eq. (3.13) by $e^{-Zt} \, dt$ and integrate from 0 to ∞. Then, the left-hand member becomes

$$\int_0^\infty \dot{u}(t) e^{-Zt} \, dt = \int_0^\infty \left(\frac{d}{dt} + Z \right) \left[u(t) e^{-Zt} \right] dt$$

$$= -u(0) + ZU(Z)$$

provided that the real part of Z is sufficiently large. The right-hand member becomes

$$\int_0^\infty Au(t)e^{-Zt}\,dt = AU(Z)$$

Hence
$$ZU(Z) - u(0) = AU(Z) \tag{3.15}$$

as in (3.11a).

 c. Solve Eq. (3.15) for $U(Z)$.
 d. Calculate

$$u(t) = \frac{1}{2\pi i}\oint e^{Zt}U(Z)\,dZ \tag{3.16}$$

This procedure can also be applied to equations which are not in the matrix notation and which contain higher-order derivatives. In this connection it is useful to note that

$$\int_0^\infty e^{-Zt}\left(\frac{d}{dt}\right)^n u(t)\,dt = Z^n U(Z) - \left[Z^{n-1}u(t)\right.$$
$$\left. + Z^{n-2}\frac{d}{dt}u(t) + \cdots + Z\left(\frac{d}{dt}\right)^{n-2}u(t) + \left(\frac{d}{dt}\right)^{n-1}u(t)\right]_{t=0}$$

As an example, consider
$$m\ddot{x} + kx = 0$$

Then, if $X = \displaystyle\int_0^\infty e^{-Zt}x(t)\,dt$,

$$m[Z^2 X - Zx(0) - \dot{x}(0)] + kX = 0$$

so that
$$X = \frac{Zx(0) + \dot{x}(0)}{Z^2 + \dfrac{k}{m}}$$

Consequently

$$x(t) = \frac{1}{2\pi i}\oint \frac{Zx(0) + \dot{x}(0)}{\left(Z + i\sqrt{\dfrac{k}{m}}\right)\left(Z - i\sqrt{\dfrac{k}{m}}\right)} e^{Zt}\,dZ$$

$$= \frac{i\sqrt{\dfrac{k}{m}}\,x(0) + \dot{x}(0)}{2i\sqrt{\dfrac{k}{m}}} e^{i\sqrt{\frac{k}{m}}t} + \frac{-i\sqrt{\dfrac{k}{m}}\,x(0) + \dot{x}(0)}{-2i\sqrt{\dfrac{k}{m}}} e^{-i\sqrt{\frac{k}{m}}t}$$

$$= x(0)\cos\left(\sqrt{\frac{k}{m}}\,t\right) + \dot{x}(0)\sqrt{\frac{m}{k}}\sin\left(\sqrt{\frac{k}{m}}\,t\right)$$

3.7   Inhomogeneous Equations

The problem treated in Sec. 2.9 may now be discussed:

$$\dot{u} = Au + f(t) \tag{3.17}$$

To apply the method of Laplace transforms, define, as in Sec. 3.6,

$$U(Z) = \int_0^\infty e^{-Zt} u(t)\, dt \tag{3.18}$$

and further

$$F(Z) = \int_0^\infty e^{-Zt} f(t)\, dt \tag{3.19}$$

Multiplication of (3.17) by $e^{-Zt}\, dt$ and integration from 0 to ∞ yields

$$ZU - u(0) = AU + F$$

or

$$(Z - A)U(Z) = u(0) + F(Z) \tag{3.20}$$

Once $U(Z)$ is determined from (3.20), use of the inversion formula

$$u(t) = \frac{1}{2\pi i} \oint e^{Zt} U(Z)\, dZ \tag{3.21}$$

yields $u(t)$.

As an illustration, consider the harmonic oscillator with a sinusoidal forcing term

$$m\ddot{x} + kx = \alpha \cos \omega t$$

Since

$$\int_0^\infty e^{-Zt} \cos \omega t\, dt = \frac{1}{2} \int_0^\infty \left[e^{-(Z+i\omega)t} + e^{-(Z-i\omega)t} \right] dt$$

$$= \frac{1}{2}\left(\frac{1}{Z + i\omega} + \frac{1}{Z - i\omega} \right)$$

$$= \frac{Z}{Z^2 + \omega^2}$$

the Laplace transform of x satisfies

$$m[Z^2 X - Zx(0) - \dot{x}(0)] + kX = \frac{\alpha Z}{Z^2 + \omega^2}$$

Thus, defining

$$\omega_0{}^2 = \frac{k}{m}$$

$$X = \frac{1}{Z^2 + \omega_0{}^2}\left[Zx(0) + \dot{x}(0) + \frac{(\alpha/m)Z}{Z^2 + \omega^2} \right]$$

A brief computation yields

$$x(t) = x(0) \cos \omega_0 t + \dot{x}(0) \frac{\sin \omega_0 t}{\omega_0} + \frac{\alpha}{m} \frac{\cos \omega_0 t - \cos \omega t}{\omega^2 - \omega_0^2}$$

3.8 The Convolution Theorem

In Sec. 2.9 the solution of

$$\dot{u} = Au + f(t)$$

was found to be

$$u(t) = e^{At}u(0) + \int_0^t e^{A(t-s)}f(s) \, ds$$

In Sec. 3.7 the solution was found to be

$$u(t) = \frac{1}{2\pi i} \oint \frac{e^{Zt}}{Z - A} \, dZ u(0) + \frac{1}{2\pi i} \oint \frac{e^{Zt}}{Z - A} F(Z) \, dZ$$

where

$$F(Z) = \int_0^\infty e^{-Zt}f(t) \, dt \qquad \frac{1}{Z - A} = \int_0^\infty e^{-Zt}e^{At} \, dt$$

A comparison of these solutions indicates that one must have

$$\int_0^t e^{A(t-s)}f(s) \, ds = \frac{1}{2\pi i} \oint \frac{1}{Z - A} F(Z)e^{Zt} \, dZ$$

Thus, $F(Z)$ is the transform of $f(t)$, $1/(Z - A)$ is the transform of e^{At}, and $F(Z) \cdot 1/(Z - A)$ is the transform of

$$\int_0^t e^{A(t-s)}f(s) \, ds = \int_0^t e^{As}f(t - s) \, ds$$

This result is a special case of the following.

Theorem

If $F(Z)$ is the transform of $f(t)$ and if $G(Z)$ is the transform of $g(t)$, then $F(Z) \, G(Z)$ is the transform of[1]

$$\int_0^t f(t - s)g(s) \, ds = \int_0^t f(s)g(t - s) \, ds$$

so that

$$\int_0^t f(t - s)g(s) \, ds = \frac{1}{2\pi i} \oint F(Z)G(Z)e^{Zt} \, dZ$$

[1] This integral is called the *convolution* of the functions f and g.

The proof is straightforward. Calculate the transform of

$$\int_0^t f(s)g(t-s)\,ds.$$

$$\int_0^\infty e^{-Zt}\int_0^t f(s)g(t-s)\,ds\,dt = \int_{t=0}^\infty \int_{s=0}^t e^{-Z(t-s)}e^{-Zs}f(s)g(t-s)\,ds\,dt$$

$$= \int_{s=0}^\infty \int_{t-s=0}^\infty e^{-Z(t-s)}e^{-Zs}f(s)g(t-s)\,d(t-s)\,ds$$

$$= \int_0^\infty e^{-Zs}f(s)\,ds\int_0^\infty e^{-Zu}g(u)\,du$$

$$= F(Z)G(Z)$$

as was to be shown.

As an application, consider

$$\ddot{x} + \omega^2 x = f(t) \qquad x(0) = \dot{x}(0) = 0$$

Then

$$(Z^2 + \omega^2)X = F$$

$$X = \frac{F}{Z^2 + \omega^2}$$

Since the inverse transform of $1/(Z^2 + \omega^2)$ is $\omega^{-1}\sin \omega t$

$$x(t) = \int_0^t \frac{\sin \omega(t-s)}{\omega}f(s)\,ds$$

Exercises

1. Show that the following matrix cannot be diagonalized.

$$A = \begin{pmatrix} \beta\delta & -\beta^2 \\ \delta^2 & -\beta\delta \end{pmatrix}$$

2. Find

$$\begin{pmatrix} 1 & 0 \\ 3 & 1 \end{pmatrix}^{37}$$

3. Solve the equations

$$\dot{x} = \beta\delta x - \beta^2 y$$
$$\dot{y} = \delta^2 x - \delta\beta y$$

4. Solve the equations

$$\dot{x} = \alpha x + \beta y + 1$$
$$\dot{y} = \beta x + \alpha y + 1$$
$$x(0) = y(0) = 0$$

5. Solve by the Laplace transform method Eqs. (1.13), (1.14), and (1.15) of the text.

6. If $U(Z)$ is the Laplace transform of $u(t)$, show that

$$\int_0^\infty t^n u(t)\, dt = \left[\left(-\frac{d}{dZ}\right)^n U(Z)\right]_{Z=0}$$

Thus evaluate $I_n = \int_0^\infty t^n e^{-t}\, dt$.

7. Find the Laplace transform of (a) $u(t - \alpha)(\alpha \geq 0)$ where $u(t) = 0$ for $x < 0$; (b) $u(\alpha t)(\alpha > 0)$; (c) $tu(t)$.

8. If $|Z - M| = \sum\limits_{n=0}^{N} \alpha_n Z^n \quad (\alpha_N = 1)$

show that
$$\sum_{n=0}^{N} \alpha_n M^n = 0$$

for every $N \times N$ square matrix M.

9. A circuit consists of a resistance R in series with an inductance. At time $t = 0$ an emf $\varepsilon = \alpha t$, where α is a constant, is applied. Find the current in the circuit at any time $t > 0$.

10. Consider the circuit of Exercise 9. At time $t = 0$, an emf $\varepsilon = \sin \omega t$ is applied. Find the current at any time $t > 0$.

References

Carslaw, H. S. and J. C. Jaeger: "Operational Methods in Applied Mathematics," Oxford University Press, Inc., New York, 1941.

Widder, D. V.: "The Laplace Transform," Princeton University Press, Princeton, N.J., 1941.

McLachlan, N. W.: "Complex Variable and the Operational Calculus," Cambridge University Press, Inc., New York, 1942.

Churchill, R. V.: "Operational Mathematics," 2d ed., McGraw-Hill Book Company, Inc., New York, 1958.

Doetsch, G.: "Theorie und Andwendung der Laplace-Transformation," Dover Publications, New York, 1944.

Campbell, G. A. and R. M. Foster: "Fourier Integrals for Practical Applications," D. Van Nostrand Company, Inc., Princeton, N. J., 1948.

Parodi, M.: "Applications Physiques de la Transformation de Laplace, Méthodes de Calcul," B, 1, Gauthier-Villars & Cie, Paris, 1948.

Proceedings of the Symposium on Spectral Theory and Differential Problems, Oklahoma A. and M., Stillwater, Oklahoma, 1951.

CHAPTER 4

Vector Spaces and Linear Operators

4.1 Introduction

The use of abstract vector spaces has become a powerful mathematical tool for the solution of physical problems. The procedure followed in the use of such spaces is to represent a physical system by a mathematical object called a *state vector*. This state vector completely describes the behavior of the physical system. When the state (i.e., the configuration) of the physical system changes, the state vector changes in a corresponding way. To each state of the physical system there corresponds a unique state vector and vice versa.

The state vector is an abstract quantity which may be described mathematically in a number of equivalent ways. The particular way in which the state vector is represented depends upon the coordinate system chosen. The mathematical form representing the state vector in a given coordinate system is known as the *representative* of the state vector in that coordinate system. In each permissible coordinate system there is a unique representative of the state vector.

In order to clarify the concept of the representative of the state vector consider the problem of the harmonic oscillator (Sec. 1.1). The equation of motion is

$$m\ddot{x} + Kx = 0 \tag{1.3}$$

The solution of (1.3) is

$$x(t) = x(0) \cos \sqrt{\frac{K}{m}}\, t + \frac{\dot{x}(0)}{\sqrt{K/m}} \sin \sqrt{\frac{K}{m}}\, t \tag{4.1}$$

Since, for a given $x(0)$, there are many possible values of $x(t)$, depending on the value of $\dot{x}(0)$, it is clear that the state of the system is not uniquely represented at a given time t by the quantity x alone. Two quantities

50

(i.e., coordinates), x and $\dot{x}$, are required to represent the state of the harmonic oscillator. If $y = m\dot{x}$, the equation of motion in the x,y coordinate system is

$$\begin{pmatrix} \dot{x} \\ \dot{y} \end{pmatrix} = \begin{pmatrix} 0 & 1/m \\ -K & 0 \end{pmatrix} \begin{pmatrix} x \\ y \end{pmatrix} \tag{1.14}$$

The representative of the state vector in the x,y coordinate system is the two-column

$$\begin{pmatrix} x \\ y \end{pmatrix}$$

Furthermore, the 2×2 matrix

$$\begin{pmatrix} 0 & \dfrac{1}{m} \\ -K & 0 \end{pmatrix}$$

is the representative in the x,y coordinate system of a linear operator which transforms the state vector into another vector whose representative in this same coordinate system is the two-column

$$\begin{pmatrix} \dot{x} \\ \dot{y} \end{pmatrix}$$

The solution of Eq. (1.14) is easily obtained by the Laplace transform method (cf. Sec. 3.8) or by diagonalization (cf. Sec. 2.6). Writing

$$\omega = \sqrt{\frac{K}{m}}$$

it is

$$\begin{pmatrix} x \\ y \end{pmatrix} = \frac{1}{2}\left[e^{i\omega t}\begin{pmatrix} 1 & -i/m\omega \\ iK/\omega & 1 \end{pmatrix} - e^{-i\omega t}\begin{pmatrix} -1 & -i/m\omega \\ iK/\omega & -1 \end{pmatrix} \right]\begin{pmatrix} x(0) \\ y(0) \end{pmatrix} \tag{4.2}$$

which (of course) agrees with (4.1).

In the present chapter it will be seen that the n columns and $n \times n$ matrices discussed in the preceding chapters may be considered, respectively, as the representatives of vectors and linear operators in n-dimensional spaces. The study begins with a review of the concepts of three-dimensional vector spaces—specifically of dyads (operators), transformations of coordinates, and length of a vector. The concepts of n-dimensional vector spaces will then be developed by the logical extension of those in three-dimensional spaces. In order to accomplish this, it is convenient to introduce unit vectors attached to the coordinate axes to symbolize the relevant coordinate system. In this way a vector will have meaning independent of the coordinate system.

4.2 Base Vectors and Basis

It is assumed that the reader is familiar with the concepts of the ordinary three-dimensional vector spaces. As a starting point, recall that the position of a particle in a given cartesian coordinate system $0XYZ$ is given by the vector

$$\mathbf{r} = x\mathbf{i} + y\mathbf{j} + z\mathbf{k} \tag{4.3}$$

where $\mathbf{i}$, $\mathbf{j}$, $\mathbf{k}$ are, respectively, unit vectors along the X, Y, and Z axes. These unit vectors are called *base vectors*. They define the coordinate system, or *basis*, in which x, y, z are the coordinates of the particle. Note that the base vectors $\mathbf{i}$, $\mathbf{j}$, $\mathbf{k}$ are linearly independent: If $r = 0$, then $x = y = z = 0$. Any vector in three-dimensional space may be expressed as a linear combination of the three base vectors $\mathbf{i}, \mathbf{j}, \mathbf{k}$. Note further that the number of base vectors (three) is exactly equal to the dimensionality of the space.

The square of the length of the vector $\mathbf{r}$ is, by definition,

$$r^2 = x^2 + y^2 + z^2 \tag{4.4}$$

In order to construct an algorithm which yields (4.4), it is useful to introduce a type of multiplication of vectors known as scalar multiplication, defined by the relations

$$\begin{aligned} \mathbf{i} \cdot \mathbf{j} = \mathbf{j} \cdot \mathbf{i} = \mathbf{j} \cdot \mathbf{k} = \mathbf{k} \cdot \mathbf{j} = \mathbf{k} \cdot \mathbf{i} = \mathbf{i} \cdot \mathbf{k} = 0 \\ \cdot \mathbf{i} = \mathbf{j} \cdot \mathbf{j} = \mathbf{k} \cdot \mathbf{k} = 1 \end{aligned} \tag{4.5}$$

and to require that scalar multiplication of vectors obey the distributive law in multiplication. Thus

$$\begin{aligned} r^2 = \mathbf{r} \cdot \mathbf{r} &= (x\mathbf{i} + y\mathbf{j} + z\mathbf{k}) \cdot (x\mathbf{i} + y\mathbf{j} + z\mathbf{k}) \\ &= x^2\mathbf{i} \cdot \mathbf{i} + xy\mathbf{i} \cdot \mathbf{j} + xz\mathbf{i} \cdot \mathbf{k} + yx\mathbf{j} \cdot \mathbf{i} + y^2\mathbf{j} \cdot \mathbf{j} + yz\mathbf{j} \cdot \mathbf{k} + zx\mathbf{k} \cdot \mathbf{i} \\ &\quad + zy\mathbf{k} \cdot \mathbf{j} + z^2\mathbf{k} \cdot \mathbf{k} \\ &= x^2 + y^2 + z^2 \end{aligned}$$

The first of the relations (4.5) expresses the *orthogonality* (i.e., the mutual perpendicularity) of the base vectors $\mathbf{i}, \mathbf{j}, \mathbf{k}$. The second relation expresses the *normality* (i.e., the unit length) of the base vectors. The relations (4.5) together are known as the *orthonormality condition*. The base vectors $\mathbf{i}, \mathbf{j}, \mathbf{k}$ are said to form an *orthonormal set*.

Vector analysis may be extended to apply to complex vectors in an

n-dimensional space,[1] where n is finite but arbitrary. This extension is carried out as follows:

Let $\mathbf{u}_i$ $(i = 1, 2, \ldots, n)$ be a set of linearly independent vectors in an n-dimensional vector space. Any vector $\mathbf{x}$ may be written as[2]

$$\mathbf{x} = \sum_{i=1}^{n} \mathbf{u}_i x_i \qquad (4.6)$$

The set of vectors $\mathbf{u}_i$ is said to form a basis. The x_i are the components of the vector $\mathbf{x}$ in this basis. For convenience, this basis will be called the "$\mathbf{u}_i$ basis" rather than by the more cumbersome expression, "the basis in which the $\mathbf{u}_i$ are the base vectors."

A length may be defined for the vector $\mathbf{x}$. This length should (1) reduce to (4.4) for real three-dimensional vectors, (2) be zero if and only if $x_i = 0$ for all i, and (3) be real. Such a definition of length is given by

$$x^2 = \sum_{i=1}^{n} |x_i|^2$$

In order to obtain an algorithm which yields this result it is convenient to introduce the concept of a *dual space:* To each vector $\mathbf{x}$ in the space determined by the basis $\mathbf{u}_i$ there corresponds a vector $\mathbf{x}^+$ in the dual space determined by the basis $\mathbf{u}_i^+$ such that

$$\mathbf{x}^+ = \sum_{i=1}^{n} \bar{x}_i \mathbf{u}_i^+ \qquad (4.7)$$

where $\bar{x}_i$ is the complex conjugate of x_i, and

$$\mathbf{u}_i^+ \mathbf{u}_j = \delta_{ij} \qquad (4.8)$$

The relation (4.8) defines the scalar multiplication of complex vectors in an n-dimensional vector space. If (4.8) holds, the $\mathbf{u}_i^+$ and $\mathbf{u}_i$ form a

---

[1] A vector space is, by definition, n-dimensional if there are n linearly independent vectors in the space, but any $n + 1$ vectors are linearly dependent.

[2] That this is always possible if the $\mathbf{u}_i$ are linearly independent may be demonstrated as follows: let $\mathbf{u}_1, \ldots, \mathbf{u}_n$ be linearly independent, and let $\mathbf{x}$ be any vector in the space. These $n + 1$ vectors are linearly dependent. Hence there exist scalars $\alpha, \alpha_1, \alpha_2, \ldots, \alpha_n$, not all zero, such that

$$\mathbf{x}\alpha + \mathbf{u}_1\alpha_1 + \mathbf{u}_2\alpha_2 + \cdots + \mathbf{u}_n\alpha_n = 0$$

But then, $\alpha \neq 0$, since if $\alpha = 0$ the relation would express the linear dependence of the set of $\mathbf{u}_i$ in contradiction to the hypothesis. One can therefore solve for $\mathbf{x}$ and write

$$\mathbf{x} = \sum_i \mathbf{u}_i x_i$$

where $x_i \equiv -\alpha_i/\alpha$. Hence every vector of the space is expressible as a linear combination of any n linearly independent vectors of the space.

bi-orthonormal basis. The relation (4.8) is known as the *bi-orthonormality condition.*

If $\mathbf{u}_i^+ = \mathbf{u}_i$, all i, the basis is said to be *orthonormal* and the relation (4.8) is then known as the *orthonormality condition.* The expression (4.8) then states that (1) the vectors $\mathbf{u}_i$ are *unitary*, i.e., of unit length ($\mathbf{u}_i \mathbf{u}_i = 1$), and (2) $\mathbf{u}_i$ and $\mathbf{u}_j$ are mutually orthogonal, i.e., $\mathbf{u}_i \mathbf{u}_j = 0$ for $i \neq j$. Such pairs of unitary and mutually orthogonal vectors are called *orthonormal.*

The square of the length of the vector $\mathbf{x}$ is given by the product

$$\mathbf{x}^+ \mathbf{x} = \sum_{ij} \bar{x}_i \mathbf{u}_i^+ \mathbf{u}_j x_j = \sum_{ij} \bar{x}_i \, \delta_{ij} x_j = \sum_i |x_i|^2$$

where the distributive law in multiplication has been used. The linear independence of the $\mathbf{u}_i$ is verified as follows: Suppose that

$$\mathbf{x} = \sum_i \mathbf{u}_i x_i = 0$$

Then
$$\mathbf{u}_j^+ \mathbf{x} = \sum_i \mathbf{u}_j^+ \mathbf{u}_i x_i = \sum_i \delta_{ji} x_i = x_j = 0$$

Note that multiplication of vectors is not commutative; $\mathbf{x}^+\mathbf{y}$ is quite different from $\mathbf{yx}^+$. The first is a number; the second corresponds to the dyad of ordinary vector algebra.

A very useful theorem, known as the *expansion theorem*, may be derived as follows: Multiply (4.6) by $\mathbf{u}_j^+$ from the left. Then

$$\mathbf{u}_j^+ \mathbf{x} = \sum_i \mathbf{u}_j^+ \mathbf{u}_i x_i = x_j$$

Substitute for the x_i in (4.6) by means of this result. Then

$$\mathbf{x} = \sum_{j=1}^{n} \mathbf{u}_j x_j = \sum_{j=1}^{n} \mathbf{u}_j \mathbf{u}_j^+ \mathbf{x}$$

$$\mathbf{x} = \sum_{i=1}^{n} \mathbf{u}_i \mathbf{u}_i^+ \mathbf{x}$$

which states that multiplication of any vector $\mathbf{x}$ by $\sum_i \mathbf{u}_i \mathbf{u}_i^+$ merely reproduces the vector. Hence

$$1 = \sum_i \mathbf{u}_i \mathbf{u}_i^+ \tag{4.9}$$

which is the expansion theorem desired.

The operations of multiplication of a vector $\mathbf{x}$ by a number α and the addition of two vectors $\mathbf{x}$ and $\mathbf{y}$ are defined by the relations

$$\alpha \mathbf{x} = \sum_i \mathbf{u}_i(\alpha x_i)$$

$$\mathbf{x} + \mathbf{y} = \sum_i \mathbf{u}_i x_i + \sum_i \mathbf{u}_i y_i = \sum_i \mathbf{u}_i(x_i + y_i)$$

4.3 Change of Basis

In a three-dimensional vector space, a coordinate system is indicated by the unit vectors $\mathbf{i}, \mathbf{j}, \mathbf{k}$, directed respectively along the positive x, y, and z axes. A new coordinate system may be introduced by expressing a new set of base vectors $\mathbf{i}', \mathbf{j}'$, and $\mathbf{k}'$ in terms of the old, or by expressing the old in terms of the new. Such a change of coordinates is called a *rotation of coordinates*[1] if both $\mathbf{i}, \mathbf{j}, \mathbf{k}$ and $\mathbf{i}', \mathbf{j}', \mathbf{k}'$ are orthonormal bases.

A similar change of coordinates may be introduced in an n-dimensional vector space. Thus, suppose $\mathbf{u}_i$ and $\mathbf{v}_j$ are two bases. Since $\mathbf{u}_i$ is a basis, each $\mathbf{v}_j$ may be written as a superposition of the $\mathbf{u}_i$:

$$\mathbf{v}_j = \sum_k \mathbf{u}_k t_{kj} \qquad (4.10)$$

Similarly, since $\mathbf{v}_j$ is a basis, each $\mathbf{u}_i$ may be written as a superposition of the $\mathbf{v}_j$:

$$\mathbf{u}_i = \sum_j \mathbf{v}_j s_{ji} \qquad (4.11)$$

A relation is readily deduced between the matrix s and the matrix t. Thus, if (4.10) is substituted into (4.11) one finds that

$$\mathbf{u}_i = \sum_{j,k} \mathbf{u}_k t_{kj} s_{ji}$$

or
$$ts = 1 \qquad (4.12)$$

Thus
$$t = s^{-1} \qquad s = t^{-1} \qquad (4.13)$$

This result, (4.13), was derived using only the hypothesis that $\mathbf{u}_i$ and $\mathbf{v}_j$ were bases. If they are both bi-orthonormal bases, s and t are further restricted.

If $\mathbf{u}_i$ and $\mathbf{u}_i^+$ form a bi-orthonormal basis, then the dual basis $\mathbf{u}_i^+$ is such that

$$\mathbf{u}_i^+ \mathbf{u}_j = \delta_{ij}$$

Further, if

$$\mathbf{v}_j = \sum_k \mathbf{u}_k t_{kj}$$

the dual vectors $\mathbf{v}_j^+$ are given by (4.7):

$$\mathbf{v}_j^+ = \sum_l \bar{t}_{lj} \mathbf{u}_l^+$$

---

[1] Or a change from a right-handed to a left-handed coordinate system as when

$$\mathbf{i} = \mathbf{i}' \qquad \mathbf{j} = \mathbf{j}' \qquad \mathbf{k} = -\mathbf{k}'$$

The bi-orthonormality of $\mathbf{v}_j$ leads to

$$\delta_{ji} = \mathbf{v}_j^+ \mathbf{v}_i = \sum_{k,l} \bar{t}_{lj} \mathbf{u}_l^+ \mathbf{u}_k t_{ki}$$

$$= \sum_{k,l} \bar{t}_{lj} \delta_{lk} t_{ki}$$

$$= \sum_k \bar{t}_{kj} t_{ki}$$

If the matrix t^+ (the conjugate transpose or *Hermitian adjoint* of t) is defined by

$$t_{jk}^+ = \bar{t}_{kj}$$

one has

$$\delta_{ji} = \sum_k t_{jk}^+ t_{ki}$$

or

$$t^+ t = 1 \tag{4.14}$$

A matrix satisfying (4.14) is said to be *unitary*. A real unitary matrix is *orthogonal*. Rotations of coordinates in the customary three-dimensional vector space are carried out by orthogonal matrices.

It has been shown that a change of coordinates from one bi-orthonormal basis to another is carried out with the aid of a unitary matrix t. Thus

$$\mathbf{u}_i = \sum_j \mathbf{v}_j t_{ji}^+ \qquad \mathbf{u}_i^+ = \sum_j t_{ij} \mathbf{v}_j^+$$

$$\mathbf{v}_j = \sum_i \mathbf{u}_i t_{ij} \qquad \mathbf{v}_j^+ = \sum_i t_{ji}^+ \mathbf{u}_i^+$$

With the above results in mind it is not difficult to calculate the coordinates of $\mathbf{x}$ and $\mathbf{x}^+$ in the $\mathbf{v}_j$ and $\mathbf{v}_j^+$ bases respectively. Thus, let x_i be the coordinates of $\mathbf{x}$ in the $\mathbf{u}_i$ basis and x_i' the coordinates of $\mathbf{x}$ in the $\mathbf{v}_i$ basis:

$$\mathbf{x} = \sum_i \mathbf{u}_i x_i = \sum_j \mathbf{v}_j x_j'$$

$$\mathbf{x}^+ = \sum_i \bar{x}_i \mathbf{u}_i^+ = \sum_j \bar{x}_j' \mathbf{v}_j^+$$

It is desired to express the x_i in terms of the x_j, etc.

To this end, it is useful to note that

$$\mathbf{v}_k^+ \mathbf{u}_i = \mathbf{v}_k^+ \sum_j \mathbf{v}_j t_{ji}^+ = t_{ki}^+$$

$$\mathbf{u}_k^+ \mathbf{v}_j = t_{kj}$$

Then consider

$$\mathbf{u}_k^+ \mathbf{x} = \mathbf{u}_k^+ \sum_i \mathbf{u}_i x_i = x_k$$

$$= \mathbf{u}_k^+ \sum_j \mathbf{v}_j x_j'$$

$$= \sum_j t_{kj} x_j'$$

that is,

$$x_k = \sum_j t_{kj} x_j'$$

similarly
$$x_k' = \mathbf{v}_k^+ \mathbf{x} = \sum_i t_{ki}^+ x_i$$

$$\bar{x}_k = \mathbf{x}^+ \mathbf{u}_k = \sum_j \bar{x}_j' t_{jk}^+$$

$$\bar{x}_k' = \mathbf{x}^+ \mathbf{v}_k = \sum_i \bar{x}_i t_{ik}$$

4.4 Linear Operators

An operator $\mathscr{L}$, in a vector space, is an entity which, acting upon an arbitrary vector $\mathbf{x}$, converts it into a vector $\mathbf{y}$:

$$\mathbf{y} = \mathscr{L}\mathbf{x} \tag{4.15}$$

$\mathscr{L}$ is a known operator if and only if, given $\mathbf{x}$, $\mathbf{y}$ is determined. The linearity of the operator $\mathscr{L}$ is expressed by the relations

$$\mathscr{L}(\mathbf{x} + \mathbf{y}) = \mathscr{L}\mathbf{x} + \mathscr{L}\mathbf{y} \tag{4.16}$$

and
$$\mathscr{L}(\alpha\mathbf{x}) = \alpha\mathscr{L}\mathbf{x} \tag{4.17}$$

where α is any number.[1]

Suppose $\mathscr{L}$ and $\mathscr{M}$ are two linear operators, the first of which transforms the arbitrary vector $\mathbf{x}$ into the vector $\mathbf{y}$

$$\mathscr{L}\mathbf{x} = \mathbf{y}$$

while the second transforms the vector $\mathbf{y}$ into the vector $\mathbf{z}$

$$\mathscr{M}\mathbf{y} = \mathbf{z}$$

Then the resultant operator $\mathscr{N}$ which transforms the vector $\mathbf{x}$ directly into the vector $\mathbf{z}$ is also linear and is denoted by $\mathscr{M}\mathscr{L}$:

$$\mathbf{z} = \mathscr{M}\mathbf{y} = \mathscr{M}\mathscr{L}\mathbf{x} = \mathscr{N}\mathbf{x} \tag{4.18}$$

4.5 The Representation of Linear Operators by Matrices

A linear operator $\mathscr{L}$ is determined if and only if its effect on every vector is known. In particular, its effect on each vector in the basis must be known. That is, the matrix L such that

$$\mathscr{L}\mathbf{u}_i = \sum_j \mathbf{u}_j L_{ji} \tag{4.19}$$

must be a known matrix.

[1] We may write in place of (4.16) and (4.17) the single relation $\mathscr{L}(\alpha\mathbf{x} + \mathbf{y}) = \alpha\mathscr{L}\mathbf{x} + \mathscr{L}\mathbf{y}$.

The converse is also true, a knowledge of the matrix L in a given coordinate system completely determines $\mathscr{L}$. It need merely be shown that a knowledge of L enables the evaluation of

$$y = \mathscr{L}x$$

for every x. The proof is almost trivial: Let

$$x = \sum_i \mathbf{u}_i x_i$$

then

$$y = \mathscr{L}x = \mathscr{L} \sum_i \mathbf{u}_i x_i$$

$$= \sum_i (\mathscr{L}\mathbf{u}_i) x_i$$

$$= \sum_{i,j} \mathbf{u}_j L_{ji} x_i$$

This result may be written as

$$y_i = \sum_i L_{ji} x_i$$

or

$$y = Lx \tag{4.20}$$

Thus it is clear that matrices and n columns are, respectively, the representatives of operators and vectors in a given basis.

An alternate demonstration that L determines $\mathscr{L}$ is given by the following procedure. From (4.19) it follows immediately that

$$\mathscr{L} \sum_i \mathbf{u}_i \mathbf{u}_i^+ = \sum_i \mathscr{L}\mathbf{u}_i \mathbf{u}_i^+ = \sum_{j,i} \mathbf{u}_j L_{ji} \mathbf{u}_i^+$$

From (4.9) we then have

$$\mathscr{L} = \sum_{i,j} \mathbf{u}_i L_{ij} \mathbf{u}_j^+ \tag{4.21}$$

This is a useful representation of the operator $\mathscr{L}$.

4.6   The Operator in the Dual Space

If

$$x = \sum \mathbf{u}_i x_i$$

then the corresponding vector in the dual space is

$$x^+ = \sum \bar{x}_i \mathbf{u}_i^+$$

With the definition

$$y = \mathscr{L}x$$

one has

$$y = Lx$$

or

$$y_i = \sum_i L_{ij} x_j$$

Hence

$$\bar{y}_i = \sum_j \bar{x}_j \bar{L}_{ij}$$

or

$$y^+ = x^+ L^+$$

This result suggests the notation

$$\mathbf{y}^+ = \mathbf{x}^+ \mathscr{L}^+$$

where, if

$$\mathscr{L} = \sum_{i,j} \mathbf{u}_i L_{ij} \mathbf{u}_j^+ \tag{4.21}$$

then

$$L^+ = \sum_{i,j} \mathbf{u}_i L_{ji} \mathbf{u}_j^+ = \sum_{i,j} \mathbf{u}_i L_{ij}^+ \mathbf{u}_j^+ \tag{4.22}$$

It then follows that the n-row y^+ and the matrix L^+ are, respectively, the representatives of the vector $\mathbf{y}^+$ and the linear operator $\mathscr{L}^+$ in the dual space, just as the n-column y and the matrix L are, respectively, the representatives of the vector $\mathbf{y}$ and the linear operator $\mathscr{L}$ in the n-dimensional vector space.

Note that the above development is equivalent to the algorithm

$$(\mathscr{L}\mathbf{x})^+ = \mathbf{x}^+ \mathscr{L}^+ \tag{4.23}$$

Further, the reader may wish to show that

$$(\mathscr{L}\mathscr{M})^+ = \mathscr{M}^+ \mathscr{L}^+ \tag{4.24}$$

follows directly from (4.21), (4.22), (4.23), and

$$(LM)^+ = M^+ L^+$$

Additional properties of the operation $^+$ are

$$(\mathbf{x}^+)^+ = \mathbf{x}$$
$$(\mathscr{L}^+)^+ = \mathscr{L}$$
$$\mathbf{x}^+\mathbf{y} = (\mathbf{y}^+\mathbf{x})^+ = \overline{\mathbf{y}^+\mathbf{x}}$$

Thus

$$(\mathbf{x}^+\mathscr{L}\mathbf{y})^+ = (\mathscr{L}\mathbf{y})^+\mathbf{x}$$
$$= \mathbf{y}^+\mathscr{L}^+\mathbf{x}$$

4.7 Effect of Change of Basis on the Representation of an Operator

If the general representation of the linear operator $\mathscr{L}$ in the $\mathbf{u}_i$ basis is, from (4.21),

$$\mathscr{L} = \sum_{i,j} \mathbf{u}_i L_{ij} \mathbf{u}_j^+ \tag{4.25}$$

then the general representation of $\mathscr{L}$ in the basis $\mathbf{v}_i$ defined by the relations

$$\mathbf{u}_i = \sum_j \mathbf{v}_j s_{ji} \quad \text{and} \quad \mathbf{u}_i^+ = \sum_j \bar{s}_{ji} \mathbf{v}_j^+ = \sum_j s_{ij}^+ \mathbf{v}_j^+$$

is

$$\mathscr{L} = \sum_{i,j} \left[\left(\sum_k \mathbf{v}_k s_{ki} \right) L_{ij} \left(\sum_m s_{jm}^+ \mathbf{v}_m^+ \right) \right]$$
$$= \sum_{k,m} \mathbf{v}_k (sLs^+)_{km} \mathbf{v}_m^+ \tag{4.26}$$

Thus, if in the $\mathbf{u}_i$ basis the linear operator $\mathscr{L}$ is represented by a matrix L, then in the $\mathbf{v}_i$ basis it is represented by sLs^+, where s is the matrix which effects the transformation from the $\mathbf{v}_i$ basis to the $\mathbf{u}_i$ basis.

Similarly, if $\mathscr{L}^+ = \sum_{i,j} \mathbf{u}_k L_{ji}^+ \mathbf{u}_i^+$, then

$$\mathscr{L}^+ = \sum_{k,m} \mathbf{v}_k (\sum_{i,j} s_{kj} L_{ji}^+ s_{im}^+) \mathbf{v}_m^+$$
$$= \sum_{k,m} \mathbf{v}_k (sL^+ s^+)_{km} \mathbf{v}_m^+ \tag{4.27}$$

The general representation in the $\mathbf{u}_i$ basis of the identity operator $\mathscr{I}$, defined by the relation $\mathscr{I} \mathbf{x} = \mathbf{x}$ for any vector $\mathbf{x}$, is the unit matrix, since

$$\mathscr{I} = \sum_{i,j} \mathbf{u}_i \, \delta_{ij} \mathbf{u}_j^+ = \sum_i \mathbf{u}_i \mathbf{u}_i^+ \tag{4.28}$$

in agreement with the expansion theorem (4.9). Clearly in the $\mathbf{v}_i$ basis one has

$$\mathscr{I} = \sum_i \mathbf{v}_i \mathbf{v}_i^+$$

4.8   The Spectral Representation of an Operator

If an operator $\mathscr{L}$ and a nonvanishing vector $\mathbf{x}$ are so related that

$$\mathscr{L} \mathbf{x} = \lambda \mathbf{x} \tag{4.29}$$

where λ is a number (that is, if $\mathbf{x}$ when operated on by $\mathscr{L}$ is transformed into a numerical multiple of itself), then $\mathbf{x}$ is said to be an *eigenvector* of the operator $\mathscr{L}$, λ is called an *eigenvalue* of the operator $\mathscr{L}$, and the eigenvector $\mathbf{x}$ and the eigenvalue λ of $\mathscr{L}$ are said to belong to each other.

Suppose the eigenvectors of a linear operator $\mathscr{L}$, denoted by $\mathbf{u}_l$, form a bi-orthonormal basis. Then

$$\mathscr{L} \mathbf{u}_l = l \mathbf{u}_l \tag{4.30}$$

where l is the eigenvalue of $\mathscr{L}$ belonging to the eigenvector $\mathbf{u}_l$, and the general representation of $\mathscr{L}$ is

$$\mathscr{L} = \sum_l \mathbf{u}_l l \mathbf{u}_l^+ \tag{4.31}$$

This representation of the operator $\mathscr{L}$ displays all the characteristics of the operator (i.e., its eigenvalues and eigenvectors) in a convenient manner. It is known as the *spectral representation* of the operator $\mathscr{L}$.

The conditions under which (4.31) may hold are discussed below in Sec. 4.9.

The spectral representation of $\mathscr{L}^+$, the Hermitian adjoint of the operator $\mathscr{L}$, in the eigenvector basis $\mathbf{u}_l$ is

$$\mathscr{L}^+ = \sum_l \mathbf{u}_l \bar{l} \mathbf{u}_l^+ \tag{4.32}$$

The representation of the operator $\mathscr{L}$ in the basis $\mathbf{v}_i$ defined by the relations

$$\mathbf{u}_l = \sum_j \mathbf{v}_j s_{jl} \qquad \text{and} \qquad \mathbf{u}_l^+ = \sum_k s_{lk}^+ \mathbf{v}_k^+ \qquad (4.33)$$

is

$$\mathscr{L} = \sum_{j,k} \mathbf{v}_j \Big(\sum_l s_{jl} l s_{lk}^+ \Big) \mathbf{v}_k^+ \qquad (4.34)$$

From (4.31) it follows that

$$\mathscr{L}^n = \sum_l \mathbf{u}_l l^n \mathbf{u}_l^+ \qquad n = \text{integer} \qquad (4.35)$$

so that for any power series and therefore by definition for any function of $\mathscr{L}$

$$f(\mathscr{L}) = \sum_l \mathbf{u}_l f(l) \mathbf{u}_l^+ \qquad (4.36)$$

It then follows that the representation of $f(\mathscr{L})$ in the v_i basis defined by (4.33) is given by

$$f(\mathscr{L}) = \sum_{j,k} \mathbf{v}_j \Big(\sum_l s_{jl} f(l) s_{lk}^+ \Big) \mathbf{v}_k^+ \qquad (4.37)$$

4.9 The Formation of a Basis by Eigenvectors of a Linear Operator

In the preceding section it was supposed that the eigenvectors of the linear operator $\mathscr{L}$ formed a bi-orthonormal basis. This is not true for all operators. However, it is true for operators $\mathscr{L}$ which satisfy the condition

$$\mathscr{L}\mathscr{L}^+ = \mathscr{L}^+\mathscr{L} \qquad (4.38)$$

Operators satisfying this condition are known as *normal operators*.

We shall prove the theorem: $\mathscr{L}^+\mathscr{L} = \mathscr{L}\mathscr{L}^+$ *is a necessary and sufficient condition that the eigenvectors of the operator $\mathscr{L}$ form a bi-orthonormal basis.*

The necessity of the condition (4.38) is demonstrated as follows: Let the eigenvectors of $\mathscr{L}$ be $\mathbf{u}_l$. Then in terms of the basis which they form

$$\mathscr{L} = \sum_l \mathbf{u}_l l \mathbf{u}_l^+ \qquad \text{and} \qquad \mathscr{L}^+ = \sum_l \mathbf{u}_l \bar{l} \mathbf{u}_l^+$$

hence $\qquad \mathscr{L}\mathscr{L}^+ = \sum_l \mathbf{u}_l l \mathbf{u}_l^+ \sum_{l'} \mathbf{u}_{l'} \bar{l}' \mathbf{u}_{l'}^+ = \sum_l \mathbf{u}_l |l|^2 \mathbf{u}_l^+ = \mathscr{L}^+\mathscr{L}$

That (4.38) is also a sufficient condition is proved after the lemmas.

Lemma I

Any operator has at least one eigenvector.

Let the vectors $\mathbf{v}_i$ form a basis. Then one may write

$$\mathscr{L} = \sum \mathbf{v}_i L_{ij} \mathbf{v}_j^+$$
$$\mathbf{u}_l = \sum \mathbf{v}_i a_i$$

Then
$$\mathscr{L}\mathbf{u}_i = \mathbf{u}_i l$$

implies
$$\sum \mathbf{v}_i L_{ij} a_j = l \sum \mathbf{v}_i a_i$$

or
$$La = la \tag{4.39}$$

The necessary and sufficient condition that (4.39) have a nontrivial solution is that

$$|L - l| = 0$$

Since this always is satisfied for at least one value of l, so is (4.39).

Lemma II

If $\mathbf{v}_i$ is an orthonormal basis and $\mathbf{a} = \Sigma \mathbf{v}_i a_i$, $\Sigma |a_i|^2 = \mathbf{a}^+\mathbf{a} = 1$, there exists an orthonormal basis $\mathbf{w}_i$ with $\mathbf{w}_1 = \mathbf{a}$.

This lemma may be proven by the construction of the desired basis. Without loss of generality, assume $a_1 \neq 0$. Define successively

$$\mathbf{w}_1 = \mathbf{a}$$

$$\mathbf{u}_i = \mathbf{v}_i - \sum_{j=1}^{i-1} \mathbf{w}_j(\mathbf{w}_j^+ \mathbf{v}_i) \qquad i = 2, 3, \ldots, N$$

$$\mathbf{w}_i = \frac{\mathbf{u}_i}{(\mathbf{u}_i^+ \mathbf{u}_i)^{1/2}}$$

In order to carry out this program, one must have all $\mathbf{u}_i \neq 0$. Clearly each $\mathbf{u}_i$ is a linear combination of $\mathbf{a}, \mathbf{v}_2, \mathbf{v}_3, \ldots, \mathbf{v}_i$, so that its vanishing would imply $a_1 = 0$, which is contrary to assumption. Thus, $\mathbf{u}_i \neq 0$. One readily verifies that

$$\mathbf{w}_i^+ \mathbf{w}_j = \delta_{i,j}$$

so that the proof is complete.

One now may return to the demonstration that $\mathscr{L}^+\mathscr{L} = \mathscr{L}\mathscr{L}^+$ assures that the eigenvectors of $\mathscr{L}$ form a bi-orthonormal basis. The proof is as follows: Let $\mathbf{a}$ be such that

$$\mathscr{L}\mathbf{a} = l\mathbf{a} \qquad \mathbf{a}^+\mathbf{a} = 1$$

Construct a unitary basis $\mathbf{w}_1, \mathbf{w}_2, \ldots, \mathbf{w}_{N-1}, \mathbf{a} \equiv \mathbf{w}_N$. Then, in terms of this basis,

$$\mathscr{L} = \sum_{i,j} \mathbf{w}_i L_{ij} \mathbf{w}_j^+$$

$$\mathscr{L}\mathbf{a} = \sum_i \mathbf{w}_i L_{iN} = l\mathbf{a}$$

whence $L_{iN} = l\delta_{iN}$. One can also show that $L_{Ni} = l\delta_{iN}$. Thus suppose that

$$\mathscr{L}^+ = l\mathbf{a} + \mathbf{b}$$

(this defines $\mathbf{b}$). Then

$$\mathbf{a}^+ \mathscr{L} \mathbf{a} = l$$

$$\mathbf{a}^+ \mathscr{L}^+ \mathbf{a} = l + \mathbf{a}^+ \mathbf{b}$$

but

$$\mathbf{a}^+ \mathscr{L}^+ \mathbf{a} = (\mathbf{a}^+ \mathscr{L} \mathbf{a})^+ = \bar{l}$$

whence

$$\mathbf{a}^+ \mathbf{b} = 0 = \mathbf{b}^+ \mathbf{a}$$

Also

$$\mathscr{L}^+ \mathscr{L} = \mathscr{L} \mathscr{L}^+$$

$$\mathbf{a}^+ \mathscr{L}^+ \mathscr{L} \mathbf{a} = \mathbf{a}^+ \mathscr{L} \mathscr{L}^+ \mathbf{a}$$

$$(\mathscr{L} \mathbf{a})^+ (\mathscr{L} \mathbf{a}) = (\mathscr{L}^+ \mathbf{a})^+ (\mathscr{L}^+ \mathbf{a})$$

$$(l\mathbf{a})^+ (l\mathbf{a}) = (\bar{l}\mathbf{a} + \mathbf{b})^+ (\bar{l}\mathbf{a} + \mathbf{b})$$

$$|l|^2 = |l|^2 + \mathbf{b}^+ \mathbf{b}$$

Therefore

$$\mathbf{b}^+ \mathbf{b} = 0$$

or

$$\mathscr{L}^+ \mathbf{a} = \bar{l}\mathbf{a}$$

whence

$$\mathbf{a}^+ \mathscr{L} = l\mathbf{a}^+$$

From this, using $\mathscr{L} = \sum_{i,j} \mathbf{w}_i l_{ij} \mathbf{w}_j^+$, one has (since $\mathbf{a} = \mathbf{w}_N$)

$$\mathbf{a}^+ \mathscr{L} = \sum_j L_{Nj} \mathbf{w}_j^+$$

$$= l\mathbf{a}^+ = l\mathbf{w}_N^+$$

or

$$L_{Nj} = l\,\delta_{Nj}$$

If one writes

$$\mathscr{L} = \mathbf{a}l\mathbf{a}^+ + \sum_{i,j=1}^{N-1} \mathbf{w}_i L_{ij} \mathbf{w}_j^+$$

he may note that $\mathscr{L} - \mathbf{a}l\mathbf{a}^+$ has the form of an operator in an $N-1$-dimensional space with basis $\mathbf{w}_1, \mathbf{w}_2, \ldots, \mathbf{w}_{N-1}$ and will thus have an eigenvector $\mathbf{b}$ and eigenvalue l', such that $\mathbf{b}^+ \mathbf{b} = 1$. Clearly $\mathbf{a}^+ \mathbf{b} = 0$, since $\mathbf{b} = \sum_{i=1}^{N-1} \mathbf{w}_i b_i$. The process is repeated on the operator $\mathscr{L} - \mathbf{a}l\mathbf{a}^+ - \mathbf{b}l'\mathbf{b}^+$ defined in an $N-2$-dimensional space, and so on until, with $\mathbf{u}_1 = \mathbf{a}$, $\mathbf{u}_2 = \mathbf{b}$, etc.,

$$\mathscr{L} = \mathbf{u}_1 l_1 \mathbf{u}_1^+ + \mathbf{u}_2 l_2 \mathbf{u}_2^+ + \cdots$$

$$= \sum \mathbf{u}_i l_i \mathbf{u}_i^+$$

By construction

$$\mathbf{u}_i^+ \mathbf{u}_j = \delta_{ij}$$

Thus the theorem is proved.

4.10   The Diagonalization of Normal Matrices

If $A^+A = AA^+$, the matrix A is said to be a *normal matrix*. Any matrix H which satisfies the condition $H = H^+$ is called a *Hermitian matrix*. Clearly, Hermitian matrices are normal matrices. Furthermore, any real symmetric matrix is a normal matrix, since such a matrix can be considered as a special case of a Hermitian matrix.

Any matrix U such that $U^+ = U^{-1}$, or equivalently, $U^+U = UU^+ = 1$ is called a *unitary matrix*. It is obvious that unitary matrices are normal matrices.

To any normal matrix A there corresponds a normal operator which is expressed in an orthonormal basis $\mathbf{u}_i$ as

$$\mathscr{A} = \sum \mathbf{u}_i A_{ij} \mathbf{u}_j^+$$

The eigenvectors $\mathbf{x}_\sigma$ of $\mathscr{A}$ satisfy

$$\mathscr{A}\mathbf{x}_\sigma = \mathbf{x}_\sigma \lambda_\sigma$$

and may be chosen to form an orthonormal basis (cf. Sec. 4.9). If one writes

$$\mathbf{x}_\sigma = \sum_i \mathbf{u}_i s_{i\sigma}$$

then, from (4.20), $\mathscr{A}\mathbf{x}_\sigma = \mathbf{x}_\sigma \lambda_\sigma$ implies

$$As_{.\sigma} = s_{.\sigma}\lambda_\sigma$$

or
$$As = s\Lambda$$

Since $\mathbf{x}_\sigma$ and $\mathbf{u}_i$ are orthonormal bases, s is unitary. Hence, if A is normal,

$$s^+As = \Lambda \qquad s^+s = 1$$

or
$$A = s\Lambda s^+ \qquad s^+s = 1$$

Thus a normal matrix may be diagonalized by a unitary matrix.

As an aside, for future use, it will be shown that the eigenvalues of Hermitian matrices are real. Thus let

$$Hs = s\Lambda$$

whence
$$s^+Hs = \Lambda$$
$$= s^+H^+s$$
$$= (s^+Hs)^+$$
$$= \Lambda^+$$

Thus
$$\Lambda^+ = \Lambda \quad \text{or} \quad \bar{\lambda}_\sigma = \lambda_\sigma$$

Exercises

1. Given:

$$\mathscr{L} = \mathbf{u}_1\mathbf{u}_1^+ + 2\mathbf{u}_1\mathbf{u}_2^+ + 2\mathbf{u}_2\mathbf{u}_1^+ + \mathbf{u}_2\mathbf{u}_2^+$$

and

$$\mathbf{v}_1 = \frac{\sqrt{2}}{2}(\mathbf{u}_1 + i\mathbf{u}_2) \qquad \mathbf{v}_2 = \frac{\sqrt{2}}{2}(\mathbf{u}_1 - i\mathbf{u}_2)$$

(*a*) write $\mathscr{L}$ in terms of the $\mathbf{v}_i$ basis, (*b*) find $\mathscr{L}^+$, and (*c*) find λ_i and $\mathbf{w}_i$ such that $\mathscr{L} = \lambda_1\mathbf{w}_1\mathbf{w}_1^+ + \lambda_2\mathbf{w}_2\mathbf{w}_2^+$.

2. Show that a linear operator which multiplies every vector in a three-dimensional vector space by a constant α is represented by the matrix

$$\begin{pmatrix} \alpha & 0 & 0 \\ 0 & \alpha & 0 \\ 0 & 0 & \alpha \end{pmatrix}$$

3. Verify that $(\mathscr{L}\mathscr{M})^+ = \mathscr{M}^+\mathscr{L}^+$ follows directly from (4.21), (4.22), (4.23), and $(LM)^+ = M^+L^+$.

4. Given two Hermitian operators $\mathscr{L}$ and $\mathscr{M}$, such that $\mathscr{L}\mathscr{M} = \mathscr{M}\mathscr{L}$, show that if $\mathscr{M}$ is not degenerate, $\mathscr{L}$ and $\mathscr{M}$ may be simultaneously diagonalized.

5. If $\mathscr{H}$ is any Hermitian operator show that $e^{i\mathscr{H}}$ is unitary.

6. If L_x, L_y, L_z are as given in Exercise 5 of Chap. 1, show that $e^{i\mathbf{n}\cdot\mathbf{L}\,\delta}$ (where $\mathbf{n}\cdot\mathbf{L} = n_xL_x + n_yL_y + n_zL_z$ and $n_x^2 + n_y^2 + n_z^2 = 1$) represents the rotation δ about the axis $\mathbf{n}$. (*Hint:* Diagonalize $\mathbf{n}\cdot\mathbf{L}$ and consider three orthonormal vectors $\mathbf{n}, \mathbf{p}, \mathbf{q}$.)

7. Evaluate the rotation given by the Euler angles α, β, γ

$$e^{iL_z\gamma}e^{iL_y\beta}e^{iL_z\alpha}$$

as a 3×3 matrix.

8. If $\mathscr{H}$ is a Hermitian operator, show that

$$\frac{1 + i\mathscr{H}}{1 - i\mathscr{H}}$$

is unitary.

9. If U is unitary, show that

$$i\,\frac{U - 1}{U + 1}$$

is Hermitian.

66   SYSTEMS WITH A FINITE NUMBER OF DEGREES OF FREEDOM

References

Rojansky, V.: "Introductory Quantum Mechanics," chap. IX, Prentice-Hall, Inc., Englewood Cliffs, N.J., 1938.

von Neumann, J.: "Mathematische Grundlagen der Quantenmechanik," Dover Publications, New York, 1943.

Halmos, P. R.: "Finite Dimensional Vector Spaces," Princeton University Press, Princeton, N.J., 1948.

Cooke, R. G.: "Infinite Matrices and Sequence Spaces," The Macmillan Company, New York, 1950.

Hamburger, H. L., and M. E. Grimshaw: "Linear Transformations in n-Dimensional Vector Spaces," Cambridge University Press, New York, 1952.

Morse, P. M., and H. Feshbach: "Methods of Theoretical Physics," chap. 1, par. 1.6, McGraw-Hill Book Company, Inc., New York, 1953.

Cooke, R. G.: "Linear Operators," The Macmillan Company, New York, 1954.

Thrall, P. M., and L. Tornheim: "Vector Spaces and Matrices," John Wiley & Sons, Inc., New York, 1957.

CHAPTER 5

The Dirac Notation

5.1 Introduction

In this chapter is presented a notation introduced by Dirac[1] which expresses the developments in the last chapter in an exceedingly concise and simple manner. The base vectors $\mathbf{u}_i$ are denoted by $|i>$ and are called base *ket vectors*, or simply base *kets*. The base vectors in the dual space, $\mathbf{u}_i^+$, are called base *bra vectors*, or base *bras*, and are denoted by $<i|$, the mirror image of the symbol for the base kets.

Using the convention that a repeated label is to be summed over, the expansion theorem (4.9) becomes

$$1 = |i> <i| \tag{5.1}$$

in the Dirac notation. Also, the orthonormality condition (4.8) becomes

$$<i|i'> = \delta_{ii'} \tag{5.2}$$

i.e., a juxtaposition of the symbols for the base bra and ket vectors, the two vertical lines being contracted to one for brevity.

The expansion theorem (5.1) enables the writing of any arbitrary bra or ket (in the old language, any arbitrary vector) in terms of the base bras or kets. Thus, the arbitrary ket $|x>$, corresponding to the arbitrary vector $\mathbf{x}$ in the old notation, becomes

$$|x> = |i> <i|x> \tag{5.3}$$

upon multiplication of (5.1) by $|x>$ from the right. Comparison of (5.3) with the old notation, namely

$$\mathbf{x} = \sum_i \mathbf{u}_i x_i \tag{4.6}$$

[1] P. A. M. Dirac, "The Principles of Quantum Mechanics," 3d ed., Oxford University Press, New York, 1947.

67

shows that the components x_i of the arbitrary vector $\mathbf{x}$ in the $\mathbf{u}_i$ basis are denoted by $<i|x>$ in the Dirac notation.

Similarly, multiplication of (5.1) by $<x|$ from the left yields

$$<x| = <x|i> <i| \tag{5.4}$$

which corresponds to the expression

$$\mathbf{x}^+ = \sum_i \bar{x}_i \mathbf{u}_i^+ \tag{4.7}$$

in the old notation. Hence, it follows that

$$<x|i> = \overline{<i|x>} \tag{5.5}$$

5.2 The Change of Basis

Multiplication of (5.1) from the right by the base ket $|j>$ gives

$$|j> = |i> <i|j> \tag{5.6}$$

This is the Dirac notation for the change of basis

$$\mathbf{v}_j = \sum_i \mathbf{u}_i t_{ij} \tag{4.10}$$

in the old notation. Hence the bracket $<i|j>$ is identified with the elements t_{ij} of the transformation matrix t. Note that while in the old notation the base vectors in different bases are distinguished by use of different letters (e.g., $\mathbf{u}_i$, $\mathbf{v}_i$, $\mathbf{w}_i$, etc.) only different indices are used in the Dirac notation. The n different base vectors which constitute a basis are denoted by the use of primes, $|i>$, $|i'>$, $|i''>$, etc.

The change of basis in the dual space corresponding to (4.10), namely:

$$\mathbf{v}_j^+ = \sum_i \bar{t}_{ij} \mathbf{u}_i^+$$

becomes in the Dirac notation

$$<j| = \overline{<i|j>} <i| = <j|i> <i| \tag{5.7}$$

which could have been obtained by multiplication of (5.1) from the left by the base bra $<j|$.

Multiplication of (5.3) from the left by $|j> <j|$ gives

$$|x> = |j> <j|x> = |j> <j|i> <i|x> \tag{5.8}$$

Hence the components of the arbitrary ket $|x>$ in the j basis are given in terms of the components in the i basis by the relation

$$<j|x> = <j|i> <i|x> \tag{5.9}$$

The components of the arbitrary bra $<x|$ corresponding to the ket $|x>$ are given by the complex conjugate of (5.9), namely:

$$\overline{<j|x>} = \overline{<i|x>}\ \overline{<j|i>} = <x|i><i|j> \qquad (5.10)$$

5.3 Linear Operators in the Dirac Notation

The expression for any linear operator $\mathscr{L}$ in the Dirac notation is obtained by multiplying $\mathscr{L}$ from both the right and left by (5.1):

$$\mathscr{L} = |i><i|\ \mathscr{L}\ |i'><i'| \qquad (5.11)$$

Comparison of (5.11) with the expression for $\mathscr{L}$ in the old notation, namely,

$$\mathscr{L} = \sum_{i,i'} \mathbf{u}_i L_{ii'} \mathbf{u}_{i'}^+ \qquad (4.21)$$

shows that the matrix elements $L_{ii'}$ are denoted by $<i|\ \mathscr{L}\ |i'>$ in the Dirac notation.

Similarly, the Dirac notation for the operator $\mathscr{L}^+$, the conjugate transpose or Hermitian adjoint of $\mathscr{L}$, is

$$\mathscr{L}^+ = |i><i|\ \mathscr{L}^+\ |i'><i'| \qquad (5.12)$$

This corresponds to the expression

$$\mathscr{L}^+ = \sum_{i,i'} \mathbf{u}_i \bar{L}_{i'i} \mathbf{u}_{i'}^+ = \sum_{i,i'} \mathbf{u}_i L_{ii'}^+ \mathbf{u}_{i'}^+ \qquad (4.22)$$

in the old notation. Hence it follows that

$$<i|\ \mathscr{L}^+\ |i'> = \overline{<i'|\ \mathscr{L}\ |i>} \qquad (5.13)$$

It should be noted that if $\mathscr{L}$ is the identity operator, (5.11) becomes

$$\mathscr{I} = |i><i|\ \mathscr{I}\ |i'><i'| = |i><i|i'><i'|$$
$$= |i> \delta_{ii'} <i'| = |i><i|$$

in agreement with (5.1).

The result of the operation of $\mathscr{L}$ on an arbitrary ket $|x>$ is given by

$$\mathscr{L}\ |x> = |i><i|\ \mathscr{L}\ |i'><i'|x> \qquad (5.14)$$

which corresponds to

$$\mathscr{L}\mathbf{x} = \sum_{i,i'} \mathbf{u}_i L_{ii'} x_{i'}$$

in the old notation.

The Hermitian adjoint of (5.14) is

$$<x|\ \mathscr{L}^+ = <x|i><i|\ \mathscr{L}^+\ |i'><i'|$$
$$= \overline{<i|x>}\ \overline{<i'|\ \mathscr{L}\ |i>}<i'| \qquad (5.15)$$

which could also have been obtained directly from (5.14).

5.4   Eigenvectors and Eigenvalues

In the last chapter it was pointed out that if $\mathscr{L}\mathbf{u}_l = l\mathbf{u}_l$, then $\mathbf{u}_l$ is said to be the eigenvector of the operator $\mathscr{L}$ belonging to the eigenvalue l. In the Dirac notation this relation becomes

$$\mathscr{L} \, |l> \; = |l> \, l$$

Then, in any basis i,

$$\mathscr{L} \, |i'> \, <i'|l> \; = |i'> \, <i'|l> \, l$$

$$|i> \, <i| \, \mathscr{L} \, |i'> \, <i'|l> \; = |i> \, <i|i'> \, <i'|l> \, l$$

so that

$$<i| \, \mathscr{L} \, |i'> \, <i'|l> \; = <i|i'> \, <i'|l> \, l$$

$$= <i|l> \, l \tag{5.16}$$

is the matrix equation from which the eigenvalues l may be determined.

5.5   The Spectral Representation of an Operator

In the old notation the representation of a linear operator $\mathscr{L}$ in the basis l whose base vectors are the eigenvectors of $\mathscr{L}$ is given by

$$\mathscr{L} = \sum_l \mathbf{u}_l l \mathbf{u}_i^+ \tag{4.31}$$

The corresponding Dirac expression is

$$\mathscr{L} = |l> \, l \, <l| \tag{5.17}$$

The representation of $\mathscr{L}$ in terms of an arbitrary basis i is then

$$\mathscr{L} = |i> \, <i|l> \, l \, <l|i'> \, <i'| \tag{5.18}$$

It follows that the representation of $\mathscr{L}^n$ in this basis is

$$\mathscr{L}^n = |i> \, <i|l> \, l^n \, <l|i'> \, <i'| \tag{5.19}$$

and, in general, the representation of any function of $\mathscr{L}$, say $f(\mathscr{L})$, is

$$f(\mathscr{L}) = |i> \, <i|l> \, f(l) \, <l|i'> \, <i'| \tag{5.20}$$

5.6   Theorems on Hermitian Operators

As a demonstration of the ease of manipulation in the Dirac notation we shall prove two important and useful theorems on Hermitian operators. A linear operator $\mathscr{H}$ which satisfies the condition $\mathscr{H} = \mathscr{H}^+$ is called a *Hermitian operator*.

Theorem a.

The eigenvalues of a Hermitian operator are real.

Consider the equation

$$\mathcal{H}\,|h> = |h>\,h \tag{5.21}$$

Multiplication of (5.21) from the left by the bra $<h|$ gives

$$<h|\,\mathcal{H}\,|h> = h \tag{5.22}$$

Since $\mathcal{H}$ is Hermitian it follows that

$$<h|\,\mathcal{H}\,|h> = <h|\,\mathcal{H}^+\,|h> = \overline{<h|\,\mathcal{H}\,|h>} = \bar{h} \tag{5.23}$$

Hence, equating the right-hand members of (5.22) and (5.23), $h = \bar{h}$, and the theorem is proved.

Theorem b.

The necessary and sufficient condition that two Hermitian operators can be diagonalized by the same unitary transformation is that they commute.

1. If $\mathcal{H} = |\lambda>\,h(\lambda)\,<\lambda|$ and $\mathcal{J} = |\lambda>\,j(\lambda)\,<\lambda|$, then $\mathcal{H}\mathcal{J} = \mathcal{J}\mathcal{H}$.

Proof:

$$\mathcal{H}\mathcal{J} = |\lambda>\,h(\lambda)\,<\lambda|\lambda'>\,j(\lambda')\,<\lambda'| = |\lambda>\,h(\lambda)j(\lambda)\,<\lambda|$$
$$= |\lambda>\,j(\lambda)h(\lambda)\,<\lambda| = \mathcal{J}\mathcal{H}$$

2. If $\mathcal{H}\mathcal{J} = \mathcal{J}\mathcal{H}$ then there exists a basis λ such that

$$\mathcal{H} = |\lambda>\,h(\lambda)\,<\lambda| \quad \text{and} \quad \mathcal{J} = |\lambda>\,j(\lambda)\,<\lambda|$$

Proof: If h is a nondegenerate eigenvalue of $\mathcal{H}$, then $\mathcal{H}\,|h> = |h>\,h$ and $\mathcal{H}\mathcal{J}\,|h> = \mathcal{J}\mathcal{H}\,|h> = \mathcal{J}\,|h>\,h$. But this states that the ket $\mathcal{J}\,|h>$ is an eigenket of $\mathcal{H}$ belonging to the eigenvalue h and is thus a multiple of $|h>$. Therefore

$$\mathcal{J}\,|h> = |h>\,j(h)$$

If h is a degenerate eigenvalue of $\mathcal{H}$ label the various eigenkets with an index λ thus,

$$\mathcal{H}\,|h,\lambda> = |h,\lambda>\,h$$

or

$$\mathcal{H} = |h,\lambda>\,h\,<h,\lambda|$$

Then write

$$\mathcal{J} = |h,\lambda>\,<h,\lambda|\,\mathcal{J}\,|h',\lambda'>\,<h',\lambda'|$$

and form

$$<h,\lambda|\,\mathcal{H}\mathcal{J} - \mathcal{J}\mathcal{H}\,|h',\lambda'> = (h - h')\,<h,\lambda|\,\mathcal{J}\,|h',\lambda'> = 0$$

It follows, then, that those elements $<h,\lambda|\; \mathcal{J}\; |h',\lambda'>$ for which $h \neq h'$ must vanish.[1] Thus

$$\mathcal{J} = |h,\lambda> \;<h,\lambda|\; \mathcal{J}\; |h,\lambda'> \;<h,\lambda'|$$

Look for eigenkets of $\mathcal{J}$ which are also eigenkets of $\mathcal{H}$ (no sums over h):

$$\mathcal{J}\; |h,j> = |h,j> j \qquad |h,j> = |h,\lambda> \;<h,\lambda|h,j>$$

and
$$<h,\lambda|\; \mathcal{J}\; |h,\lambda'> \;<h,\lambda'|h,j> = <h,\lambda|h,j> j$$

This last equation is solved for $<h,\lambda|h,j>$ and j to find $|h,j>$. It is easy to see that $|h,j>$ is a simultaneous eigenket of $\mathcal{H}$ and $\mathcal{J}$. By definition $\mathcal{J}\; |h,j> = |h,j> j$. Also

$$\begin{aligned}
\mathcal{H}\; |h,j> &= \mathcal{H}\; |h,\lambda> \;<h,\lambda|h,j> \\
&= |h,\lambda> h \;<h,\lambda|h,j> = h\; |h,j>
\end{aligned}$$

This completes the proof of Theorem b.

A set of operators $\mathcal{H}$, $\mathcal{J}$, $\mathcal{K}$, $\mathcal{L}$, etc., such that their simultaneous eigenkets are nondegenerate[2] is called a *complete set of commuting observables*. The eigenkets of a complete set of commuting observables are uniquely determined, except for an arbitrary complex multiplicative scalar of unit magnitude.

It is often easier to diagonalize an operator $\mathcal{J}$ commuting with $\mathcal{H}$ after $\mathcal{H}$ has been diagonalized. Thus if $\mathcal{H}$ is nondegenerate, $\mathcal{J}$ is automatically diagonal, whereas if $\mathcal{H}$ is degenerate, $\mathcal{J}$ may be represented, for each eigenvalue h of $\mathcal{H}$, by an $n \times n$ matrix, where n is the number of equal eigenvalues h possessed by $\mathcal{H}$. One need merely diagonalize this $n \times n$ matrix.

References

Dirac, P. A. M.: "The Principles of Quantum Mechanics," Oxford University Press, New York, 1947.

Corson, E. M.: "Perturbation Methods in the Quantum Mechanics of n-Electron Systems," chaps. 1 and 2, Blackie & Sons, Ltd., Glasgow, 1950.

[1] This means that in the discussions which follow many considerations will involve fixed h.

[2] For any pair of eigenkets $|h,j,k,l>$, $|h',j',k',l'>$, $h - h'$, $j - j'$, $k - k'$, $l - l'$ are not all zero.

CHAPTER 6

Periodic Structures

6.1 Motivation

Although repetitive or periodic structures have a great deal of interest in their own right, the interest here stems from one major circumstance—by appropriate limiting procedures the structures of interest may be made to approximate continuous systems as closely as desired. In Part Two this circumstance will be used in order to extend many of the considerations of Part One to systems with infinite numbers of degrees of freedom, i.e., to continuous systems. Specifically, meaning will be given to functions of operators in a manner analogous to that used in Part One, although in some cases the situation will be clouded by questions of existence and rigor.

In Part Three reference will again be made to Chap. 6, in this case to make use of the manner in which a periodic system approximates a continuous system in order to study a numerical method of solving problems involving complex continuous systems. In the remainder of this chapter little reference will be made to either of these possibilities.

The considerations to follow will be restricted to two problems—the lumped RC line and the loaded string. By a suitable limiting process (Part Two) one will obtain the problems of heat conduction and wave propagation in one dimension.

6.2 The RC Line

Consider the network shown in Fig. 6.1. Then one might be interested in solving the following problem:
Given:

$$e_i(0) \quad \text{and} \quad E(t)$$

To find:

$$e_i(t)$$

The equations of motion are written without much difficulty:

$$C\frac{de_i}{dt} = \frac{e_{i+1} - e_i}{R} + \frac{e_{i-1} - e_i}{R} \qquad i = 2, 3, \ldots, n-1 \qquad (6.1)$$

$$C\frac{de_1}{dt} = \frac{e_2 - e_1}{R} + \frac{E - e_1}{R_s} \qquad (6.2)$$

$$C\frac{de_n}{dt} = -\frac{e_n}{R_L} + \frac{e_{n-1} - e_n}{R} \qquad (6.3)$$

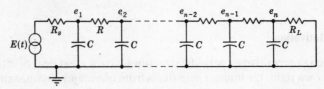

Figure 6.1

If $(e)t$ is an n column with elements $e_i(t)$, these equations may be written in the form

$$\frac{de}{dt} = Me + P(t) \qquad (6.4)$$

where, with $\quad \mu = 1/RC, \quad \mu_L = 1/R_LC, \quad \mu_s = 1/R_sC,$

$$M = \begin{matrix}
-\mu_s - \mu & \mu & \mu & 0 & \ldots & 0 & 0 & 0 \\
\mu & -2\mu & \mu & \mu & \ldots & 0 & 0 & 0 \\
0 & \mu & -2\mu & \mu & \ldots & 0 & 0 & 0 \\
0 & 0 & \mu & -2\mu & \ldots & 0 & 0 & 0 \\
\vdots & & & & & & & \vdots \\
0 & 0 & 0 & 0 & \ldots & -2\mu & \mu & 0 \\
0 & 0 & 0 & 0 & \ldots & \mu & -2\mu & \mu \\
0 & 0 & 0 & 0 & \ldots & 0 & \mu & -\mu - \mu_L
\end{matrix} \qquad (6.5)$$

and

$$P_i = \delta_{i,1}\mu_s E \qquad (6.6)$$

The formal solution of (6.4) is (cf. Sec. 2.9)

$$e(t) = e^{Mt}e(0) + \int_0^t e^{M(t-s)}P(s)\,ds \qquad (6.7)$$

In effect the problem has been solved, provided e^{Mt} can be evaluated. Since M is a Hermitian matrix [as is clearly seen by examination of (6.5)], there exist matrices S and Λ (Λ is diagonal with real elements) such that $M = S\Lambda S^{+}$, $SS^{+} = 1$. The periodicity of the structure, which is responsible for the simple form of M, will be utilized in the next section to find S and Λ.

6.3 Diagonalizing M

M is completely specified if and only if, given arbitrary x, $y = Mx$ is known. Either from (6.1), (6.2), and (6.3) or from (6.5) it is clear that

$$y_i = \mu(x_{i-1} - 2x_i + x_{i+1}) \qquad i = 2, \ldots, n-1$$
$$y_1 = \mu(x_2 - x_1) - \mu_s x_1$$
$$y_n = \mu(x_{n-1} - x_n) - \mu_L x_n$$

By a simple subterfuge it is possible to write these equations in a more useful form:

$$y_i = \mu(x_{i-1} - 2x_i + x_{i+1}) \qquad i = 1, 2, \ldots, n-1, n \qquad (6.8)$$

$$x_0 = \left(1 - \frac{\mu_s}{\mu}\right)x_1 \qquad (6.9)$$

$$x_{n+1} = \left(1 - \frac{\mu_L}{\mu}\right)x_n \qquad (6.10)$$

Here Eqs. (6.8) are known as *difference equations* whereas (6.9) and (6.10) are called *boundary conditions*.

To diagonalize M, an x must be found such that $Mx = \lambda x$. That is, x satisfies (6.9), (6.10), and

$$\lambda x_i = \mu(x_{i-1} - 2x_i + x_{i+1}) \qquad i = 1, \ldots, n \qquad (6.11)$$

There are many approaches to the solution of an equation like (6.11). One that fits in well with the spirit of this book is as follows: Rewrite (6.11) as

$$\begin{pmatrix} x_{i+1} \\ x_i \end{pmatrix} = \begin{pmatrix} 2 + \lambda/\mu & -1 \\ 1 & 0 \end{pmatrix}\begin{pmatrix} x_i \\ x_{i-1} \end{pmatrix}$$

Clearly $\qquad \begin{pmatrix} x_{i+1} \\ x_i \end{pmatrix} = \begin{pmatrix} 2 + \lambda/\mu & -1 \\ 1 & 0 \end{pmatrix}^i\begin{pmatrix} x_1 \\ x_0 \end{pmatrix} \qquad (6.12)$

Since it may be necessary to consider λ/μ such that the matrix cannot be diagonalized, this matrix had best be raised to the ith power by means of the Cauchy formula:

$$\begin{pmatrix} 2 + \lambda/\mu & -1 \\ 1 & 0 \end{pmatrix}^k = \frac{1}{2\pi i} \oint \begin{pmatrix} z - 2 - \lambda/\mu & 1 \\ -1 & z \end{pmatrix}^{-1} z^k \, dz$$

$$= \frac{1}{2\pi i} \oint \frac{z^k}{z(z - 2 - \lambda/\mu) + 1} \begin{pmatrix} z & -1 \\ 1 & z - 2 - \lambda/\mu \end{pmatrix} dz$$

Now let the roots of

$$z\left(z - 2 - \frac{\lambda}{\mu}\right) + 1 = 0$$

be α, α^{-1}. Clearly

$$\alpha + \alpha^{-1} = 2 + \frac{\lambda}{\mu^1} \tag{6.13}$$

so that

$$\begin{pmatrix} 2 + \lambda/\mu & -1 \\ 1 & 0 \end{pmatrix}^k = \frac{1}{2\pi i} \oint \frac{z^k}{(z - \alpha)(z - \alpha^{-1})} \begin{pmatrix} z & -1 \\ 1 & z - \alpha - \alpha^{-1} \end{pmatrix} dz$$

$$= \begin{pmatrix} \alpha^{k+1} - \alpha^{-k-1} & -\alpha^k + \alpha^{-k} \\ \alpha^k - \alpha^{-k} & -\alpha^{k-1} + \alpha^{-k+1} \end{pmatrix} \frac{1}{\alpha - \alpha^{-1}} \tag{6.14}$$

Using (6.9), (6.10), (6.12), and (6.14), there results for arbitrary x_1

$$\begin{pmatrix} 1 - \mu_L/\mu \\ 1 \end{pmatrix} x_n = \begin{pmatrix} \alpha^{n+1} - \alpha^{-n-1} & -\alpha^n + \alpha^{-n} \\ \alpha^n - \alpha^{-n} & -\alpha^{n-1} + \alpha^{-n+1} \end{pmatrix} \frac{1}{\alpha - \alpha^{-1}} \begin{pmatrix} 1 \\ 1 - \mu_s/\mu \end{pmatrix} x_1$$

But

$$(1 \quad -1 + \mu_L/\mu) \begin{pmatrix} 1 - \mu_L/\mu \\ 1 \end{pmatrix} x_n = 0$$

so that

$$0 = (1 \quad -1 + \mu_L/\mu) \begin{pmatrix} \alpha^{n+1} - \alpha^{-n-1} & -\alpha^n + \alpha^{-n} \\ \alpha^n - \alpha^{-n} & -\alpha^{n-1} + \alpha^{-n+1} \end{pmatrix} \begin{pmatrix} 1 \\ 1 - \mu_s/\mu \end{pmatrix} \frac{1}{\alpha - \alpha^{-1}} \tag{6.15}$$

Equation (6.15) determines the proper values of α and thus, from (6.13), of λ. Upon multiplying out, one has

$$0 = \left(\alpha - \frac{1}{\alpha}\right)^{-1} \left\{ \left[\frac{1}{\alpha} - \left(1 - \frac{\mu_L}{\mu}\right)\right] \left[\frac{1}{\alpha} - \left(1 - \frac{\mu_s}{\mu}\right)\right] \alpha^{-n+1} \right.$$

$$\left. - \left[\alpha - \left(1 - \frac{\mu_L}{\mu}\right)\right] \left[\alpha - \left(1 - \frac{\mu_s}{\mu}\right)\right] \alpha^{n-1} \right\} \tag{6.16}$$

The solution of (6.16) is seen by inspection if $\mu_L = \mu_s = \mu$. For this case,

$$\alpha^{n+1} = \alpha^{-n-1} \quad \text{or} \quad \alpha^{2n+2} = 1$$

whence $\qquad \alpha = e^{i\pi\sigma/(n+1)} \qquad \sigma = 1, \ldots, n$

This solution may be checked. $Mx = \lambda x$ is satisfied by a λ_σ and $x_{,\sigma}$ such that, from (6.13),

$$\lambda_\sigma = \left(2\cos\frac{\pi\sigma}{n+1} - 2\right)\mu \tag{6.17}$$

Further, from (6.14) (since $1 - \mu_s/\mu = 0$)

$$x_{k\sigma} = \frac{\sin\left[\pi k\sigma/(n+1)\right]}{\sin\left[\pi\sigma/(n+1)\right]} x_{1\sigma} \tag{6.18}$$

For the present case $x_0 = x_{n+1} = 0$, which follows immediately from (6.18). Thus (6.9) and (6.10) are satisfied. For (6.11) there results

$$x_{k-1} - 2x_k + x_{k+1} = \frac{x_1}{\sin\left[\pi\sigma/(n+1)\right]} \left[\sin\frac{\pi\sigma}{n+1}(k+1) - 2\sin\frac{\pi\sigma}{n+1}k \right.$$

$$\left. + \sin\frac{\pi\sigma}{n+1}(k-1)\right]$$

$$= \frac{x_1}{\sin\left[\pi\sigma/(n+1)\right]} \left(2\cos\frac{\pi\sigma}{n+1} - 2\right)\sin\frac{\pi\sigma}{n+1}k$$

$$= \frac{\lambda_\sigma}{\mu} x_k$$

which checks (6.11).

In order to complete the diagonalization of M, the solution (6.18) must be normalized. (The orthogonality of the solution is assured by the Hermitian nature of M.) Now

$$\sum_{k=1}^{n} \sin^2\frac{\pi k\sigma}{n+1} = -\frac{1}{4}\sum_{1}^{n}\left[e^{i\pi k\sigma/(n+1)} - e^{-i\pi k\sigma/(n+1)}\right]^2$$

$$= \frac{1}{4}\sum_{0}^{n}\left[2 - e^{-2i\pi k\sigma/(n+1)} - e^{2i\pi k\sigma/(n+1)}\right]$$

$$= \frac{n+1}{2} - \frac{1}{4}\frac{1 - e^{-2i\pi\sigma}}{1 - e^{-2i\pi\sigma/(n+1)}} - \frac{1}{4}\frac{1 - e^{2i\pi\sigma}}{1 - e^{+2i\pi\sigma/(n+1)}}$$

$$= \frac{n+1}{2}$$

so that $\qquad M = S\Lambda S^+ \qquad S^+S = SS^+ = 1$

where
$$S_{k\sigma} = \sqrt{\frac{2}{n+1}} \sin \frac{\pi k\sigma}{n+1} \tag{6.19}$$

$$\lambda_\sigma = -\mu\left(2 - 2\cos\frac{\pi\sigma}{n+1}\right) \tag{6.20}$$

Returning now to the formal solution of (6.4) as given in (6.7) one has

$$e_i(t) = \frac{2}{n+1} \sum_{\sigma=1}^{n} \sin\frac{\pi i\sigma}{n+1} e^{+\lambda_\sigma t}\left[\sum_{k=1}^{n} \sin\frac{\pi k\sigma}{n+1} e_k(0)\right.$$

$$\left. + \mu \sin\frac{\pi\sigma}{n+1} \int_0^t e^{-\lambda_\sigma s} E(s)\, ds\right]$$

$$\lambda_\sigma = -\mu\left(2 - 2\cos\frac{\pi\sigma}{n+1}\right) \tag{6.21}$$

6.4   The Loaded String

If one has a string of tension T (Fig. 6.2) where the ith particle is of mass m and has a displacement from equilibrium of y_i, then the equations of motion may be written, for small vibrations, as

$$m\ddot{y}_i = T\frac{y_{i+1} - y_i}{a} + T\frac{y_{i-1} - y_i}{a} \qquad i = 1, 2, \ldots, n \tag{6.22}$$

provided that the boundary conditions

$$y_0 = y_{n+1} = 0 \tag{6.23}$$

are imposed.

In matrix form
$$\ddot{y} = My \tag{6.24}$$

where, with
$$\mu = \frac{T}{ma} \tag{6.25}$$

$$M = \begin{bmatrix} -2\mu & \mu & 0 & \cdots & 0 & 0 & 0 \\ \mu & -2\mu & \mu & \cdots & 0 & 0 & 0 \\ 0 & \mu & -2\mu & \cdots & 0 & 0 & 0 \\ \cdot & \cdot & \cdot & \cdot & \cdot & \cdot & \cdot \\ 0 & 0 & 0 & \cdots & -2\mu & \mu & 0 \\ 0 & 0 & 0 & \cdots & \mu & -2\mu & \mu \\ 0 & 0 & 0 & \cdots & 0 & \mu & -2\mu \end{bmatrix} \tag{6.26}$$

The formal solution of (6.24) is given by

$$y(t) = \cos \sqrt{-M} t \, y(0) + \frac{\sin \sqrt{-M} t}{\sqrt{-M}} \, \dot{y}(0) \tag{6.27}$$

Since M is Hermitian, there exists an S such that $SS^+ = 1$, $M = S\Lambda S^{-1}$. Comparing (6.26) with (6.5) one sees that M here is the same as in (6.5)

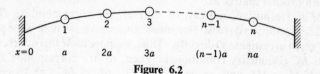

$$x = 0 \qquad a \qquad 2a \qquad 3a \qquad (n-1)a \qquad na$$

Figure 6.2

with $\mu_s = \mu_L = \mu$. Thus S and Λ are given in (6.19) and (6.20). Using these, the solution (6.27) becomes

$$y_i(t) = \frac{2}{n+1} \sum_{\sigma=1}^{n} \sin \frac{\pi \sigma i}{n+1} \left[\cos (\sqrt{-\lambda_\sigma} t) \sum_{k=1}^{n} \sin \frac{\pi \sigma k}{n+1} \, y_k(0) \right.$$

$$\left. + \frac{\sin (\sqrt{-\lambda_\sigma} t)}{\sqrt{-\lambda_\sigma}} \sum_{k=1}^{n} \sin \frac{\pi \sigma k}{n+1} \, \dot{y}_k(0) \right] \tag{6.28}$$

where, as before,

$$-\lambda_\sigma = \left(2 - 2 \cos \frac{\pi \sigma}{n+1} \right) \mu$$

That (6.28) satisfies (6.22) and (6.23) may be verified by direct substitution. Furthermore, it is easily seen that the initial conditions are correctly included.

6.5 Difference Operators

The matrix M defined in (6.5) was of large order and had mostly zero elements. It was thus found convenient to write, instead of

$$y = Mx$$

or

$$y_i = \sum_i M_{ij} x_j$$

Eqs. (6.8), (6.9), and (6.10)

$$y_i = \mu \, \delta^2 x_i \qquad i = 1, 2, \ldots, n \tag{6.8}$$

$$x_0 = \left(1 - \frac{\mu_s}{\mu} \right) x_1 \tag{6.9}$$

$$x_{n+1} = \left(1 - \frac{\mu_L}{\mu} \right) x_n \tag{6.10}$$

where

$$\delta^2 x_i = x_{i+1} - 2x_i + x_{i-1} \tag{6.29}$$

Thus, the matrix M has been eliminated, and instead the difference operator δ^2 with boundary conditions (6.9) and (6.10) has been introduced.

Such a procedure, of writing a difference equation $y_i = Dx_i$ and boundary conditions to eliminate auxiliary variables x_0, $x_{-1}, \ldots$, etc., as introduced in the difference equations, is often more convenient than using an explicit matrix M.

If M is Hermitian, unitary, or normal, the corresponding D (with boundary conditions) is also Hermitian, unitary, or normal. One prefers, however, to investigate D directly. Thus, suppose to M there corresponds D and BC (boundary conditions). Then, to M^+ corresponds D^+ and BC^+. If $M = M^+$, one can write $D = D^+$, $BC = BC^+$, and vice versa.

To find a direct definition of D^+ and BC^+, one may proceed thus. *The equation $y^+Mx - (M^+y)^+x = 0$ for arbitrary x and y may be considered a definition of M^+*, as is seen by writing the equation in detailed form

$$0 = \sum_{i,j} \bar{y}_i M_{ij} x_j - \sum_{i,j} \overline{M_{ji}^+ y_i} x_j$$

$$= \sum_{i,j} \bar{y}_i (M_{ij} - \bar{M}_{ji}^+) x_j$$

Since y_i, x_j are arbitrary, one has

$$M_{ij} = \bar{M}_{ji}^+$$

which indeed defines M^+.

Similarly D^+ and BC^+ may be determined from the requirement that

$$\sum_i \bar{f}_i Dg_i - \sum_i \overline{D^+ f_i} g_i = 0 \tag{6.30}$$

for arbitrary g_i satisfying BC and arbitrary f_i satisfying BC^+. Specifically, if D (with BC) is Hermitian, then

$$\sum_{i=1}^n \bar{f}_i Dg_i = \sum_{i=1}^n \overline{Df_i} g_i \tag{6.31}$$

for arbitrary f_i and g_i satisfying BC, and further if (6.31) holds, D (with BC) is Hermitian. That δ^2 (with $x_0 = x_{n+1} = 0$) is Hermitian is seen in Sec. 7.4.

Exercises

1. If
$$x_{n+1} = \alpha x_n + \beta x_{n-1}$$
$$x_0 = 0 \qquad x_1 = 1$$

find x_n explicitly.

2. If the $N \times N$ matrix M is defined by

$$u_0 = \rho u_1 \qquad u_{N+1} = \sigma u_N$$
$$M_n.u = \alpha_n u_{n+1} + \beta_n u_n + \gamma_n u_{n-1}$$

find r, s, a_n, b_n, and c_n such that

$$v_0 = r v_1 \qquad v_{N+1} = s v_N$$
$$M_n^+ . v = a_n v_{n+1} + b_n v_n + c_n v_{n-1}$$

3. From the results of the preceding problem, find the conditions on α_n, β_n, γ_n, ρ, σ, such that M is Hermitian.

4. Suppose a sequence of polynomials $P_n(x)$ is defined by

$$x P_n = \alpha_n P_{n+1} + \beta_n P_n + \gamma_n P_{n-1} \qquad n = 0, 1, 2, \ldots$$
$$P_0 = 1 \qquad P_{-1} = 0$$

Show that the eigenvalues of the matrix

$$M = \begin{matrix}
\beta_0 & \alpha_0 & 0 & 0 & 0 & \cdots & 0 & 0 & 0 \\
\gamma_1 & \beta_1 & \alpha_1 & 0 & 0 & \cdots & 0 & 0 & 0 \\
0 & \gamma_2 & \beta_2 & \alpha_2 & 0 & \cdots & 0 & 0 & 0 \\
\cdot & \cdot & \cdot & \cdot & \cdot & \cdot & \cdot & \cdot & \cdot \\
0 & 0 & 0 & 0 & 0 & \cdots & \gamma_{N-2} & \beta_{N-2} & \alpha_{N-2} \\
0 & 0 & 0 & 0 & 0 & \cdots & 0 & \gamma_{N-1} & \beta_{N-1}
\end{matrix}$$

are given by the roots of $P_N(x) = 0$.

5. Apply the results of Exercise 4 to (6.26) with $N = 5$.

6. Show that the recurrence formula

$$T_{i+1} - x T_i + \tfrac{1}{4} T_{i-1} = 0 \qquad i = 1, 2, \ldots$$

where $T_0 = 2$ and $T_1 = x$ is satisfied by the Tchebycheff polynomials

$$T_i(x) = \frac{1}{2^{i-1}} \cos (i \cos^{-1} x)$$

when $|x| \leq 1$, and by

$$T_i(x) = \frac{1}{2^{i-1}} \left[\cosh (i \cosh^{-1} |x|) \right]$$

when $|x| \geq 1$. In both cases write in explicit polynomial form the T_i for $i = 2, 3, 4$, and 5.

7. Solve the difference equation

$$x_{n+3} - 3 x_{n+2} - x_{n+1} + 3 x_n = 0$$

Given: $\qquad x_0 = a \qquad x_1 = b \qquad x_2 = c$

Part Two

SYSTEMS WITH AN INFINITE NUMBER OF DEGREES OF FREEDOM

CHAPTER 7

The Transition to Continuous Systems

7.1 Introduction

The theory of n-dimensional vector spaces developed in Part One was devised to treat systems with a finite number of degrees of freedom, i.e., systems with a finite number of coordinates. There are a large number of problems, however, which involve continuous systems. Two examples of continuous systems are the finite transmission line with uniformly distributed constants and the vibrating string. The methods of Part One require modification if they are to be used in the study of continuous systems. It is possible to deduce the equations of motion of continuous systems in various ways. An approach which has the advantage of enabling us to build on the results of Part One is (1) to approximate the continuous system by one containing discrete units, (2) to study the discrete system, and (3) to examine the changes induced as the continuous limit is approached. In the following section this procedure is applied to the problem of the RC line with uniformly distributed constants.

7.2 The RC Line—Change of Notation

Consider the finite transmission line with lumped constants discussed in Sec. 6.2. For the purpose of making the transition from such a line to a line in which the resistances and capacitances are not lumped but rather are distributed uniformly along the length of the line, the following change of notation is introduced. Let the length of each section in the line be Δx so that the total length of the line is given by $L = n\,\Delta x$, where n is the total number of sections. Also, let ρ and γ be defined by the equations $R = \rho\,\Delta x$ and $C = \gamma\,\Delta x$. Finally, let the distance of the jth capacitance from the beginning of the line be denoted by $x_j = j\,\Delta x$ and let the voltage across this capacitance be $e(x_j,t)$. The network of Fig. 7.1 then becomes that of Fig. 7.2.

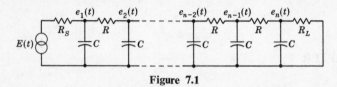

Figure 7.1

Before rewriting (6.1), (6.2), and (6.3) in terms of the new notation, it is useful first to write them in the form, as suggested by (6.8), (6.9), and (6.10), of a difference equation with boundary conditions. Thus, in the original notation

$$C \frac{de_i}{dt} = \frac{e_{i+1} - 2e_i + e_{i-1}}{R} \qquad i = 1, 2, \ldots, n \qquad (7.1)$$

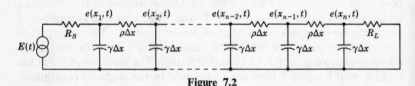

Figure 7.2

where the equations with $i = 1$ and n define respectively e_0 and e_{n+1}:

$$\frac{e_0}{R} = C \frac{de_1}{dt} - \frac{e_2}{R} + \frac{2e_1}{R}$$

$$\frac{e_{n+1}}{R} = C \frac{de_n}{dt} - \frac{e_{n-1}}{R} + \frac{2e_n}{R}$$

A comparison of these results with (6.2) and (6.3) leads immediately to the boundary conditions

$$-\frac{e_1 - e_0}{R} = \frac{E - e_1}{R_S} \qquad (7.2)$$

$$\frac{e_{n+1} - e_n}{R} = -\frac{e_n}{R_L} \qquad (7.3)$$

Equations (7.1), (7.2), and (7.3) are clearly equivalent to Eqs. (6.1), (6.2), and (6.3).

A simple translation of notation now leads to

$$\rho\gamma \frac{de(x_i,t)}{dt} = \frac{e(x_i + \Delta x, t) - 2e(x_i,t) + e(x_i - \Delta x, t)}{(\Delta x)^2} \tag{7.4}$$

$$\frac{e(\Delta x,t) - e(0,t)}{\Delta x} = \frac{\rho}{R_S} [e(\Delta x,t) - E(t)] \tag{7.5}$$

$$\frac{e(L + \Delta x, t) - e(L,t)}{\Delta x} = -\frac{\rho}{R_L} e(L,t) \tag{7.6}$$

7.3   The RC Line—Transition to the Continuous Case

Equations (7.4), (7.5), and (7.6) in the previous section have been written so as to be all independent of n but dependent on Δx. Thus the limiting case can be obtained by considering the limit as Δx approaches zero:

$$\rho\gamma \frac{\partial}{\partial t} e(x,t) = \frac{\partial^2}{\partial x^2} e(x,t) \tag{7.7}$$

$$\left.\frac{\partial e}{\partial x}\right|_{x=0} = \frac{\rho}{R_S} [e(0,t) - E(t)] \tag{7.8}$$

$$\left.\frac{\partial e}{\partial x}\right|_{x=L} = -\frac{\rho}{R_L} e(L,t) \tag{7.9}$$

It may be noted that these are indeed the appropriate equations to be used in the description of a transmission line with resistance ρ per unit length and capacitance γ per unit length. The line is fed from a voltage source E (internal resistance R_S) at $x = 0$ and is terminated at $x = L$ in a resistance R_L.

7.4   Solution of the Discrete Problem

It has been shown that the problem described by Eqs. (7.7), (7.8), and (7.9) can be considered as the limit, as $\Delta x \to 0$, of the problem described by Eqs. (7.4), (7.5), and (7.6). The method which has been developed for solving the latter (discrete) problem might be expected, in the limit as $\Delta x \to 0$, to lead to a procedure for solving the former (continuous) problem. In this section, the discrete problem will be solved in such a way as to readily be interpreted in the limit as $\Delta x \to 0$.

For simplicity, the case where $E(t) = 0$, $R_L = R_S = \rho \Delta x$ will be considered. Thus, the problem to be solved is to determine $e(x_i,t)$, given $e(x_i,0)$, from the equations of motion

$$\rho\gamma\dot{e}(x_i,t) = \frac{\delta^2}{(\Delta x)^2} e(x_i,t) \qquad i = 1, 2, \ldots, n$$

$$e(0,t) = e(L + \Delta x, t) = 0$$

(7.10)

where

$$x_i = i \Delta x$$

$$L = n \Delta x = x_n$$

$$\delta^2 e(x_i,t) = e(x_{i+1},t) - 2e(x_i,t) + e(x_{i-1},t)$$

The solution of these equations is carried out as follows. The formal solution is

$$e(x_i,t) = e^{t\delta^2/[\rho\gamma(\Delta x)^2]}e(x_i,0)$$

(7.11)

In order to evaluate any function $f(\delta^2)$ of the difference operator δ^2 it is necessary to find the eigencolumns and eigenvalues of δ^2 (with its accompanying boundary conditions). In so doing, the boundary conditions are an implicit part of the definition of δ^2. This follows directly from the manner of their introduction in Sec. 6.3.

It is thus necessary to find $s_\sigma(x_i)$ such that

$$\delta^2 s_\sigma(x_i) = \lambda_\sigma s_\sigma(x_i)$$

$$s_\sigma(0) = s_\sigma(L + \Delta x) = 0$$

$$i,\sigma = 1, 2, \ldots, n$$

(7.12)

Once the s_σ are found, the voltage at $t = 0$, $e(x_i,0)$, is written as a superposition of them:

$$e(x_i,0) = \sum_{\sigma=1}^{n} s_\sigma(x_i)A_\sigma$$

(7.13)

The formula

$$f(\delta^2)s_\sigma(x_i) = f(\lambda_\sigma)s_\sigma(x_i)$$

may then be applied to evaluate (7.11):

$$e(x_i,t) = e^{t\delta^2/[\rho\gamma(\Delta x)^2]} \sum_{\sigma=1}^{n} s_\sigma(x_i)A_\sigma$$

$$= \sum_{\sigma=1}^{n} e^{t\lambda_\sigma/[\rho\gamma(\Delta x)^2]}s_\sigma(x_i)A_\sigma$$

(7.14)

The solution (7.14) still contains the A_σ introduced in (7.13). These remain to be evaluated. This is done most directly by showing that δ^2 [with the boundary conditions (BC)] is Hermitian [see Sec. (6.5)].

$$\sum_{i=1}^{n} \left[\overline{f(x_i)}\, \delta^2 g(x_i) - g(x_i)\, \overline{\delta^2 f(x_i)} \right] = \sum_{i=1}^{n} \left[\overline{f(x_i)}g(x_{i+1}) + \overline{f(x_i)}g(x_{i-1}) \right.$$
$$\left. - g(x_i)\overline{f(x_{i+1})} - g(x_i)\overline{f(x_{i-1})} \right]$$
$$= \overline{f(x_n)}g(x_{n+1}) + \overline{f(x_1)}g(0)$$
$$- g(x_n)\overline{f(x_{n+1})} - g(x_1)\overline{f(0)}$$

so that
$$\sum_{i=1}^{n} \left[\overline{f(x_i)}\, \delta^2 g(x_i) - g(x_i)\, \overline{\delta^2 f(x_i)} \right] = 0$$

for arbitrary f and g satisfying

$$f(0) = f(x_{n+1}) = g(0) = g(x_{n+1}) = 0$$

Since, as just shown, δ^2 (with BC) is Hermitian, its eigencolumns may be taken as orthonormal:

$$\sum_{i=1}^{n} \overline{s_\sigma(x_i)}s_\tau(x_i) = \delta_{\sigma\tau}$$

Multiplication of (7.13) by $\overline{s_\tau(x_i)}$ and summation over i then yield

$$\sum_{i=1}^{n} \overline{s_\tau(x_i)}e(x_i,0) = \sum_{\sigma=1}^{n} \delta_{\sigma,\tau}A_\sigma = A_\tau \qquad (7.15)$$

This completes the solution of the problem, although one may wish to substitute (7.15) into (7.14) to obtain

$$e(x_i,t) = \sum_{\sigma=1}^{n} \sum_{j=1}^{n} e^{t\lambda_\sigma/[\rho\gamma(\Delta x)^2]}s_\sigma(x_i)\overline{s_\sigma(x_j)}e(x_j,0)$$

Of course, $s_\sigma(x_i)$ and λ_σ are as found in Sec. 6.3:

$$s_\sigma(x_i) = \sqrt{\frac{2}{n+1}} \sin \frac{\pi i \sigma}{n+1} = \sqrt{\frac{2\,\Delta x}{L+\Delta x}} \sin \frac{\pi \sigma x_i}{L+\Delta x}$$

$$\lambda_\sigma = 2 \cos \frac{\pi\sigma}{n+1} - 2 = 2 \cos \frac{\pi\sigma\,\Delta x}{L+\Delta x} - 2$$

7.5 Solution in the Limit (Continuous Problem)

In the work below, the process of solution given in Sec. 7.4 is repeated. Then, one step at a time, the limit is taken as $\Delta x \to 0$ to compare with the process used in the continuous problem.

Discrete Problem

(1) $$\rho\gamma\dot{e}(x_i,t) = \frac{\delta^2}{(\Delta x)^2} e(x_i,t) \qquad i = 1, 2, \ldots, n$$

$$e(0,t) = e(L + \Delta x, t) = 0$$

(2) $$\frac{\delta^2}{(\Delta x)^2} s_\sigma(x_i) = \frac{\lambda_\sigma}{(\Delta x)^2} s_\sigma(x_i)$$

$$s_\sigma(0) = s_\sigma(L + \Delta x) = 0$$

But δ^2 is Hermitian so that we may require

$$\sum_i \overline{s_\sigma(x_i)} s_\tau(x_i) = \delta_{\sigma\tau} = \sum_i \Delta x \frac{\overline{s_\sigma(x_i)}}{\sqrt{\Delta x}} \frac{s_\tau(x_i)}{\sqrt{\Delta x}}$$

whence $$\frac{s_\sigma(x_i)}{\sqrt{\Delta x}} = \sqrt{\frac{2}{L + \Delta x}} \sin \frac{\pi\sigma x_i}{L + \Delta x}$$

$$\frac{\lambda_\sigma}{(\Delta x)^2} = -2 \frac{1 - \cos\left[\pi\sigma \Delta x/(L + \Delta x)\right]}{(\Delta x)^2}$$

(3) $$e(x_i,0) = \sum_\sigma \frac{s_\sigma(x_i)}{\sqrt{\Delta x}} \sum_j \Delta x \frac{\overline{s_\sigma(x_j)}}{\sqrt{\Delta x}} e(x_j,0)$$

$$= \frac{2}{L + \Delta x} \sum_\sigma \sin \frac{\pi\sigma x_i}{L + \Delta x} \sum_j \Delta x \sin \frac{\pi\sigma x_j}{L + \Delta x} e(x_j,0)$$

(4) $$e(x_i,t) = \exp\left[\frac{\delta^2}{\rho\gamma(\Delta x)^2} t\right] e(x_i,0)$$

$$= \frac{2}{L + \Delta x} \sum_\sigma \exp\left[\frac{\lambda_\sigma}{(\Delta x)^2} \frac{t}{\rho\gamma}\right] \sin \frac{\pi\sigma x_i}{L + \Delta x} \sum_j \Delta x$$

$$\times \sin \frac{\pi\sigma x_j}{L + \Delta x} e(x_j,0)$$

Continuous Problem

(1a) $$\rho\gamma\dot{e}(x,t) = \frac{\partial^2}{\partial x^2} e(x,t) \qquad 0 < x < L$$

$$e(0,t) = e(L,t) = 0$$

(2a) $$\frac{\partial^2}{\partial x^2} S_\sigma(x) = \omega_\sigma S_\sigma(x)$$

$$S_\sigma(0) = S_\sigma(L) = 0$$

(Note that ω_σ replaces $\lambda_\sigma/(\Delta x)^2$ and S_σ corresponds to $s_\sigma/\sqrt{\Delta x}$ so that limiting processes follow through conveniently.)

$$\int_0^L \overline{S_\sigma(x)} S_\tau(x)\, dx = \delta_{\sigma,\tau}$$

whence
$$S_\sigma(x) = \sqrt{\frac{2}{L}} \sin \frac{\pi\sigma x}{L}$$

$$\omega_\sigma = -\lim_{\Delta x \to 0} 2\, \frac{1 - \cos\left[\pi\sigma\,\Delta x/(L + \Delta x)\right]}{(\Delta x)^2}$$

$$= -\frac{\pi^2 \sigma^2}{L^2}$$

(3a) Suppose $e(x,0) = \sum_\tau A_\tau S_\tau(x)$. Then

$$\int_0^L e(x,0)\overline{S_\sigma(x)}\, dx = \sum_\tau \delta_{\sigma,\tau} A_\tau = A_\sigma$$

whence
$$e(x,0) = \sum_\sigma S_\sigma(x) \int_0^L \overline{S_\sigma(x')} e(x',0)\, dx'$$

$$= \frac{2}{L} \sum_\sigma \sin \frac{\pi\sigma x}{L} \int_0^L \sin \frac{\pi\sigma x'}{L}\, e(x',0)\, dx'$$

(4a) $e(x,t) = \exp\left(\dfrac{t}{\rho\gamma} \dfrac{\partial^2}{\partial x^2}\right) e(x,0)$

$$= \frac{2}{L} \sum_\sigma \exp\left(-\frac{t}{\rho\gamma} \frac{\pi^2\sigma^2}{L^2}\right) \sin \frac{\pi\sigma x}{L} \int_0^L \sin \frac{\pi\sigma x'}{L}\, e(x',0)\, dx'$$

Remarks

(2), (2a) δ^2 (with *BC*) is Hermitian means that

$$\sum_i \overline{f(x_i)}\, \delta^2 g(x_i) = \sum_i \overline{\delta^2 f(x_i)} g(x_i)$$

provided that $f(0) = f(L + \Delta x) = g(0) = g(L + \Delta x) = 0$. In the limit as $\Delta x \to 0$ this becomes

$$\int_0^L \overline{f(x)}\, \frac{d^2}{dx^2}\, g(x)\, dx = \int_0^L \overline{\frac{d^2 f(x)}{dx^2}}\, g(x)\, dx$$

if $f(0) = f(L) = g(0) = g(L) = 0$, which is readily seen to be true. Thus d^2/dx^2 (with *BC* as given) is Hermitian. We may use this result to prove orthogonality directly:

$$0 = \int_0^L \overline{S_\tau(x)}\, \frac{d^2}{dx^2}\, S_\sigma(x)\, dx - \int_0^L \overline{\frac{d^2}{dx^2}\, S_\tau(x)} S_\sigma(x)\, dx$$

$$= (\omega_\sigma - \bar{\omega}_\tau) \int_0^L \overline{S_\tau(x)} S_\sigma(x)\, dx$$

whence (from $\sigma = \tau$) ω_σ is real, and (from $\sigma \neq \tau$) nondegenerate solutions are orthogonal.

(3*a*) This is the well-known Fourier series expansion. The proof that such an expansion is always possible for normal matrices (as given in Chap. 4) does not hold for infinite dimensional spaces [$n + 1 = \lim_{\Delta x \to 0} (L + \Delta x)/\Delta x = \infty$]. A proof is given for the present case in Sec. 9.4.

7.6 The Fourier Transform

It was seen in the preceding section that if

$$G_\sigma = \frac{2}{L} \int_0^L g(x) \sin \frac{\pi \sigma x}{L} \, dx \tag{7.16}$$

then

$$g(x) = \sum_{\sigma=1}^{\infty} G_\sigma \sin \frac{\pi \sigma x}{L} \tag{7.17}$$

Here G_σ is called the (finite) Fourier sine transform of $g(x)$, and $g(x)$ is called the inverse transform of G_σ.

To evaluate $f(d^2/dx^2)g(x)$ one may use the transform of $g(x)$. Thus, from (7.17)

$$f(d^2/dx^2)g(x) = \sum_{\sigma=1}^{\infty} f\left(\frac{-\sigma^2 \pi^2}{L^2}\right) G_\sigma \sin \frac{\pi \sigma x}{L}$$

whence the Fourier transform of $f(d^2/dx^2)g(x)$ is given by[1] $f(-\sigma^2\pi^2/L^2)G_\sigma$.

---

[1] This result may also be obtained from (7.16), if f is expressible as a polynomial or series in d^2/dx^2, by integration by parts a suitable number of times. This follows from the Hermiticity of d^2/dx^2:

$$\int_0^L h(x) \left(\frac{d^2}{dx^2}\right)^n g(x) \, dx = \int_0^L g(x) \left(\frac{d^2}{dx^2}\right)^n h(x) \, dx$$

for $h(x)$ and $g(x)$ satisfying the boundary conditions

$$h(0) = h(L) = g(0) = g(L) = 0$$

Thus also, for any f expressible in power series,

$$\int_0^L h(x) f\left(\frac{d^2}{dx^2}\right) g(x) \, dx = \int_0^L g(x) f\left(\frac{d^2}{dx^2}\right) h(x) \, dx$$

whence $\int_0^L \sin \frac{\pi \sigma x}{L} f\left(\frac{d^2}{dx^2}\right) g(x) \, dx = \int_0^L \left[f\left(\frac{d^2}{dx^2}\right) \sin \frac{\pi \sigma x}{L} \right] g(x) \, dx$

$$= f\left(\frac{-\pi^2 \sigma^2}{L^2}\right) \int_0^L \sin \frac{\pi \sigma x}{L} g(x) \, dx$$

as was to be shown.

To solve

$$\rho\gamma\dot{e}(x,t) = \frac{\partial^2}{\partial x^2}\, e(x,t) \qquad 0 < x < L$$

one may take the Fourier transform of both sides of the equation. Since

$$E_\sigma(t) = \frac{2}{L}\int_0^L \sin\frac{\pi\sigma x}{L}\, e(x,t)\, dx$$

and

$$\dot{E}_\sigma(t) = \frac{2}{L}\int_0^L \sin\frac{\pi\sigma x}{L}\, \dot{e}(x,t)\, dx$$

it follows that

$$\rho\gamma\dot{E} = \frac{2}{L}\int_0^L \sin\frac{\pi\sigma x}{L}\, \frac{\partial^2}{\partial x^2}\, e(x,t)\, dx = -\frac{\pi^2\sigma^2}{L^2}\, E_\sigma$$

This equation is readily solved:

$$E_\sigma(t) = e^{-[(\pi^2\sigma^2)/(L^2\rho\gamma)]t}E_\sigma(0)$$

where

$$E_\sigma(0) = \frac{2}{L}\int_0^L \sin\frac{\pi\sigma x}{L}\, e(x,0)\, dx$$

Having $E_\sigma(t)$, one takes the inverse Fourier transform to obtain

$$e(x,t) = \sum_{\sigma=1}^{\infty} E_\sigma(t)\sin\frac{\pi\sigma x}{L}$$

The procedure just outlined is clearly completely equivalent to that used in Sec. 7.5. Its main advantage is that it eliminates the need for writing down a formal solution as, for example, in (6.27). As an example, consider a vibrating string described by the equations

$$\ddot{y}(x,t) = c^2\, \frac{\partial^2}{\partial x^2}\, y(x,t) \qquad 0 < x < L$$

$$y(0,t) = y(L,t) = 0$$

Let

$$Y_\sigma(t) = \frac{2}{L}\int_0^L y(x,t)\sin\frac{\pi\sigma x}{L}\, dx \qquad (7.18)$$

then

$$\ddot{Y}_\sigma(t) = -c^2\, \frac{\pi^2\sigma^2}{L^2}\, Y_\sigma(t)$$

whence $\qquad Y_\sigma(t) = \cos\left(\frac{\pi\sigma c}{L}\, t\right) Y_\sigma(0) + \frac{L}{\pi\sigma c}\sin\left(\frac{\pi\sigma c}{L}\, t\right)\dot{Y}_\sigma(0)$

.

then $y(x,t) = \sum_\sigma \sin \dfrac{\pi \sigma x}{L} Y_\sigma(t)$

$\qquad\qquad = \sum_\sigma \sin \dfrac{\pi \sigma x}{L} \left[Y_\sigma(0) \cos \dfrac{\pi \sigma c}{L} t + \dot{Y}_\sigma(0) \dfrac{L}{\pi \sigma c} \sin \dfrac{\pi \sigma c}{L} t \right]$

where $Y_\sigma(0)$ and $\dot{Y}_\sigma(0)$ are obtained from (7.18).

The equivalent method of Sec. 7.5 proceeds as follows:

$$y(x,0) = \sum_\sigma Y_\sigma(0) \sin \dfrac{\pi \sigma x}{L}$$

$$\dot{y}(x,0) = \sum_\sigma \dot{Y}_\sigma(0) \sin \dfrac{\pi \sigma x}{L}$$

where $Y_\sigma(0)$ and $\dot{Y}_\sigma(0)$ are given by (7.18). Then, using the formal solution

$$y(x,t) = \cos \sqrt{-c^2 \dfrac{d^2}{dx^2}} \, t y(x,0) + \left(-c^2 \dfrac{d^2}{dx^2} \right)^{-\frac{1}{2}} \sin \sqrt{-c^2 \dfrac{d^2}{dx^2}} \, t \dot{y}(x,0)$$

we obtain

$$y(x,t) = \sum_\sigma \sin \dfrac{\pi \sigma x}{L} \left[Y_\sigma(0) \cos \dfrac{\pi \sigma c}{L} t + \dot{Y}_\sigma(0) \dfrac{L}{\pi \sigma c} \sin \dfrac{\pi \sigma c}{L} t \right]$$

as before.

Exercises

1. Solve the problem of the temperature distribution in a slab of length L, given that the initial temperature is an arbitrary function of x, but that at all times after $t = 0$ the two faces (at $x = 0$ and $x = L$) are maintained at temperature $T = 0$.

2. Consider the linear flow of heat in a solid bounded by the two parallel planes $x = 0$ and $x = L$ when its faces are thermally insulated and its initial temperature is $f(x)$. That is, solve the equation

$$\dfrac{\partial}{\partial t} T(x,t) = \varkappa \dfrac{\partial^2}{\partial x^2} T(x,t) \qquad 0 < x < L \qquad t > 0$$

with the boundary conditions

$$\left. \dfrac{\partial}{\partial t} T(x,t) \right|_{x=0} = \left. \dfrac{\partial}{\partial t} T(x,t) \right|_{x=L} = 0 \qquad t > 0$$

and the initial condition

$$T(x,0) = f(x) \qquad 0 < x < L$$

3. Solve Exercise 1 approximately by considering a discrete system with three interior points.

4. Solve Exercise 2 approximately by considering a discrete system with three interior points.

5. Consider the system shown below:

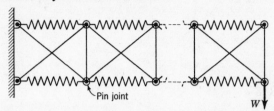

~Pin joint

W↓

which is constructed of rigid links and springs. (The links do not interact where they cross.) Assuming the structure is periodic, find the vertical displacement of the load W (assumed small). Find the equations in the continuous limit.

6. Solve the equations

$$c \frac{de_i}{dt} = \frac{e_{i+1} - 2e_i + e_{i-1}}{R} \qquad i = 1, 2, \ldots, n \qquad (a)$$

$$e_0 = e_{n+1} = 0.$$

using the discrete analogue of Sec. 7.6.

Thus show that

(1) if
$$\varepsilon_\sigma = \sum_i e_i \sqrt{\frac{2}{N+1}} \sin \frac{\pi i \sigma}{n+1}$$

then

$$e_i = \sum_\sigma \varepsilon_\sigma \sqrt{\frac{2}{N+1}} \sin \frac{\pi i \sigma}{n+1}$$

(2) Show that

$$c \frac{d\varepsilon_\sigma}{dt} = \left(2 - 2\cos \frac{\pi\sigma}{n+1}\right) \varepsilon_\sigma$$

$\left[\textit{Hint:} \text{ Multiply Eq. } (a) \text{ by } \sqrt{\dfrac{2}{N+1}} \sin \dfrac{\pi i \sigma}{n+1} \text{, sum over } i, \text{ collect coeffi-} \right.$

cients of e_i, and use $\sin \dfrac{\pi\sigma}{n+1}(i+1) - 2\sin \dfrac{\pi\sigma}{n+1}i + \sin \dfrac{\pi\sigma}{n+1}(i-1)$

$= -\left(2 - 2\cos \dfrac{\pi\sigma}{n+1}\right) \sin \dfrac{\pi\sigma}{n+1}i. \Big]$

References

Slater, J. C., and N. H. Frank: "Introduction to Theoretical Physics," secs. 80–82, McGraw-Hill Book Company, Inc., New York, 1933.
Morse, P. M., and H. Feshbach: "Methods of Theoretical Physics," pp. 131–136, McGraw-Hill Book Company, Inc., New York, 1953.

CHAPTER 8

Operators in Continuous Systems

8.1 Introduction

In the last chapter there were indications as to how one might extend the matrix concepts of Part One to continuous systems. In the present chapter this process will be developed in a consistent manner. The analogue of the column u of the finite dimensional space is, in a continuous system, a function f, satisfying certain boundary conditions. One may construct also the analogues of matrices, changes of coordinates, and so forth in continuous systems.

In order to proceed with such a program, it is useful to reinterpret the concepts of columns, matrices, and operators introduced in Part One. Thus, it is now convenient to think of a column with elements f_i as a function f of the discrete variable i and to adopt the notation $f(i)$. Similarly, it is now convenient to think of a matrix L with elements $l_{i,j}$ as a function l of the discrete variables i,j and to use the notation $l(i,j)$.

In Chap. 4 an operator $\mathscr{L}$ was introduced such that if

$$\mathbf{f} = \sum_i \mathbf{u}_i f(i) \qquad \text{and} \qquad \mathbf{g} = \sum_i \mathbf{u}_i g(i)$$

then

$$\mathbf{g} = \mathscr{L}\mathbf{f} = \sum_{i,j} \mathbf{u}_i l(i,j) f(j)$$

meant

$$g(i) = \sum_j l(i,j) f(j)$$

In Chap. 4 it was convenient to think of $\mathscr{L}$ as operating on the $\mathbf{u}_i$. Here it is more convenient to think of $\mathscr{L}$ as operating on the function $f(i)$ to produce the function $g(i)$. This is a redefinition of $\mathscr{L}$. Thus, one writes

$$g(i) = \mathscr{L}f(i) \tag{8.1}$$

as equivalent to

$$g(i) = \sum_j l(i,j) f(j) \tag{8.2}$$

It is sometimes convenient to define the operator $\mathscr{L}$ by means other than the matrix L. Thus, in Chap. 6 it was found more convenient to define $\mathscr{L}$ by the relation

$$g(i) = \mu\, \delta^2 f(i) = \mu[f(i+1) - 2f(i) + f(i-1)] \qquad i = 1, 2, \ldots, n \quad (8.3)$$

with the boundary conditions[1]

$$f(0) = f(n+1) = 0 \qquad (8.4)$$

on the $f(i)$, instead of by the matrix

$$L = \begin{bmatrix} -2\mu & \mu & 0 & 0 & \cdots & 0 & 0 & 0 \\ \mu & -2\mu & \mu & 0 & \cdots & 0 & 0 & 0 \\ 0 & \mu & -2\mu & \mu & \cdots & 0 & 0 & 0 \\ 0 & 0 & \mu & -2\mu & \cdots & 0 & 0 & 0 \\ \cdot & \cdot & \cdot & \cdot & \cdot & \cdot & \cdot & \cdot \\ 0 & 0 & 0 & 0 & \cdots & -2\mu & \mu & 0 \\ 0 & 0 & 0 & 0 & \cdots & \mu & -2\mu & \mu \\ 0 & 0 & 0 & 0 & \cdots & 0 & \mu & -2\mu \end{bmatrix}$$

In this case then $g(i) = \mathscr{L}f(i)$ is equivalent to[2]

$$g(i) = \mu\, \delta^2 f(i)$$
$$f(0) = f(n+1) = 0$$

8.2 Operators on Functions

If x is a continuous variable and $f(x)$ and $g(x)$ are functions of x, one might define an operator $\mathscr{L}$ by

$$g(x) = \mathscr{L}f(x) \qquad (8.5)$$

in analogy with (8.1).

The expression analogous to (8.2) is obtained by replacing the summation by an integration:

$$g(x) = \int l(x,x')f(x')\,dx' \qquad (8.6)$$

[1] Note that $f(0)$ and $f(n+1)$ are auxiliary variables defined by these boundary conditions.

[2] Note that the statement "$\mathscr{L}$ is Hermitian" means either (a) L is a Hermitian matrix or (b) $\mu\,\delta^2$ *with the boundary conditions* (8.4) is Hermitian. It is incorrect to omit the italic phrase. The boundary conditions are part of the definition of the operator.

When an operator $\mathscr{L}$ is defined by (8.6), the function $l(x,x')$ is known as the *kernel* of the operator $\mathscr{L}$. The function $l(x,x')$ may also be thought of as the assemblage of elements of a matrix L such that

$$g = Lf \tag{8.6a}$$

Other methods of representing operators on functions are well known. For example,

$$g(x) = \frac{d}{dx} f(x)$$

enables the calculation of $g(x)$, given $f(x)$. As another example, the equation of the RC line might be written as

$$\rho\gamma\dot{e}(x,t) = \mathscr{L}e(x,t)$$

where $\mathscr{L}$ is defined so that if $g(x) = \mathscr{L}f(x)$, then

$$g(x) = \frac{d^2}{dx^2} f(x) \tag{8.7}$$

$$f(0) = f(L) = 0 \tag{8.8}$$

These relations have an obvious similarity to (8.3) and (8.4).

That $\mathscr{L}$ as defined in (8.7) and (8.8) cannot be readily put in the form (8.6) is clear. A simpler $\mathscr{L}$ for which the form (8.6) appears to fail is the identity operation such that

$$g(x) = f(x)$$

Here one would like a function $\delta(x,x')$ such that

$$f(x) = \int \delta(x,x')f(x')\,dx' \tag{8.9}$$

for every function f. No such function $\delta(x,x')$ exists.

The way out of this difficulty is discussed in Sec. 8.3. There it will be demonstrated that the difficulty may be resolved by permitting $\delta(x,x')$ as a *symbolic function*. The adjective "symbolic" indicates that the function $\delta(x,x')$ is not a function of x according to the usual mathematical definition which requires a function to have a definite value at each point in its domain. The symbolic function $\delta(x,x')$ is defined in terms of limiting processes such that each function in the limiting sequence is a function in the usual sense. The limit does not exist in the usual sense.

8.3   The Dirac δ Function

Suppose that

$$\int_{-\infty}^{\infty} D(x)\,dx = 1 \tag{8.10}$$

Then for continuous functions $f(x)$

$$\lim_{a\to\infty}\int_{-\infty}^{\infty}aD[a(x'-x)]f(x')\,dx' = \lim_{a\to\infty}\int_{-\infty}^{\infty}D[a(x'-x)]f\left(\frac{ax'}{a}\right)d(ax')$$

$$= \lim_{a\to\infty}\int_{-\infty}^{\infty}D(t)f\left(\frac{t}{a}+x\right)dt$$

$$= f(x)$$

Thus, if one could interchange the limiting process with the integration he would have

$$f(x) = \int_{-\infty}^{\infty}\left\{\lim_{a\to\infty}aD[a(x'-x)]\right\}f(x')\,dx'$$

or
$$\delta(x,x') = \delta(x'-x) = \lim_{a\to\infty}aD[a(x'-x)] \qquad (8.11)$$

for any D satisfying (8.10). A sequence of functions $aD[a(x'-x)]$ is shown in Fig. 8.1. It should be noted that all the curves have unit area. With the understanding that the limit should be held off until after an integration, (8.11) may be taken as defining $\delta(x'-x)$.

An alternate reversal of order of processes which yields such a function is as follows. Consider $\eta(x)$ such that

$$\eta(x) = 1 \qquad x > 0$$
$$\eta(x) = 0 \qquad x < 0 \qquad (8.12)$$

Then for $f(x)$ such that $\int_{-\infty}^{\infty}f(x)\,dx$ converges absolutely

$$\int_{-\infty}^{\infty}f(x')\eta(x-x')\,dx' = \int_{-\infty}^{x}f(x')dx'$$

whence

$$f(x) = \frac{d}{dx}\int_{-\infty}^{\infty}f(x')\eta(x-x')\,dx'$$

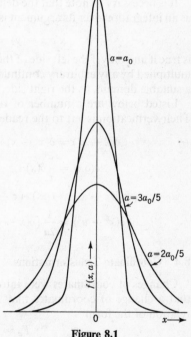

Figure 8.1

This suggests writing, by differentiation under the integral sign,

$$\delta(x-x') = \frac{d}{dx}\eta(x-x') \qquad (8.13)$$

which yields

$$f(x) = \int_{-\infty}^{+\infty} \delta(x - x') f(x') \, dx' \tag{8.14}$$

The function $\delta(x - x')$ was first introduced by Dirac[1] and is known as the *Dirac delta function*. It is defined equally well by (8.11), (8.13), or (8.14). From these definitions it is evident that $\delta(x - x')$ must vanish for $x \neq x'$ and must be infinite for $x = x'$. Thus $\delta(x - x')$ is not well defined at $x = x'$ and is not a function in the conventional meaning of the term. We therefore call it a symbolic function.

The range of integration in (8.14) need not be from $-\infty$ to $+\infty$ but may be over any domain surrounding the critical point x' at which the delta function does not vanish. In the future the limits of integration in such expressions will usually be omitted, it being understood that the domain of integration is a suitable one.

It is necessary to note that the delta function has meaning only so long as an integration over its argument is carried out. Thus any result such as

$$x \, \delta(x - y) = y \, \delta(x - y)$$

is true if and only if the left side of the equation gives the same result when multiplied by any arbitrary continuous function $f(y)$ and integrated over a suitable domain, as the right side.

Listed below are a number of relations concerning delta functions. Their verification is left to the reader.

$$\delta(x - x') = \delta(x' - x)$$

$$\delta(ax) = \frac{1}{a} \, \delta(x) \qquad\qquad a > 0$$

$$f(x) \, \delta(x - x') = f(x') \, \delta(x - x') \tag{8.15}$$

$$\delta(x^2 - a^2) = \frac{1}{2a} \left[\delta(x - a) + \delta(x + a) \right] \qquad a > 0$$

8.4   Coordinate Transformations

Changes of coordinates were introduced in Sec. 4.3, where it was seen that a change of coordinates may be associated with a matrix S by a relation of the form

$$F_\sigma = \sum_i s_{\sigma i} f_i \tag{8.16}$$

---

[1] P. A. M. Dirac, "The Principles of Quantum Mechanics," 2d ed., p. 71, Oxford University Press, New York, 1935; 3d ed., p. 58, 1947. In the form of $(d/dx)\eta(x - x')$ it was introduced by Heaviside at a much earlier date (cf., O. Heaviside, "Electrical Papers," Copley Publishers, Boston, 1925).

If $ST = TS = 1$, then the inverse transformation is given by

$$f_i = \sum_\sigma t_{i\sigma} F_\sigma \qquad (8.17)$$

In a similar manner, one might consider a transformation of a function f into a function F as given by a matrix S:

$$F(y) = \int s(y,x) f(x)\, dx \qquad (8.18)$$

or $\qquad\qquad\qquad\qquad F = Sf \qquad (8.18a)$

The inverse transformation is given by a matrix T:

$$f(x) = \int t(x,y) F(y)\, dy \qquad (8.19)$$

or $\qquad\qquad\qquad\qquad f = TF \qquad (8.19a)$

Substitution of (8.18) into (8.19) yields

$$f(x) = \int \left[\int t(x,y) s(y,x')\, dy \right] f(x')\, dx' \qquad (8.20)$$

or $\qquad\qquad\qquad\qquad f = TSf \qquad (8.20a)$

It then follows that one must have

$$\int t(x,y) s(y,x')\, dy = \delta(x - x') \qquad (8.21)$$

or equivalently $\qquad\qquad TS = 1 \qquad (8.21a)$

Similarly, substitution of (8.19) into (8.18) yields

$$\int s(y,x) t(x,y')\, dx = \delta(y - y') \qquad (8.22)$$

or equivalently $\qquad\qquad ST = 1 \qquad (8.22a)$

In Sec. 7.5 a transformation of coordinates from a continuous to a discrete variable was considered. There one had

$$F_\sigma = \int_0^L s_\sigma(x) f(x)\, dx$$

or $\qquad\qquad\qquad\qquad F = Sf$

and the inverse transformation

$$f(x) = \sum_{\sigma=1}^\infty t_\sigma(x) F_\sigma$$

or $\qquad\qquad\qquad\qquad f = TF$

From $F = STF$ it follows that

$$\int_0^L s_\sigma(x)t_{\sigma'}(x)\,dx = \delta_{\sigma,\sigma'} \tag{8.23}$$

while from $f = TSf$ it follows that

$$\sum_{\sigma=1}^\infty t_\sigma(x)s_\sigma(x') = \delta(x - x') \tag{8.24}$$

It should be noted that in a finite dimensional space (cf. Sec. 1.8), if S and T are square matrices such that $ST = 1$, then of necessity $TS = 1$.[1] In an infinite dimensional space, however, little meaning can be given to the statement "S and T are square matrices." Thus, $ST = 1$ does not imply $TS = 1$.

An example of a case where $ST = 1$, $TS \neq 1$ is given by

$$T = \begin{pmatrix} 0 & 0 & 0 & 0 & \cdot \\ 1 & 0 & 0 & 0 & \\ 0 & 1 & 0 & 0 & \\ 0 & 0 & 1 & 0 & \cdot \\ \cdot & \cdot & \cdot & \cdot & \end{pmatrix} \qquad S = \begin{pmatrix} 0 & 1 & 0 & 0 & \cdot \\ 0 & 0 & 1 & 0 & \cdot \\ 0 & 0 & 0 & 1 & \cdot \\ 0 & 0 & 0 & 0 & \cdot \\ \cdot & \cdot & \cdot & \cdot & \end{pmatrix}$$

$$ST = \begin{pmatrix} 1 & 0 & 0 & 0 & \cdot \\ 0 & 1 & 0 & 0 & \\ 0 & 0 & 1 & 0 & \cdot \\ 0 & 0 & 0 & 1 & \cdot \\ \cdot & \cdot & \cdot & \cdot & \end{pmatrix} = 1 \qquad TS = \begin{pmatrix} 0 & 0 & 0 & 0 & \cdot \\ 0 & 1 & 0 & 0 & \cdot \\ 0 & 0 & 1 & 0 & \cdot \\ 0 & 0 & 0 & 1 & \cdot \\ \cdot & \cdot & \cdot & \cdot & \end{pmatrix} \neq 1$$

The effect of a coordinate transformation on an operator is readily evaluated. Thus suppose

$$g(x) = \mathscr{L}f(x) = \int l(x,x')f(x')\,dx'$$

---

[1] For nonsquare matrices, $ST = 1$ and $TS = 1$ cannot simultaneously hold. An example of nonsquare matrices S and T such that $ST = 1$ is given by $S = (1 \quad 0)$ and $T = \begin{pmatrix} 1 \\ 0 \end{pmatrix}$.

Clearly $$TS = \begin{pmatrix} 1 & 0 \\ 0 & 0 \end{pmatrix} \neq \begin{pmatrix} 1 & 0 \\ 0 & 1 \end{pmatrix}$$

and let
$$F(y) = \int s(y,x)f(x)\,dx$$

$$f(x) = \int t(x,y)F(y)\,dy$$

Then
$$G(y) = \int s(y,x)g(x)\,dx$$

$$= \int\int s(y,x)l(x,x')f(x')\,dx\,dx'$$

$$= \int\int\int s(y,x)l(x,x')t(x',y')F(y')\,dx\,dx'\,dy'$$

so that $\mathscr{L}$ has the kernel

$$l'(y,y') = \int\int s(y,x)l(x,x')t(x',y')\,dx\,dx'$$

in the new coordinate system. Note that $\mathscr{L}$ is represented by the matrix SLT, as in the finite dimensional case. An alternate form arises if one notes that

$$\int l(x,x')t(x',y')\,dx' = \mathscr{L}t(x,y)$$

so that
$$l'(y,y') = \int s(y,x)\mathscr{L}t(x,y')\,dx$$

8.5   Adjoints

It was seen in Sec. 6.5 that L^{+}, the adjoint of the matrix L, may be defined by

$$\sum_{i,j} \overline{f(i)}l(i,j)g(j) = \sum_{i,j} \overline{l^{+}(j,i)f(i)}g(j)$$

Thus, if
$$\mathscr{L}g(i) = \sum_{j} l(i,j)g(j)$$

then $\mathscr{L}^{+}$ is defined by

$$\sum_{i} \overline{f(i)}\mathscr{L}g(i) = \sum_{j} \overline{\mathscr{L}^{+}f(j)}g(j)$$

which must hold for all f and g.

A similar relation holds for functions of a continuous variable:

$$\int \overline{f(x)}\mathscr{L}g(x)\,dx = \int \overline{\mathscr{L}^{+}f(x)}g(x)\,dx \tag{8.25}$$

If $\mathscr{L}^{+} = \mathscr{L}$, $\mathscr{L}$ is a Hermitian operator.

If
$$\mathscr{L}f(x) = \int l(x,x')f(x')\,dx'$$

then
$$\int \bar{f} \mathscr{L} g \, dx = \int \int \overline{f(x)} l(x,x') g(x') \, dx \, dx'$$

$$= \int \int \overline{\overline{l(x,x')}f(x)} g(x') \, dx \, dx'$$

$$= \int \left[\int \overline{\overline{l(x',x)}f(x')} \, dx' \right] g(x) \, dx$$

whence
$$\mathscr{L}^+ f(x) = \int l^+(x,x') f(x') \, dx'$$

$$= \int \overline{l(x',x)} f(x') \, dx'$$

for arbitrary $f(x)$. Thus

$$l^+(x,x') = \overline{l(x',x)} \tag{8.26}$$

as in the finite dimensional case.

8.6   Orthogonality of Eigenfunctions

If $\mathscr{L}$ is Hermitian, it is readily shown (cf. Sec. 7.5) that its eigenvalues are real and that eigenfunctions belonging to different eigenvalues are orthogonal. Thus, let

$$\mathscr{L}^+ = \mathscr{L}$$
$$\mathscr{L}f(x) = \lambda f(x)$$
$$\mathscr{L}g(x) = \mu g(x)$$

Then
$$\int \bar{f} \mathscr{L} f \, dx = \lambda \int \bar{f} f \, dx$$

$$= \int \overline{\mathscr{L}^+ f} f \, dx = \int \overline{\mathscr{L} f} f \, dx$$

$$= \bar{\lambda} \int \bar{f} f \, dx$$

whence $\lambda = \bar{\lambda}$. Also

$$\int \bar{f} \mathscr{L} g \, dx = \mu \int \bar{f} g \, dx$$

$$= \int \overline{\mathscr{L}^+ f} g \, dx = \int \overline{\mathscr{L} f} g \, dx$$

$$= \lambda \int \bar{f} g \, dx$$

or
$$(\lambda - \mu) \int \bar{f} g \, dx = 0$$

Independent eigenfunctions belonging to the same eigenvalue may be selected to be orthogonal. Thus, suppose $f_1(x), f_2(x), \ldots, f_n(x)$ all satisfy

$$\mathscr{L}f_i = \lambda f_i$$

for the same eigenvalue λ. Furthermore, suppose the f_i are independent so that

$$\sum_{i=1}^{n} a_i f_i(x) = 0 \qquad (8.27)$$

implies $a_i = 0$ for all i. An orthogonal set is easily constructed (cf. Sec. 4.9). Thus, let

$$g_1 = f_1$$

$$g_{i+1} = f_{i+1} - \sum_{j=1}^{i} h_j \int \bar{h}_j f_{i+1}\, dx$$

$$h_i = g_i \bigg/ \left(\int \bar{g}_i g_i\, dx \right)^{\frac{1}{2}}$$

If any g_i vanishes, (8.27) holds with nonzero coefficients (the coefficient of f_1 is 1) contrary to hypothesis. Hence this process yields $h_1, h_2, \ldots, h_n$. These are readily seen to satisfy

$$\int \bar{h}_i h_j\, dx = \delta_{ij}$$

It has thus been shown that if $\mathscr{L} = \mathscr{L}^+$ and if

$$\mathscr{L}f_\sigma(x) = \lambda_\sigma f_\sigma(x)$$

one may always have

$$\int f_\sigma f_\tau\, dx = 0 \qquad \text{for} \qquad \sigma \neq \tau$$

or, by normalization,

$$\int \bar{f}_\sigma f_\tau\, dx = \delta_{\sigma\tau}$$

8.7 Functions of Operators

Suppose

$$\mathscr{L}s_\sigma(x) = \lambda_\sigma s_\sigma(x)$$

and that there exists a T such that

$$TS = ST = 1$$

Then the evaluation of $f(\mathscr{L})g(x)$ is straightforward. Let

$$G_\sigma = \int t_\sigma(x)g(x)\,dx$$

then

$$g(x) = \sum_\sigma s_\sigma(x)G_\sigma$$

and

$$f(\mathscr{L})g(x) = f(\mathscr{L})\sum_\sigma s_\sigma(x)G_\sigma$$

$$= \sum_\sigma f(\lambda_\sigma)s_\sigma(x)G_\sigma$$

$$= \sum_\sigma f(\lambda_\sigma)s_\sigma(x)\int t_\sigma(x')g(x')\,dx'$$

Two methods may be used to solve the equation

$$\dot{y}(x,t) = \mathscr{L}y(x,t)$$

The formal solution is

$$y(x,t) = e^{t\mathscr{L}}y(x,0)$$

$$= e^{t\mathscr{L}}\sum_\sigma s_\sigma(x)\int t_\sigma(x')y(x',0)\,dx'$$

$$= \sum_\sigma e^{t\lambda_\sigma}s_\sigma(x)\int t_\sigma(x')y(x',\sigma)\,dx'$$

The Fourier transform method goes as follows:

$$Y_\sigma(t) = \int t_\sigma(x)y(x,t)\,dx$$

$$\dot{Y}_\sigma(t) = \int t_\sigma(x)\dot{y}(x,t)\,dx$$

To evaluate

$$I = \int t_\sigma(x)\mathscr{L}y(x,t)\,dx$$

note that

$$\mathscr{L}y(x,t) = \mathscr{L}\sum_\sigma s_\sigma(x)Y_\sigma(t)$$

$$= \sum_\sigma \lambda_\sigma s_\sigma(x)Y_\sigma(t)$$

so that

$$I = \lambda_\sigma Y_\sigma(t)$$

Thus, from

$$\int t_\sigma(x)\dot{y}(x,t)\,dx = \int t_\sigma(x)\mathscr{L}y(x,t)\,dx$$

one obtains

$$\dot{Y}_\sigma(t) = \lambda_\sigma Y_\sigma(t)$$

which has for solution

$$Y_\sigma(t) = e^{\lambda_\sigma t}Y_\sigma(0)$$

Then, by the inverse transform,

$$y(x,t) = \sum_\sigma s_\sigma(x) Y_\sigma(t)$$

$$= \sum_\sigma s_\sigma(x) e^{\lambda_\sigma t} \int t_\sigma(x') y(x',0) \, dx'$$

as before.

In some examples, it will turn out that the eigenvalues of $\mathscr{L}$ are continuous:

$$\mathscr{L} s(x,\omega) = \omega s(x,\omega)$$

In this case, if $t(\omega,x)$ exists such that

$$\int s(x,\omega) t(\omega,x') \, d\omega = \delta(x - x')$$

$$\int t(\omega,x) s(x,\omega') \, dx = \delta(\omega - \omega')$$

then

$$g(x) = \int s(x,\omega) \left[\int t(\omega,x') g(x') \, dx' \right] d\omega$$

and

$$f(\mathscr{L}) g(x) = \int f(\omega) s(x,\omega) \left[\int t(\omega,x') g(x') \, dx' \right] d\omega$$

Note that if $\mathscr{M} = f(\mathscr{L})$, then

$$\mathscr{M} g(x) = \int m(x,x') g(x') \, dx'$$

where

$$m(x,x') = \int s(x,\omega) f(\omega) t(\omega,x') \, d\omega$$

This kernel can be evaluated more directly from

$$m(x,x') = \mathscr{M} \, \delta(x - x')$$

$$= f(\mathscr{L}) \int s(x,\omega) t(\omega,x') \, d\omega$$

8.8 Three-dimensional Continuous Systems

The discussion thus far has treated continuous systems in a single variable x. It is clear from the development in Chap. 7 that this variable may be used to represent the coordinate in one-dimensional physical systems. Since many problems involve two- or three-dimensional physical systems, an extension of the preceding development to cover such cases is required. This extension is straightforward. The results of the preceding sections are valid upon replacement of x by $\mathbf{r}$, the position vector in a cartesian space.

Thus, for the case of three-dimensional continuous systems, the relations analogous to (8.5) and (8.6) are

$$g(\mathbf{r}) = \mathscr{L}f(\mathbf{r}) \tag{8.28}$$

and

$$g(\mathbf{r}) = \int l(\mathbf{r},\mathbf{r}')f(\mathbf{r}') \, d\mathbf{r}' \tag{8.28a}$$

where $l(\mathbf{r},\mathbf{r}')$ is the kernel of the operator $\mathscr{L}$. The Dirac delta function is defined by the relation

$$\delta(\mathbf{r} - \mathbf{r}') = \lim_{a \to \infty} a D[a(\mathbf{r} - \mathbf{r}')] \tag{8.29}$$

for any function D satisfying

$$\int_{\text{all } \mathbf{r}} D(\mathbf{r}) \, d\mathbf{r} = 1 \tag{8.30}$$

where $d\mathbf{r}$ denotes a volume element in the cartesian space. The operator $\mathscr{L}^+$ which is adjoint to the operator $\mathscr{L}$ is defined by

$$\int \overline{f(\mathbf{r})} \mathscr{L} g(\mathbf{r}) \, d\mathbf{r} = \int \overline{\mathscr{L}^+ f(\mathbf{r})} g(\mathbf{r}) \, d\mathbf{r} \tag{8.31}$$

where f and g are arbitrary functions satisfying the boundary conditions associated with $\mathscr{L}$. Finally, the solution of the equation

$$\frac{\partial}{\partial t} y(\mathbf{r},t) = \mathscr{L} y(\mathbf{r},t) \tag{8.32}$$

is

$$y(\mathbf{r},t) = \int \mathscr{S}_\sigma s(\mathbf{r},\boldsymbol{\sigma}) e^{\lambda_\sigma t} t(\boldsymbol{\sigma},\mathbf{r}') y(\mathbf{r}',0) \, d\mathbf{r}' \tag{8.33}$$

where

$$\mathscr{L} s(\mathbf{r},\boldsymbol{\sigma}) = \lambda_\sigma s(\mathbf{r},\boldsymbol{\sigma}) \tag{8.34}$$

$$\mathscr{S}_\sigma s(\mathbf{r},\boldsymbol{\sigma}) t(\boldsymbol{\sigma},\mathbf{r}') = \delta(\mathbf{r} - \mathbf{r}') \tag{8.35}$$

in which the symbol $\mathscr{S}_\sigma$ represents Σ_σ if $\boldsymbol{\sigma}$ is a discrete variable and $\int d\boldsymbol{\sigma}$ if it is a continuous variable.

8.9   Differential Operators

Much of the remainder of the text will be concerned with differential equations such as

$$\mathscr{D}(\mathbf{r})f(\mathbf{r}) = g(\mathbf{r}) \tag{8.36}$$

in which $g(\mathbf{r})$ is a given function and $\mathscr{D}$ is a differential operator of the form

$$\mathscr{D}(\mathbf{r}) \equiv \alpha \nabla^2 + \beta \qquad (8.37)$$

where α and β are constants and ∇^2 is the Laplacian operator

$$\nabla^2 \equiv \frac{\partial^2}{\partial x^2} + \frac{\partial^2}{\partial y^2} + \frac{\partial^2}{\partial z^2} \qquad \text{(cartesian coordinates)}$$

$$\equiv \frac{1}{r^2} \frac{\partial}{\partial r} r^2 \frac{\partial}{\partial r} + \frac{1}{r^2 \sin \theta} \frac{\partial}{\partial \theta} \sin \theta \frac{\partial}{\partial \theta} + \frac{1}{r^2 \sin^2 \theta} \frac{\partial^2}{\partial \varphi^2} \quad \text{(spherical coordinates)}$$

$$\equiv \frac{1}{r} \frac{\partial}{\partial r} r \frac{\partial}{\partial r} + \frac{1}{r^2} \frac{\partial^2}{\partial \theta^2} + \frac{\partial^2}{\partial z^2} \qquad \text{(cylindrical coordinates)}$$

If the operator $\mathscr{L}$ has the kernel $l(\mathbf{r},\mathbf{r}')$ given by

$$l(\mathbf{r},\mathbf{r}') = \mathscr{D}(\mathbf{r}) \, \delta(\mathbf{r} - \mathbf{r}')$$

the operator equation $\qquad \mathscr{L}f(\mathbf{r}) = g(\mathbf{r})$

reduces to the conventional (ordinary or partial) differential equation

$$\mathscr{D}(\mathbf{r})f(\mathbf{r}) = g(\mathbf{r})$$

Similarly, the equation

$$\frac{\partial}{\partial t} f(\mathbf{r},t) = \mathscr{L}f(\mathbf{r},t)$$

reduces to $\qquad \dfrac{\partial}{\partial t} f(\mathbf{r},t) = \mathscr{D}(\mathbf{r})f(\mathbf{r},t)$

It is clear, therefore, that these conventional differential equations may be solved by the methods developed in the preceding sections.

Exercises

1. Let the operator $\mathscr{F}$ be defined by

$$\mathscr{F}g(x) = \int_{-\infty}^{\infty} f(|x - x'|)g(x') \, dx'$$

Show that

$$\mathscr{F} \sin \lambda x = K(\lambda) \sin \lambda x$$
$$\mathscr{F} \cos \lambda x = K(\lambda) \cos \lambda x$$

where

$$K(\lambda) = \int_{-\infty}^{\infty} f(|t|) \cos \lambda t \, dt$$

2. If

$$\mathscr{L}g(x) = \int l(x,y)g(y)\,dy$$

$$\mathscr{M}g(x) = \int m(x,y)g(y)\,dy$$

and if $\mathscr{P} = \mathscr{L}\mathscr{M}$ is defined by

$$\mathscr{P}g(x) = \mathscr{L}(\mathscr{M}g(x)) = \int p(x,y)g(y)\,dy$$

show that

$$p(x,y) = \int l(x,z)m(z,y)\,dz$$

References

Dirac, P. A. M.: "The Principles of Quantum Mechanics," 3d ed., sec. 15, Oxford University Press, New York, 1947.

Morse, P. M., and H. Feshbach: "Methods of Theoretical Physics," pp. 122–123 and 771–774, McGraw-Hill Book Company, Inc., New York, 1953.

CHAPTER 9

The Laplacian (∇^2) in One Dimension

9.1 Introduction

The discussion of the RC line in Chap. 7 led to consideration of the partial differential equation

$$\rho\gamma \frac{\partial f(x,t)}{\partial t} = \frac{\partial^2 f(x,t)}{\partial x^2} \qquad 0 \leq x \leq L$$

with the boundary conditions

$$\frac{\partial f}{\partial x}\bigg|_{x=0} = C_1 f(0,t)$$

$$\frac{\partial f}{\partial x}\bigg|_{x=L} = C_2 f(L,t)$$

In these equations $f(x,t)$ represented the voltage across the line at the distance x from the beginning of the line at the time t and C_1 and C_2 were given constants. The equations of heat conduction in an insulated bar of length L are of the same form, with f representing the temperature. The equation of wave propagation in one dimension is

$$\frac{\partial^2}{\partial t^2} f(x,t) = c^2 \frac{\partial^2}{\partial x^2} f(x,t)$$

where $f(x,t)$ represents the amplitude of the wave at x at time t and c is the phase velocity of propagation of the waves.

In these problems, as well as in others such as that of neutron diffusion in one dimension, one is led to consider the one-dimensional Laplacian $\nabla^2 \equiv \partial^2/\partial x^2$ in four different domains:

1. The infinite domain, $-\infty < x < +\infty$

   $f(x,t)$ satisfies the boundary conditions that it remain finite as x approaches $\pm\infty$.

2. The semi-infinite domain, $0 \leq x < +\infty$

$f(x,t)$ must remain finite as x approaches $+\infty$ and, at $x = 0$, must satisfy the condition

$$\frac{\partial f}{\partial x}\bigg|_{x=0} = Cf(0,t)$$

where C is a constant.

3. The finite domain, $0 \leq x \leq L$

The boundary conditions on the functions $f(x,t)$ in this domain are

$$\frac{\partial f}{\partial x}\bigg|_{x=0} = C_1 f(0,t) \qquad \text{and} \qquad \frac{\partial f}{\partial x}\bigg|_{x=L} = C_2 f(L,t)$$

where C_1 and C_2 are constants.

4. The circular domain

In this domain the boundary conditions are $f(0,t) = f(L,t)$ and

$$\frac{\partial f}{\partial x}\bigg|_{x=0} = \frac{\partial f}{\partial x}\bigg|_{x=L}$$

In this chapter the spectral representation of the Laplacian for the above four cases will be obtained and then used to write directly the solutions of various problems.

9.2   The Infinite Domain, $-\infty < x < +\infty$

Consider the eigenvalue equation

$$\frac{\partial^2}{\partial x^2} s(x,\omega) = -\omega^2 s(x,\omega) \qquad -\infty < x < +\infty \qquad (9.1)$$

where the eigenfunctions $s(x,\omega)$ must satisfy the boundary conditions that $s(\pm\infty,\omega)$ be finite. This equation has as solutions

$$s(x,\omega) = e^{i\omega x} \qquad -\infty < \omega < +\infty \qquad (9.2)$$

where the condition that $s(\pm\infty,\omega)$ be finite requires ω to be real.

Since ω has a continuous spectrum from $-\infty$ to $+\infty$, the inverse of the matrix S, denoted by T, must satisfy the pair of relations

$$\int_{-\infty}^{+\infty} s(x,\omega)t(\omega,x')\, d\omega = \delta(x - x') \qquad (9.3)$$

$$\int_{-\infty}^{+\infty} t(\omega,x)s(x,\omega')\, dx = \delta(\omega - \omega') \qquad (9.4)$$

In order to find $t(\omega,x)$ consider the integral

$$a\,D(ax) = \frac{1}{2\pi} \int_{-a}^{+a} e^{i\omega x}\,d\omega$$

$$= \frac{1}{2\pi} \frac{e^{iax} - e^{-iax}}{ix} = \frac{a}{\pi} \frac{\sin ax}{ax}$$

Since

$$\int_{-\infty}^{+\infty} \frac{\sin y}{y}\,dy = \pi$$

it follows that

$$\int_{-\infty}^{+\infty} D(x)\,dx = 1$$

Hence, from (8.11),

$$\lim_{a\to\infty} a\,D(ax) = \frac{1}{2\pi} \int_{-\infty}^{+\infty} e^{i\omega x}\,d\omega = \delta(x)$$

or

$$\frac{1}{2\pi} \int_{-\infty}^{+\infty} e^{i\omega x} e^{-i\omega x'}\,d\omega = \delta(x - x')$$

This suggests, upon inspection of (9.3), that if $s(x,\omega) = e^{i\omega x}$ then $t(\omega,x) = \frac{1}{2\pi} e^{-i\omega x}$. A more symmetric formulation is obtained by writing

$$s(x,\omega) = \frac{1}{\sqrt{2\pi}} e^{i\omega x}$$

$$t(\omega,x) = \overline{s(x,\omega)} = s^+(\omega,x) = \frac{1}{\sqrt{2\pi}} e^{-i\omega x} \qquad (9.5)$$

Since ω and x occur in the same manner in these definitions, Eq. (9.4) holds as well as (9.3). Thus

$$\int_{-\infty}^{+\infty} s(x,\omega)s^+(\omega,x')\,d\omega = \delta(x - x')$$

$$\int_{-\infty}^{+\infty} s^+(\omega,x)s(x,\omega')\,dx = \delta(\omega - \omega') \qquad (9.6)$$

where $s(x,\omega)$ and $s^+(\omega,x)$ are defined in (9.5). This completes the basic study of the Laplacian $\partial^2/\partial x^2$ in the infinite domain.

The above results will now be used to solve two problems: First consider the problem of the temperature distribution in an infinitely long thermally insulated bar lying along the x axis, given that the initial temperature is an arbitrary function of x vanishing at infinity, $T(x,0)$, and that at all times after $t = 0$ $T(\pm\infty,t)$ vanishes.[1] If there is no generation of heat in the bar, the temperature $T(x,t)$ at the point x at time t satisfies the partial differential equation

$$\frac{\partial}{\partial t} T(x,t) = a \frac{\partial^2}{\partial x^2} T(x,t) \qquad -\infty < x < +\infty \tag{9.7}$$

where $a = \kappa/\rho c$ in which κ is the thermal conductivity, ρ the density, and c the specific heat of the material composing the bar.

It is desired to solve Eq. (9.7) subject to the boundary conditions that $T(\pm\infty,t)$ vanish and the initial condition that $T(x,0)$ is known at all points x.

The formal solution of (9.7) is

$$T(x,t) = e^{at\,\partial^2/\partial x^2} T(x,0) \tag{9.8}$$

Since

$$\frac{1}{2\pi} \int_{-\infty}^{+\infty} e^{i\omega(x-x')}\, d\omega = \delta(x - x')$$

it is clear that

$$T(x,0) = \frac{1}{2\pi} \int_{-\infty}^{+\infty} \int_{-\infty}^{+\infty} e^{i\omega(x-x')} T(x',0)\, dx'\, d\omega$$

Hence (9.8) becomes

$$T(x,t) = e^{at\,\partial^2/\partial x^2} \frac{1}{2\pi} \int_{-\infty}^{+\infty} \int_{-\infty}^{+\infty} e^{i\omega(x-x')} T(x',0)\, dx'\, d\omega$$

But

$$f(\partial^2/\partial x^2)e^{i\omega x} = f(-\omega^2)e^{i\omega x}$$

Hence

$$T(x,t) = \frac{1}{2\pi} \int_{-\infty}^{+\infty} \int_{-\infty}^{+\infty} e^{-at\omega^2} e^{i\omega(x-x')} T(x',0)\, dx'\, d\omega \tag{9.9}$$

This result may be put into a more useful form by noting that

$$\frac{1}{2\pi} \int_{-\infty}^{+\infty} e^{-at\omega^2} e^{i\omega(x-x')}\, d\omega$$

$$= \frac{1}{2\pi} \int_{-\infty}^{+\infty} \exp\left[-\left(\sqrt{at}\,\omega - i\frac{x-x'}{2\sqrt{at}}\right)^2\right] e^{-(x-x')^2/4at}\, d\omega$$

$$= \frac{1}{\sqrt{4\pi at}} e^{-(x-x')^2/4at}$$

Then

$$T(x,t) = \frac{1}{\sqrt{4\pi at}} \int_{-\infty}^{+\infty} e^{-(x-x')^2/4at} T(x',0)\, dx' \tag{9.9a}$$

[1] That is, there is no source at infinity.

As a second example, one may solve the equation of wave propagation

$$\frac{\partial^2}{\partial t^2} y = \frac{\partial^2}{\partial x^2} y \qquad -\infty < x < +\infty \tag{9.10}$$

by the transform method (cf. Sec. 8.7). That is, use is to be made of the pair of relations

$$Y(\omega,t) = \int_{-\infty}^{+\infty} s^+(\omega,x)y(x,t)\,dx$$

$$y(x,t) = \int_{-\infty}^{+\infty} s(x,\omega)Y(\omega,t)\,d\omega \tag{9.11}$$

First, (9.10) is multiplied by $s^+(\omega,x)$ and integrated with respect to x. The left side of the equation becomes $\partial^2 Y/\partial t^2$. For the right side, one notes from the second of Eqs. (9.11) that[1]

$$\frac{\partial^2}{\partial x^2} y = \int_{-\infty}^{+\infty} (-\omega^2)s(x,\omega)Y(\omega,t)\,d\omega$$

so that, from the first of Eqs. (9.11),

$$\int_{-\infty}^{+\infty} s^+(\omega,x)\frac{\partial^2}{\partial x^2} y(x,t)\,dx = -\omega^2 Y(\omega,t)$$

Thus the transform of (9.10) is the equation

$$\frac{\partial^2}{\partial t^2} Y + \omega^2 Y = 0$$

which has for solution

$$Y(\omega,t) = Y(\omega,0)\cos \omega t + \dot{Y}(\omega,0)\frac{\sin \omega t}{\omega}$$

[1] Equivalently, one may evaluate

$$\int_{-\infty}^{+\infty} s^+(\omega,x)\frac{\partial^2}{\partial x^2} y(x,t)\,dx$$

by integration by parts. This is readily accomplished by noting that

$$\int_a^b \left(f\frac{\partial^2}{\partial x^2}g - g\frac{\partial^2}{\partial x^2}f \right)dx = \left(f\frac{\partial}{\partial x}g - g\frac{\partial}{\partial x}f \right)\Bigg|_a^b$$

Since one desires a solution $y(x,t)$ which vanishes at $x = \pm\infty$, it follows that

$$\int_{-\infty}^{+\infty} s^+\frac{\partial^2}{\partial x^2} y\,dx = \int_{-\infty}^{+\infty} y\frac{\partial^2}{\partial x^2} s^+\,dx$$

$$= -\omega^2 Y$$

Use of the second of Eqs. (9.11) then yields

$$y(x,t) = \int_{-\infty}^{+\infty} s(x,\omega) \left[Y(\omega,0) \cos \omega t + \dot{Y}(\omega,0) \frac{\sin \omega t}{\omega} \right] d\omega$$

where
$$Y(\omega,0) = \int_{-\infty}^{+\infty} s^+(\omega,x) y(x,0) \, dx$$

$$\dot{Y}(\omega,0) = \int_{-\infty}^{+\infty} s^+(\omega,x) \dot{y}(x,0) \, dx$$

It may be noted that thus far the question as to the self-adjointness of the operator $\partial^2/\partial x^2$ in the infinite domain has been avoided. $\partial^2/\partial x^2$ is self-adjoint in the following sense:

$$\int_{-\infty}^{+\infty} \bar{u} \frac{\partial^2}{\partial x^2} v \, dx = \int_{-\infty}^{+\infty} \left(\overline{\frac{\partial^2 u}{\partial x^2}} \right) v \, dx$$

for arbitrary u and v such that u (or v) vanishes at $\pm\infty$.

9.3   The Semi-infinite Domain, $0 \leq x < +\infty$

The Laplacian $\partial^2/\partial x^2$ is now considered in the domain $0 \leq x < +\infty$ with the associated boundary conditions that $f(+\infty,t)$ is finite and

$$\frac{\partial}{\partial x} f(x,t) \bigg|_{x=0} = \lambda f(0,t)$$

where λ is a real constant.

There are two kinds of solutions of the eigenvalue equation

$$\frac{\partial^2}{\partial x^2} s(x,\omega) = -\omega^2 s(x,\omega) \qquad 0 \leq x < +\infty \tag{9.12}$$

satisfying the boundary condition that $s(+\infty,\omega)$ be finite. These are

$$s(x,\omega) = A \cos \omega x + B \sin \omega x \qquad \omega \text{ real} \tag{9.13}$$

and $s(x,\nu) = C e^{-\nu x}$ ν real and positive   (9.14)

where A, B, and C are constants to be determined.

Application of the boundary condition at $x = 0$ to (9.13) and (9.14) yields

$$\omega B = \lambda A \tag{9.15}$$

and
$$-\nu = \lambda \tag{9.16}$$

Since ν must not be negative, Eq. (9.16) implies that the eigenfunction (9.14) is relevant if and only if $\lambda \leq 0$.

If $N = A$ and $N_0 = C$, the solutions (9.13) and (9.14) may be written as

$$s(x,\omega) = N\left(\cos \omega x + \lambda \frac{\sin \omega x}{\omega}\right) \qquad 0 < \omega < +\infty$$

$$s_0(x) = N_0 e^{\lambda x} \qquad\qquad\qquad \lambda \leq 0 \qquad\qquad (9.17)$$

$$s_0(x) = 0 \qquad\qquad\qquad\qquad \lambda > 0$$

The orthonormality conditions satisfied by the functions (9.17) are

$$\int_0^\infty s^+(\omega,x)s(x,\omega')\, dx = \delta(\omega - \omega') \qquad (9.18)$$

$$\int_0^\infty s^+(\omega,x)s_0(x)\, dx = 0 \qquad (9.19)$$

$$\int_0^\infty s_0^+(x)s_0(x)\, dx = 1 \qquad (9.20)$$

$$\int_0^\infty s(x,\omega)s^+(\omega,x')\, d\omega + \int s_0(x)s_0^+(x') = \delta(x - x') \qquad (9.21)$$

In order to verify (9.18), first note that

$$\int_0^a \cos \omega x \cos \omega' x\, dx = \frac{1}{2}\int_0^a [\cos(\omega + \omega')x + \cos(\omega - \omega')x]\, dx$$

$$= \frac{a}{2}\frac{\sin(\omega + \omega')a}{(\omega + \omega')a} + \frac{a}{2}\frac{\sin(\omega - \omega')a}{(\omega - \omega')a}$$

Hence, using (8.11),

$$\int_0^\infty \cos \omega x \cos \omega' x\, dx = \frac{\pi}{2}[\delta(\omega + \omega') + \delta(\omega - \omega')] \qquad (9.22)$$

Similarly, it may be shown that

$$\int_0^\infty \sin \omega x \sin \omega' x\, dx = \frac{\pi}{2}[\delta(\omega - \omega') - \delta(\omega + \omega')] \qquad (9.23)$$

Since neither ω nor ω' can be equal to or less than zero, the term $\delta(\omega + \omega')$ in the relations (9.22) and (9.23) may be ignored.

There remains to be considered, in order to evaluate (9.18), the cross-product terms which are proportional to

$$\int_0^\infty (\omega' \sin \omega x \cos \omega' x + \omega \sin \omega' x \cos \omega x)\, dx$$

$$= \int_0^\infty \left[\frac{\omega' + \omega}{2}\sin(\omega' + \omega)x - \frac{\omega' - \omega}{2}\sin(\omega' - \omega)x\right] dx$$

$$= \frac{1}{2}\int_0^\infty \sin t\, dt - \frac{1}{2}\int_0^\infty \sin t\, dt = 0$$

for $\omega \neq \omega'$. The integral is finite for $\omega = \omega'$.

In view of the above, substitution of the first of Eqs. (9.17) into (9.18) yields for $\omega = \omega'$

$$N^2\left(1 + \frac{\lambda^2}{\omega^2}\right)\frac{\pi}{2} = 1$$

Therefore, the first of the relations (9.17) becomes

$$s(x,\omega) = \sqrt{\frac{2}{\pi(\lambda^2 + \omega^2)}}\,(\omega\cos\omega x + \lambda\sin\omega x) \qquad 0 < \omega < \infty \quad (9.24)$$

Substitution of the second of the relations (9.17) into (9.20) yields

$$N_0^{\,2}\int_0^\infty e^{2\lambda x}\,dx = \frac{N_0^{\,2}}{-2\lambda} = 1 \qquad\qquad (9.25)$$

Hence the second and third of the relations (9.17) may be written

$$
\begin{aligned}
s_0(x) &= \sqrt{-2\lambda}\,e^{\lambda x} & \lambda &< 0 \\
s_0(x) &= 0 & \lambda &\geq 0
\end{aligned}
\qquad (9.26)
$$

The verification of (9.19) is left as an exercise for the reader.

Substitution of (9.24) into the left-hand member of (9.21) gives

$$\frac{2}{\pi}\int_0^\infty \cos\omega x\cos\omega x'\,d\omega + \frac{2}{\pi}\lambda\int_0^\infty \frac{\omega\sin\omega(x+x') - \lambda\cos\omega(x+x')}{\omega^2 + \lambda^2}\,d\omega$$

$$+ s_0(x)s_0^+(x) \quad (9.27)$$

The first integral is equal to $\delta(x + x') + \delta(x - x')$, of which $\delta(x + x')$ may be omitted [cf. Eq. (9.22)]. The second integral is equal to

$$\frac{\lambda}{2\pi i}\int_{-\infty}^{+\infty}\frac{(\omega - i\lambda)e^{i\omega(x+x')} - (\omega + i\lambda)e^{-i\omega(x+x')}}{(\omega - i\lambda)(\omega + i\lambda)}\,d\omega$$

$$= \frac{\lambda}{2\pi i}\left[\int_{-\infty}^{+\infty}\frac{e^{i\omega(x+x')}}{\omega + i\lambda}\,d\omega - \int_{-\infty}^{+\infty}\frac{e^{-i\omega(x+x')}}{\omega - i\lambda}\,d\omega\right]$$

$$= 2\lambda e^{\lambda(x+x')} \equiv -s_0(x)s_0^+(x') \qquad \text{if } \lambda < 0$$

$$= 0 \qquad\qquad \text{if } \lambda \geq 0$$

Hence the verification of (9.21) is complete.

To summarize, the eigenfunctions

$$s(x,\omega) = s^+(\omega,x) = \sqrt{\frac{2}{\pi(\omega^2 + \lambda^2)}}\,(\omega\cos\omega x + \lambda\sin\omega x) \qquad 0 < \omega < \infty$$

$$
\begin{aligned}
s_0(x) = s_0^+(x) &= \sqrt{-2\lambda}\,e^{\lambda x} & \lambda &< 0 \\
&= 0 & \lambda &\geq 0
\end{aligned}
$$

satisfy the eigenvalue equations

$$\frac{\partial^2}{\partial x^2} s(x,\omega) = -\omega^2 s(x,\omega)$$

$$\frac{\partial^2}{\partial x^2} s_0(x) = \lambda^2 s_0(x)$$

with the boundary conditions

$$\frac{\partial}{\partial x} s(x,\omega)\bigg|_{x=0} = \lambda s(0,\omega)$$

$$\frac{\partial}{\partial x} s_0(x)\bigg|_{x=0} = \lambda s_0(0)$$

and the orthonormality relations (9.18) to (9.21).

It should be noted that the spectrum of the eigenvalues of $\partial^2/\partial x^2$ in the semi-infinite domain contains, for $\lambda < 0$, the isolated point eigenvalue λ^2 as well as the continuous set $-\omega^2$, all ω real and positive.

9.4   The Finite Domain, $0 \leq x \leq L$

Consider the Laplacian $\partial^2/\partial x^2$ in the finite domain $0 \leq x \leq L$ for such functions $f(x)$ that

$$\frac{\partial}{\partial x} f(x,t)\bigg|_{x=0} = \alpha f(0,t)$$

$$\frac{\partial}{\partial x} f(x,t)\bigg|_{x=L} = \beta f(L,t) \tag{9.28}$$

where α and β are constants. For any two functions, f and g, which satisfy (9.28), one has

$$\int_0^L \left(\bar{f}\frac{\partial^2}{\partial x^2} g - g \frac{\partial^2}{\partial x^2}\bar{f} \right) dx = \left(\bar{f}\frac{\partial}{\partial x} g - g \frac{\partial}{\partial x}\bar{f} \right)\bigg|_{x=0}^{x=L}$$

$$= (\beta - \bar{\beta})\bar{f}(L)g(L) - (\alpha - \bar{\alpha})\bar{f}(0)g(0)$$

Hence, if $\alpha = \bar{\alpha}$ and $\beta = \bar{\beta}$, the Laplacian $\partial^2/\partial x^2$ is self-adjoint with the boundary conditions (9.28).

Except for the cases in which $\alpha = 0$ or ∞, $\beta = 0$ or ∞, the problem under consideration becomes obscured in algebra. For simplicity, consider the case $\alpha = \beta = \infty$ and seek the spectral representation of $\partial^2/\partial x^2$ in the domain $0 \leq x \leq L$ for such functions $f(x)$ that satisfy the boundary conditions

$$f(0) = f(L) = 0 \tag{9.29}$$

Denote the eigenfunctions and eigenvalues belonging to the Laplacian $\partial^2/\partial x^2$ by $s_n(x)$ and $-\omega_n{}^2$, respectively. Then one must solve the eigenvalue equation

$$\frac{\partial^2}{\partial x^2} s_n(x) = -\omega_n{}^2 s_n(x) \qquad (9.30)$$

with the boundary conditions

$$s_n(0) = s_n(L) = 0 \qquad (9.31)$$

Clearly, Eqs. (9.30) and (9.31) will be satisfied only by

$$s_n(x) = C_n \sin \frac{n\pi x}{L} \qquad n = 1, 2, \dots \qquad (9.32)$$

where the C_n are normalization constants to be determined. Note that

$$\omega_n = \frac{n\pi}{L} \qquad (9.33)$$

i.e., the eigenvalues are discrete.

The normalization condition

$$\int_0^L s_n(x) s_n^+(x) \, dx = 1 \qquad (9.34)$$

yields

$$C_n{}^2 = \frac{2}{L}$$

Hence, finally

$$s_n(x) \equiv \,<x|n> \, = \sqrt{\frac{2}{L}} \sin \frac{n\pi x}{L} \qquad n = 1, 2, \dots \qquad (9.35)$$

In order to demonstrate the completeness of these solutions one must show that

$$\sum_{n=1}^{\infty} s_n(x) s_n^+(x') = \delta(x - x') \qquad 0 \le x, x' \le L \qquad (9.36)$$

To accomplish this, consider

$$\sum_{n=1}^{A} s_n(x) s_n^+(x')$$

$$= \frac{1}{2L} \left[\frac{\sin (A + 1/2)(\pi/L)(x - x')}{\sin (1/2)(\pi/L)(x - x')} - \frac{\sin (A + 1/2)(\pi/L)(x + x')}{\sin (1/2)(\pi/L)(x + x')} \right]$$

Then let $a = (\pi/L)(A + 1/2)$ and rearrange terms to obtain

$$\sum_{n=1}^{A} s_n(x) s_n^+(x') = \frac{(1/2)(\pi/L)(x - x')}{\sin (1/2)(\pi/L)(x - x')} \left[\frac{a}{\pi} \frac{\sin a(x - x')}{a(x - x')} \right]$$

$$- \frac{(1/2)(\pi/L)(x + x')}{\sin (1/2)(\pi/L)(x + x')} \left[\frac{a}{\pi} \frac{\sin a(x + x')}{a(x + x')} \right]$$

Note that in the limit as $a \to \infty$ the quantities within the brackets become, respectively, $\delta(x - x')$ and $\delta(x + x')$. Since $f(x)\,\delta(x) = f(0)\,\delta(x)$, it then follows that

$$\lim_{A \to \infty} \sum_{n=1}^{A} s_n(x)s_n^+(x') = \delta(x - x') - \delta(x + x')$$

which verifies (9.36).

It should be noted that the classical theory of Fourier series for the boundary conditions (9.31) is contained in (9.36):[1]

$$\frac{2}{L} \sum_{n=1}^{\infty} \sin \frac{n\pi x}{L} \sin \frac{n\pi x'}{L} = \delta(x - x') \qquad 0 \le x, x' \le L \qquad (9.37)$$

To apply the above results to the problem of the vibrating string, take the string as lying along the x axis from $x = 0$ to $x = L$ and denote by $y(x,t)$ the displacement at right angles to the axis at any point x at any time t. The equation of motion is

$$\frac{\partial^2}{\partial t^2} y(x,t) = c^2 \frac{\partial^2}{\partial x^2} y(x,t) \qquad (9.38)$$

where $c \equiv \sqrt{T/\rho}$, in which T is the tension in the string and ρ the mass per unit length. If the string is held fixed at its ends $x = 0$ and $x = L$, one must find solutions of (9.38) subject to the boundary conditions

$$y(0,t) = y(L,t) = 0 \qquad (9.39)$$

and the initial conditions

$$y(x,0) \text{ and } \dot{y}(x,0) \text{ specified for all } x. \qquad (9.40)$$

The formal solution is

$$y(x,t) = \cos\left(\sqrt{\frac{-\partial^2}{\partial x^2}}\, ct\right) y(x,0) + \frac{\sin\left(\sqrt{-\partial^2/\partial x^2}\, ct\right)}{c\sqrt{-\partial^2/\partial x^2}}\, \dot{y}(x,0) \qquad (9.41)$$

The actual solution may be written

$$y(x,t) = \int_0^L f(x,x'\,;\,t)y(x',0)\,dx' + \int_0^L g(x,x'\,;\,t)\dot{y}(x',0)\,dx' \qquad (9.42)$$

where, using (9.37),

$$f(x,x'\,;\,t) = \cos\left(\sqrt{\frac{-\partial^2}{\partial x^2}}\, ct\right) \delta(x - x')$$

$$= \frac{2}{L} \sum_{n=1}^{\infty} \cos \frac{n\pi ct}{L} \sin \frac{n\pi x}{L} \sin \frac{n\pi x'}{L} \qquad (9.43)$$

The evaluation of $g(x,x'\,;\,t)$ is left as an exercise for the reader.

[1] See also Sec. 2B.5 of Appendix 2B.

It is interesting to note that the results of this section, as L becomes infinite, approach those of Sec. 9.3 for λ becoming infinite. In particular, (9.36) may be written as (with $\omega_n = n\pi/L$)

$$\delta(x - x') = \sum_{n=1}^{\infty} \frac{2}{L} \sin \omega_n x \sin \omega_n x'$$

$$= \frac{2}{\pi} \sum_{n=1}^{\infty} (\omega_{n+1} - \omega_n) \sin \omega_n x \sin \omega_n x'$$

which becomes, for infinite L,

$$\frac{2}{\pi} \int_0^{\infty} \sin \omega x \sin \omega x' \, d\omega = \delta(x - x')$$

This result is the same as that given by (9.23).

9.5 The Circular Domain

In this domain the boundary conditions associated with $\partial^2/\partial x^2$ are

$$f(0,t) = f(L,t)$$

$$\frac{\partial}{\partial x} f(x,t) \bigg|_{x=0} = \frac{\partial}{\partial x} f(x,t) \bigg|_{x=L} \tag{9.44}$$

A general solution of the eigenvalue equation

$$\frac{\partial^2}{\partial x^2} s(x) = -\omega^2 s(x) \tag{9.45}$$

is given by

$$s(x) = Ae^{i\omega x} + Be^{-i\omega x}$$

Application of the boundary conditions (9.44) yields

$$A + B = Ae^{i\omega L} + Be^{-i\omega L}$$
$$A - B = Ae^{i\omega L} - Be^{-i\omega L}$$

so that $e^{\pm i\omega L} = 1$ or

$$\omega_n = \frac{2\pi n}{L} \qquad n = 0, \pm 1, \pm 2, \ldots \tag{9.46}$$

The eigenfunctions are therefore

$$s_n(x) = \sqrt{\frac{1}{L}} \, e^{i(2\pi n/L)x} \qquad n = 0, \pm 1, \pm 2, \ldots \tag{9.47}$$

They have the property that

$$\int_0^L s_n(x) s_{n'}^+(x) \, dx = \delta_{n,n'} \tag{9.48}$$

where $s_n^+(x) = \overline{s_n(x)}$. To verify completeness one must show that

$$\sum_{n=-\infty}^{+\infty} s_n(x)\overline{s_n(x')} = \delta(x-x') \qquad 0 \le x, x' \le L \qquad (9.49)$$

Proceeding as in Sec. 9.4, one evaluates

$$\frac{1}{L}\sum_{n=-A}^{+A} e^{i(2\pi n/L)(x-x')}$$

$$= \frac{1}{L}\frac{e^{i2\pi(A+1/2)(x-x')/L} - e^{-i2\pi(A+1/2)(x-x')/L}}{e^{i\pi(x-x')/L} - e^{-i\pi(x-x')/L}}$$

$$= \frac{1}{L}\frac{\sin\left[\pi(2A+1)(x-x')/L\right]}{\sin\left[\pi(x-x')/L\right]}$$

$$= \frac{\pi(x-x')/L}{\sin\left[\pi(x-x')/L\right]}\left\{\frac{1}{\pi}\frac{\pi(2A+1)}{L}\frac{\sin\left[\pi(2A+1)(x-x')/L\right]}{\pi(2A+1)(x-x')/L}\right\}$$

Clearly, as $A \to \infty$ the material in braces becomes $\delta(x-x')$. Hence (9.49) is verified.

The result

$$\frac{1}{L}\sum_{n=-\infty}^{+\infty} e^{i(2\pi n/L)(x-x')} = \delta(x-x') \qquad 0 \le x, x' \le L \qquad (9.49a)$$

is again an expression for the validity of Fourier series; this time for the case of the boundary conditions (9.44).

The solution found for

$$\frac{\partial^2 y}{\partial t^2} = c^2 \frac{\partial^2 y}{\partial x^2}$$

is given by (9.42) where, however,

$$f(x,x'; t) = \frac{1}{L}\sum_{-\infty}^{+\infty} \cos\frac{2\pi nct}{L} e^{i(2\pi n/L)(x-x')}$$

$$g(x,x'; t) = \frac{1}{L}\sum_{-\infty}^{+\infty} \frac{\sin(2\pi nct/L)}{(2\pi nc/L)} e^{i(2\pi n/L)(x-x')}$$

9.6 The Method of Images

The left-hand member of (9.49a) is periodic in $x-x'$ with period L. Thus a version of (9.49a) valid for all x,x' is given by

$$\frac{1}{L}\sum_{n=-\infty}^{+\infty} e^{i(2\pi n/L)(x-x')} = \sum_{\sigma=-\infty}^{+\infty} \delta(x-x'-\sigma L) \qquad (9.50)$$

This expresses a set of delta functions spaced at intervals L on the x axis at the points $x' + \sigma L$. The terms for $\sigma \neq 0$ can be thought of as the images of the term $\delta(x - x')$.

If one now evaluates

$$\cos\left(\sqrt{-\frac{\partial^2}{\partial x^2}}\, ct\right) \sum_{\sigma=-\infty}^{+\infty} \delta(x - x' - \sigma L)$$

he expects to obtain the same answer when $0 \leq x,\, x' \leq L$ as if he evaluated

$$\cos\left(\sqrt{-\frac{\partial^2}{\partial x^2}}\, ct\right) \delta(x - x')$$

However, the method of evaluation may be different. Thus

$$\cos\left(\sqrt{-\frac{\partial^2}{\partial x^2}}\, ct\right) \sum_{\sigma=-\infty}^{+\infty} \delta(x - x' - \sigma L)$$

$$= \cos\left(\sqrt{-\frac{\partial^2}{\partial x^2}}\, ct\right) \sum_{\sigma=-\infty}^{+\infty} \frac{1}{2\pi} \int_{-\infty}^{+\infty} e^{i\omega(x-x'-\sigma L)}\, d\omega$$

$$= \frac{1}{2} \sum_{\sigma=-\infty}^{+\infty} \frac{1}{2\pi} \int_{-\infty}^{+\infty} \left[e^{i\omega(x-x'-ct-\sigma L)} + e^{i\omega(x-x'+ct-\sigma L)} \right] d\omega$$

$$= \frac{1}{2} \sum_{\sigma=-\infty}^{+\infty} \left[\delta(x - x' - \sigma L - ct) + \delta(x - x' - \sigma L + ct) \right]$$

This last result is interpreted as oppositely moving progressions of pulses (delta functions) traveling with speed c and spaced a distance L apart. Note that this result implies that

$$\cos\left(\sqrt{-\frac{\partial^2}{\partial x^2}}\, ct\right) f(x) = \frac{1}{2} \sum_{\sigma=-\infty}^{+\infty} \left[f(x - \sigma L - ct) + f(x - \sigma L + ct) \right]$$

The physical meaning of the above may be stated as follows. If a string is held in the shape $f(x)$ and released at $t = 0$, at later times the shape of the string may be represented as the superposition of two deflections, each of the form $1/2\, f(x)$, one of these traveling in the direction of increasing x and the other in the direction of decreasing x, the speed being c in each case.

A process similar to the above may be applied to (9.43). Thus, for all x, x',

$$\frac{2}{L} \sum_{n=1}^{\infty} \sin\frac{n\pi x}{L} \sin\frac{n\pi x'}{L} = \frac{1}{L} \sum_{n=1}^{\infty} \left[\cos\frac{n\pi(x-x')}{L} - \cos\frac{n\pi(x+x')}{L} \right]$$

$$= \sum_{\sigma=-\infty}^{+\infty} \left[\delta(x - x' - 2\sigma L) - \delta(x + x' - 2\sigma L) \right]$$

It is then clear that

$$f(x,x';t) = \frac{2}{L} \cos\left(\sqrt{-\frac{\partial^2}{\partial x^2}}\, ct\right) \sum_{n=1}^{\infty} \sin\frac{n\pi x}{L} \sin\frac{n\pi x'}{L}$$

$$= \frac{1}{2} \sum_{\sigma=-\infty}^{+\infty} \left[\delta(x - x' - 2\sigma L - ct) + \delta(x - x' - 2\sigma L + ct)\right.$$
$$\left. - \delta(x + x' - 2\sigma L - ct) - \delta(x + x' - 2\sigma L + ct)\right]$$

According to Exercise 5 at the end of the chapter,

$$\frac{\partial}{\partial t} g(x,x';t) = f(x,x';t)$$

so that

$$g(x,x';t) = \frac{1}{2c} \sum_{\sigma=-\infty}^{+\infty} \left[\eta(x - x' - 2\sigma L + ct) - \eta(x - x' - 2\sigma L - ct)\right.$$
$$\left. + \eta(x + x' - 2\sigma L - ct) - \eta(x + x' - 2\sigma L + ct)\right]$$

where
$$\eta(x) = 1 \qquad x > 0$$
$$= 0 \qquad x < 0$$

A useful form of these results is obtained as follows: Consider

$$\sum_{\sigma=-\infty}^{+\infty} \left[\int_0^L \delta(x - x' - 2\sigma L - ct)y(x',0)\, dx'\right.$$
$$\left. - \int_0^L \delta(x + x' - 2\sigma L - ct)y(x',0)\, dx'\right]$$

$$= \sum_{\sigma=-\infty}^{+\infty} \left[\int_{2\sigma L}^{(2\sigma+1)L} \delta(x - u - ct)y(u - 2\sigma L, 0)\, du\right.$$
$$\left. - \int_{(2\sigma-1)L}^{2\sigma L} \delta(x - u - ct)y(2\sigma L - u, 0)\, du\right]$$

$$= \int_{-\infty}^{+\infty} \delta(x - u - ct)y(u,0)\, du$$

$$= y(x - ct, 0)$$

if one defines y (outside the interval $0 < x < L$) by

$$y(x + 2L, 0) = y(x,0)$$
$$y(-x,0) = -y(x,0)$$

Using similar results one has

$$y(x,t) = \int_0^L f(x,x';t)y(x',0)\,dx' + \int_0^L g(x,x';t)\dot{y}(x',0)\,dx'$$

$$= \frac{1}{2}\left[y(x-ct,0) + y(x+ct,0)\right]$$

$$+ \frac{1}{2c}\int_{-\infty}^{+\infty}\left[\eta(x-u+ct) - \eta(x-u-ct)\right]\dot{y}(u,0)\,du$$

$$= \frac{1}{2}\left[y(x-ct,0) + y(x+ct,0)\right] + \frac{1}{2c}\int_{x-ct}^{x+ct}\dot{y}(u,0)\,du$$

where
$$y(x+2L,0) = y(x,0) = -y(-x,0)$$
$$\dot{y}(x+2L,0) = \dot{y}(x,0) = -\dot{y}(-x,0)$$

Note that this result tells us how to study the wave in a finite string as a superposition of waves traveling to the right and to the left. Thus the wave traveling to the right (increasing x) may be written as

$$A + \frac{1}{2}y(x-ct,0) - \frac{1}{2c}\int_\alpha^{x-ct}\dot{y}(u,0)\,du$$

and the wave traveling to the left written as

$$-A + \frac{1}{2}y(x+ct,0) + \frac{1}{2c}\int_\alpha^{x+ct}\dot{y}(u,0)\,du$$

This separation of the wave in the finite string is not unique, as indicated by the arbitrary constants A and α.

Exercises

1. Verify the self-adjointness of $\partial^2/\partial x^2$ in the semi-infinite domain $0 \le x < +\infty$.

2. Verify the relation (9.19).

3. Discuss the problem of Sec. 9.4 in each of the cases, (a) $\alpha = \beta = 0$, and (b) $\alpha = 0$, $\beta = \infty$.

4. Evaluate the function (in Sec. 9.4)

$$g(x,x';t) = \frac{\sin(\sqrt{-\partial^2/\partial x^2}\,ct)}{c\sqrt{-\partial^2/\partial x^2}}\delta(x-x')$$

5. Show that

$$\frac{\partial}{\partial t} g(x,x'; t) = f(x,x'; t)$$

so that

$$g(x,x'; t) = \frac{1}{2c} \sum_{\sigma=-\infty}^{+\infty} [\eta(x - x' - 2\sigma L + ct) - \eta(x - x' - 2\sigma L - ct)$$

$$+ \eta(x + x' - 2\sigma L - ct) - \eta(x + x' - 2\sigma L + ct)]$$

where
$$\begin{aligned}\eta(x) &= 1 \qquad x > 0 \\ &= 0 \qquad x < 0\end{aligned}$$

6. Solve the problem of heat conduction in the semi-infinite rod, $0 \leq x < +\infty$, given the initial temperature distribution $T(x,0)$, with $T(0,t) = 0$.

7. Solve Exercise 6 using the method of images, starting with the solution of the problem of heat conduction in the infinite domain.

References

Carslaw, H. S., and J. C. Jaeger: "Conduction of Heat in Solids," pp. 230–233, Oxford University Press, New York, 1948.

Morse, P. M., and H. Feshbach: "Methods of Theoretical Physics," McGraw-Hill Book Company, Inc., New York, 1953.

CHAPTER 10

The Laplacian (∇^2) in Two Dimensions

10.1 Introduction

In the last chapter the Laplacian operator in one dimension, $\nabla^2 \equiv d^2/dx^2$, was considered in some detail. The purpose of the present chapter is to treat the Laplacian operator in two dimensions: in both cartesian and plane polar coordinates and in both finite and infinite domains.

The procedure to be used is the consideration of a number of well-known problems in mathematical physics. In solving each such problem there is found in a natural manner that particular representation of the Laplacian which applies. While this procedure is not conducive to good continuity of text, it has the advantage of clearly presenting the motivation for the different representations.

In studying the present chapter the reader will find it convenient to read concurrently Appendix 2C, in which are briefly sketched the properties of the cylindrical functions which are indispensable to a study of the Laplacian in plane polar coordinates.

10.2 Conduction of Heat in an Infinite Insulated Plate. Cartesian Coordinates

Consider the conduction of heat in an infinite insulated plate lying in the x,y coordinate plane. Let c represent the specific heat, ρ the density, and κ the thermal conductivity of the matter composing the plate. Then, if there is no generation of heat in the plate, the temperature $T(x,y,t)$ at the point (x,y) at time t satisfies the partial differential equation

$$\frac{\partial}{\partial t} T(x,y,t) = a \, \nabla^2 T(x,y,t) \qquad -\infty < x,y < +\infty \qquad (10.1)$$

128

where $a \equiv \kappa/\rho c$ and

$$\nabla^2 \equiv \frac{\partial^2}{\partial x^2} + \frac{\partial^2}{\partial y^2}$$

It is desired to solve Eq. (10.1) subject to the boundary condition that $T(x,y,t)$ is bounded as $x^2 + y^2$ approaches infinity and the initial condition that $T(x,y,0)$ is known at all points (x,y).

The formal solution of (10.1) is

$$T(x,y,t) = e^{a\nabla^2 t} T(x,y,0) \tag{10.2}$$

To write the solution explicitly one must determine the eigenvalues and eigenfunctions belonging to the operator ∇^2. Denote these by $-\omega^2$ and $f_\omega(x,y)$, respectively. Then

$$\left(\frac{\partial^2}{\partial x^2} + \frac{\partial^2}{\partial y^2}\right) f_\omega(x,y) = -\omega^2 f_\omega(x,y) \tag{10.3}$$

By substitution, it is easily verified that a solution of (10.3) satisfying the boundary conditions on $T(x,y,t)$ is

$$f_\omega(x,y) \equiv <x,y|\omega_x,\omega_y> = A_\omega e^{i(\omega_x x + \omega_y y)} \tag{10.4}$$

where
$$-\infty < \omega_x, \omega_y < +\infty$$

and
$$\omega^2 = \omega_x{}^2 + \omega_y{}^2 \tag{10.5}$$

We note that because of (10.5) there are many eigenfunctions corresponding to a particular eigenvalue. However, the specification of both ω_x and ω_y makes the eigenfunction unique.

The orthonormality conditions satisfied by these eigenfunctions are

$$\begin{aligned}
\delta(x - x')\,\delta(y - y') &= <x,y|\omega_x,\omega_y> <\omega_x,\omega_y|x',y'> \\
\delta(\omega_x - \omega_x')\,\delta(\omega_y - \omega_y') &= <\omega_x,\omega_y|x,y> <x,y|\omega_x',\omega_y'>
\end{aligned} \tag{10.6}$$

They require that A_ω be equal to $1/2\pi$.

The solution (10.2) may now be written

$$T(x,y,t) = \left(\frac{1}{2\pi}\right)^2 \int_{-\infty}^{+\infty} \cdots \int_{-\infty}^{+\infty} e^{i(\omega_x x + \omega_y y)} e^{-a(\omega_x{}^2 + \omega_y{}^2)t} e^{-i(\omega_x x' + \omega_y y')}$$

$$\times\, T(x',y',0)\, d\omega_x\, d\omega_y\, dx'\, dy' \tag{10.7}$$

$$= \frac{1}{4\pi a t} \int_{-\infty}^{+\infty} \int_{-\infty}^{+\infty} e^{-\frac{1}{4at}[(x-x')^2 + (y-y')^2]} T(x',y',0)\, dx'\, dy' \tag{10.8}$$

It is left as an exercise for the reader to carry out the indicated integrations over ω_x and ω_y in (10.7) to obtain (10.8).

It is sometimes convenient to use the vector notation

$$\mathbf{r} = x\mathbf{i} + y\mathbf{j} \quad\text{and}\quad \boldsymbol{\omega} = \omega_x\mathbf{i} + \omega_y\mathbf{j}$$

Then $\boldsymbol{\omega} \cdot \mathbf{r} = \omega_x x + \omega_y y$ and the eigenfunctions of ∇^2 may be written as

$$<\mathbf{r}|\boldsymbol{\omega}> = \frac{1}{2\pi} e^{i\boldsymbol{\omega}\cdot\mathbf{r}} \tag{10.4a}$$

the orthonormality conditions as

$$\begin{aligned}\delta(\mathbf{r} - \mathbf{r}') &= <\mathbf{r}|\boldsymbol{\omega}> <\boldsymbol{\omega}|\mathbf{r}'>\\ \delta(\boldsymbol{\omega} - \boldsymbol{\omega}') &= <\boldsymbol{\omega}|\mathbf{r}> <\mathbf{r}|\boldsymbol{\omega}'>\end{aligned} \tag{10.6a}$$

and the solution (10.7) as

$$T(\mathbf{r},t) = \left(\frac{1}{2\pi}\right)^2 \int\int e^{-a\omega^2 t} e^{i\boldsymbol{\omega}\cdot(\mathbf{r}-\mathbf{r}')} T(\mathbf{r}',0)\, d\boldsymbol{\omega}\, d\mathbf{r}' \tag{10.7a}$$

10.3 The Vibrating Rectangular Membrane

In the preceding section the operator $\nabla^2 = \partial^2/\partial x^2 + \partial^2/\partial y^2$ was studied in the infinite domain $-\infty < x,y < +\infty$. The problem of the vibrating rectangular membrane whose equilibrium shape is a plane sheet furnishes one with the opportunity to study this same operator in the finite domain $0 \leq x \leq L_x$, $0 \leq y \leq L_y$. Take two cartesian coordinates x and y in the equilibrium plane of the membrane and denote by $\psi(x,y,t)$ the displacement at right angles to the plane at any point x,y at any time t. The equation of motion is the well-known *wave equation*

$$\left(c^2\nabla^2 - \frac{\partial^2}{\partial t^2}\right)\psi(x,y,t) = 0 \tag{10.9}$$

where $c \equiv \sqrt{T/m}$, in which T is the tension in the membrane and m is the mass per unit area of the membrane. If the membrane is held fixed at its boundaries $x = 0$, $x = L_x$, $y = 0$, and $y = L_y$, solutions of (10.9) are desired subject to the boundary conditions

$$\psi(0,y,t) = \psi(L_x,y,t) = \psi(x,0,t) = \psi(x,L_y,t) = 0 \tag{10.10}$$

The formal solution of Eq. (10.9) is

$$\psi(x,y,t) = \cos\left(\sqrt{-\nabla^2}\,ct\right)\psi(x,y,0) + \frac{\sin\left(\sqrt{-\nabla^2}\,ct\right)}{c\sqrt{-\nabla^2}}\,\dot{\psi}(x,y,0) \tag{10.11}$$

where $\psi(x,y,0)$ is the displacement of the membrane at time $t = 0$ and $\dot{\psi}(x,y,0) = \partial/\partial t\, \psi(x,y,t)\,|_{t=0}$. Thus, one seeks solutions of the eigenvalue equation

$$\nabla^2 f_k(x,y) = -k^2 f_k(x,y) \tag{10.12}$$

satisfying (10.10).

It is left as an exercise for the reader to verify that the normalized solutions of Eq. (10.12) which satisfy the boundary conditions (10.10) are given by

$$f_k(x,y) = <x,y|n_x,n_y> = <n_x,n_y|x,y>$$

$$= \frac{2}{\sqrt{L_x L_y}} \sin \frac{n_x \pi x}{L_x} \sin \frac{n_y \pi y}{L_y} \qquad (10.13)$$

where

$$k^2 = \left(\frac{n_x \pi}{L_x}\right)^2 + \left(\frac{n_y \pi}{L_y}\right)^2 \qquad (10.14)$$

and

$$n_x, n_y = 1, 2, 3, \ldots$$

The eigenfunctions (10.13) give the possible shapes of the membrane as it vibrates with simple harmonic motion. They satisfy the orthonormality condition

$$\delta(x - x')\,\delta(y - y') = <x,y|n_x,n_y> <n_x,n_y|x',y'>$$
$$\delta_{n_x, n_x'}\, \delta_{n_y, n_y'} = <n_x,n_y|x,y> <x,y|n_x',n_y'> \qquad (10.15)$$

The eigenvalues (10.14) give the allowed frequencies of vibration of the membrane, since the circular frequency ω is [cf., (10.11)] $c\sqrt{-\nabla^2}$

$$\nu_{n_x, n_y} = \frac{\omega_{n_x, n_y}}{2\pi} = \frac{c}{2} \sqrt{\left(\frac{n_x}{L_x}\right)^2 + \left(\frac{n_y}{L_y}\right)^2} \qquad (10.16)$$

Having found the appropriate eigenvalues and eigenfunctions of the operator ∇^2, one may write the general solution (10.11) to the wave equation (10.9) in the explicit form

$$\psi(x,y,t) = \frac{4}{L_x L_y} \sum_{n_x, n_y = 1}^{\infty} \left\{ \sin \frac{n_x \pi x}{L_x} \sin \frac{n_y \pi y}{L_y} \right.$$

$$\times \int_0^{L_x} \int_0^{L_y} \left[\psi(x',y',0) \cos \omega_{n_x, n_y} t + \frac{1}{\omega_{n_x, n_y}} \psi(x',y',0) \sin \omega_{n_x, n_y} t \right]$$

$$\left. \times \sin \frac{n_x \pi x'}{L_x} \sin \frac{n_y \pi y'}{L_y}\, dx'\, dy' \right\}$$

10.4 Conduction of Heat in an Infinite Insulated Plate; Plane Polar Coordinates

In a large number of problems on the conduction of heat in an infinite insulated plate the initial temperature distribution is a function only of the distance r from the origin of coordinates. In such cases it is much more convenient to use polar coordinates than cartesian coordinates. In general, two methods of procedure are available, namely:

1. Transform the original problem, Eq. (10.1), to polar coordinates r and θ, and then solve.

2. Transform the solution, Eq. (10.7) or (10.7a), to polar coordinates.

Consider procedure (1) first. In this case one must solve the differential equation

$$\frac{\partial}{\partial t} T(r,\theta,t) = a \nabla^2 T(r,\theta,t), \qquad 0 \leq r < \infty \qquad 0 \leq \theta \leq 2\pi \quad (10.17)$$

subject to the condition that $T(r,\theta,t)$ is bounded for all r. The initial condition is that $T(r,\theta,0)$ is known at all points (r,θ).

The first problem in solving (10.17) is to determine the representation of the operator ∇^2 in plane polar coordinates. Introduce polar coordinates r and θ such that

$$\begin{aligned} x &= r \cos \theta & r^2 &= x^2 + y^2 \\ y &= r \sin \theta & \theta &= \tan^{-1} \frac{y}{x} \end{aligned} \quad (10.18)$$

Then, since

$$\frac{\partial}{\partial \theta} = \frac{\partial x}{\partial \theta} \frac{\partial}{\partial x} + \frac{\partial y}{\partial \theta} \frac{\partial}{\partial y} = -y \frac{\partial}{\partial x} + x \frac{\partial}{\partial y}$$

$$\frac{\partial}{\partial r} = \frac{\partial x}{\partial r} \frac{\partial}{\partial x} + \frac{\partial y}{\partial r} \frac{\partial}{\partial y} = \frac{x}{r} \frac{\partial}{\partial x} + \frac{y}{r} \frac{\partial}{\partial y}$$

it follows that

$$\frac{\partial}{\partial x} = \cos \theta \frac{\partial}{\partial r} - \frac{\sin \theta}{r} \frac{\partial}{\partial \theta}$$

$$\frac{\partial}{\partial y} = \sin \theta \frac{\partial}{\partial r} + \frac{\cos \theta}{r} \frac{\partial}{\partial \theta}$$

Hence

$$\partial^+ \equiv \frac{\partial}{\partial x} + i \frac{\partial}{\partial y} = e^{i\theta} \left(\frac{\partial}{\partial r} + \frac{i}{r} \frac{\partial}{\partial \theta} \right) \quad (10.19)$$

$$\partial^- \equiv \frac{\partial}{\partial x} - i \frac{\partial}{\partial y} = e^{-i\theta} \left(\frac{\partial}{\partial r} - \frac{i}{r} \frac{\partial}{\partial \theta} \right) \quad (10.20)$$

and

$$\nabla^2 \equiv \partial^+ \partial^- \equiv \partial^- \partial^+ \equiv \frac{\partial^2}{\partial x^2} + \frac{\partial^2}{\partial y^2} = \frac{1}{r^2} \left[\left(r \frac{\partial}{\partial r} \right)^2 + \frac{\partial^2}{\partial \theta^2} \right] \quad (10.21)$$

where

$$\left(r \frac{\partial}{\partial r} \right)^2 \equiv r \frac{\partial}{\partial r} r \frac{\partial}{\partial r} = r^2 \frac{\partial^2}{\partial r^2} + r \frac{\partial}{\partial r}$$

The pair of commuting operators ∂^- and ∂^+ are quite interesting and will be used extensively in subsequent discussions. It is easily verified that they commute with the Laplacian operator, i.e.,

$$[\partial^\pm, \nabla^2] \equiv \partial^\pm \nabla^2 - \nabla^2 \partial^\pm = 0$$

It is convenient to introduce the operator

$$L = -i\frac{\partial}{\partial\theta} = -i\left(x\frac{\partial}{\partial y} - y\frac{\partial}{\partial x}\right) \qquad (10.22)$$

which also commutes with the Laplacian. Equations (10.19), (10.20), and (10.21) may then be written

$$\partial^+ = e^{i\theta}\left(\frac{\partial}{\partial r} - \frac{L}{r}\right) \qquad (10.19a)$$

$$\partial^- = e^{-i\theta}\left(\frac{\partial}{\partial r} + \frac{L}{r}\right) \qquad (10.20a)$$

$$\nabla^2 = \frac{1}{r^2}\left(r\frac{\partial}{\partial r}\right)^2 - \frac{L^2}{r^2} \qquad (10.21a)$$

Let us now assume that the operators ∇^2 and L constitute a complete set of commuting observables (as defined at the end of Sec. 5.6). On the basis of this assumption we shall look for simultaneous eigenfunctions of these operators. The two simultaneous eigenvalue equations which must be solved are then

$$\nabla^2 f(r,\theta) = -\omega^2 f(r,\theta) \qquad (10.23)$$

and
$$Lf(r,\theta) = \lambda f(r,\theta) \qquad (10.24)$$

where $f(r,\theta)$ must be finite for all r and θ.

By the use of the definition (10.22) Eq. (10.24) becomes

$$\frac{\partial}{\partial\theta}f(r,\theta) = i\lambda f(r,\theta)$$

It has for solution

$$f(r,\theta) = e^{i\lambda\theta}R(r) \qquad (10.25)$$

where $R(r)$ is an arbitrary function of r. The continuity condition, $f(r,\theta) = f(r, \theta + 2\pi)$, then requires that $\lambda = n$, a positive or negative integer or zero. Substitution of this result into the eigenvalue equation (10.23) then yields

$$\left(\frac{d^2}{dr^2} + \frac{1}{r}\frac{d}{dr} + \omega^2 - \frac{n^2}{r^2}\right)R(r) = 0$$

where use has been made of (10.21a). The substitution, $\rho = \omega r$, and the replacement, $P(\rho)$ for $R(r)$, reduces this equation to

$$\left(\frac{d^2}{d\rho^2} + \frac{1}{\rho}\frac{d}{d\rho} + 1 - \frac{n^2}{\rho^2}\right)P(\rho) = 0 \tag{10.26}$$

the well-known *equation of Bessel*.

The class of functions which are solutions of Eq. (10.26) are known as the *cylindrical functions of integral order n* and denoted by $Z_n(\rho) \equiv Z_n(\omega r)$. Of these functions only that particular one known as the Bessel function and denoted by $J_n(\omega r)$, where ω is a real quantity, remains finite for all r. The properties of these functions are discussed in subsequent sections of the text and in Appendix 2C. For our present purposes we require only the property $J_n(-\omega r) = (-1)^n J_n(\omega r)$, which allows us to consider ω in the range of positive real quantities only ($0 \le \omega < \infty$).

The simultaneous eigenfunctions of the operators ∇^2 and L are, therefore,

$$f_{n,\omega}(r,\theta) = A_{n,\omega}e^{in\theta}J_n(\omega r) \tag{10.27}$$

where $0 \le r < \infty$, $0 \le \theta \le 2\pi$, $0 \le \omega < \infty$, and $n = 0, \pm1, \pm2, \ldots$, and the coefficients $A_{n,\omega}$ are normalization constants to be determined.

The normalization of the eigenfunctions $f_{n,\omega}(r,\theta)$ will be carried out in the following section where some important theorems on cylindrical functions are also derived. In Sec. 10.6 we shall conclude our discussion of the solution in polar coordinates of the problem of heat conduction in an infinite insulated plate.

10.5 Theorems on Cylindrical Functions (of Integral Order n)

The cylindrical functions are sometimes defined not as the solutions of Bessel's equation (10.26) but rather as those functions which satisfy a certain set of recurrence formulae [Eqs. (10.32) and (10.33)]. The two definitions are, of course, equivalent. The first task in this section will be the derivation of the recurrence formulae.

The technique to be used here has many applications. The properties of Hermite polynomials, Laguerre polynomials, and Legendre functions are often studied in a similar manner. See further Sec. 11.4.

For the present purposes it is convenient to make use of the operators ∂^+ and ∂^- defined by Eqs. (10.19) and (10.20). Note that

$$\partial^\pm\nabla^2 f_{n,\omega} = \nabla^2\partial^\pm f_{n,\omega} = -\omega^2\partial^\pm f_{n,\omega} \tag{10.28}$$

that is, if $f_{n,\omega}$ is an eigenfunction of the operator ∇^2 belonging to the eigenvalue $-\omega^2$ so is $\partial^{\pm}f_{n,\omega}$. Further note that

$$[\partial^-,L] \equiv \partial^- L - L\partial^- = \frac{\partial}{\partial x} - i\frac{\partial}{\partial y} = \partial^-$$

$$[\partial^+,L] \equiv \partial^+ L - L\partial^+ = -\frac{\partial}{\partial x} - i\frac{\partial}{\partial y} = -\partial^+$$

(10.29)

Therefore
$$L\partial^- f_{n,\omega} \equiv (L\partial^- - \partial^- L)f_{n,\omega} + \partial^- L f_{n,\omega}$$
$$= -\partial^- f_{n,\omega} + n\partial^- f_{n,\omega} = (n-1)\partial^- f_{n,\omega}$$

where the first of Eqs. (10.29) and the eigenvalue equation $Lf_{n,\omega} = nf_{n,\omega}$ have been used. Thus, if $f_{n,\omega}$ is the eigenfunction of the operator L belonging to the eigenvalue n, $\partial^- f_{n,\omega}$ is the eigenfunction of L belonging to the eigenvalue $(n-1)$. One may then write

$$\partial^- f_{n,\omega} = Cf_{n-1,\omega}$$

where C is any arbitrary constant. If one lets $C = \omega$ he obtains

$$\partial^- f_{n,\omega} = \omega f_{n-1,\omega}$$

(10.30)

Then
$$\nabla^2 f_{n,\omega} = -\omega^2 f_{n,\omega}$$
$$= \partial^+ \partial^- f_{n,\omega} = \omega \partial^+ f_{n-1,\omega}$$

so that
$$\partial^+ f_{n-1,\omega} = -\omega f_{n,\omega}$$

or

$$\partial^+ f_{n,\omega} = -\omega f_{n+1,\omega}$$

(10.31)

If one now writes $f_{n,\omega}(r,\theta) = Z_n(\omega r)e^{in\theta}$, the recurrence formulae for the functions $Z_n(\omega r)$ may be derived as follows: From the definition (10.19) of ∂^+ one obtains

$$\partial^+ f_{n,\omega} = e^{i\theta}\left(\frac{\partial}{\partial r} + \frac{i}{r}\frac{\partial}{\partial \theta}\right)Z_n(\omega r)e^{in\theta}$$

$$= e^{i(n+1)\theta}\left(\frac{d}{dr} - \frac{n}{r}\right)Z_n(\omega r)$$

But, from Eq. (10.31),

$$\partial^+ f_{n,\omega} = -\omega Z_{n+1}(\omega r)e^{i(n+1)\theta}$$

Hence
$$Z_{n+1}(\omega r) = \frac{1}{\omega}\left(\frac{n}{r} - \frac{d}{dr}\right)Z_n(\omega r)$$

or, with $\rho \equiv \omega r$,

$$Z_{n+1}(\rho) = \left(\frac{n}{\rho} - \frac{d}{d\rho}\right)Z_n(\rho)$$

(10.32)

In a like manner, by the use of Eq. (10.30) and the definition (10.20) of ∂^-, one finds that

$$Z_{n-1}(\rho) = \left(\frac{n}{\rho} + \frac{d}{d\rho}\right) Z_n(\rho) \qquad (10.33)$$

It is easily verified that the functions $Z_n(\rho)$ defined by the recurrence formulae (10.32) and (10.33) are the cylindrical functions. First write Eq. (10.32) with n replacing $n+1$,

$$Z_n(\rho) = \left(\frac{n-1}{\rho} - \frac{d}{d\rho}\right) Z_{n-1}(\rho)$$

Then substitute for $Z_{n-1}(\rho)$ in the right-hand member of this equation by means of (10.33),

$$Z_n(\rho) = \left(\frac{n-1}{\rho} - \frac{d}{d\rho}\right)\left(\frac{n}{\rho} + \frac{d}{d\rho}\right) Z_n(\rho)$$

$$= \left[\frac{n(n-1)}{\rho^2} + \frac{n-1}{\rho}\frac{d}{d\rho} - \frac{d}{d\rho}\frac{n}{\rho} - \frac{d^2}{d\rho^2}\right] Z_n(\rho)$$

$$= \left[\frac{n(n-1)}{\rho^2} + \frac{n-1}{\rho}\frac{d}{d\rho} + \frac{n}{\rho^2} - \frac{n}{\rho}\frac{d}{d\rho} - \frac{d^2}{d\rho^2}\right] Z_n(\rho)$$

or

$$\left(\frac{d^2}{d\rho^2} + \frac{1}{\rho}\frac{d}{d\rho} + 1 - \frac{n^2}{\rho^2}\right) Z_n(\rho) = 0$$

which is the Bessel equation satisfied by the cylindrical functions of integral order n.

As noted previously, the Bessel functions $J_n(\rho)$ are those cylindrical functions which remain finite for all real ρ. Since it is clear that the cylindrical function of any order n may be obtained from the cylindrical function of order zero by repeated use of the appropriate recurrence formula (10.32) or (10.33), to obtain all the Bessel functions only $J_0(\rho)$ need be specified. Thus, the Bessel functions are obtained from the recurrence formulae (10.32) and (10.33) when one specifies that $Z_0(0) \equiv J_0(0) = 1$.

The next problem is to demonstrate that the functions

$$f_{n,\omega}(r,\theta) = J_n(\omega r) e^{in\theta} \qquad (10.34)$$

are a complete set of functions in the r,θ coordinate system. To do this, recall that the functions $e^{i(\omega_x x + \omega_y y)}$ form a complete set in the x,y coordinate system and try to find a_n such that

$$\psi \equiv e^{i(\omega_x x + \omega_y y)} = \sum_{n=-\infty}^{+\infty} a_n f_{n,\omega}(r,\theta) \qquad (10.35)$$

Then one finds, as necessary conditions for the validity of (10.35), the values of the a_n. Thus

$$\partial^+ \psi = \left(\frac{\partial}{\partial x} + i \frac{\partial}{\partial y}\right) e^{i(\omega_x x + \omega_y y)}$$

$$= i(\omega_x + i\omega_y)\psi$$

$$= \sum_{n=-\infty}^{\infty} i(\omega_x + i\omega_y) a_n f_{n,\omega}$$

On the other hand

$$\partial^+ \psi = \sum_{n=-\infty}^{\infty} a_n \, \partial^+ f_{n,\omega}$$

$$= - \sum_{n=-\infty}^{\infty} a_n(\omega f_{n+1,\omega})$$

$$= - \sum_{n=-\infty}^{\infty} \omega a_{n-1} f_{n,\omega}$$

whence[1]

$$a_n = \frac{i\omega}{\omega_x + i\omega_y} a_{n-1} \tag{10.36}$$

Similarly, from

$$\partial^- \psi = \sum_n a_n i(\omega_x - i\omega_y) f_{n,\omega} = \omega \sum_n a_{n+1} f_{n,\omega}$$

one obtains

$$a_n = \frac{i(\omega_x - i\omega_y)}{\omega} a_{n-1} \tag{10.37}$$

Equating (10.36) to (10.37) then gives

$$\frac{i\omega}{\omega_x + i\omega_y} = \frac{i(\omega_x - i\omega_y)}{\omega}$$

or

$$\omega^2 = \omega_x{}^2 + \omega_y{}^2 \tag{10.38}$$

Substitution of (10.37) into (10.35) yields

$$\psi = e^{i(\omega_x x + \omega_y y)} = a_0 \sum_{n=-\infty}^{\infty} \left(\frac{\omega_y + i\omega_x}{\omega}\right)^n f_{n,\omega} \tag{10.39}$$

To determine a_0 let $x = y = 0$ so that (10.39) reduces to

$$1 = a_0 \sum_n \left(\frac{\omega_y + i\omega_x}{\omega}\right)^n J_n(0) e^{in\theta}$$

Since $J_n(0) = 0$ for $n \neq 0$ and $J_0(0) = 1$,[2] there results $a_0 = 1$.

[1] As we have previously seen, the functions $e^{in\theta}$ form a biorthogonal set. The coefficients of the two expressions above must therefore be equal term by term.

[2] These properties of the Bessel functions are easily verified from the series expansion about the origin, Eq. (2C.26) of Appendix 2C.

It has just been demonstrated that if one can write

$$e^{i(\omega_x x + \omega_y y)}$$

in the form

$$\sum_{n=-\infty}^{\infty} a_n J_n(\omega r) e^{i n\theta}$$

then in fact the a_n are such that one has

$$\sum_{n=-\infty}^{\infty} \left(\frac{\omega_y + i\omega_x}{\omega} \right)^n J_n(\omega r) e^{i n\theta} \equiv F(r,\theta)$$

It must then be shown that this result is indeed $e^{i(\omega_x x + \omega_y y)}$: Note that the coupled partial differential equations

$$\frac{\partial \psi}{\partial x} = i\omega_x \psi \qquad \frac{\partial \psi}{\partial y} = i\omega_y \psi$$

$$\psi(0,0) = 1$$

have the unique solution

$$\psi = e^{i(\omega_x x + \omega_y y)}$$

One then verifies that $F(r,\theta)$ satisfies these equations, thus showing it is indeed $e^{i(\omega_x x + \omega_y y)}$. Clearly,

$$\partial^{\pm} F = \partial^{\pm} \sum_{-\infty}^{\infty} \left(\frac{\omega_y + i\omega_x}{\omega} \right)^n f_{n,\omega}$$

$$= \mp \sum_{-\infty}^{\infty} \left(\frac{\omega_y + i\omega_x}{\omega} \right)^n \omega f_{n\pm 1,\omega}$$

$$= \mp \left(\frac{\omega_y + i\omega_x}{\omega} \right)^{\mp 1} \omega F$$

$$\partial^{+} F = -(\omega_y - i\omega_x) F$$

$$\partial^{-} F = (\omega_y + i\omega_x) F$$

$$\frac{\partial F}{\partial x} = i\omega_x F \qquad \frac{\partial F}{\partial y} = i\omega_y F$$

Since $F(0,0) = 1$, the important result

$$e^{i(\omega_x x + \omega_y y)} = \sum_{-\infty}^{\infty} \left(\frac{\omega_y + i\omega_x}{\omega} \right)^n J_n(\omega r) e^{i n\theta} \qquad (10.39a)$$

has been established. Several interesting and useful expansions may be deduced from Eq. (10.39a). As a first example, suppose that $\omega_y = 0$ and $\omega_x = \omega = 1$. Then (10.39a) reduces to

$$e^{ix} = e^{ir\cos\theta} = \sum_{n=-\infty}^{+\infty} i^n f_{n,1}$$

or

$$e^{ir\cos\theta} = \sum_{n=-\infty}^{+\infty} i^n J_n(r) e^{in\theta} \tag{10.40}$$

By equating the real and imaginary parts of both sides of (10.40) it is found that

$$\cos(r\cos\theta) = J_0(r) + 2 \sum_{\substack{n\text{ even}\\\text{positive}}} i^n J_n(r) \cos n\theta \tag{10.41}$$

and

$$\sin(r\cos\theta) = 2 \sum_{\substack{n\text{ odd}\\\text{positive}}} i^{n-1} J_n(r) \cos n\theta \tag{10.42}$$

where the property $J_{-n}(r) = (-1)^n J_n(r)$ has been used.

Similarly, if $\omega_x = 0$ and $\omega_y = \omega = 1$, Eq. (10.39a) reduces to

$$e^{ir\sin\theta} = \sum_{n=-\infty}^{+\infty} J_n(r) e^{in\theta} \tag{10.43}$$

and, by equating the real and imaginary parts of both sides,

$$\cos(r\sin\theta) = J_0(r) + 2 \sum_{\substack{n\text{ even}\\\text{positive}}} J_n(r) \cos n\theta \tag{10.44}$$

$$\sin(r\sin\theta) = 2 \sum_{\substack{n\text{ odd}\\\text{positive}}} J_n(r) \sin n\theta \tag{10.45}$$

The left-hand members of Eqs. (10.40) and (10.43) are called *generating functions of the Bessel functions of integral order.*

If one lets $\omega_x = \omega\cos\varphi$ and $\omega_y = \omega\sin\varphi$ so that

$$\frac{\omega_y + i\omega_x}{\omega} = i(\cos\varphi - i\sin\varphi) = ie^{-i\varphi}$$

Eq. (10.39a) reduces to

$$e^{i(\omega_x y + \omega_y y)} = e^{i\omega r\cos(\theta-\varphi)} = \sum_{n=-\infty}^{+\infty} i^n J_n(\omega r) e^{in(\theta-\varphi)} \tag{10.46}$$

Note that (10.46) could have been obtained directly from (10.40) by means of the substitutions ωr for r and $\theta - \varphi$ for θ.

The orthonormality conditions satisfied by the functions $f_{n,\omega}(r,\theta)$ defined by (10.34) may be obtained as follows: Since

$$\delta(x-x')\,\delta(y-y') = \left(\frac{1}{2\pi}\right)^2 \int_{-\infty}^{+\infty}\int_{-\infty}^{+\infty} e^{i(\omega_x x + \omega_y y)} e^{-i(\omega_x x' + \omega_y y')}\, d\omega_x\, d\omega_y$$

and

$$\delta(x-x')\,\delta(y-y') = \frac{\delta(r-r')}{r}\delta(\theta-\theta')$$

one obtains from the use of (10.46) the result

$$\frac{\delta(r - r')}{r} \delta(\theta - \theta') = \left(\frac{1}{2\pi}\right)^2 \sum_{n,n'} i^{n-n'} \int_0^{2\pi} \int_0^\infty J_n(\omega r)e^{in(\theta-\varphi)}$$

$$\times J_{n'}(\omega r')e^{-in'(\theta'-\varphi)}\omega \, d\omega \, d\varphi \qquad (10.47)$$

$$= \frac{1}{2\pi} \sum_n \int_0^\infty J_n(\omega r)J_n(\omega r')e^{in(\theta-\theta')}\omega \, d\omega$$

Multiplication of both sides of (10.47) by $e^{-im(\theta-\theta')} \, d\theta$ and integration over all θ yield the result

$$\frac{\delta(r - r')}{r} = \int_0^\infty J_m(\omega r)J_m(\omega r')\omega \, d\omega \qquad (10.48)$$

From (10.47) and (10.48) it then follows that

$$\delta(\theta - \theta') = \frac{1}{2\pi} \sum_{n=-\infty}^{+\infty} e^{in(\theta-\theta')} \qquad (10.49)$$

Equation (10.47) is the orthonormality condition satisfied by the functions $f_{n,\omega}(r,\theta)$. Thus one may write

$$f_{n,\omega}(r,\theta) \equiv <r,\theta|\omega,n> = \frac{\omega}{\sqrt{2\pi}} J_n(\omega r)e^{in\theta}$$

$$<\omega,n|r,\theta> = \frac{r}{\sqrt{2\pi}} J_n(\omega r)e^{-in\theta} \qquad (10.50)$$

10.6   Conduction of Heat in an Infinite Insulated Plate;   Plane Polar Coordinates (Concluded)

The formal solution to the heat-conduction equation (10.17) is

$$T(r,\theta,t) = e^{a\nabla^2 t}T(r,\theta,0) \qquad (10.51)$$

Since the eigenfunctions of the operator ∇^2 in the domain $0 \leq r < \infty$, $0 \leq \theta \leq 2\pi$ and their inverses are now known [expressions (10.50)], the explicit solution may be written. It is

$$T(r,\theta,t) = \frac{1}{2\pi} \sum_{n=-\infty}^{+\infty} \int_0^\infty \omega \, d\omega \int_0^\infty r' \, dr' \int_0^{2\pi} d\theta' J_n(\omega r)J_n(\omega r')$$

$$\times e^{in(\theta-\theta')}e^{-a\omega^2 t}T(r',\theta',0) \quad (10.52)$$

This concludes the solution of the problem by procedure 1 of Section 10.4.

To obtain the solution of the problem by procedure 2 of Section 10.4, one must transform the solution (10.7a) to polar coordinates. Then

$$T(\mathbf{r},t) \rightarrow T(r,\theta,t)$$
$$T(\mathbf{r}',0) \rightarrow T(r',\theta',0)$$
$$d\mathbf{r}' \rightarrow r' \, dr' \, d\theta'$$
$$d\boldsymbol{\omega} \rightarrow \omega \, d\omega \, d\varphi$$

and $\quad e^{i\boldsymbol{\omega}\cdot(\mathbf{r}-\mathbf{r}')} = e^{i(\omega_x x + \omega_y y)} e^{-i(\omega_x x' + \omega_y y')}$

$$= \sum_{n=-\infty}^{+\infty} i^n J_n(\omega r) e^{in(\theta-\varphi)} \sum_{n'} (-i)^{n'} J_{n'}(\omega r') e^{-in'(\theta'-\varphi)}$$

by reason of (10.46). Substitution into (10.7a) then gives

$$T(r,\theta,t) = \left(\frac{1}{2\pi}\right)^2 \sum_{n,n'} i^{n-n'} \int_0^\infty \omega \, d\omega \int_0^{2\pi} d\varphi \int_0^\infty r' \, dr' \int_0^{2\pi} d\theta'$$
$$\times \left[e^{-a\omega^2 t} J_n(\omega r) J_{n'}(\omega r') e^{in(\theta-\varphi)} e^{-in'(\theta'-\varphi)} T(r',\theta',0) \right]$$

On carrying out the integration over φ one obtains

$$T(r,\theta,t) = \frac{1}{2\pi} \sum_n \int_0^\infty \omega \, d\omega \int_0^\infty r' \, dr' \int_0^{2\pi} d\theta' e^{-a\omega^2 t} J_n(\omega r) J_n(\omega r') e^{in(\theta-\theta')} T(r',\theta',0)$$

which is identical to (10.52), the result obtained by procedure 1.

10.7   The Circular Membrane

The differential equation for the circular membrane is the same as for the rectangular one, but the boundary condition is different: the transverse displacement ψ is always zero on a circle of radius ρ about the origin. To solve the problem, the simplest method is to introduce polar coordinates r,θ. Then, the boundary condition is that $\psi = 0$ when $r = \rho$, which is a condition easily applied. The differential equation in polar coordinates is

$$\left(c^2 \nabla^2 - \frac{\partial^2}{\partial t^2} \right) \psi(r,\theta,t) = 0 \qquad 0 \le r \le \rho \qquad 0 \le \theta \le 2\pi \qquad (10.53)$$

where ∇^2 is given by (10.21).

Just as in the case of the rectangular membrane, one seeks solutions of (10.53) which are periodic in time:

$$\psi(r,\theta,t) = f(r,\theta) e^{i\omega t} \qquad (10.54)$$

Substitution of (10.54) into (10.53) yields the eigenvalue equation for the operator ∇^2

$$\nabla^2 f_k(r,\theta) = -k^2 f_k(r,\theta) \qquad (10.55)$$

where $k \equiv \omega/c$.

From the results of Secs. 10.4 and 10.6 it is clear that the solutions to Eq. (10.55) are the eigenfunctions

$$f_{k,n}(r,\theta) = J_n(kr)e^{in\theta} \tag{10.56}$$

in which the Bessel functions must satisfy the boundary condition $J_n(k\rho) = 0$. This condition determines the eigenvalues as follows: The Bessel function $J_n(\lambda)$ is zero only for certain values of λ, say $\lambda_{n1}, \lambda_{n2}, \ldots$. From the properties of Bessel functions, it is clear that there are an infinite number of such roots. (A limited number of these are given in Table 10.1.[1]) Thus, to satisfy our boundary condition we must let $k\rho = \lambda_{n1}$, $\lambda_{n2}, \ldots$. Since the radius ρ of the membrane is fixed, the possible values of k are $\lambda_{nj}/\rho, j = 1, 2, \ldots$. Since the value of k clearly depends on two indices n and j, we henceforth label it k_{nj}.

Table 10.1. Roots of the Bessel Functions $J_n(\lambda_j)$

j \ n	0	1	2	3	4
1	2.405	3.832	5.135	6.379	7.586
2	5.520	7.016	8.417	9.760	11.064
3	8.654	10.173	11.620	13.017	14.373

Employing the results of Sec. 2B.7 of Appendix 2B, we write the normalized solutions to Eq. (10.55).

$$f(r,\theta) = <r,\theta|n,j> = \frac{J_n(k_{nj}r)}{J'_n(k_{nj}\rho)}\, e^{in\theta} \tag{10.57}$$

Their inverses are given by

$$<n,j|r,\theta> = \frac{r}{\pi\rho^2}\frac{J_n(k_{nj}r)}{J'_n(k_{nj}\rho)}\, e^{-in\theta} \tag{10.58}$$

In these relations $k_{nj} = \lambda_{nj}/\rho$, where λ_{nj} is the jth root of the Bessel function of the nth order, J_n, and $J'_n(x) = dJ_n/dx$.

The orthonormality conditions are given by

$$\delta(r - r')\,\delta(\theta - \theta') = \frac{r}{\pi\rho^2}\sum_{n,j}\frac{J_n(k_{nj}r)J_n(k_{nj}r')}{[J'_n(k_{nj}\rho)]^2}\, e^{in(\theta - \theta')}$$

$$\delta_{n,n'}\,\delta_{j,j'} = \frac{1}{\pi\rho^2}\int_0^{2\pi}\int_0^{\rho}\frac{J_n(k_{nj}r)J_{n'}(k_{n'j'}r)}{J'_n(k_{nj}\rho)J'_n(k_{n'j'}\rho)}\, e^{-i\theta(n - n')}r\, dr\, d\theta$$

[1] For a more complete list see E. Jahnke and F. Emde, "Tables of Functions with Formulae and Curves," chap. VIII, Dover Publications, New York, 1943.

THE LAPLACIAN (∇^2) IN TWO DIMENSIONS

143

The formal solution of Eq. (10.53) is

$$\psi(r,\theta,t) = \cos(\sqrt{-\nabla^2}ct)\psi(r,\theta,0) + (c\sqrt{-\nabla^2})^{-1}\sin(\sqrt{-\nabla^2}ct)\dot\psi(r,\theta,0) \quad (10.59)$$

Using the results (10.57) and (10.58) one may write the solution explicitly as

$$\psi(r,\theta,t) = \frac{1}{\pi\rho^2}\sum_{n,j}\int_0^\rho r'\,dr'\int_0^{2\pi}d\theta'\left[\psi(r',\theta',0)\cos\omega_{nj}t + \frac{\dot\psi(r',\theta',0)}{\omega_{nj}}\sin\omega_{nj}t\right]$$

$$\times \frac{J_n(\omega_{nj}r/c)J_n(\omega_{nj}r'/c)}{[J_n'(\omega_{nj}\rho/c)]^2}e^{in(\theta-\theta')} \quad (10.60)$$

10.8 The Vibrating Circular Ring and Circular Sector

In the case of the vibrating circular membrane it was seen that the transverse displacement $\psi(r,\theta,t)$ was given in terms of the eigenfunctions $f_{k,n}(r,\theta)$ where

$$f_{k,n}(r,\theta) = J_n(kr)e^{in\theta} \qquad 0 \leq r \leq a \qquad n = 0,\pm1,\pm2,\dots \quad (10.61)$$

and k satisfies the boundary condition

$$J_n(ka) = 0 \quad (10.62)$$

In the case of the circular ring the eigenfunctions are given by

$$f_{k,n}(r,\theta) = [J_n(kr) + cN_n(kr)]e^{in\theta}$$
$$0 < b \leq r \leq a \qquad n = 0,\pm1,\pm2,\dots \quad (10.63)$$

where c is a constant to be determined. The solution $N_n(kr)$ of the Bessel equation, which is irregular at the origin of coordinates $(r = 0)$, is now admissible because the membrane does not include the origin. Furthermore, both the regular and irregular solutions J_n and N_n are required to satisfy the boundary conditions:

$$f_{k,n}(a,\theta) = J_n(ka) + cN_n(ka) = 0$$
$$f_{k,n}(b,\theta) = J_n(kb) + cN_n(kb) = 0 \quad (10.64)$$

The possible values of the eigenvalues k are the roots of

$$J_n(ka)N_n(kb) - N_n(ka)J_n(kb) = 0 \quad (10.65)$$

Just as in the case of the circular membrane, there are an infinite number of such roots. The particular constant c associated with a given root k is then determined from either of Eqs. (10.64).

For the circular sector $0 \leq r \leq a$, $0 \leq \theta \leq \alpha$ one assumes that the eigenfunctions are of the form

$$f_{k,\lambda}(r,\theta) = J_\lambda(kr)(A\cos\lambda\theta + B\sin\lambda\theta)$$

where λ has been written instead of n because λ need not be integral. [In the case of the circular membrane $\lambda = n = 0, \pm1, \pm2, \ldots$ because of the single-valuedness condition on $f_{k,n}(r,\theta)$.] λ is now determined from the boundary conditions

$$f_{k,\lambda}(r,0) = J_\lambda(kr)(A \cos 0 + B \sin 0) = 0$$
$$f_{k,\lambda}(r,\alpha) = J_\lambda(kr)(A \cos \lambda\alpha + B \sin \lambda\alpha) = 0 \qquad (10.66)$$

The first of these conditions implies that $\cos \lambda \theta$ is not a permissible solution. The second requires that $\lambda\alpha = n\pi$, $n = \pm1, \pm2, \ldots$. Hence the eigenfunctions for the circular sector are

$$f_{k,\lambda}(r,\theta) = J_\lambda(kr) \sin \lambda\theta \qquad \lambda = \frac{n\pi}{\alpha} \qquad (10.67)$$

The k are determined from the condition $J_\lambda(ka) = 0$.

In the case of the circular ring sector, which is bounded by two circular arcs and two radii, $0 < b \leq r \leq a$, $0 \leq \theta \leq \alpha$, the eigenfunctions are given by

$$f_{k,\lambda}(r,\theta) = [J_\lambda(kr) + cN_\lambda(kr)] \sin \lambda\theta \qquad \lambda = \frac{n\pi}{\alpha} \qquad (10.68)$$

The radial boundary conditions,

$$f_{k,\lambda}(a,\theta) = J_\lambda(ka) + cN_\lambda(ka) = 0$$
$$f_{k,\lambda}(b,\theta) = J_\lambda(kb) + cN_\lambda(kb) = 0 \qquad (10.69)$$

then determine the possible eigenvalues k as the roots of the equation

$$J_\lambda(ka)N_\lambda(kb) - N_\lambda(ka)J_\lambda(kb) = 0 \qquad (10.70)$$

Exercises

1. Verify that the normalized solutions of (10.3) which are bounded as $x^2 + y^2$ approaches infinity are

$$f_\omega(x,y) = \frac{1}{2\pi} e^{i(\omega_x x + \omega_y y)}$$

2. Carry out the indicated operations over ω_x and ω_y in (10.7) and thus obtain (10.8).

3. Verify that the normalized solutions of Eq. (10.12) which satisfy the boundary conditions (10.10) are given by (10.13) and (10.14).

4. Compare the solutions (10.67) for a circular sector, for $\alpha = \pi$ and for $\alpha = 2\pi$ with the solutions (10.56) for the circular membrane. Plot the solutions vs. θ for fixed r in each of the three cases.

5. Plot the three lowest frequencies of a circular sector as a function of the vertex angle α.

6. Tabulate the five lowest frequencies for (*a*) a circular membrane, (*b*) a square membrane, and (*c*) a rectangular membrane twice as long as it is wide. Select the dimensions so that all membranes have the same area and the same value of *c*.

References

Schafheitlin, P.: "Besselsche Funktionen," Teubner Verlagsgesellschaft, Leipzig, 1904.

Nielsen, N.: "Zylinderfunktionen," Teubner Verlagsgesellschaft, Leipzig, 1908.

Gray, A., G. B. Mathews, and T. M. MacRobert: "Bessel Functions and Their Applications to Physics," The Macmillan Company, New York, 1922.

Watson, G. N.: "The Theory of Bessel Functions," Cambridge University Press, New York, 1922.

McLachlin, N. W.: "Bessel Functions for Engineers," Oxford University Press, New York, 1934.

Weyrich, R.: "Zylinderfunktionen und ihre Anwendungen," Teubner Verlagsgesellschaft, Leipzig, 1937.

For comprehensive summaries of the properties of cylinder functions refer to:

Jahnke, E., and F. Emde: "Tables of Functions with Formulae and Curves," chap. 8, Dover Publications, New York, 1943.

Magnus, W., and F. Oberhettinger: "Formulas and Theorems for the Special Functions of Mathematical Physics," chap. 3, Chelsea Publishing Company, New York, 1949.

CHAPTER 11

The Laplacian (∇^2) in Three Dimensions

11.1 Introduction

The present chapter could have been more correctly entitled "The Laplacian (∇^2) in Spherical Coordinates" since three-dimensional cartesian coordinates will not be considered in any detail. The reason for this omission is obvious: Having studied the Laplacian in one- and two-dimensional cartesian coordinates in previous chapters, the extension to the three-dimensional case is trivial. For example, the eigenfunctions of the operator $\partial^2/\partial x^2$ ($-\infty < x < +\infty$) belonging to the eigenvalues $-\omega_x^2$ are $e^{i\omega_x x}$; the eigenfunctions of the operator $\partial^2/\partial x^2 + \partial^2/\partial y^2$ ($-\infty < x, y < +\infty$) belonging to the eigenvalues $-\omega^2 = -(\omega_x^2 + \omega_y^2)$ are $e^{i(\omega_x x + \omega_y y)}$. Consequently, in three dimensions the eigenfunctions of the operator $\partial^2/\partial x^2 + \partial^2/\partial y^2 + \partial^2/\partial z^2$ ($-\infty < x,y,z < +\infty$) belonging to the eigenvalues $-\omega^2 = -(\omega_x^2 + \omega_y^2 + \omega_z^2)$ are $e^{i(\omega_x x + \omega_y y + \omega_z z)}$. Similarly, the normalized eigenfunctions in the one-dimensional case are

$$\frac{1}{\sqrt{2\pi}} e^{i\omega_x x}$$

in the two-dimensional case

$$\left(\frac{1}{2\pi}\right) e^{i(\omega_x x + \omega_y y)}$$

and therefore

$$\left(\frac{1}{2\pi}\right)^{3/2} e^{i(\omega_x x + \omega_y y + \omega_z z)}$$

in the case of three dimensions.

146

11.2 The Wave Equation in Three Dimensions

The wave equation is

$$\left(c^2\nabla^2 - \frac{\partial^2}{\partial t^2}\right)\psi = 0 \tag{11.1}$$

where ψ is a function of the space coordinates and the time and c is the velocity of propagation of the wave. In the case of three-dimensional cartesian coordinates the Laplacian operator is given by

$$\nabla^2 \equiv \frac{\partial^2}{\partial x^2} + \frac{\partial^2}{\partial y^2} + \frac{\partial^2}{\partial z^2} \tag{11.2}$$

and $\psi = \psi(x,y,z,t)$. If one transforms to spherical coordinates r,θ,ϕ defined by the relations

$$\begin{aligned} x &= r \sin \theta \cos \phi \\ y &= r \sin \theta \sin \phi \\ z &= r \cos \theta \end{aligned} \tag{11.3}$$

the Laplacian operator becomes

$$\nabla^2 \equiv \frac{1}{r^2}\frac{\partial}{\partial r}\,r^2\frac{\partial}{\partial r} + \frac{1}{r^2 \sin \theta}\frac{\partial}{\partial \theta}\sin \theta \frac{\partial}{\partial \theta} + \frac{1}{r^2 \sin^2 \theta}\frac{\partial^2}{\partial \varphi^2} \tag{11.4}$$

and $\psi = \psi(r,\theta,\varphi,t)$.

Since periodic solutions of (11.1) are desired, one sets

$$\psi(r,\theta,\varphi,t) = \psi(r,\theta,\varphi)e^{i\omega t}$$

Substitution into (11.1) then yields

$$\nabla^2\psi(r,\theta,\varphi) = -k^2\psi(r,\theta,\varphi) \tag{11.5}$$

where $k = \omega/c$.

It is desired to solve Eq. (11.5) subject to the condition that $\psi(r,\theta,\varphi)$ is bounded for all r. The variables r,θ and φ have the ranges $0 \le r < \infty$, $0 \le \theta \le \pi$, and $0 \le \varphi \le 2\pi$.

Rather than solve (11.5) by the conventional method of separation of variables, we use the properties of a complete set of commuting observables (cf. Sec. 10.4). By analogy with the procedure followed in the solution of the two-dimensional problem (Sec. 10.4) we introduce the operator L_z defined by the relation

$$L_z = -i\frac{\partial}{\partial \varphi} = -i\left(x\frac{\partial}{\partial y} - y\frac{\partial}{\partial x}\right) \tag{11.6}$$

It is clear from (11.4) that this operator commutes with ∇^2.

Using the symmetry of cartesian coordinates, we define two other operators, denoted by L_x and L_y, which also commute with ∇^2:

$$L_x = -i\left(y\frac{\partial}{\partial z} - z\frac{\partial}{\partial y}\right) = i\left(\sin\varphi\,\frac{\partial}{\partial\theta} + \cot\theta\cos\varphi\,\frac{\partial}{\partial\varphi}\right) \quad (11.7)$$

$$L_y = -i\left(z\frac{\partial}{\partial x} - x\frac{\partial}{\partial z}\right) = -i\left(\cos\varphi\,\frac{\partial}{\partial\theta} - \cot\theta\sin\varphi\,\frac{\partial}{\partial\varphi}\right) \quad (11.8)$$

The operators L_x, L_y, and L_z do not commute with each other. They obey the commutation rules

$$[L_x, L_y] = iL_z \qquad [L_y, L_z] = iL_x \qquad [L_z, L_x] = iL_y \quad (11.9)$$

The operator

$$
\begin{aligned}
L^2 &= L_x{}^2 + L_y{}^2 + L_z{}^2 \\
&= -r^2\nabla^2 + \frac{\partial}{\partial r}\,r^2\,\frac{\partial}{\partial r} \\
&= -\frac{1}{\sin\theta}\left(\frac{\partial}{\partial\theta}\sin\theta\frac{\partial}{\partial\theta} + \frac{1}{\sin\theta}\frac{\partial^2}{\partial\varphi^2}\right)
\end{aligned}
\quad (11.10)
$$

which is called the *Legendre operator*, or simply the *Legendrian*, is seen to commute with ∇^2, r^2, L_x, L_y, and L_z.

It, therefore, seems plausible that a complete set of commuting observables might consist of ∇^2, L^2, and L_z. Assuming that such is the case, let us look for simultaneous eigenfunctions of these operators. The three simultaneous eigenvalue equations which must be solved are then

$$
\begin{aligned}
\nabla^2\psi_{k\lambda m} &= -k^2\psi_{k\lambda m} \\
L^2\psi_{k\lambda m} &= \lambda\psi_{k\lambda m} \\
L_z\psi_{k\lambda m} &= m\psi_{k\lambda m}
\end{aligned}
\quad (11.11)
$$

However, by noting that both L^2 and L_z are independent of r, it is seen that one may first study a problem not involving r at all:

$$
\begin{aligned}
L^2\psi_{\lambda m} &= \lambda\psi_{\lambda m} \\
L_z\psi_{\lambda m} &= m\psi_{\lambda m}
\end{aligned}
\quad (11.12)
$$

The solution to (11.11) may then be obtained from the solution to (11.12) by incorporating the r dependence.

11.3 The Eigenvalues of L^2 and L_z

It is convenient to introduce the operators L_+ and L_- defined by the relations

$$L_+ = L_x + iL_y = e^{i\phi}\left(\frac{\partial}{\partial\theta} + i \cot\theta \frac{\partial}{\partial\varphi}\right) \tag{11.13}$$

$$L_- = L_x - iL_y = e^{-i\phi}\left(-\frac{\partial}{\partial\theta} + i \cot\theta \frac{\partial}{\partial\varphi}\right) \tag{11.14}$$

These operators clearly commute with L^2. Furthermore,

$$[L_z, L_+] = L_z L_+ - L_+ L_z = L_+ \tag{11.15}$$

$$[L_z, L_-] = L_z L_- - L_- L_z = -L_- \tag{11.16}$$

$$L_- L_+ = L^2 - L_z^2 - L_z \tag{11.17}$$

$$L_+ L_- = L^2 - L_z^2 + L_z \tag{11.18}$$

Now suppose that $\psi_{\lambda m}$ is a simultaneous eigenfunction of L^2 and L_z, viz.,

$$L^2 \psi_{\lambda m} = \lambda \psi_{\lambda m}$$
$$L_z \psi_{\lambda m} = m \psi_{\lambda m} \tag{11.12}$$

We assert that either $L_+\psi_{\lambda m}$ vanishes or it is an eigenfunction of L_z belonging to $m + 1$ (and, since $[L^2, L_+] = 0$, of L^2 belonging to λ). To see this, note that

$$L_z(L_+\psi_{\lambda m}) = (L_z L_+ - L_+ L_z)\psi_{\lambda m} + L_+ L_z \psi_{\lambda m}$$
$$= L_+ \psi_{\lambda m} + L_+ m \psi_{\lambda m}$$
$$= (m + 1)L_+\psi_{\lambda m} \tag{11.19}$$

Similarly

$$L_z(L_-\psi_{\lambda m}) = (m - 1)L_-\psi_{\lambda m} \tag{11.20}$$

Thus, given $\psi_{\lambda m}$, one may construct a sequence of solutions, ..., $\psi_{\lambda, m-2}$, $\psi_{\lambda, m-1}$, $\psi_{\lambda m}$, $\psi_{\lambda, m+1}$, $\psi_{\lambda, m+2}$, ..., extending indefinitely in both directions or terminating because $L_+\psi_{\lambda m}$ vanishes for some m. It is readily demonstrated that for any eigenfunction $\psi_{\lambda m}$, λ is equal to or greater than m^2 and, therefore, the sequence of solutions must terminate at both ends. From this fact the eigenvalues of L^2 and L_z are found. The eigenfunctions may then be deduced (cf. Sec. 11.4).

To show that $\lambda \geq m^2$, consider

$$\int \bar{\psi}_{\lambda m}(L^2 - L_z{}^2)\psi_{\lambda m}\, d\Omega = \int \bar{\psi}_{\lambda m}(L_x{}^2 + L_y{}^2)\psi_{\lambda m}\, d\Omega = \lambda - m^2 \quad (11.21)$$

where $d\Omega = \sin\theta\, d\theta\, d\phi$. Since the operator L_x is Hermitian[1]

$$\int \bar{\psi}_{\lambda m}L_x{}^2\psi_{\lambda m}\, d\Omega = \int \overline{L_x\psi_{\lambda m}}L_x\psi_{\lambda m}\, d\Omega \geq 0$$

Similarly $$\int \bar{\psi}_{\lambda m}L_y{}^2\psi_{\lambda m}\, d\Omega = \int \overline{L_y\psi_{\lambda m}}L_y\psi_{\lambda m}\, d\Omega \geq 0$$

Hence $$\int \bar{\psi}_{\lambda m}(L_x{}^2 + L_y{}^2)\psi_{\lambda m}\, d\Omega \geq 0$$

and, from (11.21), $\lambda - m^2 \geq 0$.

From the relations (11.19) and (11.20) it follows that

$$L_+\psi_{\lambda m} = G_\lambda{}^m \psi_{\lambda, m+1} \quad (11.22)$$

$$L_-\psi_{\lambda m} = H_\lambda{}^m \psi_{\lambda, m-1} \quad (11.23)$$

where the constants $G_\lambda{}^m$ and $H_\lambda{}^m$ are to be determined. Furthermore, in order to terminate the sequence of functions $\psi_{\lambda m}$ for some large value of m, $G_\lambda{}^m$ must vanish. $H_\lambda{}^m$ must vanish for some other m in order to terminate the sequence at small m. If the $\psi_{\lambda m}$ are normalized such that

$$\int \bar{\psi}_{\lambda m}\psi_{\lambda m}\, d\Omega = 1$$

for all m, then

$$|G_\lambda{}^m|^2 = \int \overline{L_+\psi_{\lambda m}}L_+\psi_{\lambda m}\, d\Omega$$

---

[1] For any two functions $u(\theta,\varphi)$ and $v(\theta,\varphi)$ satisfying the boundary conditions on $\psi_{\lambda m}$

$$\iint \overline{u(\theta,\varphi)}L_x v(\theta,\varphi) \sin\theta\, d\theta\, d\varphi$$

$$= \iint \overline{u(\theta,\varphi)}\left[i\left(\sin\varphi\, \frac{\partial}{\partial\theta} + \cot\theta\cos\varphi\, \frac{\partial}{\partial\varphi}\right)v(\theta,\varphi)\right]\sin\theta\, d\theta\, d\varphi$$

$$= -\iint v(\theta,\varphi)\left[i\left(\sin\varphi\, \frac{\partial}{\partial\theta} + \cot\theta\, \frac{\partial}{\partial\varphi}\cos\varphi\right)\overline{u(\theta,\varphi)}\sin\theta\right]d\theta\, d\varphi$$

$$= -\iint v(\theta,\varphi)\left[i\left(\sin\varphi\, \frac{\partial}{\partial\theta} + \cot\theta\cos\varphi\, \frac{\partial}{\partial\varphi}\right)\overline{u(\theta,\varphi)}\right]\sin\theta\, d\theta\, d\phi$$

$$= \iint \overline{L_x u(\theta,\varphi)}v(\theta,\varphi) \sin\theta\, d\theta\, d\varphi$$

Since $(L_+)^+ = L_-,$[1] one obtains on integrating by parts

$$|G_\lambda{}^m|^2 = \int \bar{\psi}_{\lambda m} L_- L_+ \psi_{\lambda m} \, d\Omega$$

$$= \int \psi_{\lambda m} (L^2 - L_z{}^2 - L_z) \psi_{\lambda m} \, d\Omega$$

$$= \lambda - m^2 - m \qquad (11.24)$$

where use has been made of (11.17). Similarly

$$|H_\lambda{}^m|^2 = \lambda - m^2 + m \qquad (11.25)$$

If $G_\lambda{}^m$ is to vanish for some m, say $m = l$, then

$$\lambda = l^2 + l = l(l + 1)$$

In order for $H_\lambda{}^m$ to vanish also, one must have

$$l(l + 1) - m^2 + m = 0$$

or $\qquad\qquad m = l + 1, -l$

Clearly, only the solution $m = -l$ is relevant.

Thus, the simultaneous eigenvalues of the operators L^2 and L_z are

$$\lambda = l(l + 1) \qquad (11.26)$$

and $\qquad\qquad -l \le m \le +l \qquad (11.27)$

It is easily demonstrated that m and, consequently, l are integers or zero. We first note [cf. Eqs. (11.19) and (11.20)] that the eigenvalues m increase or decrease in unit steps. Consequently, it follows from (11.27) that if m is an integer or zero, so is l. That m is an integer or zero is seen as follows: The eigenfunctions of the operator L_z are the solutions of the differential equation

$$L_z \psi_{lm} = -i \frac{\partial}{\partial \varphi} \psi_{lm} = m \psi_{lm}$$

namely: $\qquad\qquad \psi_{lm} = e^{im\phi} f_{lm}(\theta) \qquad (11.28)$

where $f_{lm}(\theta)$ is an arbitrary function of θ. In order to satisfy the single-valuedness condition on ψ_{lm}, m must be zero or a positive or negative integer.[2] The relations (11.26) and (11.27), therefore, become

$$\lambda = l(l + 1) \qquad l = 0, 1, 2, \dots \qquad (11.26a)$$

and $\qquad m = -l, -l + 1, \dots, -1, 0, 1, \dots, l - 1, l \qquad (11.27a)$

[1] $(L_+)^+ = (L_x + iL_y)^+ = L_x^+ - iL_y^+ = L_-$, where we have used $L_x^+ = L_x$, etc.
[2] The commutation relations on L_x, L_y, L_z, omitting the single-valuedness, require $2m$ and $2l$ to be integral. The solutions for m and l not integral are needed in the theory of spin.

From (11.24) and (11.26a), it then follows that

$$G_l{}^m = \sqrt{l(l + 1) - m(m + 1)} = \sqrt{(l - m)(l + m + 1)} \quad (11.29)$$

where $G_l{}^m$ has been taken as real. The $H_l{}^m$ are uniquely determined from the $G_l{}^m$. Thus

$$\bar{H}_l{}^m H_l{}^m = \int \overline{L_- \psi_{lm}} L_- \psi_{lm} \, d\Omega$$

$$= \int \overline{L_- \psi_{lm}} H_l{}^m \psi_{l,m-1} \, d\Omega$$

$$= \int \bar{\psi}_{lm} L_+ H_l{}^m \psi_{l,m-1} \, d\Omega$$

$$= \int \bar{\psi}_{lm} H_l{}^m G_l{}^{m-1} \psi_{lm} \, d\Omega$$

$$= H_l{}^m G_l{}^{m-1}$$

Hence $$\bar{H}_l{}^m = G_l{}^{m-1}$$

or $$H_l{}^m = \bar{G}_l{}^{m-1} = \sqrt{(l - m + 1)(l + m)} \quad (11.30)$$

11.4   The Simultaneous Eigenfunctions of L^2 and L_z

Suppose g is a polynomial satisfying

$$\nabla^2 g(x,y,z) = 0$$

Then g may be written as a sum of homogeneous polynomials f_l of degree l:

$$g = f_0 + f_1 + \cdots + f_l + \cdots$$

As is readily seen by substitution, $\nabla^2 g = 0$ implies that $\nabla^2 f_l = 0$ for each l. We are thus led to consider a homogeneous polynomial of degree l in x,y,z satisfying the equation

$$\nabla^2 f(x,y,z) = 0$$

or by the second of Eqs. (11.10)

$$\left(\frac{1}{r^2} \frac{\partial}{\partial r} r^2 \frac{\partial}{\partial r} - \frac{L^2}{r^2} \right) f = 0 \quad (11.31)$$

If one writes

$$f(x,y,z) = r^l \psi(\theta, \phi) \quad (11.32)$$

Then $\psi(\theta, \varphi)$ satisfies the equation

$$L^2 \psi(\theta, \varphi) = l(l + 1) \psi(\theta, \varphi)$$

Consequently, the function

$$\psi(\theta, \varphi) = r^{-l} f(x,y,z) \quad (11.33)$$

is an eigenfunction of the operator L^2 belonging to the eigenvalue $l(l + 1)$. Since the operators L_z and L^2 commute with one another, $\psi(\theta,\varphi)$ may also be an eigenfunction of the operator L_z. This fact enables us to determine the form of the eigenfunctions. From (11.28) it is seen that the eigenfunctions of L_z depend on φ as $e^{im\varphi}$. But from (11.3)

$$x + iy = r \sin \theta e^{i\varphi}$$
$$x - iy = r \sin \theta e^{-i\varphi}$$
$$z = r \cos \theta$$

Thus $f(x,y,z)$ must contain, for the various α such that $0 \leq 2\alpha \leq l - m$ and for the given l and m, terms of the form

$$(x + iy)^{\alpha + m} (x - iy)^{\alpha} z^{l - 2\alpha - m}$$

(which depend on φ as $e^{im\varphi}$ and are of the degree l). In particular, the eigenfunction $\psi_{l,l}(\theta,\varphi)$ is given by

$$\psi_{l,l}(\theta,\varphi) = C_l \left(\frac{x + iy}{r} \right)^l \tag{11.34}$$

where the constant C_l may be determined by normalization of the eigenfunction. It has the value[1]

$$C_l = (-1)^l \sqrt{\frac{(2l + 1)!}{4\pi}} \frac{1}{2^l l!} \tag{11.35}$$

We denote the normalized eigenfunction by $Y_l^l(\theta,\varphi)$

$$\psi_{l,l}(\theta,\varphi) \equiv Y_l^l(\theta,\varphi) = (-1)^l \sqrt{\frac{(2l + 1)!}{4\pi}} \frac{1}{2^l l!} \left(\frac{x + iy}{r} \right)^l$$

The remaining eigenfunctions, $Y_l^m(\theta,\varphi)$, are determined by use of the relation (11.23), i.e.,

$$L_- Y_l^m(\theta,\varphi) = H_l^m Y_l^{m-1}(\theta,\varphi)$$

The functions $Y_l^m(\theta,\varphi)$ are called *normalized spherical harmonics*. As we have seen, they satisfy the differential equations

$$L^2 Y_l^m(\theta,\varphi) = l(l + 1) Y_l^m(\theta,\varphi)$$
$$L_z Y_l^m(\theta,\varphi) = m Y_l^m(\theta,\varphi)$$

and the orthonormality condition

$$\int_0^{2\pi} \int_0^{\pi} \overline{Y_l^m} Y_\lambda^\mu \sin \theta \, d\theta \, d\varphi = \delta_{l\lambda} \delta_{m\mu} \tag{11.36}$$

[1] Clearly $|C_l|$ is determined by the normalization. Thus, if $C_l = |C_l| e^{i\delta}$, δ is an arbitrary real number, called the phase. The particular choice above is for convenience.

154   SYSTEMS WITH AN INFINITE NUMBER OF DEGREES OF FREEDOM

The definition of the normalized spherical harmonics given here corresponds to that of Condon and Shortley.[1] It differs from the definition in Bethe[2] and Heitler[3] by the phase factor $(-1)^m$. Since both definitions have been used in the literature, the reader is advised against indiscriminate use of relations containing the Y_l^m.

One sometimes writes the relation

$$Y_l^m(\theta,\varphi) = \Theta_l^m(\theta)\frac{e^{im\varphi}}{\sqrt{2\pi}} \tag{11.37}$$

The functions Θ_l^m so defined may be expressed in terms of the *associated Legendre* functions of the first kind, $P_l^{|m|}(\mu)$, where $\mu \equiv \cos\theta$:

$$\Theta_l^m(\theta) = (-1)^{\frac{1}{2}(m+|m|)}\sqrt{\frac{(2l+1)(l-|m|)!}{2(l+|m|)!}}\,P_l^{|m|}(\mu) \tag{11.38}$$

$$P_l^{|m|}(\mu) = \frac{1}{2^l l!}(1-\mu^2)^{|m|/2}\frac{d^{l+|m|}}{d\mu^{l+|m|}}(\mu^2-1)^l \tag{11.39}$$

In the special case $m = 0$, Eq. (11.39) reduces to

$$P_l(\mu) = \frac{1}{2^l l!}\frac{d^l}{d\mu^l}(\mu^2-1)^l \tag{11.40}$$

which is known as *Rodrigues's formula for the Legendre polynomial*, $P_l(\mu)$.

Then
$$\Theta_l^0(\theta) = \sqrt{\frac{2l+1}{2}}\,P_l(\cos\theta) \tag{11.41}$$

and
$$Y_l^0(\theta) = \sqrt{\frac{2l+1}{4\pi}}\,P_l(\cos\theta) \tag{11.42}$$

11.5 Solution of $\nabla^2\psi = 0$

According to the results of the preceding section, the solutions of the equation

$$\nabla^2\psi(x,y,z) = 0 \tag{11.43}$$

[1] E. U. Condon and G. H. Shortley, "The Theory of Atomic Spectra," p. 52, Cambridge University Press, New York, 1951.
[2] H. Bethe, "Handbuch der Physik," 2d ed., vol. 24, no. 1, p. 273, Springer-Verlag OHG, Berlin, 1933.
[3] W. Heitler, *Proc. Camb. Phil. Soc.*, **32**, 112 (1936).

may be written in terms of the normalized spherical harmonics, i.e., $r^l Y_l^m(\theta,\varphi)$, where $l = 0, 1, 2, \ldots$ and $-l \leq m \leq +l$. The general solution of (11.43) is therefore

$$\psi(x,y,z) = \sum_{l=0}^{\infty} \sum_{m=-l}^{+l} \alpha_{lm} r^l Y_l^m(\theta,\varphi) \tag{11.44}$$

where the constant coefficients α_{lm} are to be determined from the boundary conditions on $\psi(x,y,z)$.

11.6 Solution of $(\nabla^2 + k^2)\psi = 0$

In the previous section it was remarked that the solution of the equation $\nabla^2\psi = 0$ in spherical coordinates is $r_l Y_l^m(\theta,\varphi)$. For the solution of the equation

$$(\nabla^2 + k^2)\psi = 0 \tag{11.45}$$

one therefore tries $\psi = z_l(kr) Y_l^m(\theta,\varphi)$, where the z_l are functions of r which are to be determined.

Since

$$\begin{aligned} \nabla^2 &= \frac{1}{r^2}\frac{\partial}{\partial r} r^2 \frac{\partial}{\partial r} - \frac{L^2}{r^2} \\ &= \frac{1}{r}\frac{\partial^2}{\partial r^2} r - \frac{L^2}{r^2} \end{aligned} \tag{11.46}$$

where L^2 is defined by (11.10), the equation

$$(\nabla^2 + k^2) z_l(kr) Y_l^m(\theta,\varphi) = 0$$

becomes
$$\left[\frac{1}{r}\frac{d^2}{dr^2} r - \frac{l(l+1)}{r^2} + k^2 \right] z_l(kr) = 0 \tag{11.47}$$

When one introduces the new variable $\rho = kr$, (11.47) reduces to

$$\left[\frac{d^2}{d\rho^2} - \frac{l(l+1)}{\rho^2} + 1 \right] \rho z_l(\rho) = 0 \tag{11.48}$$

For convenience set $F_l(\rho) = \rho z_l(\rho)$ so that (11.48) may be written

$$\left[\frac{l(l+1)}{\rho^2} - \frac{d^2}{d\rho^2} \right] F_l = F_l \tag{11.48a}$$

In analogy with the procedure in the case of cylindrical functions (Secs. 10.4 and 10.5) try to factor the operator in the left-hand member of (11.48a): Write

$$\left(\frac{A}{\rho} + \frac{d}{d\rho} \right)\left(\frac{B}{\rho} - \frac{d}{d\rho} \right) F_l \equiv \left[\frac{l(l+1)}{\rho^2} - \frac{d^2}{d\rho^2} \right] F_l$$

where A and B are constants to be determined. Expansion of the left-hand member then gives

$$\left(\frac{AB - B}{\rho^2} + \frac{B - A}{\rho}\frac{d}{d\rho} - \frac{d^2}{d\rho^2}\right)F_l \equiv \left[\frac{l(l + 1)}{\rho^2} - \frac{d^2}{d\rho^2}\right]F_l$$

By equating the coefficients of like terms in this identity one obtains $A = B$ and

$$AB - B = B^2 - B = B(B - 1) \equiv l(l + 1)$$

so that $$A = B = -l, l + 1$$

Hence $$\left[\frac{l(l + 1)}{\rho^2} - \frac{d^2}{d\rho^2}\right]F_l \equiv \left(\frac{l + 1}{\rho} + \frac{d}{d\rho}\right)\left(\frac{l + 1}{\rho} - \frac{d}{d\rho}\right)F_l \quad (11.49)$$

$$\equiv \left(\frac{l}{\rho} - \frac{d}{d\rho}\right)\left(\frac{l}{\rho} + \frac{d}{d\rho}\right)F_l \quad (11.50)$$

It therefore follows that Eq. (11.48a) may be written as either

$$\left(\frac{l + 1}{\rho} + \frac{d}{d\rho}\right)\left(\frac{l + 1}{\rho} - \frac{d}{d\rho}\right)F_l = F_l \quad (11.51)$$

or $$\left(\frac{l}{\rho} - \frac{d}{d\rho}\right)\left(\frac{l}{\rho} + \frac{d}{d\rho}\right)F_l = F_l \quad (11.52)$$

By operating on Eq. (11.52) from the left with

$$\left(\frac{l}{\rho} + \frac{d}{d\rho}\right)$$

one obtains $$\left(\frac{l}{\rho} + \frac{d}{d\rho}\right)\left(\frac{l}{\rho} - \frac{d}{d\rho}\right)\left[\left(\frac{l}{\rho} + \frac{d}{d\rho}\right)F_l\right] = \left[\left(\frac{l}{\rho} + \frac{d}{d\rho}\right)F_l\right]$$

Comparison of this result with Eq. (11.51) shows that $\left(\frac{l}{\rho} + \frac{d}{d\rho}\right)F_l$ satisfies the same differential equation as F_{l-1}. Since the differential equation determines F_{l-1} to within a multiplicative constant (if F_{l-1} is regular at $\rho = 0$), one has

$$\left(\frac{l}{\rho} + \frac{d}{d\rho}\right)F_l = C_l F_{l-1}$$

Multiplying by $[(l/\rho) - (d/d\rho)]$ one finds that

$$\left(\frac{l}{\rho} - \frac{d}{d\rho}\right)\left(\frac{l}{\rho} + \frac{d}{d\rho}\right)F_l = F_l = C_l\left(\frac{l}{\rho} - \frac{d}{d\rho}\right)F_{l-1}$$

or $$\left(\frac{l + 1}{\rho} - \frac{d}{d\rho}\right)F_l = (C_{l+1})^{-1}F_{l+1}$$

It is convenient to take the C_l equal to unity. Then

$$F_{l-1} = \left(\frac{l}{\rho} + \frac{d}{d\rho}\right)F_l \tag{11.53}$$

and

$$F_{l+1} = \left(\frac{l+1}{\rho} - \frac{d}{d\rho}\right)F_l \tag{11.54}$$

These two equations, together with a boundary condition on $F_0(\rho)$ at $\rho = 0$, completely determine the functions $F_l(\rho)$.

The addition of (11.53) and (11.54) gives

$$\frac{2l+1}{\rho}F_l = F_{l-1} + F_{l+1} \tag{11.55}$$

Furthermore, if one multiplies (11.53) by $l + 1$ and subtracts from the result l times (11.54), he obtains

$$(2l+1)\frac{d}{d\rho}F_l = (l+1)F_{l-1} - lF_{l+1} \tag{11.56}$$

The functions $z_l = F_l/\rho$ therefore satisfy the following recurrence formulae:

from (11.53):

$$\left(\frac{l+1}{\rho} + \frac{d}{d\rho}\right)z_l = z_{l-1} \tag{11.57}$$

from (11.54):

$$\left(\frac{l}{\rho} - \frac{d}{d\rho}\right)z_l = z_{l+1} \tag{11.58}$$

from (11.55):

$$\frac{2l+1}{\rho}z_l = z_{l-1} + z_{l+1} \tag{11.59}$$

from (11.56):

$$\frac{2l+1}{\rho}\frac{d}{d\rho}(\rho z_l) = (l+1)z_{l-1} - lz_{l+1} \tag{11.60}$$

It is left as an exercise for the reader to verify that

$$z_l(\rho) = \sqrt{\frac{\pi}{2\rho}}Z_{l+\frac{1}{2}}(\rho) \tag{11.61}$$

where the $Z_{l+\frac{1}{2}}$ are the cylindrical functions defined in Appendix 2C. The spherical functions j_l, n_l, $h_l^{(1,2)}$ which are related, respectively, to the cylindrical functions $J_{l+\frac{1}{2}}$, $N_{l+\frac{1}{2}}$, $H_{l+\frac{1}{2}}^{(1,2)}$ through (11.61) are known as the *spherical Bessel, Neumann, and Hankel functions*. Of these functions only the spherical Bessel functions $j_l(kr)$ are regular at $r = 0$.

To summarize, the complete set of regular solutions of Eq. (11.45) in spherical coordinates is given by

$$\psi_{klm} = Cj_l(kr)Y_l^m(\theta,\varphi) \tag{11.62}$$

where $l = 0, 1, 2, \ldots$, $m = -l, -l + 1, \ldots, 0, \ldots, l - 1, l$, and

$$L^2 Y_l^m = l(l + 1)Y_l^m$$

$$L_z Y_l^m = mY_l^m$$

The orthonormality condition satisfied by the eigenfunctions ψ_{klm} of Eq. (11.45) is derived in Sec. 11.8, where are also derived some useful expansion formulae.

11.7 Recurrence Relations for the Spherical Harmonics

It has already been seen in Sec. 11.4 that the normalized spherical harmonics $Y_l^m(\theta,\varphi)$ satisfy the relations

$$L_+ Y_l^m = G_l^m Y_l^{m+1} \tag{11.63}$$

$$L_- Y_l^m = H_l^m Y_l^{m-1} \tag{11.64}$$

in which $$G_l^m = \sqrt{(l - m)(l + m + 1)} \tag{11.65}$$

$$H_l^m = \sqrt{(l + m)(l - m + 1)} = G_l^{-m} \tag{11.66}$$

By the use of the relation (11.37) and the definitions (11.13) and (11.14), Eqs. (11.63) and (11.64) may be written

$$\left(\frac{\partial}{\partial\theta} - m \cot\theta\right)\Theta_l^m = G_l^m\Theta_l^{m+1} \tag{11.67}$$

and $$\left(\frac{\partial}{\partial\theta} + m \cot\theta\right)\Theta_l^m = -H_l^m\Theta_l^{m-1} \tag{11.68}$$

Addition of Eqs. (11.67) and (11.68) gives

$$\frac{\partial}{\partial\theta}\Theta_l^m = \tfrac{1}{2}G_l^m\Theta_l^{m+1} - \tfrac{1}{2}H_l^m\Theta_l^{m-1} \tag{11.69}$$

while subtraction yields

$$-m \cot\theta\Theta_l^m = \tfrac{1}{2}G_l^m\Theta_l^{m+1} + \tfrac{1}{2}H_l^m\Theta_l^{m-1} \tag{11.70}$$

We list without proof[1] the following useful recurrence relations for the normalized spherical harmonics $Y_l{}^m$:

$$\cos\theta Y_l{}^m = A_l{}^m Y_{l+1}^m + B_l{}^m Y_{l-1}^m \tag{11.71}$$

$$\sin\theta e^{i\varphi} Y_l{}^m = -C_l{}^m Y_{l+1}^{m+1} + D_l{}^m Y_{l-1}^{m+1} \tag{11.72}$$

$$\sin\theta e^{-i\varphi} Y_l{}^m = E_l{}^m Y_{l+1}^{m-1} - F_l{}^m Y_{l-1}^{m-1} \tag{11.73}$$

$$\frac{\partial}{\partial z} R Y_l{}^m = A_l{}^m \alpha_l Y_{l+1}^m + B_l{}^m \beta_l Y_{l-1}^m \tag{11.74}$$

$$\partial^+ R Y_l{}^m = -C_l{}^m \alpha_l Y_{l+1}^{m+1} + D_l{}^m \beta_l Y_{l-1}^{m+1} \tag{11.75}$$

$$\partial^- R Y_l{}^m = E_l{}^m \alpha_l Y_{l+1}^{m-1} - F_l{}^m \beta_l Y_{l-1}^{m-1} \tag{11.76}$$

where $A_l{}^m = \sqrt{\dfrac{(l+1-m)(l+1+m)}{(2l+1)(2l+3)}}$ $B_l{}^m = \sqrt{\dfrac{(l-m)(l+m)}{(2l-1)(2l+1)}}$

$C_l{}^m = \sqrt{\dfrac{(l+m+1)(l+m+2)}{(2l+1)(2l+3)}}$ $D_l{}^m = \sqrt{\dfrac{(l-m)(l-m-1)}{(2l-1)(2l+1)}}$

$E_l{}^m = \sqrt{\dfrac{(l-m+1)(l-m+2)}{(2l+1)(2l+3)}}$ $F_l{}^m = \sqrt{\dfrac{(l+m)(l+m-1)}{(2l-1)(2l+1)}}$

$$\partial^+ = \frac{\partial}{\partial x} + i\frac{\partial}{\partial y} \qquad \partial^- = \frac{\partial}{\partial x} - i\frac{\partial}{\partial y}$$

$$\alpha_l = \left(\frac{d}{dr} - \frac{l}{r}\right)R \qquad \beta_l = \left(\frac{d}{dr} + \frac{l+1}{r}\right)R$$

and R is an arbitrary function of r only.

In the special case where $R = z_l(kr)$, the spherical cylindrical function, one finds by the use of Eqs. (11.57) and (11.58) that $\alpha_l = -k z_{l+1}(kr)$ and $\beta_l = k z_{l-1}(kr)$. Equations (11.74) to (11.76) then reduce to

$$\frac{1}{k}\frac{\partial}{\partial z} z_l(kr) Y_l{}^m(\theta,\varphi) = -A_l{}^m z_{l+1} Y_{l+1}^m + B_l{}^m z_{l-1} Y_{l-1}^m \tag{11.77}$$

$$\frac{1}{k}\partial^+ z_l(kr) Y_l{}^m(\theta,\varphi) = C_l{}^m z_{l+1} Y_{l+1}^{m+1} + D_l{}^m z_{l-1} Y_{l-1}^{m+1} \tag{11.78}$$

$$\frac{1}{k}\partial^- z_l(kr) Y_l{}^m(\theta,\varphi) = -E_l{}^m z_{l+1} Y_{l+1}^{m-1} - F_l{}^m z_{l-1} Y_{l-1}^{m-1} \tag{11.79}$$

---

[1] For derivations see Condon and Shortley, *op. cit.*, p. 53, and Bethe, *op. cit.*, pp. 551–560; note that Bethe's P_{lm} equals our $(-1)^m\Theta_l{}^m$.

11.8 Some Expansion Theorems

In this section the orthonormality condition satisfied by the eigen-functions ψ_{klm} [Eq. (11.62)] which are the regular solutions of Eq. (11.45) will be derived. In order to do this it is convenient to first derive some useful expansion formulae.

The expansion of a plane wave[1] $e^{i\mathbf{k}\cdot\mathbf{r}}$, traveling in an arbitrary direction α,β (i.e., $\mathbf{k}$ has components $k_x = k \sin \alpha \cos \beta$, $k_y = k \sin \alpha \sin \beta$, $k_z = k \cos \alpha$) is

$$e^{i\mathbf{k}\cdot\mathbf{r}} = 4\pi \sum_{l=0}^{\infty} \sum_{m=-l}^{+l} i^l j_l(kr) \overline{Y_l^m(\alpha,\beta)} Y_l^m(\theta,\varphi) \tag{11.80}$$

To derive this expression let[2]

$$e^{i\mathbf{k}\cdot\mathbf{r}} = \sum_{l,m} Q_l^m j_l(kr) Y_l^m(\theta,\varphi) \tag{11.81}$$

and find the functions Q_l^m. Since $\mathbf{k} \cdot \mathbf{r} = k_x x + k_y y + k_z z$, differentiation of the left-hand member of (11.81) with respect to z yields

$$ik_z e^{i\mathbf{k}\cdot\mathbf{r}} = ik_z \sum_{l,m} Q_l^m j_l(kr) Y_l^m(\theta,\varphi)$$

By Eq. (11.77) differentiation of the right-hand member with respect to z gives

$$k \sum_{l,m} Q_l^m [-A_l^m j_{l+1}(kr) Y_{l+1}^m(\theta,\varphi) + B_l^m j_{l-1}(kr) Y_{l-1}^m(\theta,\varphi)]$$
$$= k \sum_{l,m} [-A_{l-1}^m Q_{l-1}^m + B_{l+1}^m Q_{l+1}^m] j_l(kr) Y_l^m(\theta,\varphi)$$
$$= k \sum_{l,m} [-B_l^m Q_{l-1}^m + A_l^m Q_{l+1}^m] j_l(kr) Y_l^m(\theta,\varphi)$$

since, from the definitions of A_l^m and B_l^m, it is clear that $B_{l+1}^m = A_l^m$. Hence

$$i\frac{k_z}{k} Q_l^m \equiv i \cos \alpha \, Q_l^m = A_l^m Q_{l+1}^m - B_l^m Q_{l-1}^m \tag{11.82}$$

Similarly, by operating on Eq. (11.81) with ∂^- and ∂^+, respectively, one obtains

$$i\frac{k_x - ik_y}{k} Q_l^m \equiv i \sin \alpha \, e^{-i\beta} Q_l^m = -C_l^m Q_{l+1}^{m+1} + D_l^m Q_{l-1}^{m+1} \tag{11.83}$$

$$i\frac{k_x + ik_y}{k} Q_l^m \equiv i \sin \alpha \, e^{i\beta} Q_l^m = E_l^m Q_{l+1}^{m-1} + F_l^m Q_{l-1}^{m-1} \tag{11.84}$$

[1] $e^{i\mathbf{k}\cdot\mathbf{r}}$ is constant on the parallel planes $\mathbf{k} \cdot \mathbf{r} = $ constant and varies as e^{iks} along the normal to the planes, where s is distance along the normal.

[2] Note the parallelism with the derivation of Eq. (10.39a) in the two-dimensional case. The derivation assumes the completeness of the set $j_l Y_l^m$. This can be demonstrated.

Comparison of Eqs. (11.82), (11.83), and (11.84) with Eqs. (11.71), (11.72), and (11.73)[1] shows that

$$Q_l{}^m = Ci^l \overline{Y_l{}^m(\alpha,\beta)} \tag{11.85}$$

where C is a constant to be determined. Hence Eq. (11.81) becomes

$$e^{i\mathbf{k}\cdot\mathbf{r}} = C \sum_{l,m} i^l j_l(kr) \overline{Y_l{}^m(\alpha,\beta)} Y_l{}^m(\theta,\varphi) \tag{11.81a}$$

To evaluate the constant C let $x = y = z = 0$ so that (11.81a) reduces to

$$1 = C \sum_{l,m} i^l j_l(0) \overline{Y_l{}^m(\alpha,\beta)} Y_l{}^m(\theta,\varphi)$$

But $j_l(0) = 0$ for $l \neq 0$ and $j_0(0) = 1$ and $Y_0{}^0(\mu,\lambda) = 1/\sqrt{4\pi}$. Hence $C = 4\pi$ and the derivation of Eq. (11.80) is complete.

In the special case where $k_x = k_y = 0$, $k_z = k$, Eq. (11.80) reduces to

$$e^{i\mathbf{k}\cdot\mathbf{r}} \equiv e^{ikr\cos\theta} = \sum_{l=0}^{\infty} i^l \sqrt{4\pi\,(2l+1)}\, j_l(kr) Y_l{}^0(\theta) \tag{11.86}$$

since $Y_l{}^m(0) = 0$ for $m \neq 0$ and $Y_l{}^0(0) = \sqrt{(2l+1)/4\pi}$ [see Eqs. (11.37) to (11.40) and (11.42)]. The relation (11.86) is sometimes called *Bauer's formula*.

Now note that (11.86) may be thought of as the expansion of $e^{i\mathbf{k}\cdot\mathbf{r}}$ in terms of the spherical harmonics $Y_l{}^0$ of the angle between the vectors k and r. Therefore, if one calls this angle ω instead of θ and equates

$$e^{i\mathbf{k}\cdot\mathbf{r}} \equiv e^{ikr\cos\omega} = \sum_l i^l \sqrt{4\pi(2l+1)}\, j_l(kr) Y_l{}^0(\omega)$$

to (11.80) he obtains

$$Y_l{}^0(\omega) = \sqrt{\frac{4\pi}{2l+1}} \sum_{m=-l}^{+l} \overline{Y_l{}^m(\alpha,\beta)} Y_l{}^m(\theta,\varphi) \tag{11.87}$$

where ω is the angle between the directions α,β and θ,φ and is given by the relation

$$\cos\omega = \cos\theta\cos\alpha + \sin\theta\sin\alpha\cos(\varphi-\beta)$$

which is the special case of (11.87) for $l = 1$. The relation (11.87) is the well-known *addition theorem for the spherical harmonics*.

---

[1] Note that from (11.37) and (11.38) one readily finds
$$Y_l{}^m = (-1)^m\, \bar{Y}_l{}^{-m}$$

In order to derive the orthonormality condition satisfied by the functions $j_l(kr)\, Y_l^m(\theta,\varphi)$ note that the functions $e^{i\mathbf{k}\cdot\mathbf{r}}$ satisfy the orthonormality condition

$$\delta(\mathbf{r} - \mathbf{r}') = \left(\frac{1}{2\pi}\right)^3 \int e^{i\mathbf{k}\cdot(\mathbf{r}-\mathbf{r}')}d\mathbf{k}$$

i.e.,

$$\delta(x - x')\, \delta(y - y')\, \delta(z - z')$$
$$= \left(\frac{1}{2\pi}\right)^3 \int_{-\infty}^{+\infty}\int_{-\infty}^{+\infty}\int_{-\infty}^{+\infty} e^{i[k_x(x-x')+k_y(y-y')+k_z(z-z')]}\, dk_x\, dk_y\, dk_z$$

or in spherical coordinates

$$\frac{\delta(r - r')}{r^2}\frac{\delta(\theta - \theta')}{\sin\theta}\delta(\phi - \varphi') = \left(\frac{1}{2\pi}\right)^3 \int_0^{2\pi}\int_0^{\pi}\int_0^{\infty} e^{i\mathbf{k}\cdot(\mathbf{r}-\mathbf{r}')}k^2 \sin\alpha\, dk\, d\alpha\, d\beta$$

$$(11.88)$$

Substitution of (11.80) into (11.88) then gives

$$\delta(\mathbf{r} - \mathbf{r}') = \frac{2}{\pi}\sum_{l,m}\sum_{L,M}\left[i^l(-i)^L \overline{Y_L^M(\theta',\varphi')}Y_l^m(\theta,\varphi)\int_0^{\infty} j_l(kr)j_L(kr')k^2\, dk\right.$$
$$\left. \times \int_0^{2\pi}\int_0^{\pi}\overline{Y_l^m(\alpha,\beta)}Y_L^M(\alpha,\beta)\sin\alpha\, d\alpha\, d\beta\right] \quad (11.89)$$

Because of the orthonormality condition (11.36) the integration over α and β yields $\delta_{lL}\, \delta_{mM}$. Hence (11.89) reduces to

$$\delta(\mathbf{r} - \mathbf{r}') = \frac{2}{\pi}\sum_{l,m}\overline{Y_l^m(\theta',\varphi')}Y_l^m(\theta,\varphi)\int_0^{\infty} j_l(kr)j_l(kr')k^2\, dk \qquad (11.90)$$

which is the required orthonormality relation for the eigenfunctions ψ_{klm} which are the regular solutions of Eq. (11.45).

11.9 Solution of the Wave Equation

The formal solution of the wave equation

$$\left(c^2\,\nabla^2 - \frac{\partial^2}{\partial t^2}\right)\psi(r,\theta,\varphi,t) = 0 \qquad (11.1)$$

is $\psi(r,\theta,\varphi,t) = \cos(\sqrt{-\nabla^2}ct)\psi(r,\theta,\varphi,0) + \dfrac{\sin\sqrt{-\nabla^2}ct}{c\sqrt{-\nabla^2}}\,\psi(r,\theta,\varphi,0)$ (11.91)

and $\psi(r,\theta,\varphi,0) = \displaystyle\int \psi(r',\theta',\varphi',0)\,\delta(\mathbf{r} - \mathbf{r}')\, d\mathbf{r}'$ (11.92)

The explicit solution of (11.1) is obtained by substituting (11.92) and (11.90) into the right-hand member of (11.91). Thus

$$\psi(r,\theta,\varphi,t) = \frac{2}{\pi} \sum_{l,m} \int_0^\infty \int_0^\infty \int_0^\pi \int_0^{2\pi} Y_l^m(\theta,\varphi) j_l(kr)$$

$$\times\ \overline{Y_l^m(\theta',\varphi')} j_l(kr') \Big[\cos kct\, \psi(r',\theta',\varphi',0)$$

$$+\ \frac{\sin kct}{kc}\, \dot\psi(r',\theta',\varphi',0) \Big]\, d\varphi'\, \sin\theta'\, d\theta'\, r'^2\, dr'\, k^2\, dk \qquad (11.93)$$

11.10 Heat Conduction in an Infinite Solid

The formal solution of the heat conduction equation

$$\frac{\partial}{\partial t}\, T(r,\theta,\varphi,t) = a\, \nabla^2 T(r,\theta,\varphi,t) \qquad (11.94)$$

where T is bounded for all r and $0 \le r \le \infty$, $0 \le \theta \le \pi$, $0 \le \varphi \le 2\pi$, is

$$T(r,\theta,\varphi,t) = e^{a\nabla^2 t} T(r,\theta,\varphi,0) \qquad (11.95)$$

where $T(r,\theta,\varphi,0)$ is the given initial temperature distribution. The explicit solution is then

$$T(r,\theta,\varphi,t) = e^{a\nabla^2 t} \int T(r',\theta',\varphi',0)\, \delta(\mathbf{r} - \mathbf{r}')\, d\mathbf{r}'$$

where $\delta(\mathbf{r} - \mathbf{r}')$ is given by (11.90). Substitution for $\delta(\mathbf{r} - \mathbf{r}')$ yields

$$T(r,\theta,\varphi,t) = \frac{2}{\pi} \sum_{l,m} \int_0^\infty r'^2\, dr' \int_0^\pi \sin\theta'\, d\theta' \int_0^{2\pi} d\varphi'$$

$$\times\ \Big[T(r',\theta',\varphi',0) \overline{Y_l^m(\theta',\varphi')} Y_l^m(\theta,\varphi) \int_0^\infty e^{-ak^2 t} j_l(kr) j_l(kr') k^2\, dk \Big] \qquad (11.96)$$

Exercises

1. Verify that the operators L_x, L_y, and L_z satisfy the commutation rules (11.9).

2. Verify that

$$L_z L_+ - L_+ L_z = L_+$$

$$L_z L_- - L_- L_z = -L_-$$

3. Given $[L_z,P] = P$, $[L_z,Q] = Q$, $[P,Q] = 2L_z$, $[L^2,P] = [L^2,Q] = 0$, $L^2 = PQ + L_z{}^2 - L_z$, evaluate $P Y_l^m$ and $Q Y_l^m$.

SYSTEMS WITH AN INFINITE NUMBER OF DEGREES OF FREEDOM

164

4. Verify the orthonormality condition (11.36) for the normalized spherical harmonics $Y_l^m(\theta,\varphi)$.

5. Verify that $z_l(\rho) = \sqrt{\pi/2\rho}\, Z_{l+\frac{1}{2}}(\rho)$.

6. Find the 10 lowest eigenvalues of ∇^2 for functions which vanish (a) on a sphere of radius a, (b) on a cube of equal volume to a sphere of radius a, and (c) on a hemisphere of radius a.

References

Heine, E.: "Kugelfunktionen," Reimer, Berlin, 1881.

Byerly, W. E.: "Fourier's Series and Spherical, Cylindrical, and Ellipsoidal Harmonics," Ginn and Company, Boston, 1893.

MacRobert, T. M.: "Spherical Harmonics," Methuen & Co., Ltd., 1928.

Hobson, E. W.: "Spherical and Ellipsoidal Harmonics," Cambridge University Press, New York, 1931.

Prasad, G.: "Spherical Harmonics and the Functions of Bessel and Lamé," Benares City, India, 1932.

Lense, J.: "Kugelfunktionen," Akademische Verlagsgesellschaft, Berlin, 1950.

Infeld, L., and T. E. Hull: Factorization Method, *Rev. Modern Phys.*, **23**, 21 (1951).

Morse, P. M., and H. Feshbach: "Methods of Theoretical Physics," chap. 6, McGraw-Hill Book Company, Inc., New York, 1953.

CHAPTER 12

Green's Functions

12.1 Definition

Let $\mathscr{L}$ denote a differential operator and s a continuous function. Consider the problem of finding the function f which satisfies the inhomogeneous differential equation

$$\mathscr{L}f(x) = s(x) \tag{12.1}$$

and certain specified boundary conditions. If there exists a unique solution f for each s, there must exist an inverse operator $\mathscr{L}^{-1}$ such that for all s the formal solution of (12.1) is

$$f(x) = \mathscr{L}^{-1}s(x) \tag{12.2}$$

The inverse operator $\mathscr{L}^{-1}$ represents more than the operation which is inverse to that represented by $\mathscr{L}$. It denotes that operation *plus* the application of the associated boundary conditions. A simple example may make this point clear: Consider the solution of

$$\frac{d}{dx} y = 2x$$

subject to the boundary condition $y(0) = 1$. The operation inverse to d/dx is $\int dx$. But the application of this operation alone yields many functions $y = x^2 + b$, where b is a constant of integration. The application of the boundary condition determines $b = 1$ so that the unique solution to the problem is $y = x^2 + 1$.

By definition, that solution of (12.1) corresponding to $s(x) = \delta(x - x')$ is the Green's function, $G(x,x')$, for the operator $\mathscr{L}$ and the given boundary conditions. Thus the Green's function satisfies the equation

$$\mathscr{L}G(x,x') = \delta(x - x') \tag{12.3}$$

165

with the same boundary conditions as on the function f. It then follows that

$$G(x,x') = \mathscr{L}^{-1} \delta(x - x') \tag{12.4}$$

While for simplicity a one-dimensional example has been considered, the definition (12.4) is easily extended to two or more dimensions.

The Green's function is of much theoretical importance because it enables a differential equation with suitable boundary conditions to be solved by a quadrature. This may be seen as follows: By using the Dirac delta function Eq. (12.2) may be written

$$f(x) = \int \mathscr{L}^{-1} \delta(x - x')s(x') \, dx'$$

Hence, employing the definition (12.4) of the Green's function, one obtains

$$f(x) = \int G(x,x')s(x') \, dx' \tag{12.5}$$

In the subsequent sections of this chapter various methods for determining Green's functions will be introduced, and some of the properties of these functions will be studied.

12.2   The Necessary and Sufficient Condition for a Green's Function

Consider again the differential equation

$$\mathscr{L}f(x) = s(x) \tag{12.1}$$

with the specified boundary conditions on $f(x)$. If the differential operator $\mathscr{L}$ is self-adjoint, its eigenfunctions may be expected to form a complete set. Find these eigenfunctions ψ_λ and the corresponding eigenvalues λ by solving the eigenvalue problem

$$\mathscr{L}\psi_\lambda(x) = \lambda\psi_\lambda(x) \quad \text{or} \quad \mathscr{L} <x|\lambda> = <x|\lambda> \lambda \tag{12.6}$$

with the same boundary conditions on ψ_λ as on $f(x)$. Then

$$\delta(x - x') = \mathscr{S}_\lambda \psi_\lambda(x)\overline{\psi_\lambda(x')} = <x|\lambda> <\lambda|x'> \tag{12.7}$$

where $\mathscr{S}_\lambda$ represents $\int d\lambda$ if the eigenvalues form a continuous set and $\sum_\lambda$ if they form a discrete set. Hence, from (12.4), the Green's function for the operator $\mathscr{L}$ and the given boundary conditions is

$$G(x,x') = \mathscr{S}_\lambda \frac{\psi_\lambda(x)\overline{\psi_\lambda(x')}}{\lambda} = <x|\lambda> \frac{1}{\lambda} <\lambda|x'> \tag{12.8}$$

provided that $\lambda \neq 0$ and there is no infinite sequence of λ's approaching zero as a limit point. Thus the Green's functions for all Hermitian operators $\mathscr{L}$ which do not have zero as an eigenvalue have been formed.

The expression (12.8) is known as the *eigenfunction expansion* for the Green's function.

We shall now demonstrate that if the operator $\mathscr{L}$ has zero as an eigenvalue, its Green's function is not defined regardless of the method of representation.[1] Consider

$$\mathscr{L}f = g \qquad \mathscr{L}^+\varphi_0 = 0 \qquad (12.9)$$

Then

$$\int \bar{\varphi}_0 g \, dx = \int \bar{\varphi}_0 \mathscr{L}f \, dx = \int \overline{\mathscr{L}^+\varphi_0} f \, dx = 0$$

so that (12.9) has no solution for any g such that $\int \bar{\varphi}_0 g \, dx \neq 0$. In particular, for

$$g = \varphi_0 \qquad \int \bar{\varphi}_0 g \, dx \neq 0$$

To summarize: The necessary and sufficient condition that a Hermitian operator $\mathscr{L}$ have an inverse (Green's function) is that it does not have zero as an eigenvalue or as a limit point of eigenvalues.

12.3 The Operator $-\alpha^2 \, d^2/dx^2 + 1$ in an Infinite Domain

Let $\mathscr{L}$ represent the differential operator $-\alpha^2 \, d^2/dx^2 + 1$ where α is a given constant and consider the inhomogeneous differential equation

$$\mathscr{L}f(x) = s(x) \qquad (12.10)$$

in which $s(x)$ is a given continuous function of x, with the boundary conditions

$$f(\pm\infty) = s(\pm\infty) = 0 \qquad (12.11)$$

Such an equation describes, for example, the absorption density $f(x)$ of particles diffusing from a source of density $s(x)$.

In an infinite domain the set of functions $1/\sqrt{2\pi} \, e^{iwx}$ is a complete set of eigenfunctions of the operator $\mathscr{L}$ belonging to the eigenvalues $1 + \alpha^2 w^2$. The Green's function is then

$$G(x,x') \equiv \mathscr{L}^{-1} \, \delta(x - x')$$

$$= \mathscr{L}^{-1} \frac{1}{2\pi} \int_{-\infty}^{+\infty} e^{iw(x-x')} dw$$

$$= \frac{1}{2\pi} \int_{-\infty}^{+\infty} \frac{e^{iw(x-x')}}{1 + \alpha^2 w^2} \, dw \qquad (12.12)$$

Note that as $\alpha \to 0$, $G(x,x') \to \delta(x - x')$.

[1] In chap. 13 we shall see how to extend the definition of the Green's function in some problems.

To evaluate (12.12) for $\alpha \neq 0$ set $\alpha w = t$. Then

$$G(x,x') = \frac{1}{2\pi\alpha} \int_{-\infty}^{+\infty} \frac{e^{it(x-x')/\alpha}}{(t+i)(t-i)}\,dt$$

$$= \frac{1}{2\alpha} e^{-|x-x'|/\alpha} \tag{12.13}$$

Note that this Green's function is symmetrical in the variables x and x'; $G(x,x') = G(x',x)$.

The solution of Eq. (12.10) with the boundary conditions (12.11) is then

$$f(x) = \int_{-\infty}^{+\infty} G(x,x')s(x')\,dx'$$

$$= \frac{1}{2\alpha} \int_{-\infty}^{+\infty} e^{-|x-x'|/\alpha}s(x')\,dx' \tag{12.14}$$

An alternate method of finding the Green's function $G(x,x')$ without knowing the eigenfunctions of the operator $\mathscr{L}$ is often useful. This method, sometimes called the *direct method*, goes as follows: The Green's function for the operator $\mathscr{L} \equiv (-\alpha^2\,d^2/dx^2 + 1)$ satisfies the equation

$$\mathscr{L}G(x,x') = \delta(x - x') \tag{12.15}$$

with the boundary conditions $G(\pm\infty,x') = 0$. This equation is easily solved for $x \neq x'$. Thus, if $x < x'$

$$G(x,x') = e^{x/\alpha}a(x') \tag{12.16}$$

and if $x > x'$

$$G(x,x') = e^{-x/\alpha}b(x') \tag{12.17}$$

where $a(x')$ and $b(x')$ are to be determined. Introduction of the function $\eta(x - x')$ (cf. Sec. 8.3) enables one to combine Eqs. (12.16) and (12.17) into a single relation

$$G(x,x') = e^{x/\alpha}a(x')\eta(x' - x) + e^{x/\alpha}b(x')\eta(x - x') \tag{12.18}$$

Then

$$\frac{d}{dx} G(x,x') = \frac{1}{\alpha} e^{x/\alpha}a(x')\eta(x' - x) - \frac{1}{\alpha} e^{-x/\alpha}b(x')\eta(x - x')$$

$$+ \left[e^{-x/\alpha}b(x') - e^{x/\alpha}a(x')\right]\delta(x - x') \tag{12.19}$$

The quantity enclosed in the brackets must vanish for $x = x'$ since otherwise d^2G/dx^2 would contain a term proportional to $d/dx\,\delta(x - x')$ not canceled by any other term in (12.15). Hence

$$e^{-x'/\alpha}b(x') = e^{x'/\alpha}a(x') \equiv c(x')$$

and

$$\frac{d}{dx} G(x,x') = \frac{c(x')}{\alpha} \left[e^{-(x'-x)/\alpha}\eta(x' - x) - e^{-(x-x')/\alpha}\eta(x - x')\right] \tag{12.20}$$

Therefore $\qquad \dfrac{d^2}{dx^2} G(x,x') = \dfrac{1}{\alpha^2} G(x,x') - \dfrac{2}{\alpha} c(x')\, \delta(x - x')$ (12.21)

Comparison of (12.21) with (12.15) then shows that

$$2\alpha c(x') = 1$$

The expression (12.18) for the Green's function now becomes

$$G(x,x') = \frac{1}{2\alpha} \left[e^{x/\alpha} e^{-x'/\alpha} \eta(x' - x) + e^{-x/\alpha} e^{x'/\alpha} \eta(x - x') \right]$$

which is identical with the previously obtained result (12.13).

An interesting property of the first derivative of the Green's function may now be determined. From (12.20) one obtains

$$\frac{d}{dx} G(x,x') \bigg|_{x'+0} - \frac{d}{dx} G(x,x') \bigg|_{x'-0} = -\frac{2c(x')}{\alpha} = -\frac{1}{\alpha^2} \qquad (12.22)$$

where the notation

$$\frac{dG}{dx} \bigg|_{x'+0}$$

means that dG/dx is evaluated at the point x' when x' is approached from values of $x > x'$ while

$$\frac{dG}{dx} \bigg|_{x'-0}$$

is evaluated when x' is approached from the opposite direction. The relation (12.22) states that the first derivative of the Green's function for the operator $\mathscr{L} \equiv -\alpha^2\, d^2/dx^2 + 1$ is discontinuous at the point x', the discontinuity being a jump of amount $-1/\alpha^2$.

12.4 The Operator $-\alpha^2\, d^2/dx^2 + 1$ in a Finite Domain

Consider the inhomogeneous differential equation

$$\mathscr{L}f(x) \equiv \left(-\alpha^2 \frac{d}{dx^2} + 1 \right) f(x) = s(x) \qquad (12.23)$$

with the boundary conditions

$$f(0) = f(a) = 0 \qquad (12.24)$$

The Green's function $G(x,x')$ satisfies the equation

$$\mathscr{L} G(x,x') = \delta(x - x') \qquad (12.25)$$

with the boundary conditions

$$G(0,x') = G(a,x') = 0 \qquad (12.26)$$

The general solution of (12.25) satisfying the boundary conditions (12.26) is

$$G(x,x') = a(x') \sinh \frac{x}{\alpha} \eta(x' - x) + b(x') \sinh \frac{(a - x)}{\alpha} \eta(x - x')$$

where $a(x')$ and $b(x')$ are to be determined. Then

$$\frac{dG}{dx} = \frac{1}{\alpha}\left[a(x') \cosh \frac{x}{\alpha} \eta(x' - x) - b(x') \cosh \frac{a - x}{\alpha} \eta(x - x')\right]$$

$$+ \left[b(x) \sinh \frac{a - x}{\alpha} - a(x) \sinh \frac{x}{\alpha}\right] \delta(x - x')$$

so that
$$b(x') \sinh \frac{a - x'}{\alpha} = a(x') \sinh \frac{x'}{\alpha}$$

If one lets

$$b(x') = c(x') \sinh \frac{x'}{\alpha}$$

it follows that

$$a(x') = c(x') \sinh \frac{a - x'}{\alpha}$$

Then

$$\frac{d^2}{dx^2} G = \frac{1}{\alpha^2} G - \frac{c(x')}{\alpha}\left[\sinh \frac{a - x'}{\alpha} \cosh \frac{x}{\alpha} + \sinh \frac{x'}{\alpha} \cosh \frac{a - x}{\alpha}\right] \delta(x - x')$$

so that
$$\alpha c(x') = \frac{1}{\sinh a/\alpha}$$

Hence

$$G(x,x') = \frac{1}{\alpha \sinh a/\alpha}\left[\sinh \frac{a - x'}{\alpha} \sinh \frac{x}{\alpha} \eta(x' - x)\right.$$

$$\left. + \sinh \frac{x'}{\alpha} \sinh \frac{a - x}{\alpha} \eta(x - x')\right] \quad (12.27)$$

This result may be compared with the corresponding result obtained by using the eigenfunction expansion for the Green's function, namely:

$$G(x,x') = \mathscr{L}^{-1} \delta(x - x')$$

$$= \mathscr{L}^{-1} \frac{2}{a} \sum_{n=1}^{\infty} \sin \frac{n\pi x}{a} \sin \frac{n\pi x'}{a}$$

$$= \frac{2}{a} \sum_{n=1}^{\infty} \frac{\sin (n\pi x/a) \sin (n\pi x'/a)}{1 + (n\pi\alpha/a)^2} \quad (12.28)$$

A third form of the Green's function of the operator $\mathscr{L}$ and the given boundary conditions may be found using the method of images (cf. Sec. 9.6): Thus

$$\delta(x - x') = \frac{2}{a} \sum_{n=1}^{\infty} \sin \frac{n\pi x}{\alpha} \sin \frac{n\pi x'}{\alpha}$$

$$= \sum_{\sigma=-\infty}^{+\infty} [\delta(x - x' + 2\sigma a) - \delta(x + x' + 2\sigma a)]$$

$$= \sum_{\sigma=-\infty}^{+\infty} \frac{1}{2\pi} \int_{-\infty}^{+\infty} [e^{iw(x-x'+2\sigma a)} - e^{iw(x+x'+2\sigma a)}] \, dw$$

Hence $G(x,x') = \mathscr{L}^{-1} \delta(x - x')$

$$= \sum_{\sigma=-\infty}^{+\infty} \frac{1}{2\pi} \int_{-\infty}^{+\infty} \left[\frac{e^{iw(x-x'+2\sigma a)} - e^{iw(x+x'+2\sigma a)}}{1 + \alpha^2 w^2} \right] dw$$

$$= \frac{1}{2\alpha} \sum_{\sigma=-\infty}^{+\infty} [e^{-|x-x'+2\sigma a|/\alpha} - e^{-|x+x'+2\sigma a|/\alpha}] \qquad (12.29)$$

where the integral has been evaluated by the same procedure as used in obtaining the expression (12.13). This form of the Green's function is useful if $\alpha \ll a$, because in this case very few terms in the series are required for a good approximation to the Green's function. Thus, for $0 \le x, x' \le a$, and $\alpha \ll a$,

$$G(x,x') = \frac{1}{2\alpha} [e^{-|x-x'|/\alpha} - e^{-|x+x'|/\alpha} + e^{-|x-x'+2a|/\alpha} - e^{-|x+x'+2a|/\alpha} + \cdots]$$

$$(12.30)$$

12.5   The Operator $-\alpha^2 \nabla^2 + 1$ in Spherical Coordinates

Consider now the inhomogeneous partial differential equation

$$\mathscr{L}f(\mathbf{r}) \equiv (-\alpha^2 \nabla^2 + 1)f(\mathbf{r}) = s(\mathbf{r}) \qquad (12.31)$$

where $\mathbf{r}$ denotes the vector with components $r \sin \theta \cos \phi$, $r \sin \theta \sin \varphi$, $r \cos \theta$ and

$$\nabla^2 \equiv \frac{1}{r^2} \frac{\partial}{\partial r} r^2 \frac{\partial}{\partial r} + \frac{1}{r^2 \sin \theta} \frac{\partial}{\partial \theta} \sin \theta \frac{\partial}{\partial \theta} + \frac{1}{r^2 \sin^2 \theta} \frac{\partial^2}{\partial \varphi^2} \qquad (11.4)$$

It is desired to solve (12.31) subject to the condition that $f(\mathbf{r}) \equiv f(r,\theta,\varphi)$ is bounded for all r. The variables r,θ and φ have the ranges $0 \le r < \infty$, $0 \le \theta \le \pi$, and $0 \le \varphi \le 2\pi$.

For the operator $\mathscr{L}$ and the given boundary condition the Green's function $G(\mathbf{r},\mathbf{r}')$ is

$$G(\mathbf{r},\mathbf{r}') = \mathscr{L}^{-1}\,\delta(\mathbf{r} - \mathbf{r}')$$

$$= \mathscr{L}^{-1} \frac{2}{\pi} \sum_{l,m} \overline{Y_l^m(\theta',\varphi')} Y_l^m(\theta,\varphi) \int_0^\infty j_l(kr)j_l(kr')k^2\,dk$$

$$= \frac{2}{\pi} \sum_{l,m} \overline{Y_l^m(\theta',\varphi')} Y_l^m(\theta,\varphi) \int_0^\infty \frac{j_l(kr)j_l(kr')}{1 + \alpha^2 k^2} k^2\,dk \tag{12.32}$$

where (11.90) has been used.

Introducing the notation

$$g_l(r,r') \equiv \frac{2}{\pi} \int_0^{+\infty} \frac{j_l(kr)j_l(kr')}{1 + \alpha^2 k^2} k^2\,dk \tag{12.33}$$

the expression (12.32) for the Green's function may be written

$$G(\mathbf{r},\mathbf{r}') = \sum_l g_l(r,r') \sum_{m=-l}^{+l} \overline{Y_l^m(\theta',\varphi')} Y_l^m(\theta,\varphi)$$

$$= \sum_l g_l(r,r')\sqrt{\frac{2l + 1}{4\pi}}\, Y_l^0\left(\frac{\mathbf{r} \cdot \mathbf{r}'}{rr'}\right) \tag{12.34}$$

by the use of (11.87). The auxiliary Green's function $g_l(r,r')$ satisfies the equation

$$\left(-\alpha^2 \frac{1}{r^2} \frac{d}{dr} r^2 \frac{d}{dr} + \alpha^2 \frac{l(l+1)}{r^2} + 1\right) g_l(r,r') = \frac{2}{\pi} \int_0^\infty j_l(kr)j_l(kr')k^2\,dk$$

$$= \frac{\delta(r - r')}{r^2} \tag{12.35}$$

with the boundary condition $g_l(r,r')$ finite for all r. This may be verified by using (12.33) and carrying out the indicated operations.

The function $g_l(r,r')$ may be obtained either by evaluating the integral (12.33) or by solving the differential equation (12.35). We shall evaluate the integral (12.33) and leave the solution of Eq. (12.35) as an exercise for the reader.

Since the integrand in (12.33) is an even function of k we may write

$$g_l(r,r') = \frac{1}{\pi} \int_{-\infty}^{+\infty} \frac{j_l(kr)j_l(kr')}{1 + \alpha^2 k^2} k^2\,dk$$

$$= \frac{1}{\pi \alpha^3} \int_{-\infty}^{+\infty} \frac{j_l(rt/\alpha)j_l(r't/\alpha)}{1 + t^2} t^2\,dt \tag{12.36}$$

where $t = \alpha k$. We shall evaluate (12.36) by the use of contour integration (see Appendix 2A).

Consider first the case when $r > r'$. Then, since $j_l(x) = 1/2 [h_l^{(1)}(x) + h_l^{(2)}(x)]$, (12.36) may be written as

$$g_l(r,r') = \frac{1}{2\pi\alpha^3} \left[\int_{-\infty}^{+\infty} \frac{h_l^{(1)}(rt/\alpha)j_l(r't/\alpha)}{1+t^2} t^2 \, dt + \int_{-\infty}^{+\infty} \frac{h_l^{(2)}(rt/\alpha)j_l(r't/\alpha)}{1+t^2} t^2 \, dt \right]$$

$$(12.36a)$$

Since, for $x \to \infty$, $h_l^{(1)}(x) \sim e^{ix}/x$ and $h_l^{(2)}(x) \sim e^{-ix}/x$, the integrand in the first integral on the right behaves like $e^{irt/\alpha}$ while that in the second integral behaves like $e^{-irt/\alpha}$. Consequently, if r/α is positive, the contour for the first integral is completed in a counterclockwise direction along a semicircle of infinite radius, having its center at the origin and lying in the upper half of the complex plane, and encloses the pole $t = i$. In the case of the second integral the semicircle lies in the lower half of the complex plane and the contour is described in the clockwise direction enclosing the pole $t = -i$. Hence

$$g_l(r,r') = \frac{1}{2\pi\alpha^3} \left[2\pi i \frac{h_l^{(1)}(ir/\alpha)j_l(ir'/\alpha)}{2i} - 2\pi i \frac{h_l^{(2)}(-ir/\alpha)j_l(-ir'/\alpha)}{-2i} \right]$$

$$= \frac{1}{2\alpha^3} \left[h_l^{(1)}\left(\frac{ir}{\alpha}\right)j_l\left(\frac{ir'}{\alpha}\right) + h_l^{(2)}\left(\frac{-ir}{\alpha}\right)j_l\left(\frac{-ir'}{\alpha}\right) \right]$$

Since $h_l^{(2)}(\bar{z}) = \overline{h_l^{(1)}(z)}$ and $j_l(\bar{z}) = \overline{j_l(z)}$,

$$g_l(r,r') = \frac{1}{2\alpha^3} \left[h_l^{(1)}\left(\frac{ir}{\alpha}\right)j_l\left(\frac{ir'}{\alpha}\right) + \text{complex conjugate} \right] \quad r > r' \quad \frac{r}{\alpha} > 0$$

$$= \frac{1}{\alpha^3} \text{Re} \left[h_l^{(1)}\left(\frac{ir}{\alpha}\right)j_l\left(\frac{ir'}{\alpha}\right) \right] \quad r > r' \quad r/\alpha > 0 \quad (12.37)$$

When $r/\alpha < 0$, $g_l(r,r')$ is given by (12.37) with r/α replaced by $-r/\alpha$. For $r < r'$ and $r/\alpha > 0$,

$$g_l(r,r') = \frac{1}{\alpha^3} \text{Re} \left[h_l^{(1)}\left(\frac{ir'}{\alpha}\right)j_l\left(\frac{ir}{\alpha}\right) \right] \quad (12.38)$$

Obviously, the solution of (12.31) satisfying the given boundary conditions is

$$f(r,\theta,\varphi) = \int G(\mathbf{r},\mathbf{r}')s(\mathbf{r}') \, d\mathbf{r}' = \sum_l \sqrt{\frac{2l+1}{4\pi}} \int g_l(r,r') Y_l^0\left(\frac{\mathbf{r}\cdot\mathbf{r}'}{rr'}\right) s(\mathbf{r}') \, d\mathbf{r}' \quad (12.39)$$

In the special case when s is a function of r' only, (12.39) reduces to

$$f(r,\theta,\varphi) = \sum_l \sqrt{\frac{2l+1}{4\pi}} \int_{-\infty}^{+\infty} g_l(r,r')s(r')r'^2 \, dr' \int_0^{2\pi}\int_0^{\pi} Y_l^0\left(\frac{\mathbf{r}\cdot\mathbf{r}'}{rr'}\right) \sin\theta \, d\theta \, d\varphi$$

$$= \frac{1}{4\pi} \int_{-\infty}^{\infty} g_0(r,r')s(r')r'^2 \, dr' \quad (12.40)$$

where $g_l(r,r')$ is given by (12.37) and (12.38). In particular

$$g_0(r,r') = \frac{1}{\alpha^3} \operatorname{Re}\left[h_0^{(1)}\left(\frac{ir}{\alpha}\right) j_0\left(\frac{ir}{\alpha}\right)\right] = -\frac{1}{\alpha^3}\frac{e^{-r/\alpha}}{r/\alpha}\frac{\sinh r'/\alpha}{r'/\alpha}$$

for $r > r'$.

Exercises

1. Verify by substitution the solution (12.14) of (12.10).
2. Solve the differential equation (12.35) and verify that the solution is identical with (12.37) and (12.38).
3. Consider the differential equation

$$\mathcal{L}f(x) \equiv \frac{d^2}{dx^2} f(x) = s(x) \qquad 0 \le x \le 1$$

where $s(x)$ is given. Then show by the direct method that (a) the Green's function for the operator $\mathcal{L}$ and the associated boundary conditions $f(0) = f(1) = 0$ is

$$G(x,x') = (1 - x')x \qquad x \le x'$$
$$= (1 - x)x' \qquad x > x'$$

and that (b) the Green's function for the operator $\mathcal{L}$ and the associated boundary conditions

$$f(0) = \frac{df}{dx}\bigg|_{x=1} = 0$$

is

$$G(x,x') = x \qquad x \le x'$$
$$= x' \qquad x > x'$$

4. Show, by the use of the eigenfunction expansions for the Green's functions in Exercise 3, that

$$\frac{2}{\pi^2} \sum_{n=1}^{\infty} \frac{\sin n\pi x \sin n\pi x'}{n^2} = (1 - x')x \qquad x \le x'$$
$$= (1 - x)x' \qquad x > x'$$

and

$$\frac{2}{\pi^2} \sum_{n=0}^{\infty} \frac{\sin (n + \frac{1}{2})\pi x \sin (n + \frac{1}{2})\pi x'}{(n + \frac{1}{2})^2} = x \qquad x \le x'$$
$$= x' \qquad x > x'$$

5. Consider the equation

$$\left(1 - \varkappa^2 \frac{d^2}{dx^2}\right) y(x) = f(x) \qquad 0 \le x \le L$$

where $f(x)$ is given and y satisfies the boundary conditions

$$y(0) = 0 \qquad \frac{dy}{dx}\bigg|_{x=L} = 0$$

Find $G(x,x')$ such that

$$y(x) = \int_0^L G(x,x') f(x') \, dx'$$

References

Ince, E. L.: "Ordinary Differential Equations," chap. XI, Dover Publications, New York, 1944.

Sommerfeld, A.: "Partial Differential Equations in Physics," Academic Press, Inc., New York, 1949.

Courant, R., and D. Hilbert: "Methods of Mathematical Physics," vol. 1, pp. 351–387, Interscience Publishers, Inc., New York, 1953.

Morse, P. M., and H. Feshbach: "Methods of Theoretical Physics," chap. 7, McGraw-Hill Book Company, Inc., New York, 1953.

Webster, A. G.: "Partial Differential Equations of Mathematical Physics," pp. 109–142, 222–238, Dover Publications, New York, 1955.

CHAPTER 13

Radiation and Scattering Problems

13.1 The Outgoing Wave Condition

Consider the propagation of waves outward from a given source. Let c represent the velocity of propagation. Then, the amplitude of the wave $\Psi(\mathbf{r},t)$ at the point $\mathbf{r}$ at time t satisfies both the inhomogeneous wave equation

$$\left(c^2 \nabla^2 - \frac{\partial^2}{\partial t^2}\right)\Psi(\mathbf{r},t) = c^2 S(\mathbf{r},t) \tag{13.1}$$

[where the function $S(\mathbf{r},t)$ represents the source] and an appropriate boundary condition. This boundary condition must take into account the fact that the solution is to correspond to waves traveling outward from the source.

If the source is wholly contained within a region of radius a about the origin of coordinates, then at distances large compared to a one would expect the waves to be of the form

$$\Psi \cong \frac{f(r - ct)}{r} g(\theta, \phi) \tag{13.2}$$

Incoming waves, on the other hand, would be of the form

$$\Psi \cong \frac{f(r + ct)}{r} g(\theta, \varphi)$$

The condition for outgoing waves, the so-called *radiation condition*, may be written

$$\lim_{r \to \infty} \left(\frac{\partial}{\partial r}\Psi + \frac{1}{c}\frac{\partial}{\partial t}\Psi\right) = 0 \tag{13.3}$$

The problem of determining the waves from the source S is therefore that of solving Eq. (13.1) in accordance with either of the equivalent conditions (13.2) or (13.3).

Unfortunately, the conditions (13.2) and (13.3) are difficult to apply. A useful alternative is to modify Eq. (13.1) so that it describes damped waves which decrease in amplitude as they travel. Then one need only seek that solution of this modified equation which vanishes as r approaches infinity. Once this solution is obtained, the damping may be set equal to zero and the solution of (13.1) obtained. For example, one might write in place of Eq. (13.1)

$$\left[c^2\nabla^2 - \left(\frac{\partial}{\partial t} + \eta\right)^2\right]\Psi(\mathbf{r},t) = c^2 S(\mathbf{r},t) \tag{13.4}$$

where $\eta > 0$. A solution of (13.4) is, for large r,

$$r\,\Psi \cong [e^{-(\eta r/c)}f_1(r - ct) + e^{(\eta r/c)}f_2(r + ct)]g(\theta,\varphi)$$

which does indeed describe damped waves.

13.2 The Green's Function Solution

Assume, for convenience, that $S(\mathbf{r},t)$ is a radiation source of definite frequency, i.e.,

$$S(\mathbf{r},t) = (\text{Re})\, s(\mathbf{r})e^{-i\omega t} \tag{13.5}$$

[In writing (13.5) and other similar expressions we shall usually neglect to include the reminder, "Re."] Then, one may write

$$\Psi(\mathbf{r},t) = \psi(\mathbf{r})e^{-i\omega t} \tag{13.6}$$

where substitution into (13.4) shows that $\psi(\mathbf{r})$ satisfies

$$[c^2\nabla^2 - (-i\omega + \eta)^2]\psi(\mathbf{r}) = c^2 s(\mathbf{r}) \tag{13.7}$$

With the substitution

$$k_0 \equiv \frac{\omega + i\eta}{c} \equiv k + i\frac{\eta}{c} \tag{13.8}$$

Eq. (13.7) takes the simpler form

$$(\nabla^2 + k_0{}^2)\psi(\mathbf{r}) = s(\mathbf{r}) \tag{13.9}$$

A solution of Eq. (13.9) is easily obtained: One first finds the Green's function

$$G(\mathbf{r},\mathbf{r}') = (\nabla^2 + k_0{}^2)^{-1}\,\delta(\mathbf{r} - \mathbf{r}')$$

and then uses

$$\psi(\mathbf{r}) = \int G(\mathbf{r},\mathbf{r}')s(\mathbf{r}')\,d\mathbf{r}' \tag{13.10}$$

Since $k_0{}^2$ is complex and the eigenvalues of ∇^2 are real, the operator $(\nabla^2 + k_0{}^2)$ cannot have a zero eigenvalue. Hence the existence of the Green's function G is a possibility.

The Green's function is given by

$$G(\mathbf{r},\mathbf{r}') = (\nabla^2 + k_0{}^2)^{-1}\,\delta(\mathbf{r} - \mathbf{r}')$$
$$= \sum_{l,m} g_l(r,r')\,\overline{Y_l^m(\theta',\varphi')}\,Y_l^m(\theta,\varphi) \qquad (13.11)$$

where

$$g_l(r,r') = \frac{2}{\pi}\int_0^\infty \frac{j_l(\lambda r)j_l(\lambda r')}{k_0{}^2 - \lambda^2}\,\lambda^2\,d\lambda \qquad (13.12)$$

To verify (13.11) and (13.12), note that

$$(\nabla^2 + k_0{}^2)Y_l^m(\theta,\varphi)j_l(\lambda r) = (k_0{}^2 - \lambda^2)Y_l^m(\theta,\varphi)j_l(\lambda r)$$

and recall that

$$\delta(\mathbf{r} - \mathbf{r}') = \frac{2}{\pi}\sum_{l,m}\overline{Y_l^m(\theta',\varphi')}\,Y_l^m(\theta,\varphi)\int_0^\infty j_l(\lambda r)j_l(\lambda r')\lambda^2\,d\lambda \quad (11.90)$$

The auxiliary Green's function $g_l(r,r')$ may be evaluated as follows:[1] Since the integrand in the integral over λ in (13.12) is an even function of λ, this expression may be replaced by

$$g_l(r,r) = \frac{1}{\pi}\int_{-\infty}^{+\infty} \frac{j_l(\lambda r)j_l(\lambda r')}{k_0{}^2 - \lambda^2}\,\lambda^2\,d\lambda \qquad (13.12a)$$

Since

$$\frac{\lambda^2}{\lambda^2 - k_0{}^2} = \frac{\lambda}{2}\left(\frac{1}{\lambda + k_0} + \frac{1}{\lambda - k_0}\right)$$

(13.12a) may be rewritten as

$$g_l(r,r') = -\frac{1}{2\pi}\int_{-\infty}^{+\infty} j_l(\lambda r)j_l(\lambda r')\left(\frac{\lambda}{\lambda + k_0} + \frac{\lambda}{\lambda - k_0}\right)\,d\lambda$$

But

$$\frac{\lambda}{\lambda + k_0} + \frac{\lambda}{\lambda - k_0} = \frac{2\lambda}{\lambda - k_0} + \left(\frac{\lambda}{\lambda + k_0} - \frac{\lambda}{\lambda - k_0}\right)$$

Since the term in parentheses on the right is an odd function of λ, it will make no contribution to the integral. Therefore

$$g_l(r,r') = -\frac{1}{\pi}\int_{-\infty}^{+\infty} j_l(\lambda r)j_l(\lambda r')\,\frac{\lambda}{\lambda - k_0}\,d\lambda \qquad (13.13)$$

We shall integrate (13.13) by the use of contour integration. Since $j_l(x) = 1/2[h_l^{(1)}(x) + h_l^{(2)}(x)]$ and $h_l^{(1)}(x) \simeq e^{ix}/x$, $h_l^{(2)} \simeq e^{-ix}/x$ for

---

[1] See also Sec. 12.5.

$x \to \infty$, the integral will consist of terms behaving like $e^{\pm i\lambda r}e^{\pm i\lambda r'}$. Consider the case $r > r'$. Then the two parts of the term $j_l(\lambda r)$ determine how the contours are to be closed. The $h_l^{(1)}(\lambda r)$ part of $j_l(\lambda r)$ gives a contribution from $\lambda = k_0$ when the contour is closed around the upper half plane. Since the $h_l^{(2)}(\lambda r)$ part causes the contour to be closed around the lower half plane, where no pole is included, it gives zero contribution. Hence,

$$g_l(r,r') = -ik_0 h_l^{(1)}(k_0 r)j_l(k_0 r') \qquad r > r' \qquad (13.14a)$$

A similar calculation in the case where $r < r'$ yields

$$g_l(r,r') = -ik_0 h_l^{(1)}(k_0 r')j_l(k_0 r) \qquad r < r' \qquad (13.14b)$$

Then, using (13.14a and b), (13.11), (13.10), and (13.6), one obtains the amplitude $\Psi(\mathbf{r},t)$ of the damped waves. The amplitude of the undamped waves is given by the limit as $\eta \to 0$. From (13.8) it is clear that this simply requires the replacement of k_0 by $k = \omega/c$.

For $k_0 = k$, Eq. (13.14a) becomes

$$g_l(r,r') = -ik h_l^{(1)}(kr)j_l(kr') \qquad r > r' \qquad (13.15)$$

If one now allows r' to go to zero, a very useful theorem is obtained. Thus

$$g_l(r,0) = 0 \qquad \text{if } l \neq 0$$

$$g_0(r,0) = -\frac{e^{ikr}}{r}$$

Hence $\qquad\qquad G(\mathbf{r},0) = -\frac{1}{4\pi}\frac{e^{ikr}}{r}$

Since the origin of coordinates is irrelevant, it follows that

$$G(\mathbf{r},\mathbf{r}') = -\frac{1}{4\pi}\frac{e^{ik|\mathbf{r}-\mathbf{r}'|}}{|\mathbf{r}-\mathbf{r}'|} \qquad (13.16)$$

A comparison of (13.16) with (13.11) and (13.15) then yields the expansion theorem

$$\frac{1}{4\pi}\frac{e^{ik|\mathbf{r}-\mathbf{r}'|}}{|\mathbf{r}-\mathbf{r}'|} = ik\sum_{l,m} h_l^{(1)}(kr)j_l(kr')\overline{Y_l^m(\theta',\varphi')}Y_l^m(\theta,\varphi) \qquad r > r' \quad (13.17)$$

13.3 The Multipole Expansion

The solution of the inhomogeneous-wave equation as given in (13.10) may be written in a perspicuous form for sources $s(\mathbf{r}')$ which vanish for

$r' > a$ and for field points $\mathbf{r}$ such that $r > a$. In such a case substitution of (13.17) into (13.10) yields

$$\psi(\mathbf{r}) = -i \sum_{l,m} k^{l+1} h_l^{(1)}(kr) Y_l^m(\theta,\varphi) A_l^m \qquad (13.18)$$

where

$$A_l^m = k^{-l} \int \overline{Y_l^m(\theta',\varphi')} j_l(kr') s(\mathbf{r}') \, d\mathbf{r}' \qquad (13.19)$$

The coefficients A_l^m correspond to the 2^l-pole moments of the radiation source $s(\mathbf{r}')$. Specifically, in the limit $ka \to 0$ the A_l^m are proportional to the usual static multipole moments. Thus, in this limit,

$$A_0^0 = \sqrt{\frac{1}{4\pi}} \int s(\mathbf{r}') \, d\mathbf{r}'$$

is the monopole moment (total source strength) within a factor. Similarly,

$$A_1^0 = \frac{1}{2} \sqrt{\frac{1}{3\pi}} \int z' s(\mathbf{r}') \, d\mathbf{r}'$$

where $z' = r' \cos \theta'$, is proportional to the static dipole moment along the z' axis.

The dynamic multipole moments $(ka \neq 0)$ differ from the static moments because of the interference of waves radiated from different parts of the source.

13.4   The Radiation Far From the Source

An expression often useful for the radiation far from the source (i.e., for $r \gg a$) may be obtained as follows: Substitution of (13.16) into (13.10) yields

$$\psi(\mathbf{r}) = -\frac{1}{4\pi} \int \frac{e^{ik|\mathbf{r}-\mathbf{r}'|}}{|\mathbf{r} - \mathbf{r}'|} s(\mathbf{r}') \, d\mathbf{r}' \qquad (13.20)$$

Since, by hypothesis, $r \gg r'$ for all r' such that $s(\mathbf{r}') \neq 0$, one may set $|\mathbf{r} - \mathbf{r}'|$ equal to r in the denominator of the integrand in (13.20). Unless $ka \ll 1$ this approximation is not adequate in the exponential. Here one writes

$$|\mathbf{r} - \mathbf{r}'| = \sqrt{r^2 - 2\mathbf{r} \cdot \mathbf{r}' + r'^2}$$

$$= r \sqrt{1 - 2\mathbf{n} \cdot \frac{\mathbf{r}'}{r} + \frac{r'^2}{r^2}}$$

$$= r - \mathbf{n} \cdot \mathbf{r}' + \cdots \qquad (13.21)$$

where $\mathbf{n}$ is a unit vector along $\mathbf{r}$ and the neglected terms vanish with r'/r. Thus, as r becomes large compared to a, Eq. (13.20) may be written

$$\psi(\mathbf{r}) \simeq -\frac{1}{4\pi}\frac{e^{ikr}}{r}\int e^{-ik\mathbf{n}\cdot\mathbf{r}'}s(\mathbf{r}')\,d\mathbf{r}' \qquad (13.22)$$

Two special cases of this result are often of interest. First consider the case where ka is small. Then one may write

$$e^{-ik\mathbf{n}\cdot\mathbf{r}'} = 1 - ik\mathbf{n}\cdot\mathbf{r}' + \cdots$$

so that
$$\psi(\mathbf{r}) \simeq -\frac{1}{4\pi}\frac{e^{ikr}}{r}\int s(\mathbf{r}')\,d\mathbf{r}' \qquad (13.23)$$

unless the monopole moment vanishes. Should this occur, one obtains, to the next order,

$$\psi(\mathbf{r}) \simeq \frac{1}{4\pi}\frac{e^{ikr}}{r}\,ik\mathbf{n}\cdot\int \mathbf{r}'s(\mathbf{r}')\,d\mathbf{r}' \qquad (13.24)$$

which represents the dipole radiation.

The second special case is that of the spherically symmetric source, $s = s(r')$ only. Here

$$\psi(\mathbf{r}) \simeq -\frac{1}{4\pi}\frac{e^{ikr}}{r}\int e^{-ik\mathbf{n}\cdot\mathbf{r}'}s(r')\,d\mathbf{r}'$$

$$\simeq -\frac{1}{4\pi}\frac{e^{ikr}}{r}2\pi\int_0^\infty\int_0^\pi e^{-ikr'\cos\theta'}s(r')r'^2\sin\theta'\,d\theta'\,dr'$$

$$\simeq -\frac{e^{ikr}}{r}\int_0^\infty \frac{\sin kr'}{kr'}\,s(r')r'^2\,dr' \qquad (13.25)$$

13.5 Radiation from an Infinitely Long Cylinder

Let the origin of coordinates be on the axis of an infinitely long cylindrical source whose circular cross section is of radius a. The time-dependent inhomogeneous wave equation is

$$\left(\nabla^2 - \frac{1}{c^2}\frac{\partial^2}{\partial t^2}\right)\Psi(\mathbf{r},t) = S(\mathbf{r},t) \qquad (13.26)$$

where $\Psi(\mathbf{r},t) \equiv \Psi(r,\theta,t)$, ∇^2 is given by Eq. (10.21), and $S(\mathbf{r},t) \equiv S(r,\theta,t)$ vanishes for $r > a$. Proceeding as before, one obtains the time-independent wave equation

$$(\nabla^2 + k^2)\psi(\mathbf{r}) = s(\mathbf{r}) \qquad (13.27)$$

whose solution is

$$\psi(\mathbf{r}) = \int G(\mathbf{r},\mathbf{r}')s(\mathbf{r}')\,d\mathbf{r}' \qquad (13.28)$$

where the Green's function $G(\mathbf{r},\mathbf{r}')$ is the outgoing solution of

$$(\nabla^2 + k^2)G(\mathbf{r},\mathbf{r}') = \delta(\mathbf{r} - \mathbf{r}')$$

Since, according to (10.47),

$$\delta(\mathbf{r} - \mathbf{r}') = \frac{1}{2\pi} \sum_{n=-\infty}^{+\infty} e^{in(\theta-\theta')} \int_0^\infty J_n(\lambda r)J_n(\lambda r')\lambda \, d\lambda$$

it follows that

$$G(\mathbf{r},\mathbf{r}') = \frac{1}{2\pi} \sum_{n=-\infty}^{+\infty} e^{in(\theta-\theta')} g_n(r,r') \tag{13.29}$$

where
$$g_n(r,r') = \lim_{\eta\to 0} \int_0^\infty \frac{J_n(\lambda r)J_n(\lambda r')}{(k + i\eta/c)^2 - \lambda^2} \lambda \, d\lambda \tag{13.30}$$

One cannot use the contour integral method to find the auxiliary Green's function $g_n(r,r')$ because the integrand in (13.30) is an odd function of λ. However, as is readily verified,

$$\left(\frac{1}{r}\frac{d}{dr}r\frac{d}{dr} - \frac{n^2}{r^2} + k^2\right)g_n(r,r') = \int_0^\infty J_n(\lambda r)J_n(\lambda r')\lambda \, d\lambda$$

$$= \frac{\delta(r - r')}{r} \tag{13.31}$$

Eq. (13.31) may be solved for $g_n(r,r')$. Thus

$$g_n(r,r') = A(r')[J_n(kr)H_n^{(1)}(kr')\eta(r' - r) + J_n(kr')H_n^{(1)}(kr)\eta(r - r')] \tag{13.32}$$

where $A(r')$ is to be determined. Eq. (13.32) takes into account the outgoing waveform of the solution ($H_n^{(1)}$) and the continuity of $g_n(r,r')$ at $r = r'$ as implied by (13.31). Substitution of (13.32) into (13.31) yields

$$A(r)k[H_n^{(1)\prime}(kr)J_n(kr) - J_n'(kr)H_n^{(1)}(kr)] = \frac{1}{r} \tag{13.33}$$

where the prime denotes d/dr. But, if $u(r)$ and $v(r)$ are two independent solutions of (13.31), i.e., if

$$-\frac{d}{dr}r\frac{d}{dr}u(r) = \alpha(r)u(r)$$

$$-\frac{d}{dr}r\frac{d}{dr}v(r) = \alpha(r)v(r)$$

where $\alpha(r) = k^2r - n^2/r$, then

$$\frac{d}{dr}\left[r\left(v\frac{du}{dr} - u\frac{dv}{dr}\right)\right] = 0$$

Application of this result to (13.33) shows that A is a constant. To evaluate this constant value of A, one may use either the asymptotic forms of J_n and $H_n^{(1)}$ or the series representations near the origin. In either case, one finds that $A = -\pi i/2$. Hence

$$g_n(r,r') = -\frac{\pi i}{2} J_n(kr') H_n^{(1)}(kr) \qquad r > r'$$

$$= -\frac{\pi i}{2} J_n(kr) H_n^{(1)}(kr') \qquad r < r' \qquad (13.34)$$

Thus the solution of (13.27) as given by (13.28) is completely determined by (13.29) and (13.34), and the problem has been solved.

13.6   The Scattering Problem

The propagation of a wave of given frequency ω and uniform velocity c in free space is described by the wave equation

$$\left(\nabla^2 - \frac{1}{c^2}\frac{\partial^2}{\partial t^2}\right)\Psi(\mathbf{r},t) = 0$$

or by the Helmholtz equation

$$(\nabla^2 + k^2)\psi(\mathbf{r}) = 0 \qquad (13.35)$$

where $k = \omega/c$. The process of scattering is represented by replacing the zero on the right of (13.35) by $u(\mathbf{r})\psi(\mathbf{r})$, where the function $u(\mathbf{r})$ represents the scatterer. In the propagation of transverse waves on a two-dimensional membrane, for example, $u(\mathbf{r})$ might represent restoring forces proportional to the normal displacement of the membrane, $\psi(\mathbf{r})$. Thus, a typical scattering problem is associated with the equation

$$(\nabla^2 + k^2)\psi(\mathbf{r}) = u(\mathbf{r})\psi(\mathbf{r}) \qquad (13.36)$$

Of course, in many real problems, Eq. (13.36) is an oversimplification. Nevertheless, many of the relevant concepts and techniques may be exemplified by a consideration of this problem, i.e., the scattering of scalar waves. More general problems, such as the scattering of vector waves or electromagnetic waves, will not be treated.

Even if one grants that (13.36) is the relevant equation, one must specify the questions to be asked. A typical experiment might be to create a wave field represented by a solution of (13.35), as, for example, a plane wave traveling in the z direction:

$$\psi = Ae^{ikz}$$

Then, in the presence of the scatterer this ψ does not represent a solution of the physical problem. Rather, one may argue that as a result of the scattering of the incident wave by the scatterer there will be additional outgoing waves from the scatterer. In order to speak thusly of outgoing waves one must localize the scatterer. Only then will the phrase "outgoing waves" have meaning. Consequently, it shall be required that

$$u(\mathbf{r}) = 0 \qquad \text{if } r > a \qquad (13.37)$$

for some a. This condition is stronger than needed but not so strong as to alter many relevant considerations.

As a result of the above discussion the problem to be solved may be stated as follows: It is desired to find a function ψ satisfying the conditions

(1) $$(\nabla^2 + k^2)\psi(\mathbf{r}) = u(\mathbf{r})\psi(\mathbf{r})$$

and (2) $$\psi = \psi_{\text{incident}} + \psi_{\text{outgoing}}$$

in which ψ_{out} has the asymptotic form

$$\psi_{\text{out}} \simeq f(\theta,\varphi)\frac{e^{ikr}}{r}$$

for large r, and ψ_{inc} satisfies

$$(\nabla^2 + k^2)\psi_{\text{inc}} = 0$$

but may otherwise be arbitrarily specified.

We shall, in fact, limit our detailed considerations to the case in which

$$\psi_{\text{inc}} = e^{ikz} \qquad (13.38)$$

13.7   The Scattering Cross Section

As was pointed out in Sec. 13.6 one seeks a solution of

$$(\nabla^2 + k^2)\psi(\mathbf{r}) = u(\mathbf{r})\psi(\mathbf{r})$$

in the form

$$\psi = e^{ikz} + \psi_{\text{out}} \qquad (13.39)$$

where for r large compared with both a and $1/k$

$$\psi_{\text{out}} \simeq f(\theta,\varphi)\frac{e^{ikr}}{r} \qquad (13.40)$$

The function $f(\theta,\varphi)$ is known as the *scattering amplitude* and

$$\sigma(\theta,\varphi) = |f(\theta,\varphi)|^2 \qquad (13.41)$$

is called the *differential scattering cross section*. From (13.39) and (13.40) it is clear that $f(\theta,\varphi)$ has the dimensions of a length so that σ has the dimensions of an area.

The physical interpretation of the differential scattering cross section σ is not difficult to obtain. The incident wave of (13.39) has a density of $|\psi_{\text{inc}}|^2 = |e^{ikz}|^2 = 1$, so that it corresponds to an incident current density of $c|\psi_{\text{inc}}|^2 = c$. According to (13.40), the outgoing wave at large r corresponds to a radial outward current density of

$$c\,\frac{|f|^2}{r^2}$$

The current through an element of area dS normal to $\mathbf{r}$ is therefore

$$c\,\frac{|f|^2}{r^2}\,dS$$

Since $\dfrac{dS}{r^2}$ is the solid angle subtended at $r = 0$ by the area element dS (normal to $\mathbf{r}$), it follows that $c|f|^2$ is the scattered current density per unit solid angle due to the incident current density c per unit area. Thus, if I denotes the current density (per unit area) of an incident plane wave along the polar axis, $I\sigma(\theta,\varphi)$ is the scattered current density per unit solid angle in the direction θ,φ. The total scattered current is then

$$I\iint \sigma(\theta,\varphi)\,\sin\theta\,d\theta\,d\varphi.$$

As is clear from the above discussion, the scattering problem is basically that of determining the differential scattering cross section $\sigma(\theta,\varphi)$, although one may also have use for the scattering amplitude $f(\theta,\varphi)$. In the two following sections two different approaches to the problem will be considered.

13.8 The Method of Partial Waves

If the function $u(\mathbf{r})$ which represents the scatterer is independent of the angles θ and φ, i.e., if $u = u(r)$ only, the equation of scattering,

$$(\nabla^2 + k^2)\psi(r,\theta,\varphi) = u(r)\psi(r,\theta,\varphi) \tag{13.42}$$

can be replaced by an ordinary differential equation in r. The angular dependence is trivial. Thus, in such a case, Eq. (13.42) may be written as

$$\left(\frac{1}{r^2}\frac{\partial}{\partial r}r^2\frac{\partial}{\partial r} - \frac{L^2}{r^2} + k^2\right)\psi(r,\theta,\varphi) = u(r)\psi(r,\theta,\varphi) \tag{13.43}$$

where the Legendrian L^2 is defined by the relations (11.10).

We seek solutions of (13.43) in the form

$$\psi(r,\theta,\varphi) = Y_l^m(\theta,\varphi) f_l(r) \tag{13.44}$$

where the functions f_l satisfy

$$\left[\frac{1}{r^2}\frac{d}{dr} r^2 \frac{d}{dr} - \frac{l(l+1)}{r^2} + k^2\right] f_l(r) = u(r) f_l(r) \tag{13.45}$$

and the normalized spherical harmonics Y_l^m satisfy

$$L^2 Y_l^m(\theta,\varphi) = l(l+1) Y_l^m(\theta,\varphi) \tag{13.46}$$

Since the $Y_l^m(\theta,\varphi)$ form a complete set of functions in the variable θ and φ, any solution of (13.43) may be obtained by a superposition of solutions of the form of (13.44).

Decompose the wave function ψ of (13.44) into an incident wave ψ_{inc} and a scattered wave ψ_{out}:

$$\psi = \psi_{\text{inc}} + \psi_{\text{out}} \tag{13.47}$$

Then, since $(\nabla^2 + k^2)\psi_{\text{inc}} = 0$, it follows that (cf. Sec. 11.6)

$$\psi_{\text{inc}} = j_l(kr) Y_l^m(\theta,\varphi) \tag{13.48}$$

to within an arbitrary multiplicative constant. Hence, one seeks functions α_l such that for large r

$$f_l(r) \cong j_l(kr) + \alpha_l \frac{e^{ikr}}{r} \tag{13.49}$$

Since the asymptotic form of $j_l(kr)$ is

$$j_l(kr) \cong \frac{\cos(kr - \eta_l)}{kr}$$

$$\cong \frac{e^{i(kr-\eta_l)}}{2kr} + \frac{e^{-i(kr-\eta_l)}}{2kr}$$

where $\eta_l = (l+1)\pi/2$, Eq. (13.49) may be written in the equivalent form

$$f_l(r) \cong \frac{e^{ikr}}{r}\left(\frac{e^{-i\eta_l}}{2k} + \alpha_l\right) + \frac{e^{-ikr}}{r}\frac{e^{i\eta_l}}{2k} \tag{13.49a}$$

Once the α_l are found, it follows: if

$$\psi_{\text{inc}} = j_l(kr) Y_l^m(\theta,\varphi)$$

then

$$\psi_{\text{out}} = \alpha_l \frac{e^{ikr}}{r} Y_l^m(\theta,\varphi) \tag{13.50}$$

Before considering the determination of the α_l, it may be worthwhile to demonstrate, for the case where $\psi_{\text{inc}} = e^{ikz}$, how a knowledge of the α_l determines ψ_{out} and hence $f(\theta,\varphi)$. Use the expansion formula

$$e^{ikz} = \sum_{l=0}^{\infty} i^l \sqrt{4\pi(2l+1)} j_l(kr) Y_l^0(\theta) \qquad (11.86)$$

Then, from the result (13.50), it follows that

$$\psi_{\text{out}} = \sum_{l=0}^{\infty} \alpha_l i^l \sqrt{4\pi(2l+1)} \frac{e^{ikr}}{r} Y_l^0(\theta) \qquad (13.51)$$

and consequently $\quad f(\theta,\varphi) = \sum_{l=0}^{\infty} \alpha_l i^l \sqrt{4\pi(2l+1)} Y_l^0(\theta) \qquad (13.52)$

Thus, the solution of the scattering problem for spherically symmetric u has been reduced to the determination of the α_l. Each α_l is found, using the definition (13.49), by solving the ordinary differential equation (13.45) for f_l. This may be done numerically, if other methods fail.

As defined, α_l may be and usually is complex. However, it is easily demonstrated that only one real parameter is necessary to specify α_l. This result is a consequence of the form of (13.45). Specifically, it will be shown that the solution of Eq. (13.45) may be written in the form $Cg(r)$, where C is a constant and $g(r)$ is a real function of r. To demonstrate this, let f_l denote any solution of (13.45). Then, by taking the complex conjugate of (13.45), it is clear that $\bar{f}_l$ is also a solution. Two real solutions of (13.45) are, therefore, $f_l + \bar{f}_l$ and $i(f_l - \bar{f}_l)$. Obviously, they cannot both vanish. Hence a real solution of (13.45) has been found. Since the solution must be finite at $r = 0$, it may depend on only one arbitrary constant. The general solution therefore has the required form $Cg(r)$, with real g. Application of this result to (13.49a) shows that

$$\left| \frac{e^{-i\eta_l}}{2k} + \alpha_l \right| = \left| \frac{e^{i\eta_l}}{2k} \right|$$

or, introducing the real quantity δ_l,

$$\frac{e^{-i\eta_l}}{2k} + \alpha_l = e^{i2(\delta_l - \eta_l)} \frac{e^{i\eta_l}}{2k}$$

This form was chosen so that $\delta_l = 0$ implies $\alpha_l = 0$. Solving for α_l, one obtains

$$\alpha_l = \frac{e^{-i\eta_l}}{2k}(e^{i2\delta_l} - 1) \qquad (13.53)$$

which shows that the complex number α_l is determined uniquely by the single real parameter δ_l.

Substitution of (13.53) into (13.49a) yields

$$f_l(r) \simeq e^{i\delta_l} \frac{\cos(kr - \eta_l + \delta_l)}{kr} \tag{13.54}$$

Comparison of this result with the asymptotic form of the incident wave, namely,

$$j_l(kr) \simeq \frac{\cos(kr - \eta_l)}{kr}$$

shows that the major difference in the waves arises from a shift of amount δ_l in the values of kr at which the zeros of the solutions occur. For this reason δ_l is known as the *phase shift for the lth partial wave* which is due to the scattering potential $u(r)$. Whenever the solutions $f_l(r)$ are known, the phase shifts δ_l may be determined by an examination of these functions. This procedure is illustrated in the example below.

Before proceeding to the example, we complete the above discussion of the case where $\psi_{inc} = e^{ikz}$ by rewriting the expression (13.52) for the scattering amplitude in terms of the phase shifts δ_l:

$$f(\theta,\varphi) = \sum_{l=0}^{\infty} i^l \sqrt{4\pi(2l+1)} Y_l^0(\theta) \frac{e^{-i\eta_l}}{2k} (e^{i2\delta_l} - 1) \tag{13.55}$$

The total scattering cross section may then be written

$$\int \sigma(\theta,\varphi) \sin\theta \, d\theta \, d\varphi = \frac{4\pi}{k^2} \sum_{l=0}^{\infty} (2l+1) \sin^2 \delta_l \tag{13.56}$$

Example: Scattering by a Square Well

Consider the problem of the scattering from the spherically symmetric square-well potential

$$u(r) = \text{const} = U \qquad r < a$$
$$= 0 \qquad r > a$$

The solution of the equation of scattering for $r < a$ is

$$f_l(r) = j_l(\nu r) \qquad r < a$$

where $\nu^2 = k^2 - U$. The solution for $r > a$ may be written

$$f_l(r) = A j_l(kr) + B j_{-l-1}(kr) \qquad r > a$$

where A and B are constants to be determined.

As is evident from (13.45), both f_l and $f_l' (\equiv df_l/dr)$ are continuous at $r = a$. Therefore,

$$\frac{v j_l'(va)}{j_l(va)} = \frac{k[A j_l'(ka) + B j_{-l-1}'(ka)]}{A j_l(ka) + B j_{-l-1}(ka)}$$

so that

$$\frac{B}{A} = -\frac{v j_l'(va) j_l(ka) - k j_l'(ka) j_l(va)}{v j_l'(va) j_{-l-1}(ka) - k j_{-l-1}'(ka) j_l(va)}$$

For large r

$$krf_l \simeq A \cos(kr - \eta_l) + B \cos(kr - \eta_{-l-1})$$

$$\simeq A \cos(kr - \eta_l) + (-1)^{l+1} B \sin(kr - \eta_l)$$

But $\cos(kr - \eta_l + \delta_l) = \cos \delta_l \cos(kr - \eta_l) - \sin \delta_l \sin(kr - \eta_l)$

Hence

$$\tan \delta_l = (-1)^l \frac{B}{A}$$

which determines δ_l and so solves the problem. However, some discussion of the result is in order. First of all, consider the behavior of B/A for small ka. In this case, as is readily verified, δ_l becomes rapidly smaller as l increases. For small enough ka, one may restrict consideration to δ_0. Since

$$j_0(x) = \frac{\sin x}{x} \quad \text{and} \quad j_{-1}(x) = \frac{\cos x}{x}$$

it follows that

$$\tan \delta_0 = \frac{\cot ka - (v/k) \cot va}{(v/k) \cot va \cot ka + 1}$$

But, from the trigonometric formula for $\cot(\delta_0 + ka)$,

$$\tan \delta_0 = \frac{\cot ka - \cot(\delta_0 + ka)}{\cot(\delta_0 + ka) \cot ka + 1}$$

Therefore

$$\cot(\delta_0 + ka) = \frac{v}{k} \cot va$$

or

$$\tan(\delta_0 + ka) = \frac{k}{v} \tan va$$

and

$$\delta_0 = \tan^{-1}\left(\frac{k}{v} \tan va\right) - ka$$

As k tends to zero, so does, in general, δ_0. The total scattering cross section, $\frac{4\pi}{k^2} \sin^2 \delta_0$, however, tends to the finite limit

$$4\pi a^2 \left(\frac{\tan \sqrt{-Ua}}{\sqrt{-Ua}} - 1\right)^2$$

13.9 The Born Approximation

The method of partial waves discussed in the preceding section is useful in those cases for which ka is small. This is because in such cases the phase shifts δ_l are negligible for all but the first few values of l. This statement may be verified for the scattering by a square well considered above and may be shown to be true in general. On the other hand, the method of partial waves becomes impractical in those cases where ka is large. An approximation procedure especially designed for this domain is the so-called "Born approximation."[1]

Since one desires solutions of the equation of scattering

$$(\nabla^2 + k^2)\psi = u(\mathbf{r})\psi \tag{13.57}$$

in the form

$$\psi = \psi_{\text{inc}} + \psi_{\text{out}} \tag{13.58}$$

where ψ_{inc} satisfies

$$(\nabla^2 + k^2)\psi_{\text{inc}} = 0 \tag{13.59}$$

one may rewrite (13.57) as

$$(\nabla^2 + k^2)\psi_{\text{out}} = u(\mathbf{r})\psi \tag{13.60}$$

Since ψ_{out} must be of the form of outgoing waves, the operator $\mathscr{L} = (\nabla^2 + k^2)$ must have an inverse, $\mathscr{L}^{-1}$, such that the Green's function, $G(\mathbf{r},\mathbf{r}') = \mathscr{L}^{-1}\,\delta(\mathbf{r} - \mathbf{r}')$, is given by (13.16). Thus one has

$$
\begin{aligned}
\psi_{\text{out}} &= \mathscr{L}^{-1}u(\mathbf{r})\psi \\
&= -\frac{1}{4\pi}\int \frac{e^{ik|\mathbf{r}-\mathbf{r}'|}}{|\mathbf{r}-\mathbf{r}'|}\,u(\mathbf{r}')\psi(\mathbf{r}')\,d\mathbf{r}'
\end{aligned} \tag{13.61}
$$

To obtain an approximate solution of (13.60) proceed as follows:

$$\psi_{\text{out}} = \mathscr{L}^{-1}u(\mathbf{r})\psi = \mathscr{L}^{-1}u(\mathbf{r})\psi_{\text{inc}} + \mathscr{L}^{-1}u(\mathbf{r})\psi_{\text{out}}$$

Hence

$$(1 - \mathscr{L}^{-1}u)\psi_{\text{out}} = \mathscr{L}^{-1}u\psi_{\text{inc}}$$

and

$$
\begin{aligned}
\psi_{\text{out}} &= (1 - \mathscr{L}^{-1}u)^{-1}\mathscr{L}^{-1}u\psi_{\text{inc}} \\
&= (1 + \mathscr{L}^{-1}u + \mathscr{L}^{-1}u\mathscr{L}^{-1}u + \cdots)\mathscr{L}^{-1}u\psi_{\text{inc}}
\end{aligned}
$$

The first term in the series on the right yields the first Born approximation, the first two terms the second Born approximation, etc.

We confine our attention to the first Born approximation

$$
\begin{aligned}
\psi_{\text{out}}(\mathbf{r}) &= \mathscr{L}^{-1}u(\mathbf{r})\psi_{\text{inc}}(\mathbf{r}) \\
&= -\frac{1}{4\pi}\int \frac{e^{ik|\mathbf{r}-\mathbf{r}'|}}{|\mathbf{r}-\mathbf{r}'|}\,u(\mathbf{r}')\psi_{\text{inc}}(\mathbf{r}')\,d\mathbf{r}'
\end{aligned} \tag{13.62}
$$

[1] M. Born, *Zeits. f. Physik*, **38**, 803 (1926).

Note that (13.62) differs from (13.61) only by the replacement of ψ in the integrand of (13.61) by ψ_{inc}. One may readily make plausible physical arguments to justify this in the case of large ka.

In any case, if one accepts the approximation (13.62), the scattering amplitude $f(\theta, \varphi)$ is easily obtained. Thus, setting $\psi_{inc} = e^{ikz}$, one obtains

$$\psi_{out}(\mathbf{r}) = -\frac{1}{4\pi} \int \frac{e^{ik|\mathbf{r}-\mathbf{r}'|}}{|\mathbf{r}-\mathbf{r}'|} u(\mathbf{r}')e^{ikz'} \, d\mathbf{r}'$$

This expression is of precisely the same form as (13.20). Hence, from (13.22),

$$\psi_{out}(\mathbf{r}) \simeq -\frac{1}{4\pi} \frac{e^{ikr}}{r} \int e^{-ik\mathbf{n}\cdot\mathbf{r}'} u(\mathbf{r}')e^{ikz'} \, d\mathbf{r}'$$

$$= -\frac{1}{4\pi} \frac{e^{ikr}}{r} \int e^{ik(\mathbf{n}_0-\mathbf{n})\cdot\mathbf{r}'} u(\mathbf{r}') \, d\mathbf{r}' \tag{13.63}$$

where $\mathbf{n}$ is a unit vector in the direction of $\mathbf{r}$, and $\mathbf{n}_0$ is a unit vector along the z axis. It then follows that

$$f(\theta,\varphi) = -\frac{1}{4\pi} \int e^{ik(\mathbf{n}_0-\mathbf{n})\cdot\mathbf{r}'} u(\mathbf{r}') \, d\mathbf{r}' \tag{13.64}$$

This is the final result in the first Born approximation.

In the special case when $u(\mathbf{r}')$ is spherically symmetric, Eq. (13.64) takes on the simpler form

$$f(\theta,\varphi) = -\int_0^\infty \frac{\sin Kr}{Kr} u(r)r^2 \, dr \tag{13.65}$$

where
$$K = 2k \sin \tfrac{1}{2}\theta$$

The Born approximation may also be used in conjunction with the partial wave picture to obtain expressions for the phase shifts. Thus, Eq. (13.45) for the functions f_l may be replaced by

$$\left[\frac{1}{r^2}\frac{d}{dr}r^2\frac{d}{dr} - \frac{l(l+1)}{r^2} + k^2\right]f_{l,out} = u(r)f_l \tag{13.66}$$

since
$$\left[\frac{1}{r^2}\frac{d}{dr}r^2\frac{d}{dr} - \frac{l(l+1)}{r^2} + k^2\right]f_{l,inc} = 0$$

Then, replacing f_l in the right-hand member of (13.66) by $f_{l,inc} = j_l(kr)$ and using the auxiliary Green's function $g_l(r,r')$, one finds that

$$f_{l,out} \simeq -ikh_l^{(1)}(kr)\int_0^\infty u(r')[j_l(kr')]^2 r'^2 \, dr'$$

$$\simeq -i\frac{e^{ikr}}{r} e^{-i\eta_l}\int_0^\infty u(r')[j_l(kr')]^2 r'^2 \, dr'$$

Comparing this result with (13.49) and using (13.53) one obtains

$$e^{i2\delta_l} - 1 = -2ki \int_0^\infty u(r')[j_l(kr')]^2 r'^2 \, dr'$$

This result can hold only for small δ_l, since otherwise the left-hand side is not pure imaginary whereas the right is. Therefore, for small δ_l, the Born approximation expression for the phase shifts is

$$\delta_l = -k \int_0^\infty u(r)[j_l(kr)]^2 r^2 \, dr \tag{13.67}$$

13.10   Gratings

In the scattering of electromagnetic radiation one is often led to consider scattering from a regular array of scattering centers, e.g., the diffraction grating. While, as previously stated, vector waves will not be

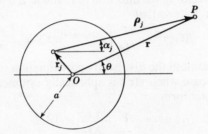

Figure 13.1

treated, we shall consider here the (simpler) corresponding problem for scalar waves. The treatment may be applied, for example, to the analysis of the diffraction of sound by an acoustical grating.

Suppose that there are n scattering centers in an incident radiation field. To a first approximation, the waves scattered by each scattering center (i.e., the outgoing waves) may be considered to be independent of the presence of the other scatterers. This approximation is certainly valid if the incident wave at the scattering center is strong compared to the waves coming from the other scatterers. In any case, this assumption will be made in the following discussion.

Let $\mathbf{r}$ denote the vector from the origin of coordinates to the field point P at which it is desired to determine the scattered wave, $\mathbf{r}_j (j = 1, 2, \ldots, n)$ the vector from the origin to the jth scatterer, and $\boldsymbol{\rho}_j$ the vector from the jth scatterer to the field point P (Fig. 13.1). Then

$$\mathbf{r} = \mathbf{r}_j + \boldsymbol{\rho}_j \tag{13.68}$$

Assume that $r_j < a$, for all scatterers, where $r \gg a$. That is, assume that all the n scatterers may be contained within a sphere of radius $a \ll r$. Then, if the incident wave is given by

$$\psi_{\text{inc}} = e^{ikz} = e^{ikr\cos\theta} \tag{13.69}$$

the asymptotic form of the wave scattered from the jth scatterer is

$$\psi_{j,\text{out}} \simeq f(\alpha_j, \beta_j) \frac{e^{ik(\rho_j + z_j)}}{\rho_j} \tag{13.70}$$

where the phase has been taken to be zero at the origin. The total scattered wave due to the n scatterers is therefore

$$\psi_{\text{out}} \simeq \sum_{j=1}^{n} f(\alpha_j, \beta_j) \frac{e^{ik(\rho_j + z_j)}}{\rho_j} \tag{13.71}$$

When $r \gg a$, this becomes to the first approximation in a/r

$$\psi_{\text{out}} \simeq f(\theta, \varphi) \frac{e^{ikr}}{r} \sum_{j=1}^{n} e^{ik(z_j - \mathbf{n} \cdot \mathbf{r}_j)} \tag{13.72}$$

where $\mathbf{n} = \mathbf{r}/r$. This result is about as far as one can go without further specification of the $\mathbf{r}_j$.

Now assume that the n scatterers are uniformly spaced along a line:

$$\mathbf{r}_j = j\mathbf{b} \qquad j = 1, 2, \ldots, n \tag{13.73}$$

Then, if $\mathbf{n}_0$ denotes a unit vector along the z direction,

$$z_j = \mathbf{n}_0 \cdot \mathbf{r}_j = j\mathbf{n}_0 \cdot \mathbf{b}$$

and (13.72) becomes

$$\psi_{\text{out}} \simeq f(\theta, \varphi) \frac{e^{ikr}}{r} \sum_{j=1}^{n} e^{ikj(\mathbf{n}_0 - \mathbf{n}) \cdot \mathbf{b}} \tag{13.74}$$

The summation in (13.74) is readily evaluated: for convenience, let $\mu \equiv k(\mathbf{n}_0 - \mathbf{n}) \cdot \mathbf{b}$. Then

$$\sum_{j=1}^{n} e^{ij\mu} = e^{i\mu(n+1)/2} \sum_{j=1}^{n} e^{i\mu[j-(n+1)/2]}$$

$$= e^{i\mu(n+1)/2} \sum_{l=-(n-1)/2}^{(n-1)/2} e^{il\mu}$$

But, for c an arbitrary constant,

$$(x^{\frac{1}{2}} - x^{-\frac{1}{2}})(x^{-c} + x^{-c+1} + \cdots + x^{c-1} + x^c) \equiv x^{c+\frac{1}{2}} - x^{-c-\frac{1}{2}}$$

Hence
$$\sum_{j=1}^{n} e^{ij\mu} = e^{i\mu(n+1)/2} \frac{e^{i\mu n/2} - e^{-i\mu n/2}}{e^{i\mu/2} - e^{-i\mu/2}}$$

$$= e^{i\mu(n+1)/2} \frac{\sin (\mu n/2)}{\sin \mu/2}$$

Therefore
$$|\psi_{\text{out}}|^2 \simeq \frac{|f(\theta,\varphi)|^2}{r^2} \frac{\sin^2 [k(\mathbf{n}_0 - \mathbf{n}) \cdot \mathbf{b}n/2]}{\sin^2 [k(\mathbf{n}_0 - \mathbf{n}) \cdot \mathbf{b}/2]} \qquad (13.75)$$

This result contains the diffraction effect which was sought.

The first factor in (13.75), $|f(\theta,\varphi)|^2/r^2$, is just the intensity pattern from a single scatterer. The new factor,

$$\frac{\sin^2 \mu n/2}{\sin^2 n/2} \equiv \frac{\sin^2 [k(\mathbf{n}_0 - \mathbf{n}) \cdot \mathbf{b}n/2]}{\sin^2 [k(\mathbf{n}_0 - \mathbf{n}) \cdot \mathbf{b}/2]}$$

the so-called "Bragg" factor, may be said to give the *interference pattern* for the n scatterers. For $\mu = 0, 2\pi, 4\pi, \ldots$, it possesses maximum values equal to n^2. It is equal to zero when $\mu = 2m\pi/n$, where m is an integer and m/n is not.

The relation
$$\mu = k(\mathbf{n}_0 - \mathbf{n}) \cdot \mathbf{b} = 2m\pi \qquad m = 0, 1, 2, \ldots \qquad (13.76)$$

is the *grating equation*. If one makes the substitutions

$$\mathbf{n}_0 \cdot \mathbf{b} = -b \sin i$$

where i is the angle of incidence, and

$$\mathbf{n} \cdot \mathbf{b} = b \sin \theta$$

where θ is the angle of diffraction, and if one recalls that $k = 2\pi/\lambda$, Eq. (13.76) takes on the more customary form

$$b(\sin i + \sin \theta) = \frac{2m\pi}{k} = m\lambda \qquad (13.77)$$

found in books on physical optics.

Consider now a regular two-dimensional array of n scatterers. Let the location of the scatterers be given by

$$\mathbf{r}_{\alpha\beta} = \alpha\mathbf{b} + \beta\mathbf{c}$$

where $\mathbf{b}$ and $\mathbf{c}$ are not collinear and $\alpha = 1, 2, \ldots, A; \beta = 1, 2, \ldots, B;$ and $AB = n$. If one applies to this situation the result (13.72) he obtains

$$\psi_{\text{out}} \simeq f(\theta,\varphi) \frac{e^{ikr}}{r} \sum_{\alpha=1}^{A} \sum_{\beta=1}^{B} e^{ik(\mathbf{n}_0 - \mathbf{n}) \cdot (\alpha\mathbf{b} + \beta\mathbf{c})}$$

The conditions for a maximum are then

$$(\mathbf{n}_0 - \mathbf{n}) \cdot \mathbf{b} = L\lambda$$
$$(\mathbf{n}_0 - \mathbf{n}) \cdot \mathbf{c} = M\lambda \qquad (13.78)$$

where L and M are integers or zero.

Provided that λ is not too large, there will always exist an $\mathbf{n}$ satisfying the conditions (13.78) in a three-dimensional problem. A more interesting problem is to determine the circumstances under which a solution to (13.78) will exist with both $\mathbf{n}_0$ and $\mathbf{n}$ lying in the $\mathbf{b},\mathbf{c}$ plane. In this case, since two components of $\mathbf{n}_0 - \mathbf{n}$ are specified by (13.78) for given L, M, and λ, $\mathbf{n}_0 - \mathbf{n}$ is determined. The additional condition that $\mathbf{n}_0$ and $\mathbf{n}$ are both unit vectors completes the determination of both $\mathbf{n}_0$ and $\mathbf{n}$. (Note that since $\mathbf{b}$ and $\mathbf{c}$ are not collinear by hypothesis, L and M cannot both be zero.)

Since the location of the various scatterers is given by the vector $\mathbf{r}_{\alpha\beta} = \alpha\mathbf{b} + \beta\mathbf{c}$, where α and β are integers, it is clear that a line with the direction $M\mathbf{b} - L\mathbf{c}$ will pass through some of the scatterers. The remaining scatterers will be on lines parallel to this direction. But by (13.78)

$$(\mathbf{n}_0 - \mathbf{n}) \cdot (M\mathbf{b} - L\mathbf{c}) = 0 \qquad (13.79)$$

Therefore, $\mathbf{n}_0 - \mathbf{n}$ is perpendicular to the line through the scatterers which has direction $M\mathbf{b} - L\mathbf{c}$. Furthermore, it follows from (13.79) and the fact that $\mathbf{n}_0$ and $\mathbf{n}$ are both unit vectors that $\mathbf{n}_0$ and $\mathbf{n}$ make equal angles with the direction $M\mathbf{b} - L\mathbf{c}$. Consequently, the diffraction may be considered as a reflection from a line in this direction.

It is further useful to calculate the distance d between two adjacent lines through the scatterers with the direction $M\mathbf{b} - L\mathbf{c}$. The distance d will be given by the minimum value (greater than zero) of the projection on $\mathbf{n}_0 - \mathbf{n}$ of any line connecting two lattice points. Thus

$$d = \text{minimum of } \mathbf{r}_{\alpha\beta} \cdot \frac{(\mathbf{n}_0 - \mathbf{n})}{|\mathbf{n}_0 - \mathbf{n}|}$$

$$= \text{minimum of } (\alpha\mathbf{b} + \beta\mathbf{c}) \cdot \frac{(\mathbf{n}_0 - \mathbf{n})}{|\mathbf{n}_0 - \mathbf{n}|}$$

$$= \text{minimum of } \frac{(\alpha L + \beta M)}{|\mathbf{n}_0 - \mathbf{n}|} \lambda$$

by reason of (13.78). If ν denotes the greatest common denominator of L and M, then the minimum positive value of $(\alpha L + \beta M)$ is ν. Hence

$$\nu\lambda = d|\mathbf{n}_0 - \mathbf{n}| = 2d \sin \theta \qquad (13.80)$$

where θ is the angle of incidence on (or, equivalently, reflection from) the line in the direction $M\mathbf{b} - L\mathbf{c}$. The integer ν is known as the *order of the diffraction*.

Exercises

1. A plane wave is traveling in a direction perpendicular to the axis of a cylinder of radius a. Discuss the problem of the scattering from the cylinder.

2. Given the spherically symmetric potentials

(a)
$$U(r) = \text{const} \qquad r \le a$$
$$= 0 \qquad r > a$$

(b)
$$U(r) = \text{const} \qquad r \le a$$
$$= \frac{e^{-\mu r}}{\mu r} \qquad r > a$$

(c)
$$U(r) = \mu(1/a - 1/r) \qquad r \le a$$
$$= 0 \qquad r > a$$

where μ is a real positive constant, find in the Born approximation the scattering amplitudes $f(\theta, \varphi)$.

3. The potential field of a nucleus of charge Ze, surrounded by a spherically symmetric distribution $\rho(r)$ of electrons, sufficient to make a neutral atom, is

$$U(r) = \frac{4\pi}{r} \int_r^\infty \rho(r) r^2 \, dr - 4\pi \int_r^\infty \rho(r) r \, dr \qquad 4\pi \int_0^\infty \rho(r) r^2 \, dr = Ze^2$$

Find the Born approximation expression for the scattering amplitude in the case of a plane wave scattered by the atom. Discuss the limiting values obtained for k large and k small.

4. Compute by the method of partial waves the scattering from a perfectly rigid sphere, which is represented by the potential

$$U(r) = +\infty \qquad r < a$$
$$= 0 \qquad r > a$$

5. Verify that the solution of Eq. (13.45) may be written

$$f_l(r) = j_l(kr) + \int_0^\infty g_l(r,r') u(r') f_l(r') r'^2 \, dr'$$

and that the phase shifts δ_l satisfy

$$\tfrac{1}{2}(e^{2i\delta_l} - 1) = -ik \int_0^\infty j_l(kr) u(r) f_l(r) r^2 \, dr$$

References

Mott, N. F., and H. S. W. Massey: "Theory of Atomic Collisions," 2d ed., chaps. II, VI, and VII, Oxford University Press, New York, 1949.

Schiff, L. I.: "Quantum Mechanics," chap. V and chap. VII, sec. 26, McGraw-Hill Book Company, Inc., New York, 1949.

Sommerfeld, A.: "Partial Differential Equations in Physics," chap. V, Academic Press, Inc., New York, 1949.

Morse, P. M., and H. Feshbach: "Methods of Theoretical Physics," pars. 9.3 and 11.3, McGraw-Hill Book Company, Inc., New York, 1953.

Part Three

APPROXIMATE METHODS

CHAPTER 14

Perturbation of Eigenvalues

14.1 Introduction

As seen in the preceding chapters, one is often concerned with the determination of the eigenvalues λ and the eigenvectors $\mathbf{f}$ belonging to an operator $\mathscr{L}$ (and its associated boundary conditions). That is, one often seeks a quantity λ such that the eigenvalue equation

$$\mathscr{L}\mathbf{f} = \lambda\mathbf{f} \tag{14.1}$$

has a nontrivial solution which satisfies certain specified boundary conditions on $\mathbf{f}$.

Some of the relatively few instances in which Eq. (14.1) can be solved exactly have been discussed in the preceding chapters. The present chapter concerns itself with the multitude of problems in which exact solutions of the eigenvalue equation cannot be obtained. Such problems are usually referred to as *perturbation problems* because they can be considered as perturbations of (i.e., deviations from) closely resembling problems which can be solved exactly. For example, suppose that Eq. (14.1) can be solved exactly. Then the perturbation problem may be represented by the eigenvalue problem

$$(\mathscr{L} + \delta\mathscr{L})(\mathbf{f} + \delta\mathbf{f}) = (\lambda + \delta\lambda)(\mathbf{f} + \delta\mathbf{f}) \tag{14.2}$$

where $\mathbf{f} + \delta\mathbf{f}$ satisfies the same boundary conditions as the $\mathbf{f}$ of Eq. (14.1). The operator $\mathscr{L} + \delta\mathscr{L}$ differs only slightly from the operator $\mathscr{L}$. The terms $\delta\mathscr{L}$, $\delta\lambda$, and $\delta\mathbf{f}$ are known, respectively, as the operator, eigenvalue, and eigenvector perturbation terms.

In a large number of perturbation problems the eigenvalue is the quantity of major interest, with knowledge of the corresponding eigenvector being relatively unimportant. The present chapter concerns itself primarily with evaluating the perturbation of the eigenvalue λ due to a given perturbation of the operator $\mathscr{L}$. Furthermore, the discussion will be restricted to problems in which the eigenvalues have a discrete spectrum. The more difficult problem of determining the perturbation of the eigenvector $\mathbf{f}$ will be treated only briefly.

14.2 Formulation of the Problem

Suppose that an eigenvalue λ_σ and the corresponding eigenvector $\mathbf{f}_\sigma$ of the operator $\mathscr{L}$ are known. That is, the solution of

$$\mathscr{L}\mathbf{f}_\sigma = \lambda_\sigma \mathbf{f}_\sigma \tag{14.3}$$

is known. Then consider operators $\mathscr{L} + \epsilon\theta$ which differ from $\mathscr{L}$ only slightly but in an arbitrary manner. By this is meant that the parameter ϵ, which measures the strength of the perturbation, is small (i.e., ϵ approaches zero) and that θ may be chosen as desired. The set of perturbation problems to be considered may then be represented by the eigenvalue equation

$$(\mathscr{L} + \epsilon\theta)(\mathbf{f}_\sigma + \epsilon\mathbf{h}) = (\lambda_\sigma + \epsilon\mu)(\mathbf{f}_\sigma + \epsilon\mathbf{h}) \tag{14.4}$$

where the eigenvector $\mathbf{f}_\sigma + \epsilon\mathbf{h}$ satisfies the same boundary conditions as $\mathbf{f}_\sigma$.

It is hoped that neither $\mathbf{h}$ nor μ becomes infinite as ϵ approaches zero. If neither limit is infinite, the values which μ and $\mathbf{h}$ take on as ϵ approaches zero are the quantities sought. If such a μ and $\mathbf{h}$ are found, the perturbation problem is solved. In what follows, such solutions are sought, bearing in mind the fact that they may not exist for all $\mathscr{L}$, $\mathbf{f}_\sigma$, and λ_σ.

Carrying out the multiplications indicated in Eq. (14.4) one obtains

$$\mathscr{L}\mathbf{f}_\sigma + \epsilon\mathscr{L}\mathbf{h} + \epsilon\theta\mathbf{f}_\sigma + \epsilon^2\theta\mathbf{h} = \lambda_\sigma\mathbf{f}_\sigma + \epsilon\lambda_\sigma\mathbf{h} + \epsilon\mu\mathbf{f}_\sigma + \epsilon^2\mu\mathbf{h}$$

Then, using (14.3) and dividing both sides of the resultant equation by ϵ, there results

$$\mathscr{L}\mathbf{h} + \theta\mathbf{f}_\sigma + \epsilon\theta\mathbf{h} = \lambda_\sigma\mathbf{h} + \mu\mathbf{f}_\sigma + \epsilon\mu\mathbf{h} \tag{14.5}$$

In (14.5) let ϵ go to zero, so that upon rearranging terms

$$(\mathscr{L} - \lambda_\sigma)\mathbf{h} = (\mu - \theta)\mathbf{f}_\sigma \tag{14.6}$$

The perturbation problem has now been reduced to that of finding $\mathbf{h}$ and μ such that Eq. (14.6) is satisfied. However, since $(\mathscr{L} - \lambda_\sigma)\mathbf{f}_\sigma = 0$, it is clear that the operator $\mathscr{L} - \lambda_\sigma$ has no inverse. Therefore, Eq. (14.6) either has no solution or it has a set of nonuniquely determined solutions. This situation will be considered further below.

14.3   A Simple Solution

There exists a nontrivial eigenvector $\mathbf{f}_\sigma$ satisfying the eigenvalue equation

$$\mathscr{L}\mathbf{f}_\sigma = \lambda_\sigma \mathbf{f}_\sigma \qquad (14.3)$$

and its associated boundary conditions, *and* there also exists a nontrivial eigenvector $\mathbf{g}_\tau$ which satisfies the eigenvalue equation

$$\mathscr{L}^+ \mathbf{g}_\tau = \xi_\tau \mathbf{g}_\tau \qquad (14.7)$$

with the same boundary conditions, at least for $\tau = \sigma$ and $\bar{\lambda}_\sigma = \xi_\sigma$. Furthermore,

$$\mathbf{g}_\tau^+ \mathbf{f}_\sigma = 0 \qquad \text{if } \xi_\tau \neq \bar{\lambda}_\sigma$$

What we would also like is that

$$\mathbf{g}_\sigma^+ \mathbf{f}_\sigma \neq 0 \qquad (14.8)$$

This relation will not always hold.[1] It may be noted that (14.8) certainly holds for all nondegenerate eigenvalues. It is only for nondegenerate eigenvalues that the simple procedure to be described applies.

If one now multiplies (14.6) by a $\mathbf{g}_\sigma^+$ satisfying (14.8) there results

$$\mu \mathbf{g}_\sigma^+ \mathbf{f}_\sigma = \mathbf{g}_\sigma^+ \theta \mathbf{f}_\sigma$$

or
$$\mu = \frac{\mathbf{g}_\sigma^+ \theta \mathbf{f}_\sigma}{\mathbf{g}_\sigma^+ \mathbf{f}_\sigma} \qquad (14.9)$$

as a necessary condition for (14.6) to hold. Consequently, if the perturbation problem has a solution in the form surmised, μ is given by Eq. (14.9).

That the result (14.9) cannot always be true is easily seen. If λ_σ is a degenerate eigenvalue of the operator $\mathscr{L}$, Eq. (14.9) will have two or more independent solutions corresponding to the same θ. Consequently, Eq. (14.9) must be incorrect in the case of a degenerate eigenvalue λ_σ. Its validity in the case of nondegenerate eigenvalues will be demonstrated in the following section.

---

[1] Consider, for example, an operator represented by the matrix $\begin{pmatrix} 2 & 0 \\ 1 & 0 \end{pmatrix}$.

14.4   Nondegenerate Eigenvalues

Consider, instead of Eq. (14.6), the more general equation

$$(\mathscr{L} - \lambda_\sigma + \alpha)\mathbf{h}' = (\mu - \theta)\mathbf{f}_\sigma \qquad (14.10)$$

where α is a constant. Eq. (14.6) then corresponds to the special case of (14.10) obtained when $\alpha = 0$. In general, a solution $\mathbf{h}'$ of Eq. (14.10) exists for all μ except in the case of those α's which are eigenvalues of the operator $\mathscr{L} - \lambda_\sigma$ (including, therefore, $\alpha = 0$ among the exceptions). This solution is easily obtained for diagonalizable operators $\mathscr{L}$. Thus, suppose that the matrix L representing the operator $\mathscr{L}$ may be written

$$L = S\Lambda S^{-1} \qquad SS^{-1} = S^{-1}S = 1$$

where Λ is diagonal, $\lambda_{11} = \lambda_\sigma$. Then, since λ_σ is nondegenerate, one may write

$$LS_{.1} = S_{.1}\lambda_\sigma \qquad \text{and} \qquad (S^{-1})_{1.}L = \lambda_\sigma(S^{-1})_{1.}$$

and make the identifications

$$f_\sigma = S_{.1} \qquad \text{and} \qquad g_\sigma^+ = (S^{-1})_{1.}$$

Therefore
$$L = \lambda_\sigma f_\sigma g_\sigma^+ + \sum_{i \neq 1} S_{.i}\lambda_{ii}(S^{-1})_{i.} \qquad (14.11)$$

and the solution of (14.10) is

$$\mathbf{h}' = (\mathscr{L} - \lambda_\sigma + \alpha)^{-1}(\mu - \theta)\mathbf{f}_\sigma$$

or
$$h' = f_\sigma \frac{1}{\alpha} g_\sigma^+(\mu - \theta)f_\sigma + \sum_{i \neq 1} S_{.i} \frac{1}{\lambda_{ii} - \lambda_\sigma - \alpha}(S^{-1})_{i.}(\mu - \theta)f_\sigma \quad (14.12)$$

This result will also hold for the case of interest, $\alpha = 0$, provided that $g_\sigma^+(\mu - \theta)f_\sigma = 0$, which is precisely the equation for μ obtained above [Eq. (14.9)]. Then Eq. (14.12) reduces to[1]

$$h = -\sum_{i \neq 1} S_{.i} \frac{1}{\lambda_{ii} - \lambda_\sigma}(S^{-1})_{i.}\theta f_\sigma \qquad (14.13)$$

or
$$\mathbf{h} = -\sum_{i \neq 1} S_{.i} \frac{1}{\lambda_{ii} - \lambda_\sigma}(S^{-1})_{i.}\theta \mathbf{f}_\sigma \qquad (14.13a)$$

It has thus been shown that when the operator $\mathscr{L}$ is diagonalizable and the eigenvalue λ_σ is nondegenerate, the simple result (14.9) is valid. Furthermore, $\mathbf{h}$ is given by (14.13a). This latter result is quite complex, since it contains the matrix S and all the eigenvalues λ_{ii}. In practice, it is often easier to obtain $\mathbf{h}$ directly from Eq. (14.6).

---

[1] Clearly, any multiple of f_σ may be added to the right-hand member of (14.13).

14.5 Change of Notation and an Extension

It will now be convenient to briefly repeat the above development in a more conventional notation. Thus, one knows the solution of the unperturbed equation

$$\mathscr{L}\mathbf{f}_\sigma = \lambda_\sigma \mathbf{f}_\sigma$$

and desires to solve the perturbed equation

$$(\mathscr{L} + \delta\mathscr{L})(\mathbf{f}_\sigma + \delta\mathbf{f}_\sigma) = (\lambda_\sigma + \delta\lambda_\sigma)(\mathbf{f}_\sigma + \delta\mathbf{f}_\sigma) \qquad (14.14)$$

neglecting the terms $\delta\mathscr{L}\,\delta\mathbf{f}_\sigma$ and $\delta\lambda_\sigma\,\delta\mathbf{f}_\sigma$. Then, Eq. (14.14) reduces to

$$(\delta\mathscr{L})\mathbf{f}_\sigma + \mathscr{L}\,\delta\mathbf{f}_\sigma = (\delta\lambda_\sigma)\mathbf{f}_\sigma + \lambda_\sigma\,\delta\mathbf{f}_\sigma \qquad (14.15)$$

One now seeks a left multiplier such that the terms

$$\mathscr{L}\,\delta\mathbf{f}_\sigma - \lambda_\sigma\,\delta\mathbf{f}_\sigma \equiv (\mathscr{L} - \lambda_\sigma)\,\delta\mathbf{f}_\sigma$$

are annihilated. Use $\mathbf{g}_\sigma^+$ such that

$$\mathbf{g}_\sigma^+(\mathscr{L} - \lambda_\sigma) = 0$$

and obtain

$$\mathbf{g}_\sigma^+(\delta\mathscr{L})\mathbf{f}_\sigma = \mathbf{g}_\sigma^+(\delta\lambda_\sigma)\mathbf{f}_\sigma \qquad (14.16)$$

or

$$\delta\lambda_\sigma = \frac{\mathbf{g}_\sigma^+(\delta\mathscr{L})\mathbf{f}_\sigma}{\mathbf{g}_\sigma^+\mathbf{f}_\sigma} \qquad \lambda_\sigma = \frac{\mathbf{g}_\sigma^+\mathscr{L}\mathbf{f}_\sigma}{\mathbf{g}_\sigma^+\mathbf{f}_\sigma} \qquad (14.17)$$

Eqs. (14.17) may be written in the even more suggestive form

$$\frac{\delta\lambda_\sigma}{\lambda_\sigma} = \frac{\mathbf{g}_\sigma^+(\delta\mathscr{L})\mathbf{f}_\sigma}{\mathbf{g}_\sigma^+\mathscr{L}\mathbf{f}_\sigma} \qquad (14.18)$$

or

$$\frac{\delta\lambda_\sigma}{\lambda_\sigma} = \frac{g_\sigma^+(\delta L)f_\sigma}{g_\sigma^+ L f_\sigma} \qquad (14.18a)$$

where L is the matrix representing $\mathscr{L}$.

A useful extension of the above procedure is to the equation (we drop the subscript σ)

$$\mathscr{L}\mathbf{f} = \lambda\mathscr{M}\mathbf{f} \qquad (14.19)$$

where $\mathscr{M}$ is also an operator. The perturbed equation is

$$(\mathscr{L} + \delta\mathscr{L})(\mathbf{f} + \delta\mathbf{f}) = (\lambda + \delta\lambda)(\mathscr{M} + \delta\mathscr{M})(\mathbf{f} + \delta\mathbf{f}) \qquad (14.20)$$

which, on neglecting the terms in $\delta\mathscr{L}\,\delta\mathbf{f}, \delta\lambda\,\delta\mathscr{M}, \delta\lambda\,\delta\mathbf{f}$, and $\delta\mathscr{M}\,\delta\mathbf{f}$, reduces to

$$(\delta\mathscr{L})\mathbf{f} - \lambda(\delta\mathscr{M})\mathbf{f} = (\delta\lambda)\mathscr{M}\mathbf{f} + (\lambda\mathscr{M} - \mathscr{L})\,\delta\mathbf{f}$$

Here, one may again annihilate the terms in $\delta\mathbf{f}$ by multiplication with a $\mathbf{g}^+$ such that

$$\mathbf{g}^+\mathscr{L} = \mathbf{g}^+\mathscr{M}\lambda \qquad (14.21)$$

There then results

$$\lambda = \frac{\mathbf{g}^+\mathscr{L}\mathbf{f}}{\mathbf{g}^+\mathscr{M}\mathbf{f}}$$

$$\frac{\delta\lambda}{\lambda} = \frac{\mathbf{g}^+(\delta\mathscr{L})\mathbf{f}}{\mathbf{g}^+\mathscr{L}\mathbf{f}} - \frac{\mathbf{g}^+(\delta\mathscr{M})\mathbf{f}}{\mathbf{g}^+\mathscr{M}\mathbf{f}} \qquad (14.22)$$

The result (14.22) clearly reduces to (14.18) when $\mathscr{M}$ is the unit operator.

14.6   An Application—The Vibrating String

As an application of the procedure described above, consider the variation in frequency and shape of a string whose mass per unit length is varied from its original condition of uniformity. The string is taken as extending along the x axis from $x = 0$ to $x = 1$. If y denotes the transverse displacement of the string, the problem may be represented by the eigenvalue equation

$$\frac{d^2}{dx^2} y = -\lambda f(x)y \qquad (14.23)$$

with the boundary conditions

$$y(0) = y(1) = 0 \qquad (14.24)$$

The eigenvalue λ represents the product $\rho\omega^2 T^{-1}$ in which ρ is the mass per unit length of the string, ω is 2π times the frequency of vibration, and T is the tension of the string. f is an arbitrary function of x.

Since the differential operator d^2/dx^2 is self-adjoint for the given boundary conditions, one obtains from (14.22)

$$\lambda = -\frac{\int_0^1 yy'' \, dx}{\int_0^1 yfy \, dx}$$

$$\frac{\delta\lambda}{\lambda} = -\frac{\int_0^1 y \, \delta fy \, dx}{\int_0^1 yfy \, dx} \qquad (14.25)$$

If $f = 1$, the solution of (14.23) is

$$y = \sin\sqrt{\lambda}x \qquad \lambda = n^2\pi^2 \qquad n = 1, 2, 3, \ldots$$

Hence, the perturbation on the lowest eigenvalue $\lambda = \pi^2$ is, from (14.25),

$$\frac{\delta\lambda}{\pi^2} = -\frac{\int_0^1 \delta f \sin^2 \pi x \, dx}{\int_0^1 \sin^2 \pi x \, dx} \tag{14.26}$$

The perturbation on the eigenfunction corresponding to the eigenvalue π^2 may be found as follows: From (14.23) one has

$$y'' + (\delta y)'' = -(\lambda + \delta\lambda)(f + \delta f)(y + \delta y)$$

or

$$(\delta y)'' + \lambda f \, \delta y = -y(f \, \delta\lambda + \lambda \, \delta f)$$

Hence, with $z \equiv \delta y$,

$$z'' + \pi^2 z = -\sin \pi x (\delta\lambda + \pi^2 \, \delta f) \tag{14.27}$$

A solution of this equation is

$$\delta y \equiv z = \frac{1}{\pi} \int_0^x \sin \pi(x' - x) \sin \pi x' (\delta\lambda + \pi^2 \, \delta f) \, dx' \tag{14.28}$$

It clearly satisfies (14.27) and the boundary conditions (14.24). An arbitrary multiple of $\sin \pi x$ may be added to the right side of (14.28).

14.7 Degenerate Eigenvalues

Return now to the problem of solving the perturbed eigenvalue equation when the eigenvalue of the unperturbed equation is n-fold degenerate. The nature of the difficulty posed by this degeneracy is readily determined from an examination of Eq. (14.13a). It is seen there that trouble arises for $\lambda_{ii} = \lambda_\sigma$ unless simultaneously $(S^{-1})_{i.}\theta \mathbf{f}_\sigma$ vanishes. Thus, for example, if λ is two-fold degenerate so that

$$\mathscr{L}\mathbf{f}^{(1)} = \lambda \mathbf{f}^{(1)} \qquad \text{and} \qquad \mathscr{L}\mathbf{f}^{(2)} = \lambda \mathbf{f}^{(2)}$$

it is also desirable that $\mathbf{g}^{(1)+}\theta \mathbf{f}^{(2)} = 0$, etc. This remark becomes useful when one recalls that after all $\mathbf{f}^{(1)}$ and $\mathbf{f}^{(2)}$ are not unique—i.e., eigenvectors belonging to degenerate eigenvalues are not uniquely determined.

Now proceed in a manner analogous to that used in Secs. 14.2 and 14.3. Thus, let

$$\mathscr{L}\mathbf{f}^{(i)} = \lambda \mathbf{f}^{(i)} \qquad i = 1, 2, \ldots, n$$
$$\mathbf{g}^{(i)+}\mathscr{L} = \lambda \mathbf{g}^{(i)+}$$
$$\mathbf{g}^{(i)+}\mathbf{f}^{(j)} = \delta_{ij}$$

define a set of eigenvectors $\mathbf{f}^{(i)}$ and $\mathbf{g}^{(i)+}$. Their existence is assured if $\mathscr{L}$ is diagonalizable.

In constructing the equation analogous to (14.4), one must incorporate explicitly the arbitrariness of the choice for the $\mathbf{f}^{(i)}$. Therefore write, as the eigenvalue equation for the perturbation problems,

$$(\mathscr{L} + \epsilon\theta)\left(\sum_i a_i \mathbf{f}^{(i)} + \epsilon\mathbf{h}\right) = (\lambda + \epsilon\mu)\left(\sum_i a_i \mathbf{f}^{(i)} + \epsilon\mathbf{h}\right)$$

where the a_i are to be determined.

Carrying out the indicated multiplications, using $\mathscr{L}\sum_i a_i\mathbf{f}^{(i)} = \lambda\sum_i a_i\mathbf{f}^{(i)}$, neglecting terms in ϵ^2, and dividing the resultant equation by ϵ, one obtains, as the analogue of Eq. (14.6),

$$(\mathscr{L} - \lambda)\mathbf{h} = (\mu - \theta)\sum_i a_i\mathbf{f}^{(i)} \qquad (14.29)$$

In accordance with the procedure in Sec. 14.3, multiply Eq. (14.29) on the left by each $\mathbf{g}^{(i)+}$ in turn. One then obtains, analogous to Eq. (14.9), the set of equations

$$\sum_{i=1}^n a_i[\mu\delta_{ji} - \mathbf{g}^{(j)+}\theta\mathbf{f}^{(i)}] = 0 \qquad (14.30)$$

This set consists of n linear homogeneous equations for the n undetermined constants a_i. They can be solved only when the determinant of the coefficients of the a_i vanishes,

$$|\mu\delta_{ji} - \mathbf{g}^{(j)+}\theta\mathbf{f}^{(i)}| = 0 \qquad (14.31)$$

Solution of this determinantal equation yields n values of μ, corresponding to the n linearly independent solutions $\mathbf{h}$ to be expected.

The demonstration by construction that this procedure leads to a valid solution of the perturbation problem follows that of Sec. 14.4. Thus

$$L = \lambda\sum_{i=1}^n \mathbf{f}^{(i)}\mathbf{g}^{(i)+} + \sum_{i>n} S_{.i}\lambda_{ii}(S^{-1})_{i.}$$

Hence, if

$$(\mathscr{L} - \lambda + \alpha)\mathbf{h}' = (\mu - \theta)\sum_{i=1}^n a_i\mathbf{f}^{(i)}$$

then

$$h' = \frac{1}{\alpha}\sum_{i,j=1}^n f^{(j)}g^{(j)+}(\mu - \theta)f^{(i)}a_i + \sum_{j>n}\sum_{i=1}^n S_{.j}\frac{1}{\lambda_{jj} - \lambda - \alpha}(S^{-1})_{j.}(\mu - \theta)f^{(i)}a_i$$

Upon allowing α to go to zero, one obtains a sensible result in view of Eq. (14.30).

Exercises

1. The lowest eigenvalue and corresponding eigenfunction of the equation

$$\left(-\frac{d^2}{dx^2} + \alpha^2 x^2\right)\psi_n = \lambda_n \psi_n \qquad -\infty < x < +\infty$$

where ψ_n is required to be finite everywhere, are

$$\lambda_n = \alpha \qquad \psi_n = e^{-\alpha x^2/2}$$

Find, approximately, the lowest eigenvalue of

$$\left(-\frac{d^2}{dx^2} + \alpha^2 x + ax^3 + bx^4\right)\varphi = \lambda\varphi \qquad -\infty < x < +\infty$$

where φ is finite everywhere and a and b are given constants.

2. Given the eigenvalue problem

$$-\frac{d^2}{d\theta^2} y_n = \lambda_n y_n \qquad y(0) = y(2\pi)$$

with solutions $y_n = e^{in\theta}$ and eigenvalues $\lambda_n = n^2$, where $n = 0, \pm 1, \pm 2, \ldots$, find, approximately, the eigenvalues of

$$\left(-\frac{d^2}{d\theta^2} + \epsilon \cos^2 \theta\right)y = \lambda y \qquad y(0) = y(2\pi)$$

3. Consider the problem

$$\left(+\frac{d}{dx} D \frac{d}{dx} + B^2\right)\varphi = 0 \qquad \text{where} \qquad \varphi(0) = \varphi(a) = 0$$

Find an approximate value of $B^2(\epsilon)$ for

$$D(x) = D_0 + \epsilon f(x)$$

4. Find the lowest frequency of a vibrating string loaded with a small mass m at its midpoint by (a) solving the problem completely, and (b) using perturbation theory, starting with the unloaded string.

5. Use perturbation theory to evaluate the eigenvalues of the matrix

$$\begin{pmatrix} \lambda_1 & \alpha & 0 & 0 \\ \alpha & \lambda_2 & \beta & 0 \\ 0 & \beta & \lambda_3 & \gamma \\ 0 & 0 & \gamma & \lambda_3 \end{pmatrix} = M$$

assuming α, β, and γ are small.

References

Schiff, L. I.: "Quantum Mechanics," chap. VII, McGraw-Hill Book Company, Inc., New York, 1949.

Courant, R., and D. Hilbert: "Methods of Mathematical Physics," vol. I, pp. 343–350, Interscience Publishers, Inc., 1953.

Morse, P. M., and H. Feshbach: "Methods of Theoretical Physics," sec. 9.1, McGraw-Hill Book Company, Inc., New York, 1953.

CHAPTER 15

Variational Estimates

15.1 Introduction

A function of a single variable x is said to be stationary at the point $x = x_0$ if the first derivative of the function with respect to x vanishes at x_0. If the functional value at x_0 is desired, the value obtained by evaluation at a point near x_0 may be expected to be a reasonably good approximation—the approximation being better the closer the point is to x_0. Similar remarks hold for functions of many variables.

The approach to the perturbation problem in the preceding chapter was one of finding stationary expressions for the eigenvalue λ. Thus if

$$\mathscr{L}\mathbf{f} = \lambda\mathscr{M}\mathbf{f} \qquad \text{and} \qquad \mathbf{g}^+\mathscr{L} = \lambda\mathbf{g}^+\mathscr{M}$$

are used to define $\mathbf{f}$, λ, and $\mathbf{g}$ for given $\mathscr{L}$ and $\mathscr{M}$, one has directly that

$$\lambda = \frac{\mathbf{g}^+\mathscr{L}\mathbf{f}}{\mathbf{g}^+\mathscr{M}\mathbf{f}} \tag{15.1}$$

If one takes the differential of (15.1) and then divides by (15.1), he obtains

$$
\begin{aligned}
\frac{\delta\lambda}{\lambda} &= \frac{(\delta\mathbf{g}^+)\mathscr{L}\mathbf{f} + \mathbf{g}^+(\delta\mathscr{L})\mathbf{f} + \mathbf{g}^+\mathscr{L}(\delta\mathbf{f})}{\mathbf{g}^+\mathscr{L}\mathbf{f}} \\
&\qquad - \frac{(\delta\mathbf{g}^+)\mathscr{M}\mathbf{f} + \mathbf{g}^+(\delta\mathscr{M})\mathbf{f} + \mathbf{g}^+\mathscr{M}(\delta\mathbf{f})}{\mathbf{g}^+\mathscr{M}\mathbf{f}} \\
&= \frac{\mathbf{g}^+(\delta\mathscr{L})\mathbf{f}}{\mathbf{g}^+\mathscr{L}\mathbf{f}} - \frac{\mathbf{g}^+(\delta\mathscr{M})\mathbf{f}}{\mathbf{g}^+\mathscr{M}\mathbf{f}} + \frac{(\delta\mathbf{g}^+)(\mathscr{L}\mathbf{f} - \lambda\mathscr{M}\mathbf{f}) + (\mathbf{g}^+\mathscr{L} - \lambda\mathbf{g}^+\mathscr{M})(\delta\mathbf{f})}{\mathbf{g}^+\mathscr{L}\mathbf{f}}
\end{aligned}
\tag{15.2}
$$

Because the terms proportional to the variations of the eigenvectors vanish, (15.1) is a stationary expression for λ and (15.2) simplifies

211

to (14.22). Note that these terms vanished because of the specific choice of the vectors $\mathbf{f}$ and $\mathbf{g}$.

Since (15.1) is a stationary expression for λ, one may estimate λ by evaluating (15.1) for appropriate values of $\mathbf{g}^+$ and $\mathbf{f}$. This estimate of λ will have an error proportional to the terms neglected in obtaining (14.22), i.e., proportional to products of $\delta\mathbf{g}^+$ with $\delta\mathbf{f}$. Expressions of the form of (15.1) having the stationary property are known as *variational principles*. Their usefulness increases greatly under some special but common circumstances which will be indicated in the remainder of this chapter.

15.2   The Rayleigh Variational Principle[1]

In this section the discussion is restricted to the estimation of the eigen-value of a Hermitian operator $\mathscr{H}$. In such a case $\mathbf{g}$ and $\mathbf{f}$ may be taken identical, since from $\mathscr{H}\mathbf{f} = \lambda\mathbf{f}$ follows directly $\mathbf{f}^+\mathscr{H} = \lambda\mathbf{f}^+$. The varia-tional principle may then be written

$$\lambda = \frac{\mathbf{f}^+\mathscr{H}\mathbf{f}}{\mathbf{f}^+\mathbf{f}} \tag{15.3}$$

It will be demonstrated that the λ calculated from (15.3) is not less than the lowest eigenvalue (say λ_1) of $\mathscr{H}$. Let H be the matrix representing the operator $\mathscr{H}$ in the given basis. Then, since a Hermitian matrix can be diagonalized by a unitary transformation, i.e.,

$$H = S\Lambda S^{-1} = S\Lambda S^+$$

(15.3) may be written as

$$\begin{aligned} \lambda &= \frac{f^+ S\Lambda S^+ f}{f^+ SS^+ f} \\ &= \frac{(S^+ f)^+ \Lambda (S^+ f)}{(S^+ f)^+ (S^+ f)} \end{aligned} \tag{15.4}$$

With the notation

$$a_i = (S^+)_{i.}\, f \qquad \Lambda_{ii} = \lambda_i$$

(15.4) becomes

$$\begin{aligned} \lambda &= \frac{\sum_i |a_i|^2 \lambda_i}{\sum_i |a_i|^2} \\ &= \lambda_1 + \frac{\sum_i |a_i|^2 (\lambda_i - \lambda_1)}{\sum_i |a_i|^2} \end{aligned}$$

[1] Lord Rayleigh, "Theory of Sound," 2d rev. ed., vol. 1, sec. 88, The Macmillan Company, New York, 1937.

Hence, if $\qquad\qquad\lambda_i \geq \lambda_1 \qquad$ all i

then $\qquad\qquad\qquad \lambda \geq \lambda_1$

as was to be demonstrated. It has therefore been proven that λ as defined by (15.3) is not less than the lowest eigenvalue of the operator $\mathscr{H}$. In a like manner, it may be demonstrated that λ is not greater than the highest eigenvalue of $\mathscr{H}$.

As an example, consider the approximate evaluation of the lowest eigenvalue ($\lambda_1 = \pi^2$) of the vibrating string problem

$$\frac{d^2}{dx^2} y = -\lambda y \qquad y(0) = y(1) = 0$$

A simple function which satisfies the boundary conditions is the parabola $y = x(1 - x)$. Substitution into (15.3) yields

$$\lambda = -\frac{\int_0^1 x(1 - x) \frac{d^2}{dx^2} [x(1 - x)] \, dx}{\int_0^1 [x(1 - x)]^2 \, dx}$$

$$= 10$$

Clearly $\lambda = 10 > \lambda_1 = \pi^2$. The error is about 1.3 per cent which is surprisingly small.

15.3   A Lower Bound[1]

As demonstrated in the preceding section, the Rayleigh variational principle yields an upper limit to the lowest eigenvalue of a Hermitian operator. This result, while clearly very useful, is not as much so as might be desired. One would also like to obtain a lower bound to the eigenvalue so that the accuracy of the approximation may be determined. In the following, it will be demonstrated how two such lower bounds may be obtained. Unfortunately, these lower bounds are not as useful in many applications as the upper bound already obtained.

The first lower bound may be obtained as follows: Let

$$\lambda = \frac{f^+ H f}{f^+ f} \tag{15.5}$$

and $\qquad\qquad\qquad \delta = \frac{(Hf)^+ (Hf)}{f^+ f} \tag{15.6}$

[1] D. H. Weinstein, *Proc. Natl. Acad. Sci.*, **20**: 529 (1934); J. K. L. MacDonald, *Phys. Rev.*, **46**: 828 (1934); W. Kohn, *Phys. Rev.*, **71**: 902 (1947).

and consider $\qquad\qquad Kf^+f \equiv [(H - \lambda)f]^+[(H - \epsilon)f]$ (15.7)

Clearly $\qquad\qquad\qquad\qquad K = \delta - \lambda^2$ (15.8)

for any value of the parameter ϵ. Furthermore, if $\epsilon = \lambda$,

$$K = \frac{\sum_i |a_i|^2(\lambda_i - \lambda)^2}{\sum_i |a_i|^2}$$

where the a_i and λ_i are as defined in Sec. 15.2. But λ will be at least as close to one λ_i (say λ_m) as to any other. Therefore

$$(\lambda - \lambda_m)^2 \le (\lambda - \lambda_i)^2 \qquad \text{all } i$$

and $\qquad\qquad K \ge \dfrac{\sum_i |a_i|^2(\lambda_m - \lambda)^2}{\sum_i |a_i|^2} = (\lambda_m - \lambda)^2$

Hence $\qquad\qquad\qquad (\lambda_m - \lambda)^2 \le \delta - \lambda^2$ (15.9)

or $\qquad\qquad \lambda - \sqrt{\delta - \lambda^2} \le \lambda_m \le \lambda + \sqrt{\delta - \lambda^2}$ (15.9a)

Now apply this result to the problem of the vibrating string (Sec. 15.2). One obtains

$$\delta = \frac{\int_0^1 \left[\dfrac{d^2}{dx^2} x(1 - x)\right]^2 dx}{\int_0^1 [x(1 - x)]^2\, dx} = 120$$

Hence, since $\lambda_1 = 10$,

$$10 - \sqrt{20} \le \lambda_m \le 10 + \sqrt{20}$$

One cannot with certitude say that this λ_m is the same eigenvalue λ_1 for which the upper bound 10 was found. However, if one knows that not more than one eigenvalue is to be found below $10 + \sqrt{20}$, he has the further result that

$$10 - \sqrt{20} \le \lambda_1 \le 10$$

This result clearly indicates that the lower limit which has been obtained is not very good.

A much better lower bound to the first eigenvalue may be obtained if one assumes knowledge of the second eigenvalue λ_2. Thus, suppose that λ and δ are defined as previously and that

$$\lambda_1 \le \lambda < \lambda_2 \le \lambda_3 \le \lambda_4 \cdots$$

One may then define K as in (15.7) and (15.8), but take $\epsilon = \lambda_1 + \lambda_2 - \lambda$, and obtain

$$K \sum_i |a_i|^2 = |a_1|^2(\lambda - \lambda_1)(\lambda_2 - \lambda) + |a_2|^2(\lambda_2 - \lambda)(\lambda - \lambda_1)$$
$$+ |a_3|^2(\lambda_3 - \lambda)(\lambda - \lambda_1 + \lambda_3 - \lambda_2)$$
$$+ |a_4|^2(\lambda_4 - \lambda)(\lambda - \lambda_1 + \lambda_4 - \lambda_2) + \cdots$$
$$\geq (\lambda - \lambda_1)(\lambda_2 - \lambda) \sum_i |a_i|^2$$

Hence
$$(\lambda - \lambda_1)(\lambda_2 - \lambda) \leq \delta - \lambda^2 \qquad (15.10)$$

Provided that one can estimate λ_2, he may apply this simple result to the problem of the vibrating string. Use the well-known fact that $\lambda_2 \sim 4\lambda_1$. Then, with $\lambda = 10$ and $\delta = 120$, one obtains from (15.10),

$$(10 - \lambda_1)(4\lambda_1 - 10) \leq 20 \qquad \lambda_1 \geq 10 - 0.15$$

If one had assumed $\lambda_2 \sim 2\lambda_1$ he would have obtained the still fairly sharp but much poorer limit

$$\lambda_1 \geq 10 - 0.5$$

A result similar to (15.10) may be obtained for the other eigenvalues. Thus, if

$$\lambda_1 \leq \lambda_2 \leq \lambda_3 \leq \cdots \leq \lambda_n \leq \lambda \leq \lambda_{n+1} \leq \cdots$$

then, by taking ϵ in (15.7) as $\lambda_n + \lambda_{n+1} - \lambda$, one finds that

$$(\lambda - \lambda_n)(\lambda_{n+1} - \lambda) \leq \delta - \lambda^2 \qquad (15.11)$$

15.4 The Ritz Method[1]

As has been seen, if λ is defined for a given $\mathbf{f}$, by the equation

$$\lambda\{\mathbf{f}\} = \frac{\mathbf{f}^+ \mathscr{H} \mathbf{f}}{\mathbf{f}^+ \mathbf{f}} \qquad (15.12)$$

or
$$\lambda\{f\} = \frac{f^+ H f}{f^+ f} \qquad (15.12a)$$

then
$$\lambda \geq \lambda_1 \qquad (15.13)$$

where λ_1 is the lowest eigenvalue of the Hermitian operator $\mathscr{H}$. Consequently, if various trial functions f are used in (15.12a), the lowest λ produced is the best approximation to λ_1. Furthermore, λ can indeed take on this value if f is the eigenfunction of H belonging to the eigenvalue

[1] W. Ritz, *Journal für die reine und angewandte Mathematik*, **135**: 1 (1909).

λ_1. Therefore, of all possible f's, the one desired is that one which minimizes $\lambda\{f\}$ as defined in (15.12a).

Now define a class of trial functions $f(\alpha,\beta,\gamma,\ldots)$ depending on the parameters $\alpha,\beta,\gamma,\ldots$. Then λ is in turn a function of these parameters, i.e., $\lambda = \lambda(\alpha,\beta,\gamma,\ldots)$. The best available estimate of λ_1 for the given class of trial functions will be given by the minimum with respect to $\alpha,\beta,\gamma,\ldots$. To obtain this minimum λ it is necessary to solve the equations

$$\frac{\partial\lambda}{\partial\alpha} = 0 \qquad \frac{\partial\lambda}{\partial\beta} = 0 \qquad \frac{\partial\lambda}{\partial\gamma} = 0,\ldots \qquad (15.14)$$

simultaneously. This task will be formidable in most cases.

The set of equations (15.14) will be linear in the parameters $\alpha,\beta,\gamma,\ldots$ provided that the parameters appear linearly in the trial functions $f(\alpha,\beta,\gamma,\ldots)$. In such a case of linear trial functions, the problem of finding the minimum value of $\lambda(\alpha,\beta,\gamma,\ldots)$ is greatly simplified. The further remarks on the Ritz method will be confined to the case of linear trial functions.

Thus, write

$$f(a_i) = \sum_{i=1}^{n} a_i \varphi_i \qquad (15.15)$$

Then, with the definitions

$$m_{ij} = \varphi_i^+ \varphi_j \qquad (15.16)$$

$$k_{ij} = \varphi_i^+ H \varphi_j \qquad (15.17)$$

one obtains

$$\lambda(a_i) = \frac{\sum_{j,k} a_j^+ a_k k_{jk}}{\sum_{l,m} a_l^+ a_m m_{lm}} \qquad (15.18)$$

Clearly, one may determine the parameters a_i in (15.18) in such a way as to minimize λ. However, a more transparent discussion may be obtained by the following somewhat different procedure.

Suppose that the φ_i had been chosen as an orthonormal set so that $m_{ij} = \delta_{ij}$. Then, in place of (15.18) one would have

$$\lambda(a_i) = \frac{\sum_{jk} a_j^+ k_{jk} a_k}{\sum_{l} a_l^+ a_l} \qquad (15.19)$$

which may be written as

$$\lambda = \frac{a^+ K a}{a^+ a} \qquad (15.20)$$

where K is the $n \times n$ Hermitian matrix with elements k_{ij} and a is the n column with elements a_i. Since Eq. (15.20) is of the form of (15.12a), it is clear that the minimum value of λ, as defined in (15.20), is the smallest eigenvalue of K. Therefore, $\lambda_{\min}$ is the least root of

$$|K - \lambda| = 0 \qquad (15.21)$$

To summarize, if the set of trial functions φ_i is orthonormal, the estimate for the lowest eigenvalue λ_1 of H is given by the least root of the determinantal equation

$$|\varphi_i^+ H \varphi_j - \lambda \delta_{ij}| = 0 \qquad (15.22)$$

In a sense one has solved a problem in the n-dimensional space spanned by the trial functions φ_i, instead of in the original space in which the operator $\mathscr{H}$ was defined, and has found the lowest value of λ in this subspace.

If the set of trial functions φ_i is not orthonormal, one can still use the result (15.22) provided that he can replace the non-orthonormal set φ_i by an orthonormal set φ_i. The procedure is as follows:

Firstly, note that the φ_i may be assumed to be linearly independent. If they were not, one of the φ_i, say φ_n, would be expressible in terms of the others,

$$\varphi_n = \sum_{i=1}^{n-1} b_i \varphi_i$$

Then, Eq. (15.15) would become

$$f = \sum_{i=1}^{n-1} a_i \varphi_i + a_n \sum_{i=1}^{n-1} b_i \varphi_i$$
$$= \sum_{i=1}^{n-1} (a_i + a_n b_i) \varphi_i$$

which is no more general than

$$f = \sum_{i=1}^{n-1} c_i \varphi_i$$

This result states that if the n trial functions φ_i are not linearly independent one of them may be omitted without loss. Consequently, it will be assumed that the φ_i are linearly independent

$$\sum_{i=1}^{n} a_i \varphi_i \neq 0 \qquad (15.23)$$

for nonzero a_i.

Secondly, it may be demonstrated that the Hermitian matrix M is positive definite, i.e., all of its eigenvalues are greater than zero. Thus, suppose that λ is an eigenvalue of M and that x is the eigencolumn belonging to λ. Then

$$Mx = \lambda x$$

or

$$\sum_j m_{ij} x_j = \lambda x_i$$

Multiplying this equation by $\bar{x}_i$ from the left and summing over all i, one obtains

$$\sum_{i,j} \bar{x}_i m_{ij} x_j = \lambda \sum_i |x_i|^2$$

or

$$\sum_{i,j} (x_i \varphi_i)^+ (x_j \varphi_j) = \left| \sum_i (x_i \varphi_i) \right|^2 = \lambda \sum_i |x_i|^2$$

where (15.16) has been used. Consequently, by (15.23),

$$\lambda = \frac{\left| \sum_i (x_i \varphi_i) \right|^2}{\sum_i |x_i|^2} > 0$$

which proves that all of the eigenvalues of the Hermitian matrix M are greater than zero. Having demonstrated this, one may write

$$M = P\Gamma^2 P^+$$

where P is a unitary matrix and Γ is real and diagonal.

Finally, one may replace the φ_i by the new set ϕ_i defined by

$$\phi_i = \sum_j \varphi_j (P\Gamma^{-1})_{ji} \tag{15.24}$$

or

$$\varphi_i = \sum_i \phi_j (\Gamma P^+)_{ji} \tag{15.25}$$

Note that Eq. (15.15) is now replaced by

$$f = \sum_{i=1}^n a_i \sum_{j=1}^n \phi_j (\Gamma P^+)_{ji}$$

$$= \sum_i \phi_i \sum_j (\Gamma P^+)_{ij} a_j = \sum_i \phi_i b_i$$

in which

$$b_i = \sum_{j=1}^n (\Gamma P^+)_{ij} a_j$$

or

$$a_i = \sum_{j=1}^n (P\Gamma^{-1})_{ij} b_j \tag{15.26}$$

$$a = P\Gamma^{-1} b \tag{15.26a}$$

That the ϕ_i are an orthonormal set is easily demonstrated: Thus

$$\phi_i^+ \phi_j = \sum_{l,m} (\Gamma^{-1}P^+)_{il}\varphi_l^+ \varphi_m(P\Gamma^{-1})_{mj}$$

$$= \sum_{l,m} (\Gamma^{-1}P^+)_{il}(P\Gamma^2P^+)_{lm}(P\Gamma^{-1})_{mj}$$

$$= (\Gamma^{-1}P^+P\Gamma^2P^+P\Gamma^{-1})_{ij}$$

$$= \delta_{ij}$$

Using (15.26) one may now write (15.18) as

$$\lambda = \frac{a^+Ka}{a^+Ma}$$

$$= \frac{b^+\Gamma^{-1}P^+KP\Gamma^{-1}b}{b^+\Gamma^{-1}P^+P\Gamma^2P^+P\Gamma^{-1}b}$$

$$= \frac{b^+Jb}{b^+b} \tag{15.27}$$

where J is the Hermitian matrix

$$J = \Gamma^{-1}P^+KP\Gamma^{-1}$$

Hence, the lowest λ for (15.27) [and, consequently, for (15.18)] is the least root of

$$|J - \lambda| = 0$$

This result may be written in a more useful form as follows. Substitution for J yields

$$|\Gamma^{-1}P^+KP\Gamma^{-1} - \lambda| = 0$$

$$|\Gamma^{-1}P^+(K - \lambda P\Gamma^2P^+)P\Gamma^{-1}| = 0$$

$$|\Gamma^{-2}||K - M\lambda| = 0$$

Hence $$|K - \lambda M| = 0$$

or $$|\varphi_i^+ H\varphi_j - \lambda\varphi_i^+ \varphi_j| = 0 \tag{15.28}$$

The result, that λ is to be taken as the least root of (15.28), replaces (15.22) and clearly reduces to (15.22) when the φ_i are orthonormal. The form (15.28) is often useful for computation purposes. For formal purposes one might just as well take the φ_i as orthonormal, as the above discussion has indicated.

15.5   Higher Eigenvalues by the Ritz Method

The method described in the preceding section may also be used to obtain approximate values for the higher eigenvalues. The procedure was to consider the various λ for which

$$\lambda = \frac{f^+ H f}{f^+ f}$$

was stationary for

$$f = \sum_{i=1}^{N} a_i \varphi_i$$

For an orthonormal set φ_i, it was found that the a_i satisfied the equation

$$\sum_j \varphi_i^+ H \varphi_j a_j = \lambda a_i$$

Now write the N solutions as

$$\sum_j \varphi_i^+ H \varphi_j a_{j\sigma} = \mu_\sigma a_{i\sigma} \qquad \begin{array}{l} \sigma = 1, 2, 3, \ldots, N \\ \mu_1 \le \mu_2 \le \mu_3 \le \cdots \le \mu_N \end{array} \qquad (15.29)$$

Furthermore, define N functions ϕ_σ by

$$\phi_\sigma = \sum_i a_{i\sigma} \varphi_i$$

The set of trial functions ϕ_σ are equivalent to the set φ_i and will lead to the same roots.

Now consider, with $n \le N$, the trial functions

$$f = \sum_{\sigma=1}^{n} b_\sigma \phi_\sigma \qquad (15.30)$$

Since

$$\phi_\sigma^+ H \phi_\tau = \sum_{i,j} \bar{a}_{i\sigma} \varphi_i^+ H a_{j\tau} \varphi_j = \sum_i \bar{a}_{i\sigma} \mu_\tau a_{i\tau} = \delta_{\sigma\tau} \mu_\tau$$

the eigenvalues determined by these trial functions are the roots of the determinantal equation

$$|\delta_{\sigma\tau}\mu_\tau - \delta_{\sigma\tau}\lambda| = 0$$

i.e., the roots are $\mu_1, \mu_2, \ldots, \mu_n$.

Now note that the variational principle becomes

$$\lambda = \frac{f^+ H f}{f^+ f} = \frac{\displaystyle\sum_{\sigma=1}^{n} |b_\sigma|^2 \mu_\sigma}{\displaystyle\sum_{\sigma=1}^{n} |b_\sigma|^2}$$

so that μ_n is the largest value of λ obtainable with

$$f = \sum_{\sigma=1}^{n} b_\sigma \phi_\sigma$$

But if the f_α are the eigenfunctions of H belonging to the eigenvalue λ_σ, i.e., if

$$Hf_\alpha = \lambda_\alpha f_\alpha \qquad \lambda_1 \le \lambda_2 \le \lambda_3 \le \cdots$$

one may expand the ϕ_σ in terms of the complete set of f_α's,

$$\phi_\sigma = \sum_{\alpha=1}^{\infty} A_{\sigma\alpha} f_\alpha$$

If one now chooses the b_σ in (15.30) so that

$$f = \sum_{\sigma=1}^{n} \sum_{\alpha=1}^{\infty} b_\sigma A_{\sigma\alpha} f_\alpha$$

does not contain $f_1, f_2, \ldots, f_{n-1}$, i.e., if one arranges that

$$\sum_{\sigma=1}^{n} b_\sigma A_{\sigma\alpha} = 0 \qquad \text{for} \qquad \alpha = 1, 2, \ldots, n-1$$

the trial function so constructed has the form

$$f = \sum_{\alpha=n}^{\infty} C_\alpha f_\alpha$$

The corresponding λ, which is certainly not greater than μ_n, is given by

$$\lambda = \frac{\displaystyle\sum_{\alpha=n}^{\infty} |C_\alpha|^2 \lambda_\alpha}{\displaystyle\sum_{n}^{\infty} |C_\alpha|^2} \ge \lambda_n$$

Hence, $\mu_n \ge \lambda_n$. It follows, therefore, that the ith root of (15.22) or (15.28) is as great as or greater than the ith eigenvalue of H.

15.6 Example of the Ritz Method

As an illustration of the Ritz method consider again the problem of the vibrating string. The eigenvalue problem is to solve the differential equation

$$\frac{d^2}{dx^2} y = -\lambda y \qquad 0 \le x \le 1$$

with the boundary conditions $y(0) = y(1) = 0$. The exact solution is

$$y_n = \sqrt{2} \sin n\pi x \qquad \lambda_n = n^2\pi^2 \qquad n = 1, 2, 3, \ldots. \qquad (15.31)$$

The equivalent variational problem is

$$\lambda = -\frac{\int_0^1 y \dfrac{d^2}{dx^2} y \, dx}{\int_0^1 y^2 \, dx} = \frac{\int_0^1 \left(\dfrac{dy}{dx}\right)^2 dx}{\int_0^1 y^2 \, dx} \qquad (15.32)$$

Approximate eigenvalues and eigenfunctions can be obtained by the Ritz method as follows: Choose an orthonormal set of functions φ_i as polynomials, namely

$$\varphi_1 = \alpha_0 + \alpha_1 x + \alpha_2 x^2$$
$$\varphi_2 = \beta_0 + \beta_1 x + \beta_2 x^2 + \beta_3 x^3$$
$$\varphi_3 = \gamma_0 + \gamma_1 x + \gamma_2 x^2 + \gamma_3 x^3 + \gamma_4 x^4, \text{ etc.}$$

The boundary condition at $x = 0$ requires that $\alpha_0 = \beta_0 = \gamma_0 = \cdots = 0$. The boundary condition at $x = 1$ requires that $\sum_i \alpha_i = \sum_i \beta_i = \sum_i \gamma_i = \cdots = 0$. Hence the functions φ_i reduce to

$$\varphi_1 = \alpha_1 x(1 - x)$$
$$\varphi_2 = \beta_1 x(1 - x^2) + \beta_2 x^2(1 - x)$$
$$\varphi_3 = \gamma_1 x(1 - x^3) + \gamma_2 x^2(1 - x^2) + \gamma_3 x^3(1 - x), \text{ etc.}$$

The condition φ_1 normalized to unity leads to $\alpha_1 = \sqrt{30}$. The two conditions φ_2 orthogonal to φ_1 and φ_2 normalized to unity lead to $\beta_1 = \sqrt{210}$ and $\beta_2 = -3\sqrt{210}$. The three conditions φ_3 orthogonal to φ_1, φ_3 orthogonal to φ_2, and φ_3 normalized to unity lead to $\gamma_1 = 9\sqrt{10}$, $\gamma_2 = -51\sqrt{10}$, and $\gamma_3 = 84\sqrt{10}$. Thus

$$\varphi_1 = \sqrt{30}x(1 - x)$$
$$\varphi_2 = \sqrt{210}x(1 - 3x + 2x^2) \qquad (15.33)$$
$$\varphi_3 = 3\sqrt{10}x(3 - 17x + 28x^2 - 14x^3)$$

The integrals

$$k_{ij} = -\int_0^1 \varphi_i \frac{d^2}{dx^2} \varphi_j = \int_0^1 \frac{d\varphi_i}{dx} \frac{d\varphi_j}{dx} dx$$

yield on substitution for the φ's, $k_{11} = 10$, $k_{12} = k_{21} = 0$, $k_{13} = k_{31} = 2\sqrt{3}$, $k_{22} = 42$, $k_{23} = k_{32} = 0$, and $k_{33} = 102$.

If only the first basic function φ_1 is used, the determinantal equation (15.22) reduces to $k_{11} - \lambda = 0$. Since $k_{11} = 10$, the first approximate eigenvalue is $\lambda_1 = 10$, a close approximation to the correct value π^2. The corresponding approximate eigenfunction $f_1 = \varphi_1$ is a good approximation to the correct eigenfunction $y_1 = \sqrt{2} \sin \pi x$.

To obtain additional approximate eigenvalues and eigenfunctions one may use φ_2 as well as φ_1. The determinantal equation (15.22) then becomes

$$\begin{vmatrix} 10 - \lambda & 0 \\ 0 & 42 - \lambda \end{vmatrix} = 0$$

with solutions $\lambda_1 = 10$, $\lambda_2 = 42$ corresponding to the correct values $\lambda_1 = \pi^2$, $\lambda_2 = 4\pi^2$. The approximate eigenfunctions are $f_1 = \varphi_1$ and $f_2 = \varphi_2$.

Since $k_{13} = k_{31} \neq 0$, one may obtain better, as well as additional, approximate eigenvalues and eigenfunctions by using φ_3 in addition to φ_1 and φ_2. The determinantal equation (15.22) now becomes

$$\begin{vmatrix} 10 - \lambda & 0 & 2\sqrt{3} \\ 0 & 42 - \lambda & 0 \\ 2\sqrt{3} & 0 & 102 - \lambda \end{vmatrix} = 0$$

with solutions $\lambda_1 = 9.87$, $\lambda_2 = 42$, and $\lambda_3 = 102.13$. The corresponding approximate eigenfunctions are $f_1 = 0.999\varphi_1 - 0.038\varphi_3$, $f_2 = \varphi_2$, and $f_3 = -0.038\varphi_1 + 0.999\varphi_3$.

The reader will observe that more accurate eigenvalues were obtained by taking additional functions φ_i and not by correcting previous ones. Unfortunately, as more functions φ_i are included, the labor of computation increases enormously.

Exercises

1. Use the function e^{-cx^2}, where c is a constant, in the Rayleigh variational principle to obtain an upper limit to the lowest eigenvalue of

$$\left(-\frac{d^2}{dx^2} + \alpha^2 x + ax^3 + bx^4\right)\psi = \lambda\psi \qquad -\infty < x < +\infty$$

where ψ is required to be finite at $\pm\infty$. Minimize this upper limit by finding c such that $d\lambda/dc = 0$. Compare the value of λ so obtained with that obtained in Exercise 1 of Chap. 14.

2. Find a lower bound for the eigenvalue of Exercise 1.

3. Use the function $a + b \cos \theta + c \sin \theta$, where a, b, and c are constants, in the Rayleigh variational principle to obtain an upper limit to the lowest eigenvalue of

$$-\frac{d^2y}{d\theta^2} = (\lambda - \epsilon \cos^2 \theta)y \qquad y(0) = y(2\pi)$$

Minimize this upper limit.

4. Evaluate approximately the lowest eigenvalue of the vibrating-string problem

$$\frac{d^2y}{dx^2} + \lambda \rho y = 0 \qquad y(0) = y(1) = 0 \qquad \begin{array}{l} \rho = 1 \text{ for } 0 \leq x \leq 1/2 \\ \rho = 2 \text{ for } 1/2 < x \leq 1 \end{array}$$

Use the Rayleigh variational principle and carry out the evaluation for each of the functions $x(1 - x)$, $x(1 - x^2)$, and $\sin \pi x$.

5. Evaluate the eigenvalue of Exercise 4 using the Ritz method and each of the trial functions $(1 - x)(\alpha_1 x + \alpha_2 x^2)$ and $\alpha_1 \sin \pi x + \alpha_2 \sin 2\pi x$.

References

Pauling, L., and E. B. Wilson: "Introduction to Quantum Mechanics," pp. 180–190, McGraw-Hill Book Company, Inc., New York, 1935.

Courant, R., and D. Hilbert: "Methods of Mathematical Physics," vol. I, chap. 6, Interscience Publishers, Inc., New York, 1953.

Morse, P. M., and H. Feshbach: "Methods of Theoretical Physics," sec. 9.4, McGraw-Hill Book Company, Inc., New York, 1953.

CHAPTER 16

Iteration Procedures

16.1 Introduction

The variational estimates of the lowest eigenvalue of an operator, given in the preceding chapter, are limited by one's ability to select good trial functions. For this reason, methods of improving trial functions are of interest. One such method, that of iteration, is the subject of this chapter. It has many variants and may be applied to a wide class of problems. Some of these will be discussed below.

16.2 Eigenvalue Problems

One of the first successful iteration methods, that due to Cayley-Sylvester, may be used in the case of discrete systems to determine the largest (in magnitude) eigenvalue and the corresponding eigencolumn of a (matrix) operator $\mathscr{L}$. It proceeds as follows: It is desired to solve the eigenvalue problem

$$\mathscr{L}y = \lambda y \tag{16.1}$$

for its largest (in magnitude) eigenvalue λ_m and its corresponding eigencolumn y_m. If the operator $\mathscr{L}$ has a complete set of eigencolumns ϕ_σ $(\sigma = 1, 2, \ldots, m)$ such that

$$\mathscr{L}\phi_\sigma = \lambda_\sigma \phi_\sigma \tag{16.2}$$

$$|\lambda_1| \leq |\lambda_2| \leq \cdots \leq |\lambda_m| \tag{16.3}$$

one may write, for arbitrary y_0,

$$y_0 = \sum_\sigma a_\sigma \phi_\sigma \tag{16.4}$$

Then
$$\mathscr{L}y_0 = \sum_{\sigma} a_\sigma \lambda_\sigma \phi_\sigma = \alpha_1 y_1$$

say, where α_1 is a constant and y_1 is the first approximation to the eigencolumn y_m. Further

$$\mathscr{L}y_1 = \frac{1}{\alpha_1}\sum_{\sigma} a_\sigma \lambda_\sigma^{\,2} \phi_\sigma = \alpha_2 y_2$$

or in general
$$\mathscr{L}y_{i-1} = \frac{1}{\alpha_1 \alpha_2 \ldots \alpha_{i-1}}\sum_{\sigma} a_\sigma \lambda_\sigma^{\,i} \phi_\sigma = \alpha_i y_i$$

Hence
$$y_i = \frac{1}{\alpha_1 \alpha_2 \ldots \alpha_i}\sum_{\sigma} a_\sigma \lambda_\sigma^{\,i} \phi_\sigma$$

$$= \frac{\lambda_m^{\,i}}{\alpha_1 \alpha_2 \ldots \alpha_i}\sum_{\sigma} a_\sigma \left(\frac{\lambda_\sigma}{\lambda_m}\right)^i \phi_\sigma \qquad (16.5)$$

Since λ_m is the eigenvalue of largest magnitude, the powers $(\lambda_0/\lambda_m)_i$ tend to zero when $\sigma \neq m$, and the right-hand member of (16.5) tends to a multiple of ϕ_m as i increases except in the very special case when the initial assumption y_0 happens to be exactly orthogonal to ϕ_m so that $a_m = 0$. If λ_m is a multiple eigenvalue, the process will still lead to *one* corresponding eigencolumn.

As an example of the method, solve the eigenvalue problem (16.1) where (cf. Sec. 2.6)

$$\mathscr{L} = \begin{pmatrix} -15 & 12 \\ -24 & 19 \end{pmatrix}$$

Begin by guessing a solution, say $y_0 = \begin{pmatrix} 1 \\ 1 \end{pmatrix}$. If this guess were correct, $\mathscr{L}y_0 = \lambda y_0$ and the problem would be solved. Actually, one finds that

$$\mathscr{L}y_0 = \begin{pmatrix} -3 \\ -5 \end{pmatrix} = -3\begin{pmatrix} 1 \\ 5/3 \end{pmatrix} = -3y_1$$

say. Since the first guess was wrong, apply $\mathscr{L}$ to y_1:

$$\mathscr{L}y_1 = \begin{pmatrix} 5 \\ 7.6 \end{pmatrix} = 5\begin{pmatrix} 1 \\ 1.52 \end{pmatrix} = 5y_2$$

Hence y_1 is not an eigencolumn either. However, one notes that y_2 is much closer to y_1 than y_1 was to y_0, indicating that it is a better approximation to the eigencolumn. Continuing in this manner, one obtains

$$\mathscr{L}y_2 = \begin{pmatrix} 3.25 \\ 4.9 \end{pmatrix} = 3.25 \begin{pmatrix} 1 \\ 1.5 \end{pmatrix} = 3.25y_3$$

$$\mathscr{L}y_3 = \begin{pmatrix} 3 \\ 4.5 \end{pmatrix} = 3 \begin{pmatrix} 1 \\ 1.5 \end{pmatrix} = 3y_3$$

Hence $$y = \begin{pmatrix} 1 \\ 1.5 \end{pmatrix} \quad \text{or} \quad y = \begin{pmatrix} 2 \\ 3 \end{pmatrix}$$

is an eigencolumn of $\mathscr{L}$, and $\lambda = 3$ is the corresponding eigenvalue. Comparison with the results of Sec. 2.6 shows that the largest eigenvalue of $\mathscr{L}$ and its eigencolumn have indeed been found.

The iteration method of Cayley-Sylvester as described above suffers from several defects: In general, many iterations are required to obtain only an approximate solution; only the largest eigenvalue and its eigencolumn are determined, whereas in many problems it is the lowest eigenvalue and its eigencolumn which are of interest; the method cannot be applied to continuous systems involving differential operators. Some methods for overcoming these defects are indicated below.

The rate of convergence of the method clearly depends upon the magnitude of the ratio λ_{m-1}/λ_m. If this ratio is near unity, the convergence rate will be slow. It may be increased by a trick: Consider instead of (16.1)

$$\mathscr{L}^p y = \lambda^p y \tag{16.6}$$

where p is an integer. The eigenvalues of the new matrix $\mathscr{L}^p$ are then $\lambda_1^p, \lambda_2^p, \ldots, \lambda_m^p$ and the ratio is clearly increased.

In the case of a positive definite matrix (one which has only positive eigenvalues) the method may be extended to determination of the smallest eigenvalue and its eigencolumn by another trick: Having determined λ_m, one forms the matrix

$$\mathscr{L}' = \lambda_m 1 - \mathscr{L} \tag{16.7}$$

$\mathscr{L}'$ has the eigenvalues $\lambda_1' = \lambda_m - \lambda_m$, $\lambda_2' = \lambda_m - \lambda_{m-1}$, ..., $\lambda_m' = \lambda_m - \lambda_1$. $\mathscr{L}'$ may now be treated in the same manner as $\mathscr{L}$ was treated above. By determining its highest eigenvalue λ_m', one also obtains $\lambda_1 = \lambda_m - \lambda_m'$. The associated eigencolumn y_m' is seen to be identical with that belonging to the smallest eigenvalue λ_1 of $\mathscr{L}$ as follows: $\mathscr{L}'y_m' = (\lambda_m - \lambda_1)y_m'$ implies $\mathscr{L}y_m' = \lambda_1 y_m'$, that is, $y_m' = y_1$.

In many problems one is interested solely in the lowest eigenvalue of $\mathscr{L}$ and its eigencolumn. If the matrix operator $\mathscr{L}$ has an inverse the eigenvalue problem (16.1) may be replaced by the problem

$$\mathscr{L}^{-1}y = \lambda^{-1}y \qquad (16.8)$$

Clearly, the largest eigenvalue of $\mathscr{L}^{-1}$ to which the iteration method converges yields the lowest eigenvalue of $\mathscr{L}$. Unfortunately, the labor of inverting $\mathscr{L}$ in the case of discrete systems is usually so great that the method is inferior to the former approach. In the case of continuous systems involving differential operators, however, the method is quite simple to apply.

As an example, consider the standard problem of the vibrating string

$$\frac{d^2}{dx^2} y = -\lambda y \qquad y(0) = y(1) = 0$$

Begin by guessing a solution

$$y_0 = x(1 - x) = x - x^2$$

which satisfies the boundary conditions. Then, integrating twice and applying the boundary conditions one obtains

$$y_1 = -\tfrac{1}{12}x + \tfrac{1}{6}x^3 - \tfrac{1}{12}x^4 = -\tfrac{1}{12}(x - 2x^3 + x^4) \equiv -\tfrac{1}{12}y_2''$$

Continuing this process, one obtains the successive iterates:

$$y_2 = -\tfrac{1}{10}x + \tfrac{1}{6}x^3 - \tfrac{1}{10}x^5 + \tfrac{1}{30}x^6$$

$$= -\tfrac{1}{10}(x - \tfrac{5}{3}x^3 + x^5 - \tfrac{1}{3}x^6) \equiv -\tfrac{1}{10}y_3''$$

$$y_3 = -\tfrac{17}{168}x + \tfrac{1}{6}x^3 - \tfrac{1}{12}x^5 + \tfrac{1}{42}x^7 - \tfrac{1}{168}x^8$$

$$= -\tfrac{17}{168}(x - \tfrac{28}{17}x^3 + \tfrac{14}{17}x^5 - \tfrac{4}{17}x^7 + \tfrac{1}{17}x^8)$$

Thus one has obtained as successive approximations to the smallest eigenvalue of the operator $-d^2/dx^2$ (with its associated boundary conditions) the values 12, 10, and 168/17. The last is about 0.1 per cent greater than the exact eigenvalue π^2.

The approximate eigenfunction y_3 may now be used in the variational principle to obtain a better approximation to the eigenvalue. It yields the value 306/31, which is about 0.01 per cent greater than π^2.

In general, iteration methods will lead to good approximate eigenfunctions. It is harder to obtain good approximate eigenfunctions than good eigenvalues by variational methods.

16.3 Inverses by Iteration

The problem of finding the inverse $\mathscr{L}^{-1}$ of an operator $\mathscr{L}$ arises when it is required to solve the equation

$$\mathscr{L}x = y \tag{16.9}$$

for x. In many cases an iterative method may be successfully applied. One such method proceeds as follows: Let

$$\mathscr{L} = \mathscr{P} + \mathscr{Q} \tag{16.10}$$

where $\mathscr{P}$ is chosen to be a nonsingular matrix which can readily be inverted. Then the exact solution is

$$x = \mathscr{L}^{-1}y = (1 + \mathscr{P}^{-1}\mathscr{Q})^{-1}\mathscr{P}^{-1}y \tag{16.11}$$

where 1 is the unit operator. If one lets $\mathscr{M} = \mathscr{P}^{-1}\mathscr{Q}$ and $z = \mathscr{P}^{-1}y$, then

$$x = (1 + \mathscr{M})^{-1}z = (1 - \mathscr{M} + \mathscr{M}^2 - \mathscr{M}^3 + \cdots)z \tag{16.12}$$

provided that the series expansion converges.

The condition for convergence is easily found: To solve the problem

$$(1 + \mathscr{M})\psi = S \tag{16.13}$$

for ψ, consider, for arbitrary ψ_0, the sequence

$$\psi_{n+1} = S - \mathscr{M}\psi_n \tag{16.14}$$

Suppose

$$\mathscr{M}\phi_\sigma = \lambda_\sigma\phi_\sigma$$

where the ϕ_σ form a complete set. Then write

$$\psi_0 = \sum a_\sigma\phi_\sigma$$
$$S = \sum s_\sigma\phi_\sigma$$

Then, as is readily verified,

$$\psi_n = \sum_\sigma \left[\frac{s_\sigma}{1 + \lambda_\sigma} + \left(a_\sigma - \frac{s_\sigma}{1 + \lambda_\sigma} \right)(-\lambda_\sigma)^n \right]\phi_\sigma$$

It is clear that if $|\lambda_\sigma| < 1$, this process converges to the solution

$$\psi = \sum_\sigma \frac{s_\sigma}{1 + \lambda_\sigma}\phi_\sigma$$

Thus, the process converges if all eigenvalues of $\mathscr{M}$ are less than unity.

A useful assumption for ψ_0 is often $\psi_0 = S$, or $a_\sigma = s_\sigma$. In this case

$$\psi_n = \sum_\sigma \frac{s_\sigma}{1 + \lambda_\sigma} [1 - (-\lambda_\sigma)^{n+1}]\phi_\sigma$$

$$= \sum_\sigma s_\sigma \phi_\sigma [1 - \lambda_\sigma + \lambda_\sigma{}^2 - \cdots + (-\lambda_\sigma)^n]$$

$$= [1 - \mathcal{M} + \mathcal{M}^2 - \cdots + (-\mathcal{M})^n]S$$

Of course, if an approximate solution is already known, its use as the first approximation instead of $\psi_0 = S$ will shorten the computations.

In recapitulation, to solve the problem

$$\mathscr{L}x = y \qquad\qquad (16.9)$$

for x, transform into the problem

$$(1 + \mathcal{M})x = z \qquad\qquad (16.15)$$

as described in (16.10) through (16.12). The successive approximations to x are then obtained from the sequence

$$x_{n+1} = z - \mathcal{M}x_n \qquad\qquad (16.16)$$

As an application of the method to discrete systems, consider (16.9) with

$$\mathscr{L} = \begin{pmatrix} 5 & 0.4 & 0.2 \\ 0.4 & 2 & 0.2 \\ 0.2 & 0.2 & 0.8 \end{pmatrix} \quad \text{and} \quad y = \begin{pmatrix} 3.45 \\ 3.15 \\ 2.15 \end{pmatrix}$$

Choose the matrices $\mathscr{P}$ and $\mathscr{Q}$ such that

$$\mathscr{P} = \begin{pmatrix} 5 & 0 & 0 \\ 0.4 & 2 & 0 \\ 0.2 & 0.2 & 0.8 \end{pmatrix} \quad \mathscr{Q} = \begin{pmatrix} 0 & 0.4 & 0.2 \\ 0 & 0 & 0.2 \\ 0 & 0 & 0 \end{pmatrix}$$

Then

$$\mathscr{P}^{-1} = \begin{pmatrix} 0.2 & 0 & 0 \\ -0.04 & 0.5 & 0 \\ -0.04 & -0.125 & 1.25 \end{pmatrix}$$

$$\mathcal{M} = \mathscr{P}^{-1}\mathscr{Q} = \begin{pmatrix} 0 & 0.08 & 0.04 \\ 0 & -0.016 & 0.092 \\ 0 & -0.016 & -0.033 \end{pmatrix}$$

$$z = \mathscr{P}^{-1}y = \begin{pmatrix} 0.69 \\ 1.437 \\ 2.15575 \end{pmatrix}$$

The successive approximations to x are then (to slide-rule accuracy)

$$x_0 = \begin{pmatrix} 0.69 \\ 1.437 \\ 2.15575 \end{pmatrix} \qquad x_1 = \begin{pmatrix} \cdots \\ 1.2620 \\ 2.2497 \end{pmatrix} \qquad x_2 = \begin{pmatrix} \cdots \\ 1.2500 \\ 2.2502 \end{pmatrix} \qquad x_3 = \begin{pmatrix} 0.500 \\ 1.250 \\ 2.250 \end{pmatrix}$$

Note that since in the iteration process the leading element in x_n is always multiplied by zero, it is unnecessary to compute it until the final step is reached.

As an illustration of the application of the method to continuous systems, consider the solution of the equation

$$\frac{d^2}{dx^2} y + \alpha y = s(x) \tag{16.17}$$

with the boundary conditions

$$y(0) = y(1) = 0 \tag{16.18}$$

Rewrite (16.17) as

$$\left(1 + \frac{1}{\alpha}\frac{d^2}{dx^2}\right)y = \frac{1}{\alpha} s(x) \tag{16.17a}$$

The eigenvalues of the operator d^2/dx^2 with the boundary conditions (16.18) are $-n^2\pi^2$ with $n = 1, 2, 3, \ldots$. Clearly the operator $\frac{1}{\alpha} d^2/dx^2$ is large compared to unity for all α less than π^2. The inverse operator, $\mathscr{L}^{-1}$ say, is then small compared to unity. In such a case one may write in place of (16.17a)

$$(1 + \mathscr{L}^{-1})y = \frac{1}{\alpha}\mathscr{L}^{-1}s(x) \tag{16.19}$$

and apply the iteration method. Then

$$y_{n+1}(x) = \frac{1}{\alpha}\mathscr{L}^{-1}s(x) - \mathscr{L}^{-1}y_n(x)$$

$$= \frac{1}{\alpha}\left\{\mathscr{L}^{-1}[s(x) - \alpha y_n(x)]\right\}$$

$$= \int_0^x \int_0^t [s(u) - \alpha y_n(u)] \, du \, dt - \int_0^1 \int_0^t [s(u) - \alpha y_n(u)] \, du \, dt$$

$$= \int_0^x (x - t)[s(t) - \alpha y_n(t)] \, dt - x\int_0^1 (1 - t)[s(t) - \alpha y_n(t)] \, dt$$

$$= -(1 - x)\int_0^x t[s(t) - \alpha y_n(t)] \, dt - x\int_x^1 (1 - t)[s(t) - \alpha y_n(t)] \, dt$$

$$\tag{16.20}$$

The iteration process may now be applied, starting with an arbitrary y_0 which satisfies the boundary conditions.

If an approximate inverse to $\mathscr{L}$, say $\mathscr{N}$, is known, the equation

$$\mathscr{L}x = y \qquad (16.9)$$

may be solved by still another iterative method. Thus, if $1 - \mathscr{N}\mathscr{L}$ is small, one may write

$$\mathscr{N}\mathscr{L}x = \mathscr{N}y$$
$$= x + (\mathscr{N}\mathscr{L} - 1)x$$

so that $\qquad\qquad x = \mathscr{N}y + (1 - \mathscr{N}\mathscr{L})x$

The iterative solution is then

$$x_{n+1} = \mathscr{N}y + (1 - \mathscr{N}\mathscr{L})x_n$$

Exercises

1. By iteration, find the largest eigenvalue of

$$M = \begin{pmatrix} 5 & 2 \\ 1 & 5 \end{pmatrix}$$

2. Find the lowest eigenvalue of M by iteration.
3. By iteration, find the solution of

$$Mx = \begin{pmatrix} 1 \\ 1 \end{pmatrix}$$

4. Find the lowest eigenvalue of

$$y'' + \lambda\rho y = 0$$

for $\qquad\qquad y(0) = y(1) = 0$

with $\qquad\qquad \rho(x) = 0.8 + 0.4x$

Work until two iterates yield eigenvalues differing by less than 2 per cent.

References

Kármán, T. V., and M. A. Biot: "Mathematical Methods in Engineering," McGraw-Hill Book Company, Inc., New York, 1940.

Frazer, R. A., W. J. Duncan, and A. R. Collar: "Elementary Matrices," Cambridge University Press, New York, 1947.

Hildebrand, F. B.: "Methods of Applied Mathematics," Prentice-Hall, Inc., Englewood Cliffs, N.J., 1952.

Morse, P. M., and H. Feshbach: "Methods of Theoretical Physics," chap. 9, McGraw-Hill Book Company, Inc., New York, 1953.

CHAPTER 17

Construction of Eigenvalue Problems

17.1 Introduction

Many useful methods of handling eigenvalue problems have been discussed in Chaps. 14 to 16. In this chapter we shall show how some problems may be transformed into eigenvalue problems and, therefore, solved by the previously discussed methods.

17.2 The Method

Suppose that one wishes to calculate

$$\mu^{-1} \equiv \mathbf{Q}^+\boldsymbol{\psi} \tag{17.1}$$

in which $\mathbf{Q}$ is a given vector and $\boldsymbol{\psi}$ is the solution of the inhomogeneous equation

$$\mathscr{L}\boldsymbol{\psi} = \mathbf{S} \tag{17.2}$$

where both the operator $\mathscr{L}$ and the function $\mathbf{S}$ are given. The quantity μ may be found as an eigenvalue in a suitable equation. For example consider the equation

$$\mathscr{L}\boldsymbol{\varphi} = \mu \mathbf{S}\mathbf{Q}^+\boldsymbol{\varphi} \tag{17.3}$$

We assert that $\boldsymbol{\psi}$ satisfies (17.3) and that the corresponding μ is given by (17.1). Furthermore, any solution $\boldsymbol{\varphi}$ of (17.3) leads to a solution of (17.2),

$$\boldsymbol{\psi} = \frac{\boldsymbol{\varphi}}{\mu \mathbf{Q}^+\boldsymbol{\varphi}} \tag{17.4}$$

It then follows that if Eq. (17.2) has a unique solution, Eq. (17.3) has a unique eigenvalue μ and, furthermore, has a solution $\boldsymbol{\varphi}$ which is unique to within a multiplicative constant factor.

A variational principle for μ follows directly from Eqs. (14.19) and (14.21). Thus, one has

$$\mathscr{L}\boldsymbol{\varphi} = \mu S Q^+ \boldsymbol{\varphi}$$

$$\boldsymbol{\chi}^+ \mathscr{L} = \mu \boldsymbol{\chi}^+ S Q^+$$

and the variational principle

$$\mu = \frac{\boldsymbol{\chi}^+ \mathscr{L} \boldsymbol{\varphi}}{(S^+ \boldsymbol{\chi})^+ Q^+ \boldsymbol{\varphi}}$$

$$\frac{\delta\mu}{\mu} = \frac{\boldsymbol{\chi}^+ (\delta\mathscr{L}) \boldsymbol{\varphi}}{\boldsymbol{\chi}^+ \mathscr{L} \boldsymbol{\varphi}} - \frac{\boldsymbol{\chi}^+ \, \delta(SQ^+) \boldsymbol{\varphi}}{\boldsymbol{\chi}^+ SQ^+ \boldsymbol{\varphi}}$$

It may be useful to note that, if one so desires, he can write an equation for $\boldsymbol{\chi}$ analogous to (17.2) for $\boldsymbol{\psi}$. Thus, if $\boldsymbol{\chi}$ is normalized so that

$$\mu \boldsymbol{\chi}^+ S = 1$$

then

$$\boldsymbol{\chi}^+ \mathscr{L} = Q^+$$

Hence, in place of Eqs. (17.1) and (17.2) one may write

$$\mu^{-1} = (S^+ \boldsymbol{\chi})^+$$

$$\mathscr{L}^+ \boldsymbol{\chi} = Q$$

This latter formulation may be particularly useful if one wants to calculate μ for a wide variety of functions S, but for only one weighting function Q.

17.3   Application to the Scattering Problem

A rather interesting application of the results of the preceding section is to the scattering problem (cf., Secs. 13.6 to 13.9), where we were interested in a function ψ satisfying

$$\psi(r) = j_l(kr) + \int_0^\infty g_l(r,r')u(r')\psi(r')r'^2 \, dr' \qquad (17.5)$$

and phase shifts δ_l, which satisfied

$$\lambda^{-1} \equiv \tfrac{1}{2}(e^{2i\delta_l} - 1) = -ik \int_0^\infty j_l(kr)u(r)\psi(r)r^2 \, dr \qquad (17.6)$$

We thus have the eigenvalue problem

$$\psi(r) - \int_0^\infty g_l(r,r')u(r')\psi(r')r'^2 \, dr' = -ik\lambda j_l(kr) \int_0^\infty j_l(kr')u(r')\psi(r')r'^2 \, dr' \quad (17.7)$$

Multiplication of Eq. (17.7) by $\psi(r)u(r)r^2\,dr$ and integration over all r lead to the variational principle

$$-ik\lambda = \frac{\displaystyle\int_0^\infty \psi(r)u(r)\psi(r)r^2\,dr - \int_0^\infty\int_0^\infty \psi(r)u(r)g_l(r,r')u(r')\psi(r')r^2r'^2\,dr\,dr'}{\left[\displaystyle\int_0^\infty j_l(kr')u(r')\psi(r')r'^2\,dr'\right]^2}$$

(17.8)

A somewhat more useful form of (17.8), which is completely real, may be obtained as follows:

$$\begin{aligned}
g_l(r,r') &= -ikh_l^{(1)}(kr)j_l(kr') \qquad\qquad r' < r\\
&= -ik[j_l(kr) + in_l(kr)]j_l(kr')\\
&= -ikj_l(kr)j_l(kr') + kn_l(kr)j_l(kr')\\
&= -ikj_l(kr)j_l(kr') + G_l(r,r')
\end{aligned}$$

hence

$$\psi(r) - \int_0^\infty G_l(r,r')u(r')\psi(r')r'^2\,dr' = -ik(\lambda+1)j_l(kr)\int_0^\infty j_l(kr')u(r')\psi(r')r'^2\,dr'$$

and

$$-ik(\lambda+1) = \frac{\displaystyle\int_0^\infty \psi(r)u(r)\psi(r)r^2\,dr - \int_0^\infty\int_0^\infty \psi(r)u(r)G_l(r,r')u(r')\psi(r')r^2r'^2\,dr\,dr'}{\left[\displaystyle\int_0^\infty j_l(kr')u(r')\psi(r')r'^2\,dr'\right]^2}$$

But

$$\lambda + 1 = \frac{e^{2i\delta_l}+1}{e^{2i\delta_l}-1} = -i\cot\delta_l$$

Therefore

$$-k\cot\delta_l = \frac{\displaystyle\int_0^\infty \psi(r)u(r)\psi(r)r^2\,dr - \int_0^\infty\int_0^\infty \psi(r)u(r)G_l(r,r')u(r')\psi(r')r^2r'^2\,dr\,dr'}{\left[\displaystyle\int_0^\infty j_l(kr')u(r')\psi(r')r'^2\,dr'\right]^2}$$

(17.9)

which is the desired form.

CHAPTER 18

Numerical Procedures

18.1 Introduction

The purpose of this chapter is to give, by illustration, a very cursory indication of the use of numerical procedures in the solution of eigenvalue problems. The illustrative example will be the standard problem of the vibrating string. Two methods by which the actual equation involving an infinite number of degrees of freedom may be replaced by similar ones which involve only a finite number of degrees of freedom will be discussed. The advantage of such a replacement lies in the fact that problems with a finite number of degrees of freedom can always be handled numerically, if one is willing to work hard enough, whereas problems in continuous systems may not admit of any other direct attack.

In Sec. 18.2 it is shown how an alteration of the model of the vibrating string leads to a system with a finite number of degrees of freedom and how one may then proceed to the determination of an approximate value for the eigenvalues. In Sec. 18.3 it is shown how, beginning with the variational expression for the eigenvalue, a specific set of trial functions in a Rayleigh-Ritz procedure leads to a set of difference equations for the determination of the eigenvalue.

18.2 Simplification of the Model

It is desired to find the frequency and displacement of a finite vibrating string whose density is an arbitrary (but specified) function of position along the string. If one adopts the viewpoint that the precise form of the density variation along the string is unimportant, he may replace the arbitrary given density distribution by a distribution which is more suitable to numerical methods.

One such replacement is suggested by the results of Chaps. 6 and 7. Thus, let the string lie along the x axis in the region $0 \leq x \leq a$, and let the density distribution be denoted by $\rho(x)$. Then, the actual string might be approximated by a weightless string loaded with n masses m_i at the points

$$x_i = ih \qquad i = 0, 1, 2, 3, \ldots, n \qquad h = \frac{a}{n} \tag{18.1}$$

One would then expect that an approximate mass m_i to associate with the point x_i is the total mass of the actual string included between $x_i - (1/2)h$ and $x_i + (1/2)h$. Hence

$$m_i = \int_{x=x_i-\frac{1}{2}h}^{x_i+\frac{1}{2}h} \rho(x) \, dx \equiv \bar{\rho}_i h \tag{18.2}$$

With the notation $y(x_i) \equiv y_i$ for the displacement of the loaded string at the point x_i, the equations of motion are

$$m_i \ddot{y}_i = \frac{T}{h}(y_{i+1} - 2y_i + y_{i-1})$$

or

$$\bar{\rho}_i \ddot{y}_i = T \frac{y_{i+1} - 2y_i + y_{i-1}}{h^2} \tag{18.3}$$

with the boundary conditions

$$y_0 = y_n = 0 \tag{18.4}$$

Equations (18.3) and (18.4) bear a striking resemblance to the equations for the actual string:

$$\rho \ddot{y} = T \frac{d^2 y}{dx^2} \qquad y(0) = y(a) = 0$$

especially when it is noted that, with $x_i = x$

$$\lim_{h \to 0} \frac{y_{i+1} - 2y_i + y_{i-1}}{h^2} = \lim_{h \to 0} \frac{y(x+h) - 2y(x) + y(x-h)}{h^2}$$

$$= \frac{d^2}{dx^2} y(x)$$

and

$$\lim_{h \to 0} \bar{\rho}_i = \rho(x)$$

This sort of approach may be readily applied to the approximate determination of the eigenvalues λ in the eigenvalue problem

$$\frac{d^2}{dx^2} y + \lambda y = 0 \qquad y(0) = y(1) = 0 \tag{18.5}$$

which represents the problem of a string of uniform density per unit length. The corresponding difference equations are

$$h^{-2}(y_{i+1} - 2y_i + y_{i-1}) + \lambda y_i = 0 \qquad \begin{matrix} y_0 = y_n = 0 \\ i = 1, 2, \ldots, n-1 \quad nh = 1 \end{matrix} \qquad (18.6)$$

These equations are a set of $n-1$ linear equations for $n-1$ unknowns y_i. In order for them to have a solution other than the trivial one, $y_i = 0$ for all i, the determinant of the coefficients must vanish. Thus

$$\begin{vmatrix} h^2\lambda - 2 & 1 & 0 & 0 & \cdots & 0 & 0 \\ 1 & h^2\lambda - 2 & 1 & 0 & \cdots & 0 & 0 \\ 0 & 1 & h^2\lambda - 2 & 1 & \cdots & 0 & 0 \\ 0 & 0 & 0 & 0 & \cdots & h^2\lambda - 2 & 1 \\ 0 & 0 & 0 & 0 & \cdots & 1 & h^2\lambda - 2 \end{vmatrix} = 0 \quad (18.7)$$

This determinantal equation has $n-1$ solutions λ, which may be shown to be real. They are approximations to the first $n-1$ eigenvalues of (18.5).

As a first approximation, take $n = 2$, $h = 1/2$. Equation (18.7) then reduces to $(1/4)\lambda - 2 = 0$. Hence $\lambda = 8$ is the first approximation to the exact value π^2. This result is astonishingly good considering the nature of the approximation and the amount of labor involved.

For $n = 3$, $h = 1/3$, Eq. (18.4) reduces to

$$\begin{vmatrix} \tfrac{1}{9}\lambda - 2 & 1 \\ 1 & \tfrac{1}{9}\lambda - 2 \end{vmatrix} = 0$$

The solutions of this determinantal equation are the approximate eigenvalues $\lambda_1 = 9$, $\lambda_2 = 27$ which correspond, respectively, to the exact values π^2 and $4\pi^2$.

For $n = 4$, $h = 1/4$, the determinantal equation

$$\begin{vmatrix} \tfrac{1}{16}\lambda - 2 & 1 & 0 \\ 1 & \tfrac{1}{16}\lambda - 2 & 1 \\ 0 & 1 & \tfrac{1}{16}\lambda - 2 \end{vmatrix} = 0$$

has solutions $\lambda_1 = 9.37$, $\lambda_2 = 32$, and $\lambda_3 = 54.63$.

One notes that increasing the total number of lattice points, i.e., increasing n, not only gives additional approximate eigenvalues but also gives better approximations for the previously determined ones.

An analytical expression for the approximate eigenvalues λ may be obtained by noting that Eqs. (18.6) are identical in form with Eqs. (6.11), in which λ is given by (6.17). In the present notation, Eq. (6.17) reads

$$\lambda_i = \frac{2}{h^2}\left(1 - \cos\frac{\pi i}{n}\right) = 2n^2\left(1 - \cos\frac{\pi i}{n}\right) \tag{18.8}$$

or

$$\lambda_i = \frac{4}{h^2}\sin^2\frac{\pi i h}{2} \tag{18.8a}$$

[n appears in (18.8) in place of the $(n + 1)$ of (6.17) since $i = 0, 1, 2, \ldots$, $n - 1$ in Eq. (18.6) whereas $i = 1, 2, \ldots, n$ in Eq. (6.11).] In the limit of an infinite number of lattice points, $n \to \infty$, $h \to 0$, Eq. (18.8a) reduces to $\lambda = i^2\pi^2$, the exact values of the eigenvalues of (18.5).

The displacement y_i of the ith lattice point may be obtained by replacing $(n + 1)$ in Eq. (6.18) by n. Thus

$$y_{ki} = \frac{\sin \pi k i/n}{\sin \pi i/n}\, y_{1i} \qquad k = 1, 2, \ldots, n,$$

$$= \frac{\sin \pi k i h}{\sin \pi i h}\, y_{1i}$$

or

$$y_k(x_i) = \frac{\sin \pi k x_i}{\sin \pi x_i}\, y_{1i}$$

Other approximations to $\rho(x)$, in addition to the point mass discussed above, are readily imagined. Thus, one might take in place of $\rho(x)$

$$p(x) = \bar{\rho}_i \qquad x_i - \frac{1}{2h} < x < x_i + \frac{1}{2h}$$

In such a case, the differential equations may be solved in each region where p is constant and fitted together at the points where p changes.

18.3 Difference Equations from the Variational Principle

As was shown in Chaps. 14 and 15, the variational principle

$$\lambda = \frac{\displaystyle\int_0^a \left(\frac{dy}{dx}\right)^2 dx}{\displaystyle\int_0^a \rho y^2\, dx} \tag{18.9}$$

is completely equivalent to the eigenvalue problem

$$\frac{d^2y}{dx^2} + \lambda\rho y = 0 \qquad y(0) = y(a) = 0 \tag{18.10}$$

Approximate values of λ and y may be obtained from (18.9) by means of the Rayleigh-Ritz procedure. A method of doing this which yields difference equations for solution is described below.

Use as a trial function in (18.9) a $y(x)$ which is linear between the lattice points $x_i = ih$ and continuous at the points x_i. Thus, with $x_i = ih$ and $h = a/n$, use

$$y(x) = y_i + (y_{i+1} - y_i)\left(\frac{x - x_i}{h}\right) \qquad x_i \leq x \leq x_i + h$$

with
$$y(0) = y_0 = 0 \qquad y(a) = y_n = 0$$

This form for $y(x)$ may be substituted into (18.9) as a Ritz trial function (depending on the parameters $y_1, y_2, \ldots, y_n$). Since y is continuous at the points $x = x_i$, there will be no contribution to the numerator of (18.9) at these points. A brief computation then yields

$$\lambda = \frac{h \sum_{i=0}^{n-1} [(y_{i+1} - y_i)/h]^2}{\begin{aligned} h \sum_{i=0}^{n-1} \big[&\bar{\rho}_{i+\frac{1}{2}} \tfrac{1}{3}(y_i{}^2 + y_i y_{i+1} + y_{i+1}{}^2) + \overline{\rho t}_{i+\frac{1}{2}}(y_{i+1}{}^2 - y_i{}^2) \\ &+ \overline{\rho(t^2 - \tfrac{1}{12})}_{i+\frac{1}{2}}(y_{i+1} - y_i)^2 \big] \end{aligned}}$$

in which
$$\overline{\rho t_{i+\frac{1}{2}}^{\sigma}} \equiv \int_{-\frac{1}{2}}^{+\frac{1}{2}} t^{\sigma} \rho(x_i + \tfrac{1}{2}h + ht)\,dt$$

If this expression for λ is minimized with respect to $y_1, y_2, \ldots, y_{n-1}$, one finds the following difference equation for the y_i:

$$\frac{y_{i+1} - 2y_i + y_{i-1}}{h^2} + \lambda\{\tfrac{1}{6}[\bar{\rho}_{i+\frac{1}{2}}(2y_i + y_{i+1}) + \bar{\rho}_{i-\frac{1}{2}}(2y_i + y_{i-1})]$$

$$+ \rho(\bar{t}_{i-\frac{1}{2}} - \overline{\rho t}_{i+\frac{1}{2}})y_i + \overline{\rho(t^2 - \tfrac{1}{12})}_{i+\frac{1}{2}}(y_i - y_{i+1})$$

$$+ \overline{\rho(t^2 - \tfrac{1}{12})}_{i-\frac{1}{2}}(y_i - y_{i-1})\} = 0 \quad (18.11)$$

While this equation is substantially more complex than the corresponding result of Sec. 18.2, it does have the advantage that the λ obtained is an upper bound for the true eigenvalue.

As an example, let $\rho = 1$, $a = 1$, and $h = 1/n$, so that (18.11) reduces to

$$\frac{y_{i+1} - 2y_i + y_{i-1}}{h^2} + \frac{\lambda}{6}(y_{i+1} + 4y_i + y_{i-1}) = 0$$

with the boundary conditions $y_0 = y_n = 0$. These equations may be solved by the method of Chap. 6 to obtain as upper bounds for the lowest root

$$\lambda = 6 \frac{1 - \cos \pi/n}{2 + \cos \pi/n} n^2$$

In Table 18.1 these values are tabulated as λ'. For comparison the approximate values λ, obtained in Sec. 18.2, are also tabulated.

Table 18.1

n	2	3	4	5	6	∞
λ	8	9	9.37	9.55	9.65	9.87
λ'	12	10.8	10.37	10.20	10.09	9.87

It is interesting to note that the values of λ' are just about as high above π^2 as the corresponding values of λ are below.

Equations (18.11) are just one of a variety of sets of difference equations which can be produced by suitable approximate evaluation of the integrals in (18.9). For example,

$$\lambda = \frac{h \sum_i [(y_{i+1} - y_i)/h]^2}{h \sum_i \rho_i y_i^2}$$

leads to the difference equations of Sec. 18.2, but with ρ_i replacing $\bar{\rho}_i$.

Exercises

1. Find approximately the lowest eigenvalue satisfying

$$\frac{d^2}{dx^2} y + \lambda x^2 y = 0 \qquad 0 \le x \le 1$$

where

$$\left.\frac{dy}{dx}\right|_{x=0} = 0 \qquad \text{and} \qquad y(1) = 0$$

2. Use the method of Sec. 18.3 to solve Exercise 4 of Chap. 16.
3. Consider a tightly stretched string loaded at N equally spaced points $x_n = nk$ $(n = 1, 2, \ldots, N)$ by forces f_n, and attached to the x axis

at the points $x_0 = 0$ and $x_{N+1} = (N+1)k = L$. For small deflections the problem is described by the difference equation

$$y_{n+1} - 2y_n + y_{n-1} = \frac{k}{T} f_n \qquad (1 \le n \le N)$$

where k is the horizontal spacing and T the (constant) tension, and the end conditions

$$y_0 = 0 \qquad y_{N+1} = 0$$

Assuming that the mass of the string may be neglected and that all the forces f_n are equal, find y_n as a function of x_n. Show that in the limiting case as $k \to 0$, the solution reduces to

$$y = -\frac{p}{2T} x(L - x)$$

where p is the uniform force per unit length.

APPENDIX 1A

Determinants

It is customary to introduce the concept of determinants from the point of view of the solution of linear equations. For example, if the equations

$$a_{11}x_1 + a_{12}x_2 = y_1$$
$$a_{21}x_1 + a_{22}x_2 = y_2$$

are to be solved for x_1 and x_2 where the other quantities are given, the process of elimination leads to the solutions

$$x_1 = \frac{a_{22}y_1 - a_{12}y_2}{D(A)}$$

$$x_2 = \frac{a_{11}y_2 - a_{21}y_1}{D(A)}$$

where $D(A) = a_{11}a_{22} - a_{12}a_{21}$. It is then customary to introduce the notation

$$D(A) = |A| = \begin{vmatrix} a_{11} & a_{12} \\ a_{21} & a_{22} \end{vmatrix}$$

with the understanding that this is an abbreviation and that the value of $|A|$ is obtained by evaluating the sum

$$|A| = \sum_{i,j} \varepsilon_{ij} a_{1i} a_{2j}$$

where $\varepsilon_{12} = 1$, $\varepsilon_{21} = -1$, and $\varepsilon_{11} = \varepsilon_{22} = 0$. $|A| = |a_{ij}|$ is called the determinant of the coefficients a_{ij}. In this notation

$$|A|x_1 = \begin{vmatrix} y_1 & a_{12} \\ y_2 & a_{22} \end{vmatrix}$$

$$|A|x_2 = \begin{vmatrix} a_{11} & y_1 \\ a_{21} & y_2 \end{vmatrix}$$

243

That is, the solutions are ratios of two determinants wherein the numerators are formed from $|A|$ by replacing the first or second column by the y_i as indicated.

In order to extend this procedure to n variables $x_i\,(i = 1\cdots n)$ so that the equations whose solution is required are

$$\sum_{j=1}^{n} a_{ij}x_j = y_i$$

one needs define an $n \times n$ determinant. By definition

$$|A| = \sum \varepsilon_{i_1,i_2,\ldots,i_n} a_{1i_1}a_{2i_2}\ldots a_{ni_n} \equiv \begin{vmatrix} a_{11} & a_{12} & \cdots & a_{1n} \\ a_{21} & a_{22} & \cdots & a_{2n} \\ \cdot & \cdot & \cdot & \cdot \\ \cdot & \cdot & \cdot & \cdot \\ \cdot & \cdot & \cdot & \cdot \\ a_{n1} & a_{n2} & \cdots & a_{nn} \end{vmatrix} \qquad (1A.1)$$

where $\varepsilon_{i_1 i_2,\ldots,i_n}$ is $+1$ if $i_1, i_2, \ldots, i_n$ is an even permutation of the numbers $1, 2, \ldots, n$ and is -1 for an odd permutation.[1] $\varepsilon_{i_1,i_2,\ldots,i_n}$ vanishes if any two subscripts are equal. Alternately ε may be defined by

$$\varepsilon_{i_1\cdots i_\sigma\cdots i_\tau\cdots i_n} = -\varepsilon_{i_1\cdots i_\tau\cdots i_\sigma\cdots i_n}$$

$$\varepsilon_{1,2,3,\ldots,n} = 1$$

The sum in (1A.1) is over all $n!$ permutations. Stated otherwise, the expansion of the square array in (1A.1) is obtained by taking sums of all possible products of elements a_{ij} of the determinant in such a way that each term contains one and only one element from each row and from each column where each such product is given the plus or minus sign according as the number of transpositions of the second subscripts is even or odd when the first subscripts are in the natural order as in the principal diagonal.

The sum of the signed products described in the definition is called the expansion of the determinant. Since there are $n!$ permutations of the n seconp subscripts, the expansion of a determinant of the nth order contains $n!$ terms.

---

[1] An even (odd) permutation of $1, 2, \ldots, n$ is one which can be obtained from $1, 2, \ldots, n$ by an even (odd) number of interchanges (transpositions) of pairs of numbers in this set. Thus for $n = 4$, 1243, 1324, and 4123 are examples of odd permutations of 1234 while 3412, 1342, and 2143 are examples of even permutations. It is clear that any cyclic interchange is even (odd) for n odd (even).

A more useful form of the definition (1A.1) may be derived. Consider

$$F_{i_1,i_2,\ldots,i_n} = \sum_{j_1,j_2,\ldots,j_n} a_{i_1 j_1} a_{i_2 j_2} \cdots a_{i_n j_n} \varepsilon_{j_1,j_2,\ldots,j_n}$$

$$= \begin{vmatrix} a_{i_1 1} & a_{i_1 2} & \cdots & a_{i_1 n} \\ a_{i_2 1} & a_{i_2 2} & \cdots & a_{i_2 n} \\ \cdot & \cdot & \cdot & \cdot \\ \cdot & \cdot & \cdot & \cdot \\ \cdot & \cdot & \cdot & \cdot \\ a_{i_n 1} & a_{i_n 2} & \cdots & a_{i_n n} \end{vmatrix} \qquad (1A.2)$$

Clearly $F_{1,2,3,\ldots,n} = |A|$. Further

$$\begin{aligned} F_{i_1 \cdots i_\sigma \cdots i_\tau \cdots i_n} &= \sum_{j,i} a_{i_1 j_1} \cdots a_{i_\sigma j_\sigma} \cdots a_{i_\tau j_\tau} \cdots a_{i_n j_n} \varepsilon_{j_1 \cdots j_\sigma \cdots j_\tau \cdots j_n} \\ &= \sum_{j,i} a_{i_1 j_1} \cdots a_{i_\tau j_\tau} \cdots a_{i_\sigma j_\sigma} \cdots a_{i_n j_n} \varepsilon_{j_1 \cdots j_\sigma \cdots j_\tau \cdots j_n} \\ &= -\sum_{j,i} a_{i_1 j_1} \cdots a_{i_\tau j_\tau} \cdots a_{i_\sigma j_\sigma} \cdots a_{i_n j_n} \varepsilon_{j_1 \cdots j_\tau \cdots j_\sigma \cdots j_n} \\ &= -F_{i_1 \cdots i_\tau \cdots i_\sigma \cdots i_n} \qquad (1A.3) \end{aligned}$$

Thus F is proportional to ε:

$$F_{i_1,i_2,\ldots,i_n} = \varepsilon_{i_1,i_2,\ldots,i_n} |A|$$

or $$\sum_{j_1,j_2,\ldots,j_n} a_{i_1 j_1} a_{i_2 j_2} \cdots a_{i_n j_n} \varepsilon_{j_1,j_2,\ldots,j_n} = \varepsilon_{i_1,i_2,\ldots,i_n} |A| \qquad (1A.4)$$

Determinants have the following properties which are direct consequences of the definition:

I. *The value of a determinant is not changed if corresponding rows and columns are interchanged;* $|D| = |D^T|$, where D^T is the matrix formed from D by interchanging corresponding rows and columns ($d_{ij}^T = d_{ji}$) and is called the *transpose* of D.

Thus, from (1A.4)

$$\sum_{i_1,i_2,\ldots,i_n} (\varepsilon_{i_1,i_2,\ldots,i_n})^2 |A| = \sum_{i_1,i_2,\ldots,i_n} \sum_{j_1 j_2} \varepsilon_{i_1,i_2,\ldots} \varepsilon_{j_1,j_2,\ldots} a_{i_1 j_1} a_{i_2 j_2}$$

which is clearly unchanged by replacing each a_{ij} with a_{ji}. Since further $\Sigma(\varepsilon_{i_1,i_2,\ldots})^2 > 0$, property I is established.

From property I it follows that for every theorem concerning the rows of a determinant there is a corresponding theorem concerning the columns. Hence, we shall state the following properties as true for both rows and columns, but shall prove only that part referring to rows.

II. *An interchange of any two rows (or columns) of a determinant will merely change the sign of the determinant.* In the light of (1A.2) this property is identical with (1A.3).

III. *If any two rows (or columns) of a determinant are identical, the value of the determinant is zero.*

Denote the value of the determinant by $|D|$. If one interchanges the two identical rows (or columns), the value of the determinant is unchanged. But, by property II, such an interchange changes $|D|$ into $-|D|$. Hence, $|D| = -|D|$ or $|D| = 0$.

IV. *If all the elements of any row (or column) are multiplied by the same number λ, the value of the determinant is multiplied by λ.* This follows directly from (1A.1).

From properties III and IV, it follows that the value of a determinant is zero if any two rows (or columns) have corresponding elements proportional.

V. *If all the elements of any row (or column) are zero, the value of the determinant is zero.*

Each term of the expansion of the determinant is zero, because each term contains one factor from the row (or column) of zeros.

VI. *If each element of any row (or column) of a determinant is written as the sum of two numbers, then the determinant may be written as the sum of two determinants.*

Each term of the expansion of the determinant may be separated into two terms, because each term contains one factor from the row (or column) whose elements are written as the sum of two numbers. Thus one has two expansions (i.e., two determinants) whose sum equals the original expansion (determinant).

VII. *If each element of any row (or column) of a determinant is multiplied by a given number λ and added to (or subtracted from) the corresponding element of another row (or column), the value of the determinant is unchanged.*

Apply property VI to the resultant determinant to obtain the original determinant plus another determinant having two rows (or columns) with corresponding elements proportional. By properties III and IV this latter determinant is zero.

If, in the determinant $|D|$, one strikes out the row and column that contain the element d_{ij}, the remaining determinant of order $n-1$ is called the *minor* of the element d_{ij}. The product of the minor of d_{ij} by $(-1)^{i+j}$ is called the *cofactor* of d_{ij} and is denoted by D_{ij}. From (1A.1) the coefficient of d_{nn} in $|D|$ is given by

$$\sum_{i_1, \ldots, i_{n-1}=1}^{n-1} d_{1i_1}, d_{2i_2}, \ldots, d_{n-1,i_{n-1}} \, \varepsilon_{i_1,i_2,\ldots,i_{n-1}}$$

which is clearly its cofactor D_{nn}. That the coefficient of d_{ij} is its cofactor D_{ij} may be seen as follows: In $|D|$ interchange the nth and ith rows and then the nth and jth columns, so as to make the element a_{ij} the lower right element in the new determinant. According to property II there have been $(n - i) + (n - j)$ changes of sign. It follows, therefore, that the coefficient of d_{ij} is the product of its minor by $(-1)^{2n-i-j} = (-1)^{i+j}$, i.e., its cofactor D_{ij}. Hence the theorem:

VIII. *The expansion of a determinant of order n may be written as the algebraic sum of n products formed by multiplying each element of any one row (or column) by its cofactor*:

$$|D| = \sum_{i=1}^{n} d_{ij}D_{ij} = \sum_{j=1}^{n} d_{ij}D_{ij} \qquad (1\text{A}.5)$$

This expansion of a determinant is known as the *simple Laplace expansion*.

Consider the sum

$$\sum_{j=1}^{n} d_{ij}D_{kj} \qquad k \neq i$$

Each term of this sum is the product of an element in the ith row of a determinant $|D|$ by the cofactor of the corresponding element in the kth row. It is the expansion of a determinant whose ith and kth rows are identical and whose value is therefore zero. Hence the theorem:

IX.   *The sum* $\sum_{j=1}^{n} d_{ij}D_{kj} = 0 \qquad k \neq i.$ $\qquad\qquad (1\text{A}.6)$

Similarly, it follows that

$$\sum_{i=1}^{n} d_{ij}D_{ik} = 0 \qquad k \neq j \qquad (1\text{A}.7)$$

One may now proceed to prove the properties of determinants listed in Sec. 1.7 of the text. The numbering used in the text is given in brackets after the property:

1. *The determinant $|z - M|$ is a polynomial of degree n in z with its leading term z^n.* [5]

The proof follows directly from the definition of a determinant which states that each term in the expansion contains as factors one and only one element from each row and column. z will then appear as a factor a maximum number of times (n times in a determinant of nth order) in that term of the expansion which contains as factors the diagonal elements. This term is equal to $\prod_i(z - m_{ii})$, which is a polynomial of degree n in z with leading term z^n. All other terms in the expansion must be of degree $m < n$ since they cannot have as factors all the diagonal elements.

2. *For a given column y, the necessary and sufficient condition that the equation Mx = y have a unique solution is that* $|M| \neq 0$. [2]

The matrix equation $Mx = y$ is an abbreviation for the set of equations

$$\sum_{j=1}^{n} m_{ij}x_j = y_i \qquad i = 1, 2, 3, \ldots, n \qquad (1A.8)$$

The theorem following on property 2 may now be stated as follows: A system of n nonhomogeneous linear equations in n unknowns has a unique solution if and only if the determinant of the coefficients $|M|$ is unequal to zero.

Thus we demonstrate the existence of a solution when $|M| \neq 0$ by construction. Multiply the ith equation of (1A.8) by M_{ik}, the cofactor of m_{ik}, and the sum over all i. Then, interchanging the order of summation,

$$\sum_j \left(\sum_i m_{ij}M_{ik} \right) x_j = \sum_i M_{ik}y_i$$

or
$$\sum_j |M|\, \delta_{jk}x_j = |M|x_k = \sum_i M_{ik}y_i$$

by (1A.5) and (1A.7).

If $|M| \neq 0$, then

$$x_k = \frac{1}{|M|} \sum_i M_{ik}y_i \qquad (1A.9)$$

This result may be shown to be equivalent to the well-known rule of Cramer, namely: each x_k is a quotient, the denominator of which is the determinant $|M|$ formed by the coefficients of the unknowns in the system of equations, the numerator being a determinant obtained from $|M|$ by substituting the column y for the kth column of $|M|$. The reader will note the equivalence of this with the solution previously given for two equations in two unknowns.

To demonstrate the uniqueness of the solution, we suppose that $x_i + \xi_i$ is another solution

$$\sum m_{ij}(x_j + \xi_j) = y_i$$

Then the ξ_i must satisfy
$$\sum m_{ij}\xi_j = 0$$

Suppose at least one of the ξ_i is not zero (say ξ_1). One may write, by use of property IV and by repeated use of property VII,

$$|M| = \frac{1}{\xi_1} \begin{vmatrix} m_{11}\xi_1 + m_{12}\xi_2 + \cdots & m_{12} & m_{13} & \cdots \\ m_{21}\xi_1 + m_{22}\xi_2 + \cdots & m_{22} & m_{23} & \cdots \\ m_{31}\xi_1 + m_{32}\xi_2 + \cdots & m_{32} & m_{33} & \cdots \end{vmatrix}$$

Since the first column is zero, it follows from V that $|M| = 0$, a contradiction. Thus $\xi_i = 0$, all i, whence the solution is unique.

Thus far it has been demonstrated that $|M| \neq 0$ is a sufficient condition for a system of n nonhomogeneous linear equations in n unknowns to have a unique solution. This result may be summarized in matrix notation as follows: If $Mx = y$ and $|M| \neq 0$, then $x = M^{-1}y$ where

$$(M^{-1})_{ij} = \frac{M_{ji}}{|M|}$$

and defines the inverse of the matrix M.

In order to show that $|M| \neq 0$ is also a necessary condition it is convenient to use property 3 below. The proof of necessity is therefore postponed until the truth of property 3 has been established.

3. *A necessary and sufficient condition that a column $x \neq 0$ exist satisfying $Mx = 0$ is that $|M| = 0$.* [3]

First assume $|M| \neq 0$. Then from (1A.9) one finds $x_k = 0$, since all the y_i are zero. Therefore, if there is some solution where the unknowns are not all zero, it is impossible to have $|M| \neq 0$. This demonstrates necessity.

For convenience in consideration of sufficiency, let us now introduce the idea of *rank of a matrix M*. If $|M|$ is of the nth order, a determinant obtained from $|M|$ by suppressing m rows and m columns is called a minor of order $n - m$; $|M|$ itself may be called the minor of order n, and any single element is a minor of order 1. If there exists at least one minor of order $r (\equiv n - m)$ that is not zero, whereas all minors of order higher than r are zero, the matrix M is said to be of rank r. Obviously, the rank of a matrix can be zero only if all elements are zero.

Suppose now that $|M| = 0$ and that M is of rank r. Interchange the rows and columns of $|M|$ so that the nonvanishing minor is composed of the first r rows and columns of the resultant determinant. Then the equations

$$Mx = 0$$

or

$$\sum_j m_{ij}x_j = 0$$

may be written

$$\sum_{j=1}^{r} m_{ij}x_j = -\sum_{\kappa=r+1}^{n} m_{i\kappa}x_\kappa \qquad i = 1, 2, \ldots, r \qquad (1A.10)$$

$$\sum_{k=1}^{n} m_{ik}x_k = 0 \qquad i = r+1, \ldots, n \qquad (1A.11)$$

For any arbitrarily chosen set of values of x_κ ($\kappa = r + 1, \ldots, n$), the set (1A.10) has a unique solution, namely:

$$x_k = -\sum_{i=1}^{r} \frac{M'_{ik}}{|M'|} \sum_{\kappa=r+1}^{n} m_{i\kappa}x_\kappa \qquad k = 1, 2, \ldots, r \qquad (1A.12)$$

where $|M'|$ is the rth order determinant of the coefficients on the left of (1A.10) and M'_{ik} is the cofactor of m_{ik} in the determinant $|M'|$.

Substitution into the left side of (1A.11) yields, for $i > r$,

$$\sum_{k=1}^{n} m_{ik}x_k = -\sum_{k=1}^{n} \sum_{p=1}^{r} \frac{M'_{pk}}{|M'|} m_{ik} \sum_{\kappa=r+1}^{n} m_{p\kappa}x_\kappa + \sum_{\kappa=r+1}^{n} m_{i\kappa}x_\kappa$$

$$= \sum_{\kappa=r+1}^{n} \frac{x_\kappa}{|M'|} \left(|M'|m_{i\kappa} - \sum_{p=1}^{r} \sum_{k=1}^{r} m_{ik}m_{pk}m_{p\kappa} \right) \qquad (1A.13)$$

Consider now the following minor of order $r + 1$, and expand in terms of the last row and column:

$$\begin{vmatrix} m_{11} & m_{12} & \cdots & m_{1r} & m_{1\kappa} \\ m_{21} & m_{22} & \cdots & m_{2r} & m_{2\kappa} \\ \cdot & \cdot & \cdots & \cdot & \cdot \\ m_{r1} & m_{r2} & \cdots & m_{rr} & m_{r\kappa} \\ m_{i1} & m_{i2} & \cdots & m_{ir} & m_{i\kappa} \end{vmatrix} \qquad (1A.14)$$

The coefficient of $m_{i\kappa}$ in the expansion of this minor is $|M'|$. The coefficient of $m_{ik}m_{p\kappa}$ is the negative of the coefficient of $m_{i\kappa}m_{pk}$, which is $-M'_{pk}$. Hence the coefficient of $x_\kappa/|M'|$ in (1A.13) is a minor of order $r + 1$ of the original determinant, which vanishes by hypothesis. Thus if the matrix M is of rank r less than n, $n - r$ of the unknowns can be assigned arbitrarily and the remainder are homogeneous linear functions of them.

Having verified property 3 we may return to our considerations of property 2 and demonstrate that $|M| \neq 0$ is also a necessary condition for the equation $Mx = y$ to have a unique solution. Suppose that $|M| = 0$ and that $Mx = y$ has a solution x_0. Since $|M| = 0$ there exists an x_1 such that $Mx_1 = 0$. Therefore, $x = x_0 + \alpha x_1$, where α is an arbitrary constant, is also a solution of $Mx = y$. Hence the solution x_0 is not unique whence $|M| \neq 0$ is a necessary condition for a unique solution.

4. *The determinant of the product of two matrices is equal to the product of the determinants of the matrices;* if $A = XY$, $|A| = |X| \cdot |Y|$. [4]

We refer to the definition (1A.1) and also use (1A.4).

$$|A| = \sum \varepsilon_{i_1, i_2, \ldots, i_n} a_{1i_1} a_{2i_2} a_{3i_3} \ldots a_{ni_n}$$

$$= |a_{ij}| = \left| \sum_m x_{im} y_{mj} \right|$$

$$= \sum_{j_1, j_2, \ldots, j_n} \varepsilon_{j_1, j_2, \ldots, j_n} \left(\sum_{m_1} x_{1m_1} y_{m_1 j_1} \right) \left(\sum_{m_2} x_{2m_2} y_{m_2 j_2} \right) \ldots \left(\sum_{m_n} x_{nm_n} y_{m_n j_n} \right)$$

$$= \sum_{j_1, j_2, \ldots} \sum_{m_1, m_2, \ldots} \varepsilon_{j_1, j_2, \ldots} x_{1m_1} y_{m_1 j_1} x_{2m_2} y_{m_2 j_2} \cdots$$

$$= \sum_{m_1, m_2, \ldots} x_{1m_1} x_{2m_2} \ldots x_{nm_n} \sum_{j_1 j_2} \varepsilon_{j_1, j_2, \ldots} y_{m_1 j_1} y_{m_2 j_2} \cdots$$

$$= \sum_{m_1, m_2, \ldots} x_{1m_1} x_{2m_2} \ldots x_{nm_n} \varepsilon_{m_1, m_2, \ldots, m_n} |Y|$$

$$= |X| \cdot |Y|$$

Furthermore, since $|M^T| = |M|$, we have the equally possible equivalents $|MP^T|$, $|M^TP|$, $|M^TP^T|$, for $|M|\,|P|$. Thus determinant multiplication can be carried out row into row, column into column, and column into row, as well as by the usual row into column way of matrices.

Convergence of Matrix Power Series

The problem is to investigate the convergence of a power series of the form

$$S = \sum_{\sigma=0}^{\infty} c_\sigma A^\sigma$$

where A is an $n \times n$ matrix and the c_σ are numbers. Clearly S (if it exists) is also an $n \times n$ matrix.

Suppose now that B is also an $n \times n$ matrix and that

$$|a_{ij}| \leq a \qquad i,j = 1, 2, \ldots, n$$
$$|b_{ij}| \leq b \qquad i,j = 1, 2, \ldots, n$$

where the vertical bars indicate magnitude (not determinant). Then

$$|(AB)_{ij}| = \left| \sum_k a_{ik} b_{kj} \right|$$
$$\leq \sum_k |a_{ik}| \, |b_{kj}|$$
$$\leq nab$$

Thus

$$|(A^2)_{ij}| \leq na^2$$
$$|(A^3)_{ij}| \leq n^2 a^3$$

$$|(A^\sigma)_{ij}| \leq \frac{1}{n}(na)^\sigma \qquad \sigma > 0$$

But

$$|S_{ij}| = \left| \left(\sum_{\sigma=0}^{\infty} c_\sigma A^\sigma \right)_{ij} \right|$$
$$\leq |c_0| + \frac{1}{n} \sum_{\sigma=1}^{\infty} |c_\sigma|(na)^\sigma$$

Hence the power series for each element of S converges if

$$\sum_{\sigma} |c_{\sigma}|(na)^{\sigma}$$

converges.

As an example consider

$$e^{At} = \sum_{\sigma} \frac{1}{\sigma!} A^{\sigma} t^{\sigma}$$

Here $c_{\sigma} \equiv t^{\sigma}/\sigma!$. Since $\sum_{\sigma} (nat)^{\sigma}/\sigma!$ is convergent for any a and all t, it follows that e^{At} converges for any A and all t.

APPENDIX 1C

Remarks on Theory of Functions of Complex Variables

1C.1 Analytic Functions

A function $f(z)$ of the complex variable $z = x + iy$ which possesses a continuous derivative throughout a region R is called *analytic* or *monogenic* in the region R. Equivalently, considering the expression for the derivative,

$$f(z) = \lim_{\Delta z \to 0} \frac{f(z + \Delta z) - f(z)}{\Delta z} \tag{1C.1}$$

we state that the function is analytic at z if the above limit is independent of the path by which $z + \Delta z$ approaches z. Functions which do not obey this rule are called *polygenic*.

It is easy to obtain a pair of *necessary conditions* that the function

$$f(z) = u(x,y) + iv(x,y) \tag{1C.2}$$

have a derivative at z. In (1C.1) let $\Delta y = 0$ and let $\Delta z = \Delta x$ tend to zero. Then

$$f'(z) = \lim_{\Delta x \to 0} \frac{u(x + \Delta x, y) + iv(x + \Delta x, y) - u(x,y) - iv(x,y)}{\Delta x}$$

$$= \frac{\partial u}{\partial x} + i \frac{\partial v}{\partial x} \tag{1C.3}$$

Next, let $\Delta x = 0$ and let $\Delta z = i\Delta y$ tend to zero. Then,

$$f'(z) = \lim_{\Delta y \to 0} \frac{u(x, y + \Delta y) + iv(x, y + \Delta y) - u(x,y) - iv(x,y)}{i\Delta y}$$

$$= \frac{1}{i} \frac{\partial u}{\partial y} + \frac{\partial v}{\partial y} = -i \frac{\partial u}{\partial y} + \frac{\partial v}{\partial y} \tag{1C.4}$$

254

Equating (1C.3) to (1C.4), we obtain

$$\frac{\partial u}{\partial x} + i\frac{\partial v}{\partial x} = -i\frac{\partial u}{\partial y} + \frac{\partial v}{\partial y}$$

(1C.5)

or

$$\frac{\partial u}{\partial x} = \frac{\partial v}{\partial y} \quad \text{and} \quad \frac{\partial v}{\partial x} = -\frac{\partial u}{\partial y}$$

These relations are known as the *Cauchy-Riemann equations* and are the necessary conditions we set out to obtain.

If we assume that the real functions $u = u(x,y)$ and $v = v(x,y)$ are continuous, together with their first partial derivatives, then Eqs. (1C.5) form, conversely, a sufficient condition that $f = u + iv$ have a derivative and, equivalently, that the function be analytic. If we give to x and y any increments whatever, Δx, Δy, we can write

$$\Delta u = \frac{\partial u}{\partial x}\Delta x + \frac{\partial u}{\partial y}\Delta y + \epsilon_1\Delta x + \epsilon_2\Delta y$$

$$\Delta v = \frac{\partial v}{\partial x}\Delta x + \frac{\partial v}{\partial y}\Delta y + \epsilon_1'\Delta x + \epsilon_2'\Delta y$$

where the ϵ's are variables which approach zero with Δx and Δy. Since Eqs. (1C.5) are assumed to hold, it is clear that

$$\left(\frac{\partial u}{\partial x}\Delta x + \frac{\partial u}{\partial y}\Delta y\right) + i\left(\frac{\partial v}{\partial x}\Delta x + \frac{\partial v}{\partial y}\Delta y\right) = \left(\frac{\partial u}{\partial x} + i\frac{\partial v}{\partial y}\right)(\Delta x + i\Delta y)$$

so that the quotient

$$\frac{\Delta f}{\Delta z} = \frac{\Delta u + i\Delta v}{\Delta x + i\Delta y}$$

becomes

$$\frac{\Delta f}{\Delta z} = \frac{\partial u}{\partial x} + i\frac{\partial v}{\partial y} + (\epsilon_1 + i\epsilon_1')\frac{\Delta x}{\Delta z} + (\epsilon_2 + i\epsilon_2')\frac{\Delta y}{\Delta z}$$

Now $|\Delta x| \leqslant |\Delta z|$ and $|\Delta y| \leqslant |\Delta z|$, and the factors $\epsilon_1 + i\epsilon_1'$ and $\epsilon_2 + i\epsilon_2'$ are approaching zero as $\Delta x \to 0$ and $\Delta y \to 0$, respectively. Hence $\Delta f/\Delta z$ approaches a limit when $\Delta z \to 0$, and thus the function f is seen to possess a derivative and is analytic at z.

1C.2 The Cauchy Integral Theorem and Corollary

Let two points z_1 and z_2 be joined by a path C given in parametric form by $z = z(t)$, where t is a real variable, and let $z_1 = z(t_1)$ and $z_2 = z(t_2)$. Then the line integral taken along the path C, written

$$\int_C f(z)\, dz \quad \text{or} \quad \int_{z_1}^{z_2} f(z)\, dz$$

represents the integral

$$\int_{t_1}^{t_2} f[z(t)] \frac{dz}{dt}\, dt$$

An integral that is taken along a closed path or contour is indicated by the symbol $\oint$. If $f(z)$ is an analytic function within and on a closed contour C, then

$$\oint f(z)\, dz = 0 \tag{1C.6}$$

This is a statement of the Cauchy integral theorem. The proof is as follows:

$$\oint f(z)\, dz = \oint (u + iv)(dx + i\, dy) = \oint (u\, dx - v\, dy) + i \oint (v\, dx + u\, dy) \tag{1C.7}$$

Application of Stokes' theorem[1] to (1C.7) yields

$$\oint f(z)\, dz = \int\int \left(-\frac{\partial v}{\partial x} - \frac{\partial u}{\partial y} \right) dx\, dy + i \int\int \left(\frac{\partial u}{\partial x} - \frac{\partial v}{\partial y} \right) dx\, dy$$

Since $f(z)$ is analytic, the Cauchy-Riemann equations apply, the integrands of the double integrals vanish, and the theorem is proven.

An important corollary follows at once. If C_1 and C_2 are two closed contours, C_2 lying completely inside C_1, then

$$\int_{C_1} f(z)\, dz = \int_{C_2} f(z)\, dz \tag{1C.8}$$

provided that $f(z)$ is analytic between the two contours C_1 and C_2 and continuous on approaching them.

1C.3 Singularities

Suppose a function $f(z)$ is analytic throughout a closed region S, except possibly at a finite number of exceptional points. These points are called the *singular points* or *singularities* of the function. If there are no singularities within the domain S, the function is said to be *regular* in the domain. If a circle can be drawn about the singular point as center, so as to enclose no other singularity of the function, the singularity is said to be *isolated*.

[1] See, for example, H. and B. S. Jeffreys, "Methods of Mathematical Physics," pp. 170 and 319, Cambridge University Press, New York, 1946.

One type of singularity is known as a *branch point*. By definition, a point $z = \alpha$ is a branch point of $f(z)$ if $f(z)$ fails to return to its original value when z moves around α in a circle of arbitrarily small (nonzero) radius. As an example, consider the function $f(z) = z^{1/2}$ where $z = \rho e^{i\theta}$. Clearly, $f(z)$ has two values, namely:

$$f_1(z) = \rho^{1/2}\left(\cos\frac{\theta}{2} + i\sin\frac{\theta}{2}\right)$$

$$f_2(z) = \rho^{1/2}\left[\cos\left(\frac{\theta+2\pi}{2}\right) + i\sin\left(\frac{\theta+2\pi}{2}\right)\right] = -f_1(z)$$

These are known as the *branches* of the two-valued function $f(z)$. As θ varies continuously from 0 to 2π, $f_1(z)$ varies from $\rho^{1/2}$ to $-\rho^{1/2}$ and $f_2(z)$ varies from $-\rho^{1/2}$ to $\rho^{1/2}$. Thus a revolution of z about the origin (the branch point of $z^{1/2}$) interchanges the branches $f_1(z)$ and $f_2(z)$. Since we cannot attach a single value to $z^{1/2}$ at every point if θ can vary by more than 2π, $z^{1/2}$ is not a single-valued function of z. In order to simplify the situation, we try to consider only paths (contours) upon which $z^{1/2}$ is single valued. To accomplish this, we may limit θ to the range $0 \le \theta < 2\pi$ by making a *cut* along the real axis from 0 to $+\infty$ across which a path is not permitted to pass. In fact, any cut extending from the origin to ∞ will suffice.

Another type of singularity is known as a *pole*. Let $f(z)$ be analytic throughout a region S, except at a single point α inside the region, and let

$$f(z) = \frac{a_{-m}}{(z-\alpha)^m} + \frac{a_{-m+1}}{(z-\alpha)^{m-1}} + \cdots + \frac{a_{-1}}{(z-\alpha)} + \phi(z) \qquad (1C.9)$$

where $a_{-m} \ne 0$ and $\phi(z)$ is analytic within S. Then $f(z)$ is said to have a pole of order m at α. The terms containing negative powers of $z - \alpha$ are in the aggregate called the *principal part* of $f(z)$ near α. Poles of order unity are also called *simple poles*. If α is a pole of order m, $(z-\alpha)^m f(z)$ is analytic in the neighborhood of α and $\lim_{z\to\alpha}(z-\alpha)^m f(z) = C$, where C is the nonzero constant a_{-m}.

If no value of m can be found such that $\lim_{z\to\alpha}(z-\alpha)^m f(z) = \text{const.}$, then α is said to be an *essential singularity* of $f(z)$. An essential singularity is any point α, not a branch point or a pole, in the neighborhood of which $f(z)$ is not analytic.

1C.4 Cauchy's Integral Formula

From the corollary to the Cauchy integral theorem there may be derived a relation known as the Cauchy integral formula. Let $f(z)$ be analytic within a closed contour C and continuous on the contour C. Then if a is any arbitrary point within C

$$f(a) = \frac{1}{2\pi i} \int_C \frac{f(z)}{z-a}\,dz \qquad (1C.10)$$

This relation is known as the Cauchy integral formula. The derivation of (1C.10) is as follows: Draw a small circle γ about a. In the region between the contours γ and C, $\dfrac{f(z)}{z-a}$ is analytic. Hence, by the corollary to the Cauchy integral theorem,

$$\int_C \frac{f(z)}{z-a}\,dz = \int_\gamma \frac{f(z)}{z-a}\,dz$$

To evaluate the integral on the right, let $z - a = \rho e^{i\theta}$ where z is a point on the contour and ρ is the radius. Then

$$\int_\gamma \frac{f(z)}{z-a}\,dz = \int_0^{2\pi} \frac{f(z) i \rho e^{i\theta}}{\rho e^{i\theta}}\,d\theta = i\int_0^{2\pi} f(a + \rho e^{i\theta})\,d\theta$$

Now let ρ approach the limit zero. The last integral approaches

$$\int_0^{2\pi} f(a)\,d\theta = 2\pi f(a)$$

since the integrand is continuous in the two independent variables ρ and θ. Hence

$$\int_C \frac{f(z)}{z-a}\,dz = 2\pi i f(a)$$

which is the desired relation.

From (1C.10) one may obtain

$$f'(a) = \frac{d}{da}\frac{1}{2\pi i}\oint \frac{f(z)}{z-a}\,dz$$

$$= \frac{1}{2\pi i}\oint f(z)\frac{d}{da}\frac{1}{z-a}\,dz$$

or $\qquad\qquad f'(a) = \frac{1}{2\pi i}\int_C \frac{f(z)}{(z-a)^2}\,dz \qquad (1C.11)$

The process may be repeated indefinitely; and thus one obtains

$$f^{(n)}(a) = \frac{n!}{2\pi i}\int_C \frac{f(z)}{(z-a)^{n+1}}\,dz \qquad (1C.12)$$

1C.5 The Theorem of Residues

Consider a function $f(z)$ which has a pole of order m at $z = \alpha$. Then, by (1C.9), the integral $\oint f(z)\, dz$, where the path of integration is a circle whose center is at α and whose radius ρ is so small that $\phi(z)$ is analytic inside and on the circle, becomes

$$\oint f(z)\, dz = a_{-1} \oint \frac{dz}{z - \alpha} + \sum_{n=2}^{m} a_{-n} \oint \frac{dz}{(z - \alpha)^n} + \oint \phi(z)\, dz \quad (1C.13)$$

The last integral on the right is zero by reason of (1C.6). Hence, setting $z - \alpha = \rho e^{i\theta}$, (1C.13) becomes

$$\oint f(z)\, dz = a_{-1} \int_0^{2\pi} i\, d\theta + \sum_{n=2}^{m} a_{-n} \int_0^{2\pi} i\rho^{-n+1} e^{i(1-n)\theta}\, d\theta$$

$$= 2\pi i a_{-1} \quad (1C.14)$$

Hence the integral of $f(z)$ about its pole α depends wholly on the value of the coefficient of $(z - \alpha)^{-1}$ in its principal part. This coefficient is called the *residue* of the function at the pole.

We shall sometimes find it necessary to evaluate integrals of the form

$$I = \oint \frac{f(z)}{g(z)}\, dz$$

where $f(z)$ is analytic within the closed contour and continuous on the contour and $g(z)$ is a polynomial in z. The method of integration consists in breaking up the fraction $1/g(z)$ into an algebraic sum of simpler fractions or, as it is designated, into "partial fractions." The reader is referred to any standard text on the calculus for details. We limit our discussion to two illustrations: First, suppose $g(z) = C(z - a)(z - b)$ where C is a constant and $a \neq b$. Then

$$\frac{1}{g(z)} = \frac{1}{C(z - a)(z - b)} = \frac{1}{C}\frac{1}{b - a}\left(\frac{1}{z - b} - \frac{1}{z - a}\right)$$

Hence

$$I = \oint \frac{f(z)}{g(z)}\, dz = \frac{1}{C}\left[\frac{1}{a - b}\oint \frac{f(z)}{z - a}\, dz + \frac{1}{b - a}\oint \frac{f(z)}{z - b}\right]dz$$

$$= \frac{2\pi i}{C}\left[\frac{f(a)}{a - b} + \frac{f(b)}{b - a}\right]$$

by the Cauchy integral formula (1C.10).

Next, suppose $g(z) = (z - a)^2(z - b)$ where $a \neq b$. Then

$$\frac{1}{g(z)} = \frac{A}{z - a} + \frac{B}{(z - a)^2} + \frac{C}{z - b}$$

where

$$A = \frac{-1}{(a - b)^2}$$

$$B = \frac{1}{(a - b)}$$

$$C = \frac{1}{(a - b)^2}$$

Therefore

$$I = \oint \frac{f(z)}{g(z)} \, dz = A \oint \frac{f(z)}{z - a} \, dz + B \oint \frac{f(z)}{(z - a)^2} \, dz + C \oint \frac{f(z)}{z - b} \, dz$$

$$= 2\pi i [Af(a) + Bf'(a) + Cf(b)]$$

where the second integral on the right was evaluated by the use of (1C.11).

References

Copson, E. T.: "Theory of Functions of a Complex Variable," Oxford University Press, New York, 1944.

Hurwitz, A., and R. Courant: "Allgemeine Funktionentheorie," Interscience Publishers, Inc., New York, 1944.

Bierbach, L.: "Lehrbuch der Funktionentheorie," 4th ed., band I, Chelsea Publishing Company, New York, 1945.

APPENDIX 2A

Evaluation of Integrals of the Form $\int_{-\infty}^{+\infty} F(x)e^{ixt}\,dx$

The integral

$$I = \int_{-\infty}^{+\infty} F(x)e^{ixt}\,dx \tag{2A.1}$$

is representative of an oft-encountered class of integrals which may be evaluated by means of contour integration.

We first consider the case when the function $F(z)$ of the complex variable $z = x + iy$ is such that (1) it is analytic except at a finite number of poles, (2) it has no poles on the real axis, and (3) it goes to zero as $|z|$ goes to infinity. In this case we form the integral of $F(z)e^{izt}$ along a contour C which extends from $-R$ to $+R$, $R \to \infty$, along the real axis and returns from $+R$ to $-R$ along a semicircle of radius R with center at the origin. Then

$$\int_C F(z)e^{izt}\,dz = \lim_{R\to\infty}\left[\int_{-R}^{+R} F(x)e^{ixt}\,dx + \int_0^{\pm\pi} F(Re^{i\theta})e^{iRt\cos\theta - Rt\sin\theta}\,iRe^{i\theta}\,d\theta\right]$$

$$= I + \lim_{R\to\infty}\int_0^{\pm\pi} F(Re^{i\theta})e^{iRt\cos\theta - Rt\sin\theta}\,iRe^{i\theta}\,d\theta \tag{2A.2}$$

since, along the semicircle of radius R

$$z = Re^{i\theta} = R\cos\theta + iR\sin\theta$$

and

$$e^{izt} = e^{iRt\cos\theta - Rt\sin\theta}$$

The sign of the upper limit of the integral over θ depends on whether the semicircle lies in the upper or lower half of the z plane. This is determined by the sign of the real part of the constant t. For simplicity we shall assume that t is purely real. Then, if t is positive $\sin\theta$ must be positive

261

and the semicircle must lie in the upper half of the z plane. Otherwise, $e^{-Rt\sin\theta}$ would approach infinity as $R \to \infty$.

We write

$$\int_0^\pi = \int_0^\epsilon + \int_\epsilon^{\pi-\epsilon} + \int_{\pi-\epsilon}^\pi$$

for fixed ϵ. Then

$$\left| \int_0^\epsilon F(Re^{i\theta})e^{iRt\cos\theta - Rt\sin\theta} \, iRe^{i\theta} \, d\theta \right| \leq \int_0^\epsilon \left| F(Re^{i\theta})e^{iRt\cos\theta - Rt\sin\theta} \, iRe^{i\theta} \right| d\theta$$

$$= \int_0^\epsilon |F(Re^{i\theta})| e^{-Rt\sin\theta} R \, d\theta$$

$$\leq \int_0^\epsilon |F(Re^{i\theta})| e^{-Rt\theta} R \, d\theta$$

$$\leq MR \int_0^\epsilon e^{-Rt\theta} \, d\theta = \frac{M}{t}(1 - e^{-Rt\epsilon})$$

where M is the least upper bound of the continuous function $|F(Re^{i\theta})|$, and

$$\lim_{R\to\infty} \left| \int_0^\epsilon F(Re^{i\theta})e^{iRt\cos\theta - Rt\sin\theta} \, iRe^{i\theta} \, d\theta \right| \leq \lim_{R\to\infty} \frac{M}{t} = 0$$

since $\lim F(z) = 0$ by hypothesis.

Similarly

$$\lim_{R\to\infty} \int_{\pi-\epsilon}^\pi F(Re^{i\theta})e^{iRt\cos\theta - Rt\sin\theta} \, iRe^{i\theta} \, d\theta = 0$$

Finally

$$\left| \int_\epsilon^{\pi-\epsilon} F(Re^{i\theta})e^{iRt\cos\theta - Rt\sin\theta} \, iRe^{i\theta} \, d\theta \right| \leq \int_\epsilon^{\pi-\epsilon} \left| F(Re^{i\theta})e^{iRt\cos\theta - Rt\sin\theta} \, iRe^{i\theta} \right| d\theta$$

$$= \int_\epsilon^{\pi-\epsilon} |F(Re^{i\theta})| e^{-Rt\sin\theta} R \, d\theta$$

$$\leq \int_\epsilon^{\pi-\epsilon} |F(Re^{i\theta})| e^{-Rt\sin\epsilon} R \, d\theta$$

$$\leq Me^{-Rt\sin\epsilon} R(\pi - 2\epsilon)$$

where M is the least upper bound of the continuous function $|F(Re^{i\theta})|$, and

$$\lim_{R\to\infty} \left| \int_\epsilon^{\pi-\epsilon} F(Re^{i\theta})e^{iRt\cos\theta - Rt\sin\theta} \, iRe^{i\theta} \, d\theta \right| \leq \lim_{R\to\infty} Me^{-Rt\sin\epsilon} R(\pi - \epsilon) = 0$$

Consequently, for positive t

$$\lim_{R\to\infty} \int_0^\pi F(Re^{i\theta})e^{iRt\cos\theta - Rt\sin\theta}\, iRe^{i\theta}\, d\theta = 0$$

Similarly, for negative t

$$\lim_{R\to\infty} \int_0^{-\pi} F(Re^{i\theta})e^{iRt\cos\theta - Rt\sin\theta}\, iRe^{i\theta}\, d\theta = 0$$

We then have, by the method of residues (Appendix 1C), that

$$I = \int_C F(z)e^{izt}\, dz = \pm 2\pi i \sum \tag{2A.3}$$

where Σ denotes the sum of the residues of $F(z)e^{izt}$ at all its poles enclosed by the contour C and the sign is plus if the contour is described in the counterclockwise direction and minus if in the clockwise direction.

As an example, let us evaluate

$$I_1 = \int_{-\infty}^{+\infty} \frac{e^{ixt}}{x^2 + a^2}\, dx \tag{2A.4}$$

We note that the integrand has poles at $z = \pm ia$. If $t > 0$ the contour is completed in a counterclockwise direction along a semicircle of infinite radius, having the center at the origin and lying in the upper half of the z plane. The only pole enclosed by the contour is then $z = +ia$.

Hence
$$I_1 = 2\pi i \frac{e^{-at}}{2ia} = \frac{\pi}{a} e^{-at} \qquad (t > 0) \tag{2A.5}$$

If $t < 0$, the semicircle lies in the lower half of the z plane. The contour is then described in the clockwise direction and encloses the pole $z = -ia$. Hence, it follows that

$$I_1 = -2\pi i \frac{e^{at}}{-2ia} = \frac{\pi}{a} e^{at} \qquad (t < 0) \tag{2A.6}$$

In some cases of interest, $F(z)$ (1) is analytic except at a finite number of poles, (2) *has simple poles on the real axis*, and (3) goes to zero as $|z|$ goes to infinity. As an example consider the problem of evaluating

$$I_2 = \int_{-\infty}^{+\infty} \frac{e^{ixt}}{x - \alpha}\, dx \tag{2A.7}$$

Clearly the integrand diverges when $x = \alpha$ and the integral is meaningless. However, one may define the related integral

$$\int_{-\infty}^{\alpha-\epsilon} \frac{e^{ixt}}{x - \alpha}\, dx + \int_{\alpha+\epsilon}^{+\infty} \frac{e^{ixt}}{x - \alpha}\, dx$$

If this integral has a limit as $\epsilon \to 0$, we call the limit the principal value of I_2 and denote it by PI_2. To find the principal value of I_2 we form the integral of $e^{izt}/(z - \alpha)$ along a contour C which extends (1) along the real axis from $-R$ to $\alpha - \rho$, (2) a semicircle with center at α and radius ρ, (3) the real axis from $\alpha + \rho$ to $+R$, and (4) a semicircle with center at the origin and radius R, where $\rho \to 0$, and $R \to \infty$. Along the real axis $z = x$, and along the two semicircles

$$z = \alpha + \rho e^{i\theta} = \alpha + \rho(\cos\theta + i\sin\theta)$$

and $$z = Re^{i\theta} = R(\cos\theta + i\sin\theta)$$

respectively.

As before, the sign of the real constant t determines whether the semicircle of radius R lies in the upper or lower half of the z plane. Let us suppose that $t \geq 0$ so that the semicircle will lie in the upper half of the z plane. We shall see that whether the semicircle of radius ρ lies in the upper or lower half of the z plane has no effect on the value of I_2.

First, let us take the semicircle of radius ρ as lying in the upper half of the z plane. Then the contour integral

$$\int_C \frac{e^{izt}}{z - \alpha} dz = \int_{-R}^{\alpha-\rho} \frac{e^{ixt}}{x - \alpha} dx + \int_{\pi}^{0} e^{i\alpha t + it(\rho e^{i\theta})} i\, d\theta + \int_{\alpha+\rho}^{R} \frac{e^{ixt}}{x - \alpha} dx$$
$$+ \int_0^{\pi} e^{itRe^{i\theta}} i\, d\theta = 0$$

since the integrand has no pole inside the contour. In the limits $\rho \to 0$, $R \to \infty$, the sum of the first and third integrals on the right becomes PI_2, the second integral approaches $-\pi i e^{i\alpha t}$ and the fourth integral approaches zero. Hence

$$PI_2 = P\int_{-\infty}^{+\infty} \frac{e^{ixt}}{x - \alpha} dx = \pi i e^{i\alpha t} \qquad t > 0 \qquad (2A.8)$$

In the event that the semicircle of radius ρ is taken in the lower half of the z plane, the contour integral becomes

$$\int_C \frac{e^{izt}}{z - \alpha} dz = \int_{-R}^{\alpha-\rho} \frac{e^{ixt}}{x - \alpha} dx + \int_{\pi}^{2\pi} e^{i\alpha t + it(\rho e^{i\theta})} i\, d\theta + \int_{\alpha+\rho}^{R} \frac{e^{ixt}}{x - \alpha} dx$$
$$+ \int_0^{\pi} e^{itRe^{i\theta}} i\, d\theta = 2\pi i e^{i\alpha t}$$

since the contour C encloses the simple pole at $z = \alpha$. Now, in the limits $\rho \to 0$, $R \to \infty$, the sum of the first and third integrals on the right becomes PI_2, the second integral approaches $+\pi i e^{i\alpha t}$ and the fourth integral approaches zero. Hence

$$PI_2 + \pi i e^{i\alpha t} = 2\pi i e^{i\alpha t}$$

or
$$PI_2 = \pi i e^{i\alpha t} \qquad t > 0$$

which is identical with the previous result (2A.8).

If $t < 0$, it is easily shown that

$$PI_2 = -\pi i e^{i\alpha t} \qquad t < 0 \tag{2A.9}$$

APPENDIX 2B

Fourier Transforms, Integrals, and Series

2B.1 Introduction

We wish to develop here the concepts of Fourier transforms, integrals, and series from the point of view of transformation of bases in linear vector spaces. The Dirac notation introduced in Chap. 5 will be used as well as the standard notion found in conventional mathematical texts. Since we shall deal here with both finite and infinite dimensional linear vector spaces, it will be necessary to extend the interpretation of the notation in Chap. 5, which dealt with finite dimensional spaces only, to cover the infinite dimensional spaces as well. The reader is therefore advised to refresh his knowledge of the contents of the first two sections of Chap. 5 before proceeding further.

Consider a finite N-dimensional linear vector space and let the set of kets $|\lambda>$ form a basis in this space. Since the space is of dimensionality N, there will be N kets in the set forming a basis and the label λ will have N admissible values which may be denoted by $\lambda_1, \lambda_2, \ldots, \lambda_N$. We call the variable λ the *spectral variable* and refer to the range of its admissible values as the *spectrum* of λ. Any arbitrary ket $|>$ may be represented in the λ basis (i.e., in the basis formed by the N kets $|\lambda>$) by

$$|> = |\lambda> <\lambda|> \tag{2B.1}$$

where $<\lambda|>$ denotes the components of the arbitrary ket $|>$ in the given basis and we use the convention that a repeated label (such as λ) is to be summed over.

If the dimensionality of the linear vector space is infinite, we may still represent an arbitrary ket $|>$ by (2B.1). However, we must note that the spectrum of λ is now continuous or discrete with an infinite number of admissible values of λ. Consequently, the repeated label λ must be integrated over or summed over an infinite number of values.

2B.2 Transforms

We begin with the representation (2B.1) of an arbitrary ket $|>$ in a given basis λ. On transformation to another basis, say the μ basis, the expression for $|>$ becomes

$$|> = |\mu> <\mu|\lambda> <\lambda|> \tag{2B.2}$$

in which $|>$ denotes the base kets and $<\mu|\lambda>$ is the transformation function for the change from the λ basis to the μ basis.

Since all bases are on an equal footing, instead of beginning with the representation of $|>$ in the λ basis, we might have started with its representation in the μ basis, namely,

$$|> = |\mu> <\mu|> \tag{2B.3}$$

Its representation in the λ basis would then be given by

$$|> = |\lambda> <\lambda|\mu> <\mu|> \tag{2B.4}$$

The transformation functions, $<\mu|\lambda>$ and its inverse $<\lambda|\mu>$, satisfy the *orthonormality conditions*

$$<\lambda|\mu> <\mu|\lambda'> = <\lambda|\lambda'> \tag{2B.5}$$

and $$<\mu|\lambda> <\lambda|\mu'> = <\mu|\mu'> \tag{2B.6}$$

where the function $<\lambda|\lambda'>$, for example, represents the Kronecker delta, $\delta_{\lambda, \lambda'}$, if the spectrum of λ is discrete, and the Dirac delta, $\delta(\lambda - \lambda')$, if the spectrum is continuous.

Comparison of (2B.1) with (2B.4) shows that

$$<\lambda|> = <\lambda|\mu> <\mu|> \tag{2B.7}$$

Similarly, comparison of (2B.2) with (2B.3) shows that

$$<\mu|> = <\mu|\lambda> <\lambda|> \tag{2B.8}$$

The functions $<\lambda|>$ and $<\mu|>$ related by (2B.7) and (2B.8) are called transforms of one another; e.g., $<\lambda|>$ is a transform of $<\mu|>$ and vice versa.

2B.3   Infinite One-dimensional Transforms

The Fourier Integral—Complex Form

Consider the transformation functions (Sec. 9.2)

$$<x|\omega> = \sqrt{\frac{1}{2\pi}}\, e^{i\omega x} \qquad <\omega|x> = \sqrt{\frac{1}{2\pi}}\, e^{-i\omega x} \qquad (2B.9)$$

where $-\infty < x < \infty$ and $-\infty < \omega < \infty$. It is easily demonstrated that the functions here defined satisfy the orthonormality conditions (2B.5) and (2B.6), i.e.,

$$\delta(\omega - \omega') = \frac{1}{2\pi}\int_{-\infty}^{+\infty} e^{-i(\omega-\omega')x}\, dx$$

$$\delta(x - x') = \frac{1}{2\pi}\int_{-\infty}^{+\infty} e^{+i(x-x')\omega}\, d\omega \qquad (2B.10)$$

For example, we verify that

$$\delta(x - x') = \frac{1}{2\pi}\lim_{a\to\infty}\int_{-a}^{+a} e^{+i(x-x')\omega}\, d\omega \qquad (2B.10a)$$

To do so we multiply both sides by an arbitrary function of x, say $f(x)$, and integrate over all x. Then

$$\int_{-\infty}^{+\infty} f(x)\, \delta(x - x')\, dx$$

$$= \frac{1}{2\pi}\lim_{a\to\infty}\int_{-\infty}^{+\infty} f(x)\, dx \int_{-a}^{+a} e^{+i(x-x')\omega}\, d\omega$$

$$= \frac{1}{2\pi}\lim_{a\to\infty}\int_{-\infty}^{+\infty} f(x)\, dx \left[\frac{e^{+i(x-x')a}}{i(x-x')} - \frac{e^{-i(x-x')a}}{i(x-x')}\right] = f(x')$$

Note that in verifying (2B.10a) we have derived the *complex form of the Fourier integral theorem*, namely:

$$f(x') = \frac{1}{2\pi}\int_{-\infty}^{+\infty}\int_{-\infty}^{+\infty} f(x)e^{i\omega(x-x')}\, d\omega\, dx \qquad (2B.11)$$

Thus, the orthonormality conditions (2B.10) and the Fourier integral theorem are completely equivalent.

The Fourier integral theorem (2B.11) may be obtained in another manner. Use the relations (2B.7) and (2B.8) and write $<x|> = f(x)$ and $<\omega|> = g(\omega)$ so as to obtain

$$f(x) = \sqrt{\frac{1}{2\pi}} \int_{-\infty}^{+\infty} g(\omega) e^{i\omega x} \, d\omega \tag{2B.12}$$

$$g(\omega) = \sqrt{\frac{1}{2\pi}} \int_{-\infty}^{+\infty} f(x) e^{-i\omega x} \, dx \tag{2B.13}$$

These functions f and g are said to be *complex Fourier transforms* of one another. By substituting for $g(\omega)$ in (2B.12) by means of (2B.13) we obtain

$$f(x') = \frac{1}{2\pi} \int_{-\infty}^{+\infty} \int_{-\infty}^{+\infty} f(x) e^{i\omega(x-x')} \, d\omega \, dx \tag{2.B11a}$$

the Fourier integral theorem.

The Fourier Integral—Real Forms

Let us rewrite (2B.13) as

$$g(\omega) = \sqrt{\frac{1}{2\pi}} \left[\int_{-\infty}^{0} f(x) e^{-i\omega x} \, dx + \int_{0}^{+\infty} f(x) e^{-i\omega x} \, dx \right]$$

The substitution of $-x$ for x in the first integral on the right then gives

$$g(\omega) = \sqrt{\frac{1}{2\pi}} \left[\int_{0}^{\infty} f(-x) e^{i\omega x} \, dx + \int_{0}^{\infty} f(x) e^{-i\omega x} \, dx \right] \tag{2B.14}$$

There are two cases to consider, namely, $f(x) = f(-x)$ and $f(x) = -f(-x)$. If $f(x) = f(-x)$, (2B.14) reduces to

$$g(\omega) = \sqrt{\frac{2}{\pi}} \int_{0}^{\infty} f(x) \cos \omega x \, dx \tag{2B.15}$$

It then follows that $g(\omega) = g(-\omega)$ and, from (2B.12),

$$f(x) = \sqrt{\frac{2}{\pi}} \int_{0}^{\infty} g(\omega) \cos \omega x \, d\omega \tag{2B.16}$$

The functions f and g in (2B.15) and (2B.16) are known as *infinite Fourier cosine transforms* of one another.

Clearly, the transformation functions are

$$<x|\omega> = \sqrt{\frac{2}{\pi}} \cos \omega x \qquad <\omega|x> = \sqrt{\frac{2}{\pi}} \cos \omega x \tag{2B.17}$$

where $0 < x < \infty$ and $0 < \omega < \infty$; and the orthonormality relations are

$$\delta(x - x') = \frac{2}{\pi} \int_0^\infty \cos \omega x \cos \omega x' \, d\omega$$

$$\delta(\omega - \omega') = \frac{2}{\pi} \int_0^\infty \cos \omega x \cos \omega' x \, dx \qquad (2B.18)$$

Substitution of (2B.15) into (2B.16) yields the real form of the Fourier integral theorem applicable to even functions $f(x) = f(-x)$

$$f(x) = \frac{2}{\pi} \int_0^\infty \int_0^\infty f(x') \cos \omega x' \cos \omega x \, d\omega \, dx' \qquad (2B.19)$$

If $f(x)$ is an odd function, $f(x) = -f(-x)$, (2B.13) reduces to

$$g(\omega) = -i \sqrt{\frac{2}{\pi}} \int_0^\infty f(x) \sin \omega x \, dx$$

or $\qquad\qquad G(\omega) \equiv ig(\omega) = \sqrt{\frac{2}{\pi}} \int_0^\infty f(x) \sin \omega x \, dx \qquad (2B.20)$

Hence $G(\omega) = -G(-\omega)$ and, from (2B.12),

$$f(x) = \sqrt{\frac{2}{\pi}} \int_0^\infty G(\omega) \sin \omega x \, d\omega \qquad (2B.21)$$

The two functions f and G are called *infinite Fourier sine transforms.*
In this case the transformation functions are

$$<x|\omega> = \sqrt{\frac{2}{\pi}} \sin \omega x \qquad <\omega|x> = \sqrt{\frac{2}{\pi}} \sin \omega x \qquad (2B.22)$$

the orthonormality relations are

$$\delta(x - x') = \frac{2}{\pi} \int_0^\infty \sin \omega x \sin \omega x' \, d\omega$$

$$\delta(\omega - \omega') = \frac{2}{\pi} \int_0^\infty \sin \omega x \sin \omega' x \, dx \qquad (2B.23)$$

and the Fourier integral theorem takes the form

$$f(x) = \frac{2}{\pi} \int_0^\infty \int_0^\infty f(x') \sin \omega x' \sin \omega x \, d\omega \, dx' \qquad (2B.24)$$

2B.4 Infinite Multidimensional Transforms—Cartesian Coordinates

Consider the transformation functions

$$<x_1 x_2|\omega_1 \omega_2> = \frac{1}{2\pi} e^{i(\omega_1 x_1 + \omega_2 x_2)} \qquad <\omega_1 \omega_2|x_1 x_2> = \frac{1}{2\pi} e^{-i(\omega_1 x_1 + \omega_2 x_2)}$$

where the ranges of x_1, x_2, ω_1, and ω_2 are from $-\infty$ to $+\infty$. These functions satisfy the orthonormality conditions

$$\delta(\omega_1 - \omega_1') \, \delta(\omega_2 - \omega_2') = \left(\frac{1}{2\pi}\right)^2 \int_{-\infty}^{+\infty} \int_{-\infty}^{+\infty} e^{-i[(\omega_1 - \omega_1')x_1 + (\omega_2 - \omega_2')x_2]} \, dx_1 \, dx_2$$

$$\delta(x_1 - x_1') \, \delta(x_2 - x_2') = \left(\frac{1}{2\pi}\right)^2 \int_{-\infty}^{+\infty} \int_{-\infty}^{+\infty} e^{+i[(x_1 - x_1')\omega_1 + (x_2 - x_2')\omega_2]} \, d\omega_1 \, d\omega_2$$

The transform relations (2B.7) and (2B.8) become in this case

$$f(x_1,x_2) = \frac{1}{2\pi} \int_{-\infty}^{+\infty} \int_{-\infty}^{+\infty} g(\omega_1,\omega_2) e^{i(\omega_1 x_1 + \omega_2 x_2)} \, d\omega_1 \, d\omega_2$$

$$g(\omega_1,\omega_2) = \frac{1}{2\pi} \int_{-\infty}^{+\infty} \int_{-\infty}^{+\infty} f(x_1,x_2) e^{-i(\omega_1 x_1 + \omega_2 x_2)} \, dx_1 \, dx_2$$

and the Fourier integral theorem becomes

$$f(x_1,x_2) = \left(\frac{1}{2\pi}\right)^2 \int_{-\infty}^{+\infty} \cdots \int_{-\infty}^{+\infty} f(x_1',x_2') e^{i[\omega_1(x_1 - x_1') + \omega_2(x_2 - x_2')]} \, d\omega_1 \, d\omega_2 \, dx_1' \, dx_2'$$

The generalization to a greater number of variables is obvious. Suppose that $f(x_1, x_2, \ldots, x_n)$ is a function of the n independent variables $x_1, x_2, \ldots, x_n$, where $-\infty < x_i < +\infty$. Then the n-dimensional complex Fourier transform of the function f is defined to be

$$g(\boldsymbol{\omega}) = \left(\frac{1}{2\pi}\right)^{n/2} \int_{-\infty}^{+\infty} \cdots \int_{-\infty}^{+\infty} f(\mathbf{r}) e^{i(\boldsymbol{\omega} \cdot \mathbf{r})} \, d\mathbf{r} \qquad (2B.25)$$

where

$$\boldsymbol{\omega} \cdot \mathbf{r} = \omega_1 x_1 + \omega_2 x_2 + \cdots + \omega_n x_n$$

and $d\mathbf{r}$ represents the "volume" element $dx_1 dx_2 \ldots dx_n$. The corresponding relation for $f(\mathbf{r})$ is

$$f(\mathbf{r}) = \left(\frac{1}{2\pi}\right)^{n/2} \int_{-\infty}^{+\infty} \cdots \int_{-\infty}^{+\infty} g(\boldsymbol{\omega}) e^{-i(\boldsymbol{\omega} \cdot \mathbf{r})} \, d\boldsymbol{\omega} \qquad (2B.26)$$

where $d\boldsymbol{\omega} = d\omega_1 d\omega_2 \ldots d\omega_n$.

The transformation functions and orthonormality relations may be written

$$<\mathbf{r}|\boldsymbol{\omega}> = \left(\frac{1}{2\pi}\right)^{n/2} e^{i\boldsymbol{\omega}\cdot\mathbf{r}} \qquad <\boldsymbol{\omega}|\mathbf{r}> = \left(\frac{1}{2\pi}\right)^{n/2} e^{-i\boldsymbol{\omega}\cdot\mathbf{r}} \qquad (2B.27)$$

and

$$\delta(\boldsymbol{\omega} - \boldsymbol{\omega}') = \left(\frac{1}{2\pi}\right)^{n} \int_{-\infty}^{+\infty} e^{-i[(\boldsymbol{\omega}-\boldsymbol{\omega}')\cdot\mathbf{r}]} \, d\mathbf{r}$$

$$(2B.28)$$

$$\delta(\mathbf{r} - \mathbf{r}') = \left(\frac{1}{2\pi}\right)^{n} \int_{-\infty}^{+\infty} e^{+i[(\mathbf{r}-\mathbf{r}')\cdot\boldsymbol{\omega}]} \, d\boldsymbol{\omega}$$

respectively. The complex form of the Fourier integral theorem is then

$$f(\mathbf{r}) = \left(\frac{1}{2\pi}\right)^{n} \int_{-\infty}^{+\infty} \int_{-\infty}^{+\infty} f(\mathbf{r}') e^{i[(\mathbf{r}-\mathbf{r}')\cdot\boldsymbol{\omega}]} \, d\boldsymbol{\omega} \, d\mathbf{r}' \qquad (2B.29)$$

2B.5 Finite One-dimensional Transforms

Fourier's Series

Consider the transformation functions

$$<\theta|n> = \sqrt{\frac{1}{2\pi}}\, e^{in\theta} \qquad <n|\theta> = \sqrt{\frac{1}{2\pi}}\, e^{-in\theta} \qquad (2B.30)$$

where $-\pi \leq \theta \leq +\pi$ and n is zero or a positive or negative integer. These functions satisfy the orthonormality conditions

$$\delta(\theta - \theta') = \frac{1}{2\pi} \sum_{n=-\infty}^{+\infty} e^{in(\theta-\theta')}$$

$$(2B.31)$$

$$\delta_{n,n'} = \frac{1}{2\pi} \int_{-\pi}^{+\pi} e^{-i(n-n')\theta} \, d\theta$$

By using the relations (2B.7) and (2B.8) and the notation $<\theta|> = f(\theta)$ and $<n|> = \sqrt{2\pi}a_n$ we obtain the transforms

$$f(\theta) = \sum_{n=-\infty}^{+\infty} a_n e^{in\theta} \qquad (2B.32a)$$

$$a_n = \frac{1}{2\pi} \int_{-\pi}^{+\pi} f(\theta) e^{-in\theta} \, d\theta \qquad (2B.32b)$$

These transforms are mathematical statements of the *complex form of Fourier's series:* Any function $f(\theta)$ in the interval $-\pi \leq \theta \leq +\pi$ which is continuous or has at most a finite number of finite discontinuities may always be represented by the series (2B.32a) in which the coefficients a_n are given by (2B.32b).

The reduction to the usual real form of Fourier's series will be carried out below. However, we shall first introduce the variable x which runs from $-L$ to $+L$ when θ goes from $-\pi$ to $+\pi$. Then the transformation functions (2B.30) may be written

$$<x|n> = \sqrt{\frac{1}{2L}}\, e^{in\pi x/L} \qquad <n|x> = \sqrt{\frac{1}{2L}}\, e^{-in\pi x/L} \quad (2B.30a)$$

where $-L \leq x \leq +L$; the orthonormality conditions become

$$\delta(x - x') = \frac{1}{2L} \sum_{n=-\infty}^{+\infty} e^{in\pi(x-x')/L}$$

$$(2B.31a)$$

$$\delta_{n,n'} = \frac{1}{2L} \int_{-L}^{+L} e^{-i(n-n')\pi x/L}\, dx$$

and the complex form of Fourier's series is given by

$$f(x) = \sum_{n=-\infty}^{+\infty} a_n e^{in\pi x/L} \qquad\qquad (2B.32a')$$

$$a_n = \frac{1}{2L} \int_{-L}^{+L} f(x) e^{-in\pi x/L}\, dx \qquad\qquad (2B.32b')$$

The expression (2B.32b') is known as the *finite complex Fourier transform* of the function $f(x)$.

To obtain the real form of Fourier's series we rewrite (2B.32a') as

$$f(x) = a_0 + \sum_{n=-1}^{-\infty} a_n e^{i\pi n x/L} + \sum_{n=1}^{\infty} a_n e^{i\pi n x/L}$$

$$= a_0 + \sum_{n=1}^{\infty} a_{-n} e^{-i\pi n x/L} + \sum_{n=1}^{\infty} a_n e^{i\pi n x/L}$$

$$= a_0 + \sum_{n=1}^{\infty} (a_n + a_{-n}) \cos\frac{n\pi x}{L} + \sum_{n=1}^{\infty} i(a_n - a_{-n}) \sin\frac{n\pi x}{L}$$

Hence

$$f(x) = b_0 + \sum_{n=1}^{\infty} b_n \cos\frac{n\pi x}{L} + \sum_{n=1}^{\infty} c_n \sin\frac{n\pi x}{L} \qquad (2B.33)$$

where

$$b_0 \equiv a_0 = \frac{1}{2L} \int_{-L}^{+L} f(x)\, dx$$

$$b_n \equiv a_n + a_{-n} = \frac{1}{L} \int_{-L}^{+L} f(x) \cos\frac{n\pi x}{L}\, dx \qquad (2B.34)$$

$$c_n = i(a_n - a_{-n}) = \frac{1}{L} \int_{-L}^{+L} f(x) \sin\frac{n\pi x}{L}\, dx$$

Finite Fourier Sine Transform

Let us rewrite (2B.32b') as

$$a_n = \frac{1}{2L} \left[\int_{-L}^{0} f(x) e^{-i\pi nx/L} \, dx + \int_{0}^{L} f(x) e^{-i\pi nx/L} \, dx \right]$$

The substitution of $-x$ for x in the first integral on the right then gives

$$a_n = \frac{1}{2L} \left[\int_{0}^{L} f(-x) e^{i\pi nx/L} \, dx + \int_{0}^{L} f(x) e^{-i\pi nx/L} \, dx \right] \qquad (2B.35)$$

If $f(x)$ is an odd function, $f(x) = -f(-x)$, (2B.35) reduces to

$$a_n = -\frac{i}{L} \int_{0}^{L} f(x) \sin \frac{\pi nx}{L} \, dx$$

Hence
$$A_n \equiv 2ia_n = \frac{2}{L} \int_{0}^{L} f(x) \sin \frac{\pi nx}{L} \, dx \qquad (2B.36)$$

and, clearly, $A_n = -A_{-n}$. Then, from (2B.32a') we obtain

$$f(x) = \sum_{n=-\infty}^{+\infty} \frac{A_n}{2i} e^{i\pi nx/L}$$

$$= \sum_{n=1}^{\infty} A_n \sin \frac{\pi nx}{L} \qquad (2B.37)$$

The relation (2B.37) is the *Fourier sine series* expansion for the function $f(x)$. The coefficients A_n are given by the expression (2B.36), which is known as the finite *Fourier sine transform* of the function $f(x)$.

The results (2B.36) and (2B.37) might have been derived directly from the transformation functions

$$<x|n> = \sqrt{\frac{2}{L}} \sin \frac{n\pi x}{L} \qquad <n|x> = \sqrt{\frac{2}{L}} \sin \frac{n\pi x}{L} \qquad (2B.38)$$

where $n = 1, 2, 3, \ldots$ and $0 \leq x \leq L$. They satisfy the orthonormality conditions

$$\delta(x - x') = \frac{2}{L} \sum_{n=1}^{\infty} \sin \frac{n\pi x}{L} \sin \frac{n\pi x'}{L}$$

$$\delta_{n,n'} = \frac{2}{L} \int_{0}^{L} \sin \frac{n\pi x}{L} \sin \frac{n'\pi x}{L} \, dx \qquad (2B.39)$$

Finite Fourier Cosine Transform

If $f(x)$ is an even function, (2B.35) reduces to

$$a_n = \frac{1}{L} \int_0^L f(x) \cos \frac{n\pi x}{L} dx$$

Clearly, $a_n = a_{-n}$. Then, from (2B.32a') we obtain

$$f(x) = a_0 + \sum_{n=1}^{\infty} 2a_n \cos \frac{n\pi x}{L}$$

$$= \frac{B_0}{2} + \sum_{n=1}^{\infty} B_n \cos \frac{n\pi x}{L} \tag{2B.40}$$

where $$B_n \equiv 2a_n = \frac{2}{L} \int_0^L f(x) \cos \frac{n\pi x}{L} \tag{2B.41}$$

The relation (2B.40) is the *Fourier cosine series* expansion for the function $f(x)$. The coefficients B_n are given by the expression (2B.41), which is known as the *finite Fourier cosine transform* of the function $f(x)$.

The Fourier sine and cosine series expansions (2B.37) and (2B.40) are equivalent in the range $0 \leq x \leq L$. They differ in that if it is desired to expand a function between $-L$ and $+L$, (2B.37) can be used only if the function is odd, (2B.40) when it is even. However, any function can be represented as the sum of an even and an odd one. Hence, if an arbitrary function $f(x)$ is to be expanded between $-L$ and $+L$, either both the sine and cosine series must be used or, equivalently, the complex form (2B.32).

2B.6 The Fourier-Bessel Integral

Thus far we have considered only cartesian coordinates. In the case of plane polar coordinates r,θ we may employ the transformation functions

$$<r,\theta|k,n> = \frac{k}{\sqrt{2\pi}} e^{in\theta} J_n(kr) \qquad <k,n|r,\theta> = \frac{r}{\sqrt{2\pi}} e^{-in\theta} J_n(kr) \tag{2B.42}$$

where $0 \leq r \leq \infty, 0 \leq \theta \leq 2\pi, 0 \leq k \leq \infty$, and n is zero or a positive or negative integer. J_n is the Bessel function of integral order n. These transformation functions satisfy the orthonormality conditions

$$\delta(r-r')\,\delta(\theta-\theta') = \frac{r}{2\pi} \sum_{n=-\infty}^{+\infty} \int_0^\infty J_n(kr)J_n(kr')e^{in(\theta-\theta')}k\,dk \tag{2B.43}$$

$$\delta(k-k')\,\delta_{n,n'} = \frac{k}{2\pi} \int_0^{2\pi} \int_0^\infty J_n(kr)J_{n'}(k'r)e^{i(n-n')\theta}r\,dr\,d\theta \tag{2B.44}$$

The verification of (2B.43) has been carried out in Sec. 10.5 of the text. The verification of (2B.44) is left as an exercise for the reader.

Let $<r,\theta|> = f(r,\theta)$ and $<k,n|> = g_n(k)$. Then the relations (2B.7) and (2B.8) yield the transforms

$$f(r,\theta) = \frac{1}{\sqrt{2\pi}} \sum_{n=-\infty}^{+\infty} \int_0^\infty g_n(k) e^{in\theta} J_n(kr) k \, dk \qquad (2B.45)$$

and

$$g_n(k) = \frac{1}{\sqrt{2\pi}} \int_0^{2\pi} \int_0^\infty f(r,\theta) e^{-in\theta} J_n(kr) r \, dr \, d\theta \qquad (2B.46)$$

In the special case where f is a function of r alone, $f(r)$, the transformation functions reduce to

$$<r|k> = k J_n(kr) \qquad <k|r> = r J_n(kr) \qquad (2B.47)$$

They satisfy the orthonormality conditions

$$\delta(r - r') = r \int_0^\infty J_n(kr) J_n(kr') k \, dk$$

$$\delta(k - k') = k \int_0^\infty J_n(kr) J_n(k'r) r \, dr \qquad (2B.48)$$

The transforms

$$f(r) = \int_0^\infty g(k) J_n(kr) k \, dk \qquad (2B.49)$$

and

$$g(k) = \int_0^\infty f(r) J_n(kr) r \, dr \qquad (2B.50)$$

are said to be a pair of *Fourier-Bessel* or *Hankel Transforms*. Substitution of (2B.50) into (2B.49) yields the *Fourier-Bessel integral*

$$f(r) = \int_0^\infty \left[\int_0^\infty f(r') J_n(kr') r' \, dr' \right] J_n(kr) k \, dk \qquad (2B.51)$$

which is the analogue of the cosine Fourier integral

$$f(x) = \frac{2}{\pi} \int_0^\infty \left[\int_0^\infty f(x') \cos \omega x' \, dx' \right] \cos \omega x \, d\omega \qquad (2B.52)$$

obtained from the transforms (2B.15) and (2B.16).

2B.7 The Fourier-Bessel Expansion

Consider the case in which the range of r is finite, $0 \leq r \leq a$, and the function $f(r)$ satisfies the conditions that $f(0)$ is finite and $f(a) = 0$. If

$$J_n(\lambda_j) = 0 \qquad \lambda_{j+1} > \lambda_j \qquad j = 1, 2, 3, \ldots$$

by analogy with the development in the discussion of Fourier's series we try as transformation functions

$$<r|j> = N_j J_n\left(\lambda_j \frac{r}{a}\right) \qquad <j|r> = r J_n\left(\lambda_j \frac{r}{a}\right) \qquad (2B.53)$$

The as yet undetermined quantity N_j must satisfy the orthonormality condition

$$\delta_{j,j'} = <j|r><r|j'> = N_j \int_0^a J_n\left(\lambda_j \frac{r}{a}\right) J_n\left(\lambda_{j'} \frac{r}{a}\right) r\, dr \qquad (2B.54)$$

Consequently, our first problem is to evaluate the integral

$$I = \int_0^a J_n(\alpha r) J_n(\beta r) r\, dr \qquad (2B.55)$$

where $J_n(\alpha a) = J_n(\beta a) = 0$. To do this we utilize Green's theorem[1]

$$\iint (u\nabla^2 v - v\nabla^2 u)\, dS \equiv \iint \nabla \cdot (u\nabla v - v\nabla u)\, dS \equiv \oint (u\nabla v - v\nabla u)_n\, ds$$

in which u and v are any two functions of space coordinates which are finite, continuous, and have continuous first and second derivatives. S represents a certain surface and s its boundary. $(u\nabla v - v\nabla u)_n$ represents the component of $(u\nabla v - v\nabla u)$ which is normal to the boundary.

Let $f(n,\alpha) \equiv J_n(\alpha r)e^{in\theta}$. Then the integral (2B.55) may be written

$$2\pi I = \int_S f(n,\alpha)\overline{f(n,\beta)}\, dS$$

where the bar denotes the complex conjugate and the surface S is a circle of radius a about the origin. But, since $(\nabla^2 + \alpha^2)f(n,\alpha) = 0$,[2] we obtain

$$2\pi I = \frac{1}{\alpha^2 - \beta^2} \int_S \left[f(n,\alpha)\nabla^2\overline{f(n,\beta)} - \overline{f(n,\beta)}\nabla^2 f(n,\alpha) \right] dS$$

Application of Green's theorem then yields

$$2\pi I = \frac{1}{\alpha^2 - \beta^2} \oint \left[f(n,\alpha)\frac{d}{dr}\overline{f(n,\beta)} - \overline{f(n,\beta)}\frac{d}{dr}f(n,\alpha) \right] ds$$

$$= \frac{1}{\alpha^2 - \beta^2} \int_0^{2\pi} \left[J_n(\alpha a)\beta J_n'(\beta a) - J_n(\beta a)\alpha J_n'(\alpha a) \right] a\, d\theta$$

or

$$I = \frac{a}{\alpha^2 - \beta^2} \left[\beta J_n(\alpha a)J_n'(\beta a) - \alpha J_n(\beta a)J_n'(\alpha a) \right] \qquad (2B.56)$$

[1] See any standard text on vector analysis.
[2] See Sec. 10.5 of the text.

where the prime denotes differentiation with respect to the argument. Hence it follows that if αa and βa are roots of $J_n(x)$, $I = 0$, unless $\alpha = \beta$. For $\alpha = \beta$ we compute the limiting values by means of L'Hôpital's rule. Then

$$I = \frac{a}{2\beta} \{\beta a[J'_n(\beta a)]^2 - J_n(\beta a)J'_n(\beta a) - \beta a J_n(\beta a)J''_n(\beta a)\} \qquad \alpha = \beta$$

$$= \frac{a^2}{2} [J'_n(\beta a)]^2 \tag{2B.57}$$

since $J_n(\beta a) = 0$.

Returning now to Eq. (2B.54) we find that

$$N_j = \frac{2}{a^2}\left[\frac{1}{J'_n(\lambda_j)}\right]^2 \tag{2B.58}$$

Hence the transformation functions (2B.53) become

$$<r|j> = \frac{2}{a^2}\left[\frac{1}{J'_n(\lambda_j)}\right]^2 J_n\left(\frac{\lambda_j r}{a}\right) \qquad <j|r> = rJ_n\left(\frac{\lambda_j r}{a}\right)$$

or better $\quad <r|j> = \dfrac{J_n(\lambda_j r/a)}{J'_n(\lambda_j)} \qquad <j|r> = \dfrac{2r}{a^2}\dfrac{J_n(\lambda_j r/a)}{J'_n(\lambda_j)} \tag{2B.59}$

Hence, the transforms are

$$f(r) = \sum_{j=1}^{\infty} a_j \frac{J_n(\lambda_j r/a)}{J'_n(\lambda_j)} \tag{2B.60}$$

and $\quad a_j = \dfrac{2}{a^2}\displaystyle\int_0^a \dfrac{J_n(\lambda_j r/a)}{J'_n(\lambda_j)} r\,dr \tag{2B.61}$

Expression (2B.60) is known as the *Fourier-Bessel expansion* of a function of r only. The coefficients a_j are given by (2B.61).

In the more general case in which $0 \leq r \leq a$, $0 \leq \theta \leq 2\pi$, and $f(r,\theta)$ satisfies the conditions $f(0,\theta)$ is finite and $f(a,\theta) = 0$, the transformation functions are

$$<r,\theta|j,n> = \frac{J_n(\lambda_j r/a)}{J'_n(\lambda_j)} e^{in\theta} \qquad <j,n|r,\theta> = \frac{r}{\pi a^2}\frac{J_n(\lambda_j r/a)}{J'_n(\lambda_j)} e^{-in\theta}$$

the orthonormality conditions are

$$\delta(r - r')\,\delta(\theta - \theta') = \frac{r}{\pi a^2}\sum_{j,n}\frac{J_n(\lambda_j r/a)J_n(\lambda_j r'/a)}{[J'_n(\lambda_j)]^2} e^{in(\theta-\theta')}$$

$$\delta_{j,j'}\,\delta_{n,n'} = \frac{1}{\pi a^2}\int_0^{2\pi}\int_0^a \frac{J_n(\lambda_j r/a)J'_{n'}(\lambda_{j'} r/a)}{J'_n(\lambda_j)J'_{n'}(\lambda_{j'})} e^{-i\theta(n-n')} r\,dr\,d\theta$$

and the transforms are

$$f(r,\theta) = \sum_{j=1}^{\infty} \sum_{n=-\infty}^{+\infty} a_{jn} \frac{J_n(\lambda_j r/a)}{J'_n(\lambda_j)} e^{in\theta} \qquad (2B.62)$$

and

$$a_{jn} = \frac{1}{\pi a^2} \int_0^{2\pi} \int_0^a f(r,\theta) \frac{J_n(\lambda_j r/a)}{J'_n(\lambda_j)} e^{-in\theta} \, r \, dr \, d\theta \qquad (2B.63)$$

The expressions (2B.62) and (2B.63) constitute the *Fourier-Bessel expansion* of a function of r and θ.

References

Carslaw, H. S.: "Fourier's Series and Integrals," The Macmillan Company, New York, 1930.

Wiener, N.: "The Fourier Integral," Cambridge University Press, New York, 1932.

Titchmarsh, E. C.: "Introduction to the Theory of Fourier Integrals," Oxford University Press, New York, 1937.

Churchill, R. V.: "Fourier Series and Boundary Value Problems," McGraw-Hill Book Company, Inc., New York, 1941.

Campbell, G. A., and R. M. Foster: "Fourier Integrals for Practical Applications," D. Van Nostrand Company, Inc., Princeton, N.J., 1948.

Sneddon, I. N.: "Fourier Transforms," McGraw-Hill Book Company, Inc., New York, 1951.

Tranter, C. J.: "Integral Transforms in Mathematical Physics," John Wiley & Sons, Inc., New York, 1951.

APPENDIX 2C

The Cylindrical Functions

2C.1 Introduction

The important class of functions which are solutions of the equation

$$\left(\frac{d^2}{d\rho^2} + \frac{1}{\rho}\frac{d}{d\rho} + 1 - \frac{\nu^2}{\rho^2}\right)f(\rho) = 0 \qquad (2C.1)$$

known as *Bessel's equation*, are called *cylindrical functions* and generally denoted by $Z_\nu(\rho)$, where the constant ν is not necessarily an integer. It is the purpose of this appendix to sketch the properties of these functions so that free application of them may be made in the solutions to physical problems in Chaps. 10, 11, et seq.

2C.2 The Integral Representation of $J_n(\rho)$

The function $J_n(\rho)$, known as the *Bessel function of integral order n*, is that particular cylindrical function of order n which is finite at $\rho = 0$.

It was shown in Sec. 10.5 of the text that

$$e^{i\rho \sin \theta} = \sum_{n=-\infty}^{+\infty} J_n(\rho)e^{in\theta} \qquad (10.43)$$

Multiplication of both sides of (10.43) by $e^{-im\theta}\,d\theta$ and integration over θ from $-\pi$ to $+\pi$ yield

$$J_m(\rho) = \frac{1}{2\pi}\int_{-\pi}^{+\pi} e^{i(\rho \sin \theta - m\theta)}\,d\theta \qquad (2C.2)$$

or $$J_n(\rho) = \frac{1}{\pi}\int_0^\pi \cos\,(\rho \sin \theta - n\theta)\,d\theta \qquad (2C.3)$$

280

The replacement of θ by $w + \pi/2$ in (2C.2) yields

$$J_n(\rho) = \frac{1}{2\pi} \int_{-3\pi/2}^{+\pi/2} e^{i(\rho \cos w - nw - n\pi/2)} \, dw \qquad (2C.4)$$

These expressions, (2C.2), (2C.3), and (2C.4), are known as the integral representations of the Bessel function of integral order.

We may use the integral representations to prove that

$$J_{-n}(\rho) = (-1)^n J_n(\rho) \qquad (2C.5)$$

as follows: In (2C.2) substitute $-n$ for m. Then

$$J_{-n}(\rho) = \frac{1}{2\pi} \int_{-\pi}^{\pi} e^{i(\rho \sin \theta + n\theta)} \, d\theta$$

The substitution $w = \pi/2 - \theta$ in this expression yields

$$J_{-n}(\rho) = \frac{e^{in\pi}}{2\pi} \int_{-3\pi/2}^{\pi/2} e^{i(\rho \cos w - nw - n\pi/2)} \, dw$$

Hence, by reason of (2C.4), we obtain

$$J_{-n}(\rho) = e^{in\pi} J_n(\rho) = (-1)^n J_n(\rho)$$

2C.3   The Integral Representations of the General Cylindrical Functions

The solution of the equation

$$(\nabla^2 + k^2)f = 0 \qquad (2C.6)$$

where k is a constant, in plane polar coordinates is

$$f(r,\theta) = Z_\nu(kr)e^{i\nu\theta} \qquad (2C.7)$$

It has already been shown in Sec. 10.7 of the text that the appropriate solution in the case of the vibrating circular membrane is $J_n(kr)e^{in\theta}$.

In order to obtain the integral representations of the general cylindrical functions Z_ν we first consider Eq. (2C.6) in cartesian coordinates. A particular solution is then

$$f(x,y) = e^{i(k_x x + k_y y)} \qquad k^2 = k_x^2 + k_y^2 \qquad (2C.8)$$

With the substitutions

$$k_x = k \cos w \qquad x = r \cos \theta$$
$$k_y = k \sin w \qquad y = r \sin \theta$$

The solution (2C.8) becomes

$$f(r,\theta) = e^{ikr \cos (w-\theta)}$$

The general solution of (2C.6) in plane polar coordinates is then

$$f(r,\theta) = Z_\nu(kr)e^{i\nu\theta} = \int_\beta^\gamma g(w)e^{ikr\cos(w-\theta)}\,dw$$

in which the coefficients $g(w)$ and the limits of integration β and γ are to be determined. With the substitution $\rho = kr$ we obtain

$$Z_\nu(\rho) = \int_\beta^\gamma g(w)e^{i[\rho\cos(w-\theta)-\nu\theta]}\,dw$$

The further replacement of w by $w + \theta$ yields

$$Z_\nu(\rho) = \int_{\beta-\theta}^{\gamma-\theta} g(w+\theta)e^{i(\rho\cos w-\nu\theta)}\,dw \qquad (2C.9)$$

Comparison of this expression with (2C.4) leads us to assume that

$$g(w+\theta) = C_\nu e^{i\nu(w+\theta)}$$

so that (2C.9) may be written

$$Z_\nu(\rho) = \int_{\beta-\theta}^{\gamma-\theta} C_\nu e^{i(\rho\cos w + \nu w)}\,dw \qquad (2C.10)$$

where the coefficient C_ν is as yet undetermined. Furthermore, since Z_ν is a function of ρ alone, the dependence of the limits of integration on θ must be removed. In the case where $\nu = n =$ an integer, this may be accomplished by setting $\beta = \gamma - 2\pi$. In the general case we let β and γ approach infinity in such a manner that the integrand vanishes at both limits. For ρ real and positive and $w = \xi + i\eta$ we obtain

$$i\rho\cos w = i\rho(\cos\xi\cos i\eta - \sin\xi\sin i\eta)$$

$$= i\rho(\cos\xi\cosh\eta - i\sin\xi\sinh\eta)$$

Hence the real part of $i\rho\cos w$ is negative if $\eta \to +\infty$ and $\sin\xi < 0$ and if $\eta \to -\infty$, $\sin\xi > 0$. Only those regions in the w plane which satisfy these conditions are allowed. These allowed regions are strips which are parallel to the imaginary axis and are indicated in Fig. 2C.1 by shading.

If ρ is not real and positive, say $\rho = ae^{i\delta}$, a real and positive, then the pattern of Fig. 2C.1 is still maintained but is shifted by $\pm\delta$ in the direction of the real axis, in which the plus and minus signs are for the upper and lower half planes. In the convergence considerations $\sin\xi$ is replaced by $\sin(\xi \mp \delta)$.

Since a change of 2π in the path of integration is irrelevant there are only three possible paths. For simplicity we define the paths, which are designated by W_0, W_1, and W_2, as follows:

$$W_0: \text{ from } -\frac{\pi}{2} + i\infty \text{ to } -\frac{\pi}{2} + i0 \text{ to } \frac{3\pi}{2} + i0 \text{ to } \frac{3\pi}{2} + i\infty$$

$$W_1: \text{ from } -\frac{\pi}{2} + i\infty \text{ to } -\frac{\pi}{2} + i0 \text{ to } \frac{\pi}{2} + i0 \text{ to } \frac{\pi}{2} - i\infty$$

$$W_2: \text{ from } \frac{\pi}{2} - i\infty \text{ to } \frac{\pi}{2} + i0 \text{ to } \frac{3\pi}{2} + i0 \text{ to } \frac{3\pi}{2} + i\infty$$

From the definitions it is clear that the path of integration W_0 is equal to $W_1 + W_2$.

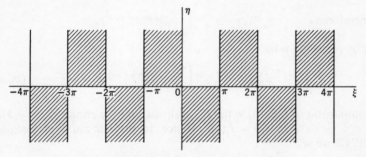

Figure 2C.1. Allowed regions in the w plane.

Expression (2C.10) for the integral representation of the cylindrical functions Z_ν may now be written

$$Z_\nu^{(j)}(\rho) = C_\nu^{(j)} \int_{W_j} e^{i(\rho \cos w + \nu w)} \, dw \qquad (2\text{C}.11)$$

It is left as an exercise for the reader to verify that (2C.11) satisfies the Bessel differential equation (2C.1).

2C.4 The Integral Representation of the Bessel Function J_ν

Let us consider the integral representation (2C.11) in the case where the path of integration is W_0. Then

$$Z_\nu^{(0)}(\rho) = C_\nu^{(0)} \int_{W_0} e^{i(\rho \cos w + \nu w)} \, dw \qquad (2\text{C}.12)$$

For $v = n =$ an integer, this becomes

$$Z_n^{(0)}(\rho) = C_n^{(0)}\left[\int_{\pi/2+i\infty}^{-\pi/2} e^{i(\rho\cos w + nw)}\,dw + \int_{-\pi/2}^{3\pi/2}\cdots + \int_{3\pi/2}^{3\pi/2+i\infty}\cdots\right]$$

In the first integral on the right let $w = it - \pi/2$. Then

$$\int_{-\pi/2+i\infty}^{-\pi/2} e^{i(\rho\cos w + nw)}\,dw = \int_{\infty}^{0} e^{-\rho\sinh t - nt - in\pi/2}\,dt$$

In the third integral on the right let $w = it + 3\pi/2$ so that

$$\int_{3\pi/2}^{3\pi/2+i\infty} e^{i(\rho\cos w + nw)}\,dw = \int_{0}^{\infty} e^{-\rho\sinh t - nt + i3n\pi/2}\,dt$$

Therefore
$$Z_n^{(0)}(\rho) = C_n^{(0)}\int_{-\pi/2}^{3\pi/2} e^{i(\rho\cos w + nw)}\,dw$$

or by replacing w by $-w$

$$Z_n^{(0)}(\rho) = C_n^{(0)}\int_{-3\pi/2}^{\pi/2} e^{i(\rho\cos w - nw)}\,dw \tag{2C.13}$$

Comparison of (2C.13) with (2C.3) shows that the choice $C_n^{(0)} = 1/2\pi\, e^{-in\pi/2}$ yields $Z_n^{(0)}(\rho) = J_n(\rho)$. Hence, in the integral representation (2C.12) we set

$$C_v^{(0)} = \frac{1}{2\pi}e^{-iv\pi/2} \tag{2C.14}$$

and define the Bessel function of order v by

$$J_v(\rho) = \frac{1}{2\pi}\int_{W_0} e^{i(\rho\cos w + vw - v\pi/2)}\,dw \tag{2C.15}$$

for all v.

2C.5 The Hankel Functions

Let us now consider the integral representations (2C.11) in the cases where the paths of integration are W_1 and W_2. The constants $C_v^{(1,2)}$ are now taken as

$$C_v^{(1,2)} = \frac{1}{\pi}e^{-iv\pi/2} \tag{2C.16}$$

The cylindrical functions which are thus defined are known as the Hankel functions of the first and second kinds, $H_\nu^{(1)}$ and $H_\nu^{(2)}$, respectively.

$$H_\nu^{(1)}(\rho) = \frac{1}{\pi} \int_{W_1} e^{i(\rho \cos w + \nu w - \nu \pi/2)} \, dw \qquad (2C.17)$$

$$H_\nu^{(2)}(\rho) = \frac{1}{\pi} \int_{W_2} e^{i(\rho \cos w + \nu w - \nu \pi/2)} \, dw \qquad (2C.18)$$

These functions differ from the Bessel function J_ν by the fact that they become infinite at $\rho = 0$.

Since, as has already been pointed out, the integral over the path W_0 is equal to the sum of the integrals over W_1 and W_2 it follows that

$$J_\nu(\rho) = \tfrac{1}{2}[H_\nu^{(1)}(\rho) + H_\nu^{(2)}(\rho)] \qquad (2C.19)$$

where the factor $1/2$ comes from the definitions (2C.14) and (2C.16) of $C_\nu^{(0)}$ and $C_\nu^{(1,2)}$, respectively. Furthermore, since the difference $H_\nu^{(1)}(\rho) - H_\nu^{(2)}(\rho)$ is a pure imaginary for real ρ and ν we define a function $N_\nu(\rho)$, called a *Neumann function*, by the relation

$$N_\nu(\rho) = \frac{1}{2i}[H_\nu^{(1)}(\rho) - H_\nu^{(2)}(\rho)] \qquad (2C.20)$$

The relations (2C.19) and (2C.20) are reminiscent of the trigonometric relations

$$\cos \theta = \tfrac{1}{2}(e^{i\theta} + e^{-i\theta})$$

$$\sin \theta = \frac{1}{2i}(e^{i\theta} - e^{-i\theta})$$

The resemblance is not accidental. As will be seen in Sec. 2C.7 the cylindrical functions for large ρ behave as sines, cosines, and exponentials.

According to (2C.17)

$$H_\nu^{(1)}(\rho) = \frac{1}{\pi} \int_{-\pi/2+i\infty}^{\pi/2-i\infty} e^{i\rho \cos w} e^{i\nu(w-\pi/2)} \, dw$$

so that the complex conjugate is

$$\overline{H_\nu^{(1)}(\rho)} = \frac{1}{\pi} \int_{-\pi/2-i\infty}^{\pi/2+i\infty} e^{-i\bar{\rho} \cos \bar{w}} e^{-i\bar{\nu}(\bar{w}-\pi/2)} \, d\bar{w}$$

The substitution $w' = \pi - \bar{w}$ then yields

$$\overline{H_\nu^{(1)}(\rho)} = \frac{1}{\pi} \int_{\pi/2-i\infty}^{3\pi/2+i\infty} e^{i\bar{\rho} \cos w'} e^{i\bar{\nu}(w'-\pi/2)} \, dw' \qquad (2C.21)$$

$$= H_{\bar{\nu}}^{(2)}(\bar{\rho})$$

Similarly, it may be shown that

$$\overline{H_\nu^{(2)}(\rho)} = H_{\bar\nu}^{(1)}(\bar\rho) \tag{2C.22}$$

For ν and ρ both real (2C.21) and (2C.22) reduce to

$$\overline{H_\nu^{(1)}(\rho)} = H_\nu^{(2)}(\rho) \qquad \nu, \rho \text{ real} \tag{2C.23}$$

Application of (2C.21) and (2C.22) to the complex conjugate of (2C.19) yields

$$\overline{J_\nu(\rho)} = J_{\bar\nu}(\bar\rho) \tag{2C.24}$$

If ν and ρ are both real, then

$$\overline{J_\nu(\rho)} = J_\nu(\rho) \qquad \nu, \rho \text{ real} \tag{2C.25}$$

2C.6 Series Expansions at the Origin

The series expansions for the cylindrical functions may be obtained either by assuming a series and determining the coefficients by substitution into the differential equation (2C.1) or directly from the integral representation. The first method is one of the conventional methods for solving differential equations and, therefore, need not be discussed here. We shall illustrate the second method by finding the series expansion of the Bessel function of integral order n: The integral representation of J_n is

$$J_n(\rho) = \frac{1}{2\pi} \int_{-\pi}^{\pi} e^{i(\rho \sin\theta - n\theta)} \, d\theta \tag{2C.2}$$

Expansion of $e^{i\rho \sin\theta}$ in the well-known power series for e^x gives

$$e^{i\rho \sin\theta} = \sum_{s=0}^{\infty} \frac{i^s \rho^s \sin^s \theta}{s!} = \sum_{s=0}^{\infty} \left(\frac{\rho}{2}\right)^s \frac{(e^{i\theta} - e^{-i\theta})^s}{s!}$$

If the factor $(e^{i\theta} - e^{i\theta})^s$ is expanded by the binomial theorem and the resultant expression for $e^{i\rho \sin\theta}$ is substituted into (2C.2), we derive

$$\begin{aligned}
J_n(\rho) &= \frac{1}{2\pi} \sum_{s=0}^{\infty} \left(\frac{\rho}{2}\right)^s \frac{1}{s!} \int_{-\pi}^{\pi} e^{-in\theta} \left[e^{is\theta} - \frac{s}{1!} e^{i(s-2)\theta} + \frac{s(s-1)}{2!} e^{i(s-4)\theta} \cdots \right] d\theta \\
&= \left(\frac{\rho}{2}\right)^n \frac{1}{n!} - \left(\frac{\rho}{2}\right)^{n+2} \frac{n+2}{(n+2)!} + \left(\frac{\rho}{2}\right)^{n+4} \frac{(n+4)(n+3)}{(n+4)! \, 2!} \cdots \\
&= \left(\frac{\rho}{2}\right)^n \frac{1}{n!} \left[1 - \left(\frac{\rho}{2}\right)^2 \frac{1}{n+1} + \left(\frac{\rho}{2}\right)^4 \frac{1}{(n+2)(n+1)2!} \cdots \right] \\
&= \left(\frac{\rho}{2}\right)^n \sum_{m=0}^{\infty} \frac{(-1)^m}{m!(n+m)!} \left(\frac{\rho}{2}\right)^{2m}
\end{aligned} \tag{2C.26}$$

The series expansion for the Bessel function of integral order n may be found in still another way. In (10.43) let $e^{i\theta} = t$ so that

$$\sin \theta = \frac{1}{2i}\left(t - \frac{1}{t}\right)$$

We then obtain the identity in t

$$e^{(\rho/2)(t-1/t)} = \sum_n J_n(\rho)t^n \qquad (2C.27)$$

The left-hand member can be expanded by Laurent's theorem.[1] The coefficient of t^n is then the Bessel function $J_n(\rho)$.

2C.7 The Asymptotic Expansions

A divergent series

$$a_0 + \frac{a_1}{z} + \frac{a_2}{z^2} + \cdots + \frac{a_n}{z^n} + \cdots$$

in which the sum of the first $(n + 1)$ terms is $S_n(z)$, is said to be an *asymptotic expansion* of a function $f(z)$ for a given range of values of arg z (if $z = re^{i\theta}$, $\theta \equiv \arg z$), if the expression

$$R_n(z) = z^n[f(z) - S_n(z)]$$

satisfies the condition

$$\lim_{|z|\to\infty} R_n(z) = 0 \qquad n \text{ fixed}$$

even though

$$\lim_{n\to\infty} |R_n(z)| = \infty \qquad z \text{ fixed}$$

We denote the fact that the series is the asymptotic expansion of $f(z)$ by writing

$$f(z) \simeq \sum_{n=0}^{\infty} a_n z^{-n}$$

One of the most important methods for obtaining asymptotic expansions is the *saddle-point method* due to Debye: Consider the integral

$$I(t) = \int_A^B X(z)e^{tf(z)}\, dz \qquad (2C.28)$$

in which t is large, real, and positive, $f(z)$ is analytic, and the path of integration is an arc or closed curve in the z plane. This path may be

---

[1] See any standard text on the functions of a complex variable.

deformed continuously without affecting the value of the integral I provided that during the deformation the path of integration does not pass through a singularity of the integrand. Let

$$z = x + iy \quad \text{and} \quad f(z) = u(x,y) + iv(x,y)$$

so that the integrand in (2C.28) may be written $X(x + iy)e^{itv}e^{tu}$. Now X does not depend on t so that, since t and u are both real, the integrand is not a rapidly oscillating function for large values of t and constant v. Furthermore, the integrand will be large when u is algebraically large. However u can never have an absolute maximum. Consider a point at which

$$\frac{\partial u}{\partial x} = \frac{\partial u}{\partial y} = 0 \tag{2C.29}$$

Because $f(z)$ is analytic we also have at this point

$$\frac{\partial v}{\partial x} = \frac{\partial v}{\partial y} = 0 \tag{2C.30}$$

and $\qquad \dfrac{\partial^2 u}{\partial x^2} = -\dfrac{\partial^2 u}{\partial y^2} \qquad \dfrac{\partial^2 v}{\partial x^2} = -\dfrac{\partial^2 v}{\partial y^2} \qquad$ (2C.31)

Because of the relations (2C.29), (2C.30), and (2C.31) such a point is given the descriptive name, *saddle point*. At such a point we also have $f'(z) = 0$.

It follows, therefore, that at least two curves along which u is constant may be drawn through a saddle point. In the sectors between these two curves, u will be alternately greater and less than at the saddle point itself. Topographically speaking, the two curves are mountain passes, and we may call the sectors where u is greater, the mountains, and those where u is lesser, the valleys. For this reason the saddle-point method is also called the *pass method*. In order to keep large values of u in as short a stretch of the path as possible we must avoid the mountains and keep to the valleys as much as possible. In the interesting case where the points A and B are in different valleys the path must go through the saddle point, i.e., the path must go through the pass in the mountains.

In order to surmount the pass in the fastest possible manner we must take the path of steepest ascent and descent for which $|\partial u/\partial s|$ is a maximum. For this reason the saddle-point method is often called the *method of steepest descent*. If we denote by θ the inclination of the path s to the x axis, we have

$$\frac{\partial u}{\partial s} = \cos \theta \frac{\partial u}{\partial x} + \sin \theta \frac{\partial u}{\partial y}$$

If $|\partial u/\partial s|$ is to be a maximum for variations in θ

$$\frac{\partial}{\partial \theta} \frac{\partial u}{\partial s} = 0 = -\sin \theta \frac{\partial u}{\partial x} + \cos \theta \frac{\partial u}{\partial y}$$

$$= -\sin \theta \frac{\partial v}{\partial y} - \cos \theta \frac{\partial v}{\partial x} = -\frac{\partial v}{\partial s}$$

Hence v is constant along the path. Such a path is called *a line of steepest ascent and descent*. There will be one into each valley.

If z_0 is a saddle point, $f(z)$ near it can be expanded in the form

$$f(z) = f(z_0) + \tfrac{1}{2}(z - z_0)^2 f''(z_0) + \cdots$$

and the direction of the path will be such that $(z - z_0)^2 f''(z_0)$ is real and negative. The integral (2C.28) may now be written as, approximately,

$$I(t) = e^{tf(z_0)} \int X(z) e^{1/2 t (z-z_0)^2 f''(z_0)} \, dz$$

With the substitutions

$$\xi^2 = -t(z - z_0)^2 f''(z_0)$$

$$\xi \, d\xi = -t(z - z_0) f''(z_0) \, dz$$

so that

$$dz = \frac{d\xi}{[-tf''(z_0)]^{1/2}}$$

the integral becomes

$$I(t) = \frac{e^{tf(z_0)}}{[-tf''(z_0)]^{1/2}} \int_{-\infty}^{+\infty} X(z) e^{-1/2 \xi^2} \, d\xi \qquad (2C.32)$$

The first term in the asymptotic expansion of the integral $I(t)$ is easily obtained. Integrating over the neighborhood of the saddle point z_0, we may replace the "slowly varying" function $X(z)$ by $X(z_0)$ so that

$$I(t) \simeq \frac{X(z_0) e^{tf(z_0)}}{[-tf''(z_0)]^{1/2}} \int_{-\infty}^{+\infty} e^{-1/2 \xi^2} \, d\xi \simeq \sqrt{\frac{2\pi}{t}} \frac{X(z_0) e^{tf(z_0)}}{[-f''(z_0)]^{1/2}} \qquad (2C.33)$$

Let us now apply the method to the integral

$$H_\nu^{(1)}(\rho) = \frac{1}{\pi} \int_{W_1} e^{i\nu(w - \pi/2)} e^{i\rho \cos w} \, dw \qquad (2C.17)$$

We assume $\rho \gg 1$ and real, and $\nu \ll \rho$. Then, with the identifications

$$X(w) = e^{i\nu(w - \pi/2)} \qquad f(w) = -i \cos w$$

and with $f'(w) = 0$ when $w = 0$, we obtain

$$H_\nu^{(1)}(\rho) \simeq \frac{1}{\pi} \sqrt{\frac{2\pi}{\rho}} \frac{e^{-i\nu\pi/2}e^{i\rho}}{\sqrt{i}}$$

$$\simeq \sqrt{\frac{2}{\pi\rho}} e^{i(\rho - \nu\pi/2 - \pi/4)} \qquad (2C.34)$$

by the use of (2C.33).

In a like manner we may obtain

$$H_\nu^{(2)}(\rho) \simeq \sqrt{\frac{2}{\pi\rho}} e^{-i(\rho - \nu\pi/2 - \pi/4)} \qquad (2C.35)$$

by applying the saddle-point method to (2C.18). Note that this result may have been obtained directly from (2C.23) and (2C.34).

Furthermore, substitution of (2C.34) and (2C.35) into (2C.19) and (2C.20) yields

$$J_\nu(\rho) \simeq \sqrt{\frac{2}{\pi\rho}} \cos(\rho - \nu\pi/2 - \pi/4) \qquad (2C.36)$$

and

$$N_\nu(\rho) \simeq \sqrt{\frac{2}{\pi\rho}} \sin(\rho - \nu\pi/2 - \pi/4) \qquad (2C.37)$$

The quickest way of obtaining the remaining terms in the asymptotic expansions is as follows: We assume

$$H_\nu^{(1,2)}(\rho) \simeq \sqrt{\frac{2}{\pi\rho}} e^{\pm i(\rho - \nu\pi/2 - \pi/4)} \left(1 + \frac{a_1}{\rho} + \frac{a_2}{\rho^2} + \cdots + \frac{a_m}{\rho^m} + \cdots\right) \quad (2C.38)$$

and substitute into the differential equation (2C.1). The a's are then found by setting the factor of each power of ρ equal to zero. They satisfy the general formula

$$\frac{a_m}{\rho^m} = \frac{(\nu,m)}{(\mp 2i\rho)^m}$$

where the symbol (ν,m), which was introduced by Hankel, represents

$$\frac{(4\nu^2 - 1)(4\nu^2 - 9) \cdots [4\nu^2 - (2m-1)^2]}{2^{2m}m!}$$

and $(\nu,0) = 1$.

The asymptotic expansions for $H^{(1)}$ and $H^{(2)}$ are then

$$H_\nu^{(1)}(\rho) \simeq \sqrt{\frac{2}{\pi\rho}}\, e^{i(\rho - \nu\pi/2 - \pi/4)} \sum_{m=0,1,2,\ldots} \frac{(\nu,m)}{(-2i\rho)^m} \qquad (2C.39)$$

and

$$H_\nu^{(2)}(\rho) \simeq \sqrt{\frac{2}{\pi\rho}}\, e^{-i(\rho - \nu\pi/2 - \pi/4)} \sum_{m=0,1,2,\ldots} \frac{(\nu,m)}{(+2i\rho)^m} \qquad (2C.40)$$

These expansions are known as *Hankel's asymptotic series*. For real positive values of ρ and ν, the error due to breaking off either series after the term $m > \frac{1}{4}(2\nu - 1)$ is smaller than the absolute value of the first term not taken.

The asymptotic expansions for J_ν and N_ν are obtained by substituting (2C.39) and (2C.40) into (2C.19) and (2C.20) respectively.

2C.8   The Asymptotic Series of Debye

The considerations in Sec. 2C.7 were restricted to the case where $\nu \ll \rho$. We wish to discuss now the case in which ν and ρ are both large. The exponent

$$f(w) = i(\rho \cos w + \nu w - \nu\pi/2)$$

in the integral representations of the Hankel functions, (2C.17) and (2C.18), now depends on two large numbers ρ and ν which, for convenience, we take to be real and positive. For the case of complex values the reader is referred to Debye's papers.[1]

Let $\beta = w - \pi/2$ so that

$$f(w) = F(\beta) = i(\nu\beta - \rho \sin \beta) \qquad (2C.41)$$

If $\nu < \rho$ we set

$$\nu = \rho \cos \alpha \qquad (2C.42)$$

so that

$$F(\beta) = i\rho(\beta \cos \alpha - \sin \beta) \qquad (2C.43)$$

The saddle point $F'(\beta) = 0$ is then given by $\cos \alpha - \cos \beta = 0$. It lies at $\beta_0 = \mp\alpha$, for $H^{(1)}$ and $H^{(2)}$, respectively. From (2C.43) we obtain

$$F''(\beta_0) = \mp i\rho \sin \alpha$$

so that $F(\beta) = \mp i\rho(\alpha \cos \alpha - \sin \alpha) \mp \frac{1}{2}i\rho \sin \alpha (\beta - \beta_0)^2 + \cdots$

$$= \mp i\rho(\alpha \cos \alpha - \sin \alpha) \mp \frac{1}{2}i\rho \sin \alpha (\beta \pm \alpha)^2 + \cdots$$

[1] *Math. Ann.*, **67** (1909); *Bayr. Akad.*, **40** (1910).

With the substitutions

$$\xi^2 = \pm i(\beta \pm \alpha)^2$$

$$\xi \, d\xi = \pm i(\beta \pm \alpha) \, d\beta$$

so that
$$d\beta = e^{\mp i\pi/4} \, d\xi$$
we obtain

$$H_\nu^{(1,2)}(\rho) = \frac{1}{\pi} \int e^{F(\beta)} \, d\beta = \frac{1}{\pi} \, e^{\mp i\rho(\alpha \cos \alpha - \sin \alpha)} \int e^{-\rho/2 \xi^2 \sin \alpha} \, e^{\mp i\pi/4} \, d\xi$$

$$= \sqrt{\frac{2}{\pi \rho \sin \alpha}} \, e^{\mp i\rho(\alpha \cos \alpha - \sin \alpha) \mp i\pi/4} \tag{2C.44}$$

In the case $\nu > \rho$, we set $\nu = \rho \cosh \alpha$ and, proceeding as above, obtain

$$H_\nu^{(1,2)}(\rho) = \sqrt{\frac{2}{\pi \rho \sinh \alpha}} \, e^{\rho(\alpha \cosh \alpha - \sinh \alpha) \mp i\pi/2} \tag{2C.45}$$

From these limiting values, (2C.44) and (2C.45), Debye deduced the asymptotic expansions. We do not develop these here. The interested reader is referred again to the papers of Debye.[1]

2C.9 The Addition Theorems for Bessel Functions

Bessel functions do not possess addition theorems in the strict sense of the term; that is, it is not possible to express $J_\nu(\rho + r)$ as an algebraic function of $J_\nu(\rho)$ and $J_\nu(r)$. There are, however, a number of formulae which are commonly described as addition theorems. We shall develop these formulae for functions of integral order n only.

Consider the triangle with sides r, ρ, and $R = \sqrt{r^2 + \rho^2 - 2r\rho \cos \varphi}$ where φ is the angle opposite side R. Let ψ be the angle opposite side ρ. Then

$$Re^{i\psi} = r - \rho e^{-i\varphi}$$

so that
$$R \cos \psi = r - \rho \cos \varphi \qquad R \sin \psi = \rho \sin \varphi \tag{2C.46}$$

Now
$$J_n(R) = \frac{1}{2\pi} \int_{-\pi}^{\pi} e^{i(R \sin \theta - n\theta)} \, d\theta \tag{2C.2}$$

[1] *Ibid.*

With the substitution $\theta = \alpha + \psi$, this becomes

$$J_n(R) = \frac{1}{2\pi} \int_{-\pi-\psi}^{\pi-\psi} e^{i[R\sin(\alpha+\psi)-n(\alpha+\psi)]}\,d\alpha$$

$$= \frac{e^{-in\psi}}{2\pi} \int_{-\pi}^{\pi} e^{i[R\sin(\alpha+\psi)-n\alpha]}\,d\alpha \tag{2C.47}$$

where, because of the periodicity of the integrand, the limits of integration have again been taken as $\pm\pi$. By the use of (2C.46) we obtain $R\sin(\alpha+\psi) = r\sin\alpha + \rho\sin(\varphi-\alpha)$. Hence (2C.47) becomes

$$e^{in\psi}J_n(R) = \frac{1}{2\pi}\int_{-\pi}^{\pi} e^{i\rho\sin(\varphi-\alpha)}e^{i(r\sin\alpha-n\alpha)}\,d\alpha$$

$$= \frac{1}{2\pi}\int_{-\pi}^{\pi} \sum_m J_m(\rho)e^{im(\varphi-\alpha)}e^{i(r\sin\alpha-n\alpha)}\,d\alpha$$

$$= \sum_m J_m(\rho)e^{im\varphi}\frac{1}{2\pi}\int_{-\pi}^{\pi} e^{i[r\sin\alpha-(n+m)\alpha]}\,d\alpha$$

$$= \sum_{m=-\infty}^{+\infty} J_m(\rho)J_{m+n}(r)e^{im\varphi} \tag{2C.48}$$

where we have used (10.43).

A number of well-known addition theorems may be obtained as special cases of (2C.48). For example, if $n = 0$,

$$J_0(R) = \sum_{m=-\infty}^{+\infty} J_m(\rho)J_m(r)e^{im\varphi} \tag{2C.49}$$

If $\psi = 0$ and $\varphi = \pi$, then $R = r + \rho$ and (2C.48) reduces to

$$J_n(r+\rho) = \sum_{m=-\infty}^{+\infty} (-1)^m J_m(\rho)J_{m+n}(r) \tag{2C.50}$$

Finally, for $n = 0$, (2C.50) becomes

$$J_0(r+\rho) = \sum_{m=-\infty}^{+\infty} (-1)^m J_m(\rho)J_m(r) \tag{2C.51}$$

References

Nielsen, N.: "Zylinderfunktionen," Teubner Verlagsgesellschaft, Leipzig, 1904.

Schafheitlin, P.: "Besselsche Funktionen," Teubner Verlagsgesellschaft, Leipzig, 1908.

Gray, A., G. B. Mathews, and T. M. MacRobert: "Bessel Functions and Their Applications to Physics," The Macmillan Company, New York, 1922.

Watson, G. N.: "The Theory of Bessel Functions," Cambridge University Press, New York, 1922.

McLachlin, N. W.: "Bessel Functions for Engineers," Oxford University Press, New York, 1934.

Weyrich, R.: "Zylinderfunktionen und ihre Anwendungen," Teubner Verlagsgesellschaft, Leipzig, 1937.

For comprehensive summaries of the properties of cylinder functions refer to:

Jahnke, E., and F. Emde: "Tables of Functions with Formulae and Curves," Chap. 8, Dover Publications, New York, 1943.

Magnus, W., and F. Oberhettinger: "Formulas and Theorems for the Special Functions of Mathematical Physics," Chap. 3, Chelsea Publishing Company, New York, 1949.

Index

Gunfire Wakes the Echoes at Ticonderoga

CHAMPLAIN, the great French explorer, was the first white man to visit Ticonderoga. In the summer of 1609, wishing to adventure southward up the valley of the Richelieu into the great lake of which he had heard the Indians speak, he joined forces with a war party of Hurons and Montagnais. These Indians, itching for a profitable skirmish with their bitter enemies, the mighty Iroquois of the Mohawk Valley, heartily welcomed the addition of the white men and their death-dealing firearms, something as yet unknown to the Iroquois. The expedition worked its way south upstream against the current of the Richelieu River until the rapids at Chambly were encountered. It soon was evident that the Frenchmen's shallop could never be gotten upstream past this obstruction. Champlain accordingly selected two companions from the crew and sent the craft back to the tiny outpost of Quebec, where his fortified garrison house had been built the year before. Sixty Indians and the three Frenchmen carried overland around the rapids their equipment and twenty-four birchbark canoes, smallish ones really, each intended to hold only two Indians and their baggage. All climbed aboard, and there could not have been much room to spare. They paddled upstream and soon met more rapids at the place later to be called Ste. Thérèse. Then something over a score of miles up the now placid river brought them to the waters of the great lake we now call Champlain.

Each night the party landed, threw up birchbark shelters, and then built a barricade of tree trunks around them. A canoe or two scouted ahead for a few miles looking for signs of an enemy, but soon returned. No further guard was maintained, and all the Indians went to sleep, trusting their "manitou" to keep them safe until morning. Each evening the medicine man made magic to prophesy, to keep away evil spirits and to put a "hex" on the Iroquois. The expedition paddled southward, keeping a weather eye out for the enemy, and soon it was decided to travel only by night, hiding in the woods during the daylight hours. No Indians lived in these regions, but they were the hunting grounds of the warring nations. Split Rock, near today's Essex, New York, was said to mark the boundary line between the Canadian and the more southern Indians. He who passed beyond this point in those early days was certain to have warlike intentions. In later years it would no longer be so, but in Champlain's day battle was the only objective of passage beyond Split Rock.

South of this point the lake becomes more narrow, and once Crown Point — Pointe à la Chevelure (Scalp Point), the French called it — is reached the width is only that of a great river. It was at about ten in the evening of nearly the last day of July that the party arrived in the vicinity of the narrows at Ticonderoga, and there they encountered a flotilla of Iroquois elm-bark canoes, headed northward and bent on mischief.

The two parties, that of the Iroquois much the larger, closed their canoes tightly together and lay to just out of arrow range. Insults, threats and badinage were exchanged, and the Indians from the Mohawk then landed on the little peninsula of Ticonderoga, where they hurriedly built a barricade of tree trunks and bushes. The Canadian Indians lashed their canoes together with long poles and held a position of safety offshore. Soon two Iroquois canoes paddled out with envoys who asked if the northerners would fight. The reply was that they would like nothing better and that that was what they had come for. How confident must the Iroquois have felt, seeing their enemy only a third of their own number, and how certain of victory. The Canadian Indians knew no fear, for they trusted in the magic of the white men's firearms, whose power they had already seen demonstrated in their northern villages. All agreed that it was foolish to attempt to fight in the dark, and that the battle must wait for daylight. The remainder of the night, according to Champlain, was passed in songs, insults and dances, although how one could do a war dance in an overloaded canoe, and at night at that, is not easy to comprehend.

At daybreak Champlain's party landed in a crowd, the Indians forming a screen in front of the explorer and his two companions. The Iroquois, some two hundred in number, rushed out from their rough barricade, expecting to overawe the invaders by their numbers alone. Three chiefs wearing great feathers on their heads led the van. The Canadian Indians rolled aside their center ranks, revealing Champlain with his arquebus, loaded this day with four leaden balls. The two companions slipped into the cover of a patch of woods on the flank. Champlain now started forward toward the Iroquois, who had halted in their mad rush at their first sight of a white man. He does not tell us whether or not he wore any armor that day, but his appearance even without a shining breastplate would have been wildly unlike anything the Iroquois had ever seen. Despite their astonishment they set arrows to their bows and prepared to let fly. But before they could the Frenchman delivered his fire from a range of only thirty yards, aiming at one of the chieftains. Two of the Iroquois leaders fell, while a third Indian was wounded, so lucky was the shot. Undaunted by the noise and smoke of this new and undreamed-of weapon, the southern Indians let fly their cloud of arrows, but no one was seriously hurt. If Champlain wore no half-armor he certainly must have had on a padded jerkin, and the Indians had wooden shields, proof against any arrow.

Then one of the Frenchmen on the flank let go with his weapon. This second clap of thunder was too much for the Iroquois, and they took to flight, pursued for a short distance by Champlain, who got off one more shot, dropping another two or three redskins. Pursuit was continued for a distance into the heavy woods, while the whooping and wildly exulting Hurons and Montagnais killed a few more of their enemies and seized about a dozen prisoners. Soon all returned to the scene of the battle, and it was found that only about fifteen or sixteen of the victors had been wounded, and that all injuries moreover were slight. It was a mighty victory, but most unfortunately for Canada it would long be remembered by the Iroquois and would lead to bitter reprisals over many years to come.

The victors feasted, sang, danced and made merry for about three hours, during which time Champlain apparently visited the little river which connects the lake of his name with Lake George, although he did not spare the time to go as far as the latter. The Iroquois were still in the vicinity in considerable numbers, and the risk of ambush existed. It is probable that he went only as far as a canoe could take him, that is, to the lowest falls on the river, where later the French would build a sawmill.

By this time it must have been about midday, and the expedition took to its canoes, now greatly overloaded with prisoners and plunder. Very likely they added a few of the elm-bark canoes of the enemy to their flotilla. After about three hours of paddling northward they went ashore, probably a bit north of the present Crown Point bridge. A fire was lit and a prisoner selected for torture. Champlain gives some of the bloody details. After listening for a while to the shrieks of the unhappy victim he begged the tormentors to put the wretch out of his misery. They objected to discontinuing their sport. At last the Frenchman could stand it no longer and his arquebus put an end to the suffering of the Iroquois. Then the Indians cut out his heart and tried to make the other prisoners eat it, but in this they had no success.

Various thoughts have been advanced over the years as to the exact location of Champlain's fight, and of course it can never be precisely determined. It obviously was somewhere on the peninsula upon which Fort Ticonderoga stands today, although claims have been made for Crown Point, largely because the latitude recorded by Champlain's crude astrolabe more nearly approaches that of this place than that of Ticonderoga. Two specific points disprove Crown Point's claim. Champlain stated that he saw the river through which Lake George discharges into Lake Champlain, and he also reported that his party returned north three hours after the battle. Thus there would not have been sufficient time to paddle on from Crown Point to Ticonderoga and to return. The other point, and a very definite one, is that on Champlain's map of 1632 he clearly marks Lake George and its outlet, and shows by a number keyed to the legend that it was on the peninsula, on the north side of this river, that the fight took place.

Champlain returned to Canada and no white man would see Ticonderoga for years to come. Not many miles to the south, however, Henry Hudson that same summer was exploring the river which was later to bear his name, and

scarcely a month after Champlain's skirmish the Englishman was in the vicinity of Albany, less than ninety miles
from Ticonderoga. The first tentacles of the two civilizations
which were to clash for nearly a century over the control of
the Champlain Valley had almost met in that year of 1609.
When at last France and Britain joined in decisive battle in
that vital valley, it was at the site of Champlain's encounter
that the issue was to be most bitterly contested. And again
in the American Revolution this same spot would be the
enemy's objective for two successive campaigns.

For years to come, however, Ticonderoga would, after
Champlain's departure, be merely a name in the wilderness,
and over a century was to pass before the white man attempted settlement in the region. Until nearly the end of
the seventeenth century the French would restrict their habi-
tations to the banks of the St. Lawrence and the northern
parts of the valley of the Richelieu. Albany was established
by the Dutch as a trading post by 1614, soon to be followed
by Fort Amsterdam at today's New York, but the Dutch-
British occupancy of the Hudson Valley would not advance
north of the Mohawk until well into the following century.
And so Ticonderoga would remain merely the name of an
almost unknown place in the forests of North America while
New France was slowly consolidating her tenuous hold on
the St. Lawrence and English immigrants were pouring into
New England to populate a new land and to establish a way
of life quite different from that existing elsewhere on the
continent.

THREE

Martyrdom on the Mohawk

FOR A GENERATION after Champlain's battle at Ticonderoga the Iroquois refrained from attack on the French, but they remembered and nourished revenge deep in their savage hearts. The Dutch at Fort Orange (now Albany) traded muskets for their furs, and by 1640 the Iroquois possessed at least thirty of these weapons with which Champlain had first confounded them in 1609. As their acquisition of firearms increased, so grew the enmity, still largely concealed, of the Iroquois against the French. With their new muskets they carried war to the Hurons of Georgian Bay and the Algonkins, but, save for a minor incident or two, they left the French alone. Then at last in the summer of 1641 the brittle peace snapped and open war broke out as Iroquois raiding parties appeared along the St. Lawrence. It was not a continuous war at all, but a sporadic one in which little parties of bloodthirsty savages suddenly burst from the woods, did what damage they could and promptly disappeared again into the wilderness.

In the early summer of 1642 Father Isaac Jogues of the Society of Jesus, a gentle and unassuming priest, timid but of an indomitable will, was sent from the Huron Mission of Ste. Marie on the shores of Georgian Bay to Quebec to secure much-needed supplies. He was returning westward with a party of two score Hurons and three lay missionaries and had passed by Trois Rivières and then Montreal Island, where only a month or two before Maisonneuve and his devoted little band had established the mission colony of Villemarie, still but a few tents and huts enclosed in a rough palisade. A little west of Montreal the Ottawa River enters the St. Lawrence through the Lake of the Two Mountains, really only a widening of the former river's shores. At the upper end of this lake there are a number of little islands, and here on the northern riverbank, Jogues's Indians noticed the tracks of some raiding Iroquois. These appeared to be relatively few in number, and the Hurons felt safe in continuing on their way.

The waters of the river here ran swiftly, and the canoes accordingly closely skirted the shore where the current was less. Suddenly some thirty Iroquois rose up from among the tall reeds and grasses along the river's margin, and poured upon the dumfounded Hurons a fusillade from their newly acquired weapons. Thirty muskets sent their bullets at forty men sitting in canoes at a distance of probably not over twenty or thirty yards. One Huron was wounded in the hand — such was Indian marksmanship on this occasion at least.

Another band of the invaders appeared on the opposite shore and the surprised and terrified Hurons splashed ashore and took to the woods in flight. Many of them escaped, and one of the four Frenchmen also was successful. Several friendly Indians, however, were killed or disabled. Father Jogues, from concealment in some bushes, watched the conclusion of the affair and could probably have remained safely in hiding until the Iroquois withdrew. But when he saw the two Frenchmen in the hands of the enemy, his conscience told him that he must share their fate, and he emerged from hiding and gave himself up to the howling savages. He immediately received a beating, and most of his fingernails were torn out by the roots, ripped off by Indian teeth. Then the Iroquois chewed one of the priest's fore-fingers until the bone was crushed and splinters of it protruded. The other Frenchmen received similar treatment, but the Hurons for the moment suffered no tortures.

The torment of the missionaries did not long continue, and soon the Iroquois with their twenty-two captives headed eastward down the St. Lawrence. They stopped at the mouth of the Richelieu, where the heads of the slain Hurons were set up on the top of stakes and crude pictures of Jogues and the other prisoners were sketched on the trunks of trees. Then the party ascended the Richelieu and went on up Lake Champlain, while the Frenchmen suffered agonies from their untended wounds and the fierce heat of summer. Eight days after the capture they met, probably a little north of Ticonderoga, a war party of two hundred Mohawks bound on a raid on the Canadian settlements. The newcomers, with shouts of excitement and a joyful volley of musketry, at once cut clubs and formed a long double line. The prisoners were forced to run the gauntlet, but the priest could make it only halfway and fell to the ground beneath the blows. Then he was further mishandled, a fingertip burned, another crunched by Indian teeth, and threatening gestures made of cutting off his nose. But soon the sport lost interest and the northward-bound party proceeded on its way. They were to meet surprise, for only eleven days after Jogues and his captors had left the Richelieu's mouth a French expedition arrived there to build a fort, the first of the many that were later to follow in the Champlain Valley. The new stockade was not quite finished when the war party got there, but it was complete except for a single gap, where the French made a successful stand, and the savages were beaten off.

Father Jogues's captors continued on to Ticonderoga and

then along Lake George, at last quitting their canoes at today's village of Lake George and continuing overland. The
priest, suffering greatly from his wounds and bruises, was
forced to carry a part of the Indian booty, the goods originally destined for the Huron Mission. They crossed the Hudson, at this time of year flowing sluggishly in its rocky bed,
and almost certainly followed the valley of the Sacandaga,
today flooded by a great reservoir, and on to where Amsterdam now stands. The lowest of the three Mohawk towns
was but a mile or two upstream. Today the great Martyr's
Shrine of Auriesville covers the site of this vanished town.
The trip from the Lake of the Two Mountains had taken
thirteen days. The prisoners were at once greeted with clubs
and stones, while the priest had his two remaining fingernails
torn off. Then all the youth of the town lined up for the
gauntlet; but now a new proceedure was introduced, as Mohawks inserted themselves at intervals in the file of prisoners
and forced them to slow their progress through the ranks of
their tormentors to a walk.

At last the center of the village was reached, and here
further torture awaited. Jogues's left thumb was hacked off
at its base, a customary Indian mayhem before the day of
firearms, since it prevented use of a bow. The next day the
captives were taken to the second village, a couple of miles
upstream, and subjected to further torments, such as being
staked out naked on the ground while Indian children tossed
hot coals at them. Two days later they were moved on to
the third town, a few miles east of today's Canajoharie. Here
Jogues, stark naked, suffered greatly from cold and wet, but
otherwise he received only minor mishandling. One of his
companions, however, was less fortunate. This man hitherto
had lost no fingers, but one of the Mohawks, noting the
fact, at once sawed off a forefinger with a clamshell.

This was the end of the priest's worst physical suffering,

but he still led a miserable existence, scantily clothed in fragments of cast-off Indian garments and eating little but unripe squashes and cornmeal mush occasionally enriched with bits of fish or sun-dried meat. The Dutch at Fort Orange soon learned of the prisoner and tried without success to ransom him from his captors. Jogues still lived in fear and received many threats, but fortunately they were only threats. One of his two companions was adopted by a Mohawk, while the other was murdered in the presence of the Jesuit, who also bowed his head for the tomahawk but was left unharmed.

Father Jogues by now had largely recovered from his injuries, although his hands would always be fearfully maimed. He was treated as a slave and taken on a fall hunting trip. The Indians had a custom of dedicating their slain deer to one of their divinities, which Jogues believed devils, and accordingly he refused to eat any of the meat, which was to his mind accursed. And so he nearly starved in the midst of plenty. His food at times was, he recorded, deer entrails, boiled fungus, frogs eaten whole and cornmeal mush. It is most probable, however, that at times his captors fared no better. By the new year of 1643 his position became somewhat less miserable; a Frenchman at Fort Orange gave him a suit of clothes, and he commenced to study the Mohawk tongue, at last feeling that he probably would be allowed to live. He even managed to secure some paper from the Dutch and wrote several letters, one of which, directed to the governor of Trois Rivières, was actually delivered by an Indian to the fort at the mouth of the Richelieu.

By some extraordinary chance Father Jogues was able to retain possession of at least two books of religion, and with these and his increasing knowledge of the Indian tongue he started missionary work, probably largely among the Huron slaves. He was now left relatively free to go where he would among the Mohawk villages, and, being an unusually swift runner, he could probably have escaped had he wished. But he felt that he now was doing some good for his faith and so decided, for the present at least, to remain. The good Dutch dominie Megapolensis of Fort Orange befriended him, and the priest even visited the Dutch settlement upon occasion.

Father Jogues at one time had accompanied a fishing party of Mohawks to the Hudson at a point some twenty miles below Fort Orange, and on returning to his village by way of this post he learned that an Iroquois raiding party had suffered disaster through, they firmly believed, the letter he had dispatched. Accordingly they were out for his blood. And so at last he decided to escape and sought safety with the Dutch.

The little outpost which was to become Albany was the northernmost settlement in the Hudson Valley in 1643. It was a puny little place, "a wretched little fort called Fort Orenge, built of logs with four or five pieces of cannon . . . and as many swivels." The entire population was but a hundred living in something over a score of houses. There was an active trade with the Indians, who for their furs received guns, kettles, knives, axes and cloth as well as many other items of trade goods.

The Dutchmen were kindly and sheltered the priest in secrecy from his searching Indian hosts, until he could safely be put on shipboard. Eventually the Indians were placated by a sizable ransom and ceased their search for the priest. At the Hudson's mouth was the Dutch settlement of New Amsterdam, and to Father Jogues, after years in the wilderness, it must have seemed a real metropolis with its fort and garrison of sixty soldiers, its large stone church, the governor's house of brick and the storehouses and barracks. The population, some scattered over the island of Manhattan, totaled four or five hundred. Jogues was told by the governor that eighteen different languages were spoken there, while half as many sects worshiped as they pleased.

After further adventures, minor in nature compared to those he had survived, Father Jogues reached France on Christmas Day of 1643, a year and a half after his capture. A few days later he knocked on the door of the Jesuit college at Rennes, where he was at first taken for a beggar. Word soon reached Paris of his extraordinary misfortunes, and the queen sent for him to tell her the story. The modest priest shrank from the homage of the Court and longed to return to Canada. Under Church law, the fearful mutilation of his hands prevented his saying mass, but a sympathetic pope granted him a special dispensation. He sailed westward again in the spring of 1644, and for the next two years was retained at various duties in the little town of Quebec.

In the early summer of 1645 Mohawk peace emissaries appeared at Trois Rivières, bringing with them that companion of Father Jogues whom the Indians had adopted. In dress and appearance he now was a Mohawk, but it was largely due to his efforts that this embassy of peace had been undertaken. Council followed council and wampum belt followed wampum belt until at last, after days and weeks of councils and feasting, peace was declared. But it was a tenuous one that would not last.

The Canadian governor in the spring of 1646 decided to send an ambassador to the Mohawks in an attempt further to cement the peace. Father Jogues, in view of his knowledge of both the language and the region, was the logical candidate. With one white companion and a few Indians he started south, wearing on the advice of the Indians a civilian doublet instead of his cassock. They reached the northern end of Lake George on the eve of Corpus Christi, and the priest, in honor of the day, named the lake St. Sacrement, a name that would endure for more than a century. From the southern end of this lake the party followed the Sacandaga trail until they reached the Hudson, where, borrowing canoes from an Indian fishing party, they started paddling down the river to Fort Orange. Here the priest received a hearty welcome from the Dutch and a few days of rest were taken. The embassy then moved up the Mohawk to the scene of the priest's former captivity. What thoughts he must have had upon seeing again the place of his torment! The reception given him by the Mohawks was such as was due an emissary of a power with which it was desired, for the moment at least, to remain at peace. His Huron converts were certainly glad to see him, and some of the Mohawks appear to have been reasonably cordial. Father Jogues delivered his belts and speeches and shortly returned to Canada without incident.

A month or two later in that same year it was decided to attempt to found a mission on the Mohawk and Father Jogues was designated as its head. He started south in the late summer. Meanwhile, there had been a change of feeling among the Mohawks and one of the clans, the Bears, believing that Jogues had put a curse on their nation, were all for war and demanded the priest's death. The Turtles and Wolves, however, defended him and wished to maintain the peace. A war party of young Bears met Father Jogues and his companions somewhere south of Lake George, seized and stripped him, and took him back prisoner to the lower Mohawk town, where he promptly met martyrdom from an Iroquois tomahawk. Such was the sad end of this gentle, timid and yet iron-willed priest, who later would be canonized by his Church.

FOUR

A Fort Rises in the Wilderness

FOR A SCORE of years after the death of Father Jogues
the Champlain Valley saw no white man, and the region
remained the hunting grounds of the Indian. Over the northern half of the region the Algonkin held sway, while to the
south the Iroquois hunted without fear of ambush. Raids
northward on the puny Canadian settlements by warriors of
the Five Nations had, by 1665, become so troublesome
that the French King at last took notice and sent a regiment,
the hard-bitten Carignan-Salières, across the ocean to curb
the raiding savage. The governor of Canada believed in
carrying the war to the enemy and in 1666 he led his forces
south in a raid on the Indian castles of the Mohawk Valley.
The expedition went astray, met a party of Dutchmen from
Albany, then two years a British possession. The Dutchmen
saved the Frenchmen from near starvation, and the disgruntled raiders struggled north again to Canada, the first
military expedition of white men ever to pass through the
narrows of Ticonderoga. Later in that same year the Frenchmen tried again with better luck, found and burned five of
the Mohawk towns and thoroughly cowed that tribe of the
Five Nations. The Mohawks never forgot their humiliation,
and, despite treaties of peace and friendship, they waited
their opportunity for vengeance. Albany and the New Neth-
erlands meanwhile passed back into Dutch hands for a brief

period before becoming, in 1674, the British province of
New York.

In 1689, fifteen hundred bloodthirsty Iroquois, mindful
still of their villages burned a generation before, hit La
Chine, a Canadian settlement a little distance upstream from
Montreal, in a bloody raid. The French governor, the fiery
and short-tempered Frontenac, convinced that the English
had incited the raid, in revenge turned his Canadians and
Indians against the little hamlet of Schenectady. This was
Canada's first attack on the British colonies, forerunner of a
half-century of bloody warfare. Britain at once retaliated with
an attempted thrust northward, which never got beyond
the southern end of Lake Champlain, and by two minor
raids on the Canadian settlements on the St. Lawrence. It
was in the course of the last of these, Peter Schuyler's raid of
1691, that Ticonderoga is again mentioned in our history,
for the raiders rested there at the narrows for a day or two on
their journey and built an additional canoe. There was a
little further, but minor, action back and forth along the
great waterway, while Canadian raids shifted eastward to
fall on the settlements in Maine. Then peace was made, a
peace which soon was broken when Queen Anne's War
erupted. Although this new struggle commenced in Europe
in 1701, no action took place in America until two years
later. A truce existed in effect along the Hudson-Champlain
Valley, for neither the French nor the Dutch of Albany
wished to interrupt the profitable smuggling trade which was
carried on between the two colonies. So for many a year the
narrows of Ticonderoga enjoyed a quiet peace, broken only
by the splash of the smuggler's paddle, and history had no
tale to tell.

Gradually the French pushed southward up the valley of
the lake until in 1731 they built a stone fort at Crown Point,
a fort which was fated to exist for a generation and yet never

see a hostile action. The British meanwhile had advanced their settlements northward up the Hudson to the region of old Saratoga, now called Schuylerville. Only some sixty miles separated the two opposing civilizations. King George's War broke out in America in 1744 and lasted for four years, but they were relatively peaceful years save for minor strife on the borders. The great event of this war was the New Englanders' capture of Louisbourg, but in the Champlain Valley little of note took place.

Peace between France and Britain endured for a few years after the Treaty of Aix-la-Chapelle in 1748, but it was a peace that could not last. Two great empires were in conflict and this was but a breathing spell. The first real clash was to come in America and beyond the Alleghenies, where the French were advancing their frontier posts and stockaded forts into the great valley of the Ohio River. In 1749 a number of Virginian and London capitalists had formed the Ohio Company in order to speculate in lands in that desirable region. Its emissaries were now pushing westward, while at the same time independent English fur traders, a rough and undisciplined crew, were encroaching more and more into lands each nation believed to be its own, and bringing out many of the furs so essential to the economy of New France. King Louis considered the Appalachian Mountains the westward boundary of the colonies of Britain, a view King George and particularly his American subjects were far from accepting.

By 1753 the French had established Fort Le Boeuf on the headwaters of the Allegheny, only a relatively short portage from Lake Erie — up to now, and for a few years yet to come, uncontested French waters. The stockaded fort was about a dozen miles south and slightly east of today's Erie, Pennsylvania. From Le Boeuf one could easily descend by water all the way to French New Orleans on the Gulf of

Mexico. The governor of Virginia in 1753 sent young
George Washington to the Ohio to order the French garrison
of Le Boeuf to cease their encroachment and depart. The
commander at the little fort of course spurned the demand,
and Washington journeyed back through peril to Williams-
burg to report the rebuff to Governor Dinwiddie.

In the spring of the next year, 1754, a party of Virginians
was despatched westward over the mountains with orders to
build a fortified post at the Forks of the Ohio, the junction
of the Allegheny and Monongahela Rivers, the Pittsburgh of
today. Scarcely had they started their work before a large
body of Frenchmen suddenly appeared, descending the Allegheny from Fort Le Boeuf. The Englishmen were quietly
and firmly ejected and told to go home across the mountains.
Meanwhile the Virginia governor had raised additional
troops and sent them west under the youthful Lieutenant
Colonel George Washington to reinforce the new British
post on the Ohio. They were too late to save the post, whose
builders had already started their long trek homeward.
Washington's little army met them, learned the news, and
then soon encountered a party of reconnoitering Frenchmen.
The first armed clash of the new war took place, a war which
at last was to end with France stripped of Canada. Reinforcements quickly arrived from Le Boeuf and Washington
was penned up in the hurriedly built Fort Necessity at the
Great Meadows, near Uniontown, Pennsylvania, besieged
and forced into surrender. This petty engagement, far away
on the frontiers of North America, opened the great "Seven
Years War," which, however, would not formally be declared in Europe until two more years had passed. In America
it really was the "Nine Years War."

Although peace officially continued between the two nations in this summer of 1754, each knew that open war was
inevitable and each made preparations to initiate it in Amer-

ica. The British King sent General Braddock and two regiments of regulars overseas. An expedition was to penetrate
to the Ohio and throw out those Frenchmen who had dared
to encroach on His Majesty's domains. Braddock was also to
chase the French away from their post near Niagara Falls
and from Crown Point on Lake Champlain. None of these
missions could be considered acts of war in British eyes.
They were merely police actions to eject unlawful intruders.
The French, of course, would believe otherwise and feel,
perhaps quite rightly, that Britain had started a war.

Paris meanwhile had been far from asleep, and an army of
nearly four thousand regular troops crossed the Atlantic
under command of General Baron von Dieskau, an officer
of considerable experience. Some five hundred of the soldiers
had the misfortune to fall prey to the ever-watchful British
navy, but the remainder reached the St. Lawrence in safety.
They would be the backbone of the army that Montcalm
would often lead to victory over the next few years. A few
reinforcements would trickle in from France, but only a
few. New France had its own regular army, the regiment of
La Marine, but it was small, of dubious quality and had
officers of little experience in formal warfare, although often
most effective in the wilderness campaign. There also was
Canadian militia, but like all militia it was a most dubious
tool, poorly armed and undisciplined. The little force of hard-
bitten French regulars was the weapon Montcalm would
wield so effectively over the next four years.

Braddock's unfortunate attempt on the new Fort Duquesne at the Forks of the Ohio is beyond the scope of this
book, but he accomplished logistic wonders in moving his
force over the mountains and nearly succeeded in his mission.
He deserves better of history than he has received.

The northern drive against Crown Point was to start from
Albany. The army, composed entirely of colonial regiments,

assembled there on the flats under command of General William Johnson, fur trader, Indian commissioner, politician and one of the great men of colonial North America. Word of this impending attack soon reached the ears of Canada's Governor Vaudreuil.

In the spring of 1755 the southern bastion of New France in the Champlain Valley was the fort at Crown Point, an unusual fort in that its principal structure was a high tower-like redoubt. It was a dozen or so miles north of the narrows at Ticonderoga. The British had no real defense north of Albany, for stockaded Fort Lydius, where the portages for Lakes Champlain and George left the Hudson, had been burned during the last war. Such had also been the fate of the post at old Saratoga. Johnson's mission was to seize Fort St. Frédéric at Crown Point, but he appreciated the threat to New York offered by the undefended Hudson corridor to the south. Accordingly he moved up the river and commenced building a new fort on the site of Lydius's stockaded post. He called it Fort Edward, and for years it was to be a main defense of the Hudson Valley.

By late summer von Dieskau had his army at Crown Point —seven hundred French regulars, sixteen hundred Canadians and seven hundred Indians. The fort, quite a small one at best, and at this time only twenty-four years old, had fallen into poor condition. Masons feared to work on its walls lest they collapse. Yet this was Canada's southern outpost on the vital Hudson-Champlain waterway. In the first week of September von Dieskau started south, hoping to surprise the workmen at the new Fort Edward. In planning his expedition the general, new to America, made a grievous mistake, for he put his trust in Canadian militia and Indians, and left all but two hundred of his regulars behind. There is no need here to go into the resulting battle at any length. Johnson had left troops to continue work on the new fort, but he took most of his men on to the southern end of Lake George. In colonial days it was a rare occasion indeed when Indians could be persuaded to attack a fort — they preferred easier game. Von Dieskau's Indians refused to have anything to do with the camp where Fort Edward was just starting to arise, even though as yet it was quite indefensible. Accordingly he moved on against Johnson's main body at Lake George, and, after successfully ambushing a large force unwisely sent forward by the colonial general, he attacked the main body of troops barricaded behind breastworks hurriedly contrived out of tree trunks, wagon bodies and bateaux on a ridge bordering the shore of the lake. The regular French troops fought valiantly and suffered terrible losses, while the Canadians and Indians earned but little glory that day. Von Dieskau's attack was foiled, and he himself was wounded and captured.

The defeated French fell back to their boats on the western arm of Lake Champlain, receiving another mauling on the way from a party of British reinforcements. They retreated north to Ticonderoga and encamped. Johnson, wounded in the battle, failed to pursue and held his army at Lake George, his mission unaccomplished. Yet his victory, the only one gained by the British in America this year, made Johnson a baronet.

Canadian Governor Vaudreuil may or may not have heard of Von Dieskau's defeat when, on 20 September, he directed his wife's nephew, de Lotbinière, a young Canadian engineer officer, to build a fort at Ticonderoga. De Lotbinière had studied military engineering in France, but he had never seen active service in the field or garrison duty in a fortress. Nevertheless the young engineer had no doubt of his ability to design and build a fort in the wilderness, and his family connections gave him a much freer hand than any other officer could have enjoyed.

The peninsula which extends southeastward into Lake Champlain at the outlet of Lake George is composed largely of rugged rock, but when de Lotbinière first saw the place it apparently was so covered with trees and bushes that one could not see more than thirty paces in any direction. Nevertheless he staked out the outline of the fort on the ground and set to work. Later, when the outer end of the peninsula was stripped bare, it became apparent that the fort could have been better located, but it was then too late.

Work on the fort began in mid-October of 1755. De Lotbinière's first care was to provide some sort of winter quarters for the workmen, and relatively little was accomplished on the actual fort that fall and winter. He had two regiments from which to draw his labor force, La Reine and Languedoc, about six hundred and fifty men in all, and there certainly must have been some civilian artisans, such as foremen and carpenters. Soldiers were paid for their labor, in addition to their regular pay. The next year at Fort Frontenac on Lake Ontario this additional pay was at first a franc, then it was lowered to fifteen sous, three-fourths of a franc, but even this latter sum was a most welcome addition to the soldiers' meager pay.

The British were not ignorant of the new fort that was building, and scouting parties kept the peninsula under observation at frequent intervals. Robert Rogers, most famous of the colonial rangers, viewed the place at the end of September and reported that there were about three thousand men camped on the point, engaged in laying the foundations for a fort. A week later he rowed up Lake George with a party of fifty but failed to get any view of Ticonderoga, although his scouts managed to observe the force camped at the head of the portage. In mid-October Rogers returned to Lake Champlain, scouted around Crown Point, scalped a soldier there in full view of the fort, and examined Ticonderoga on his return trip. He reported about two thousand men in camp there but no further details.

And so it went, frequent reports from scouts but few specific details beyond the fact that the French were obviously building a fort, until in December Thomas Poor brought back word of four barracks within the outline of the walls, and twenty-one small huts, covered with boards or shakes, outside. He saw about four hundred men, he thought, felling trees and sawing planks.

It seems highly probable that there was little further progress on the fort now that cold weather had really set in — cutting and hauling firewood would take much of the time of the troops. De Lotbinière reported that the walls were seven feet high before freezing weather put a stop to the work, but I am inclined to believe that he stretched matters considerably in view of what Montcalm found the following spring.

French documents tell us that by February of 1756 there were twelve cannon in place as well as some smaller pieces, while eight more were at hand but not yet in position. An outpost with defensive works had been established at the head of the portage coming from Lake George, and the garrison now numbered some two thousand in all. More workmen and some Indians had evidently arrived since the previous fall. The fort itself apparently as yet amounted to very little and probably consisted of scarcely more than the base upon which the walls were to be erected. It had been necessary to level off an even footing, cutting rock away here and building up masonry there to form a foundation for the wooden facings of the walls. These main walls, the major defense of the place, were composed of heavy oak timbers, fourteen or fifteen inches square, laid horizontally one on top of the other. There were two such wooden walls, ten feet apart and tied to each other with cross timbers dovetailed in place. The space between was then filled with dirt and rubble. This form of construction was cheaper and quicker than one using masonry, and from the immediate military point of view better, since cannonballs would become harmlessly imbedded in the wood instead of shattering the stone facing. The drawback, of course, was the rotting of the timbers. In the end, for a permanent fort, stone was cheaper. Initially timber was used at Ticonderoga, later to be replaced, in part at least, by stone.

The campaign of 1756 was to bring no important action to the Champlain Valley. Neither the French nor the British was yet ready for a major clash in that region. Each was busily engaged in building its major outpost, and until that was accomplished there could be no thought of aggressive action. The new French fort at Ticonderoga, first called Fort Vaudreuil, soon acquired the delightful name of Carillon, presumably, tradition tells us, because the music of the waterfall in the little river falling down from Lake George sounded like a chime of bells. Johnson's men had started their fort in 1755 at the scene of von Dieskau's defeat, and they called it Fort William Henry.

Louis Joseph, Marquis de Montcalm, reached New France in the spring of 1756 to replace von Dieskau as commander of the field army. He was subordinate to the vain and jealous Governor Vaudreuil, and the two men were to clash constantly until Montcalm died from the wounds received on the Plains of Abraham three years later. The newly arrived general was sent west this first summer to attack the important British post of Oswego on Lake Ontario, the outpost that guarded Britain's access to the Great Lakes and the fur harvest of that vast region. The mission was brilliantly achieved, the first of the memorable deeds which Montcalm accomplished before his death.

This spring another regiment of regulars, the Royal Rous-

sillon, was sent to Fort Carillon, and by July there were
some five thousand men there in all. The regulars amounted
to about two thousand, and much of the remainder must have
been Canadian militia and workmen, with only a relatively
few soldiers of La Marine, a regiment which numbered under nine hundred in all and furnished garrisons for the three
cities of Canada as well as many of the western posts.

The fort advanced slowly. On the other hand, progress
had been made, for by mid-July, 1756, all four bastions
had been raised to a height of at least seven feet, and some
thirty or more cannon were in place along the walls. Montcalm, a volatile Provençal, naturally was impatient and not
at all pleased with the youthful and inexperienced engineer
who, trusting to his most influential connections, went his
own way and did largely as he pleased.

Graft was rampant in Canada, and it had become increasingly so in the 1750's. The notorious Bigot, who had
learned his trade as commissary at Louisbourg before the
1745 siege, became the *intendant,* the economic czar, of
Canada after the peace of 1748, and he proceeded to exploit
the possibilities open to him and his associates in a grand
manner. The Canadian governor was charged by the King
with all military matters and all dealings with the Indians,
but, practically speaking, all executive, economic and police
measures were under the intendant, whose powers, in effect,
were really greater than those of the governor. When this most
important officer was dishonest, or even only unobservant, the
opportunities for peculation were vast. Bigot gathered around
himself a coterie of grafters whose operations were immense,
in scope relatively greater even than those of Tammany under
Boss Tweed. Opportunities were endless in the new land, and
even well-intentioned men were forced to sanction illicit operations to a greater or lesser extent, even if they themselves received no direct benefit. New France was considered a Utopia

for ambitious and impecunious young Frenchmen in the first half of the eighteenth century, and many a bankrupt courtier sought a Canadian appointment so that he might make or recoup a fortune. This perhaps could be done honestly, but it was soon learned that dishonest methods were quickest and were not questioned. All was excused in a land of easy morals.

While Governor Vaudreuil must have been cognizant of what was taking place, he apparently never secured any direct benefit from these operations of his friends and associates. He was, however, much to blame for not at least attempting to curb these excesses. The real answer, however, may have been that Bigot's powers actually were so much greater than those of the governor that the latter was powerless to act.

Living costs were much higher in Canada than in France, yet the pay of the regular officers, in theory the same as in Europe, was soon being disbursed in inflated paper money, and no allowance was made in any way for the greatly increased cost of mere existence. The Canadian officers also suffered, of course, but many of them engaged in extracurricular activities, usually more or less illicit. Such operations, even if desired by the more strait-laced French professional officers, were seldom if ever open to them. Thus many an officer was forced into debt.

One simple source of profit, open in practice only to officers of the Canadian regiment assigned to western posts, was to trade to the Indians for furs those goods which the French King sent as gifts. Another practice commonly available, since companies were almost always understrength, was to draw rations and equipment for the full theoretical company strength and to sell the excess. Neither of these methods would have been open to regular officers who came overseas with Montcalm. There is little doubt that some of the regulars succumbed to the opportunities they found existing and the spirit in which even the highest Canadian officials viewed illicit gain. The great majority, however, and all the senior commanders appear to have held themselves rigidly aloof from these activities.

Probably the greatest chance to make a fortune open to one not of the topmost echelon was given to the officer charged with building a fort in Canada. Several avenues were open to him, some accepted by Canadian practice as proper and correct, others less so and therefore conducted more or less under cover. The ultimate result, after all had taken their share of the spoils, was that it cost just about twice as much to build a fort in New France as it did in the home country. While some of this undoubtedly resulted from distance and the difficulty of operating in the wilderness, a very large part of the excess cost was represented by graft.

One plum considered the rightful perquisite of the officer building a fort was the canteen concession. It was particularly true in a place like Ticonderoga that a soldier had nothing upon which to spend his pay, both his regular pittance and those extra francs received for work on the fortifications, except on wine and brandy at the canteen. At Ticonderoga, Le Roux, keeper of the canteen, sold wine for just twice what it cost at Montreal and brandy three times. In the same way the farther one went away from Montreal the greater the cost of the soldier's ration. In 1756 the value of the soldier's daily portion of food was ten and one-half sous at Montreal, while at La Chine, only twelve miles upstream, it was twenty-seven sous. A small bit of this fearful increase of course was chargeable to transport costs, but most of it was due to graft. The King gave daily to each soldier about a pound each of bread and salt pork, perhaps half as much of dried peas, and an allowance of wine. Save for salt and other condiments, that was all. At times fresh beef was issued, but salt pork was usual. Sometimes when a barrel of salt pork was broached, it was found to contain only the heads and feet of pigs. In times of scarcity, and they often reigned in New France during this last war, salt cod was substituted for some of the pork and the amount of meat and bread reduced. At permanent posts vegetables were grown and there always was the chance of securing fish and game, but food at Ticonderoga in these years was neither plentiful nor very attractive. Montcalm at one time, in order to set an example, even tried eating bread made partly from *"grouillée"* (squirming) flour — flour constantly in motion from the activity of the vermin within it.

The profit of the canteen was great and continuing. The longer it took to build the fort, the greater the engineer's profit. Thus de Lotbinière had no real incentive to expedite the construction at Ticonderoga, but instead had every reason to make the work drag out. A French regular engineer officer who served at the fort estimated that the annual profits of the canteen at Carillon amounted to 100,000 francs, certainly equivalent to $150,000 today. Another moneymaking opportunity was open to anyone who had a little capital. De Lotbinière paid his workers in paper chits, rather than the usual Canadian "card" money which was bad enough in itself. If one had hard money at Carillon he could buy "card" money at a material discount, and then with this latter currency he could acquire de Lotbinière notes at anywhere from one-half to three-quarters of their face value. Then, if he sent these chits to the treasurer at Montreal, they would be exchanged for their face value in "card" money less a small discount. The process could then be repeated. It was even said that de Lotbinière kept a clerk at the fort who would expedite these various exchanges.

A third operation, illicit and open only to the engineer himself, was quite out of the ordinary. The sand used in the mortar — much of the later work at Carillon was in masonry — had to be hauled a hundred or two hundred yards from the sandpit, so horses were provided by the engineer, although presumed to be hired from various fictitious owners. De Lotbinière had to pay for the oats the horses ate, but hay and shoeing were provided by the King, as well as the supply and repair of the wagons used. Twenty-five francs, say thirty-five dollars or so in today's values, was paid for each trip, but it was considered too much trouble to bother to count the number of trips actually made, so it was assumed that each horse made sixteen or seventeen trips a day. There were at least fifteen horses in 1756 and each horse must have grossed about ten thousand francs a month. This seems almost astronomical and would be hard to believe were the figures not reported by an honest professional officer recently arrived from France. Another officer has left a record confirming this operation, but he put the proceeds at a considerably smaller figure, believing that the seven horses working in 1758 earned de Lotbinière 120,000 francs in all, a sum certainly not to be despised.

De Lotbinière, as constructing engineer, certified for all work done, and no one appears to have audited his figures. It is most probable that a material part of the engineer's immense receipts were distributed to associates and subordinates — he offered a third share in the canteen and horse concessions to a regular French officer who worked with him at Carillon, and who refused the offer in scorn — but he must have made a very sizable fortune through his operations. Today we would consider this an illegal and ill-gotten gain, but it appears that de Lotbinière stayed within the letter of the law of that day, just as did Governor Vaudreuil.

The former was not arraigned nor the latter found guilty in the wholesale trial of Bigot's crew after the fall of New France.

Montcalm returned to Carillon after his capture of Oswego, and was discouraged by the lack of progress in the fortifications. As late as the end of September he noted that it would be at least another month before the fort could be considered fit to defend itself against an attack. The general found that he had to ride herd on de Lotbinière to keep him engaged in essential work, otherwise he would be distracted into unproductive channels. The slower the progress, the greater the profit. It is quite possible that the criticism of the young engineer which has survived is unfair to him, but it comes from several sources, biased perhaps, but each of them has a reputation for accuracy. De Lotbinière was not dishonest according to the standards of New France; he was merely working a good thing for all that he could. And whatever one may say he did get Fort Carillon built.

In 1756 a lime kiln and a brick works were in operation by summer, and work was started on a sawmill at the lowest falls on the river flowing out of Lake George, Rivière la Chute, the French called it. There evidently was no experienced millwright available and the mill could not be gotten to operate this season. Water-powered sawmills were still rather a novelty in Canada; the first ones had been built by captive New Englanders or Yorkers, history does not say which.

Once the Ticonderoga peninsula had been cleared throughout its lower end in order to secure an open field of fire, it was found that the fort did not effectively command the passage through the narrows. The range was too great for accurate fire. Accordingly a redoubt, actually a small separate fort, was built this summer on the extreme tip of the neck of land. When the British at last secured Ticonderoga in 1759 this redoubt, then built of stone, was still incomplete. Hence it seems probable that in 1756 this structure, then called the Grenadier Battery, was only of log and dirt, a temporary defense, later to be replaced by a more permanent work.

By the fall of 1756 the outlines of the uncompleted fort were much as they are today with one major exception. As one enters the fort, one crosses a flat stretch, bounded on the south by a high wall lined with great bronze cannon and on the north by the southern bastions and curtain wall of the fort itself. This little plateau and the great retaining wall which holds it in place are later additions, perhaps built by the British in 1759, perhaps Revolutionary in origin. In 1756 a large storehouse stood on the original hillside just in front of the present arched entrance into the interior of the fort. It was built, like the fort walls, of squared horizontal timbers and carried cannon on its roof. Actually this storehouse was a ravelin, square rather than triangular in shape, covering the southern curtain wall and the main entrance to the fort. Its cellar, hewn out of solid rock, was used to store a great number of the casks of wine upon which the garrison depended.

As the winter of 1756-1757 approached, the fortress, still only partly completed and built of earth and logs, was at last in condition to put up a reasonable defense against an attack. There were now thirty-six cannon mounted on its walls, a third of them 18-pounders carrying a five-and-a-half-inch iron ball. The storehouse covered the southern curtain by cannon on its embrasured roof. There was now a small fort, perhaps merely a blockhouse, at the head of the falls on the east shore of Lake George. Fort Carillon no longer need fear a sudden raid. But this the British had no thought of attempting, so shocked and handicapped were they by the loss of Oswego. Their activities in the Champlain Valley this year would be limited to pushing on the construction of Fort William Henry near the scene of von Dieskau's defeat at the head of Lake George.

Montcalm returned to Carillon after his victory at Oswego, and with him came his excellent aide-de-camp Bougainville, whose voluminous journal tells us of conditions at Ticonderoga during that late summer and fall of 1756. Bougainville was a brilliant young Frenchman, trained as a lawyer but also skilled in mathematics, who had served the French ambassador in London. He knew the English and their language, was interested in everything and recorded it all in his journal. Moreover he and Montcalm were deep in each other's confidence. (The young officer transferred to the French navy after the end of the war, explored the South Seas, introduced the Bougainvillea flower to Europe, and died an admiral and a count of Napoleon's empire.)

The general and his aide reached Fort Carillon on 10 September. Progress since his earlier visit seemed to the general to be very slight. Although about five hundred men were working daily on the defenses, little appeared to have been accomplished since late spring. Montcalm, moreover, thought that the fort should be about twice its actual size, capable of holding a garrison of five hundred instead of the three hundred that the present structure could shelter. Three of the four bastions, those spurs which projected out from each corner of the square fort and provided flanking fire along the face of the curtain walls, were in a practical state. There was a camp at the foot of Lake George, where an enemy coming from the south must land, with an advance camp a mile farther south along the lake shore, whence two bateaux daily reconnoitered the waters of Lake George. Over eleven hundred men were deployed at these outposts out of a total force of less than three thousand, but this still left an

A Fort Rises in the Wilderness 51

ample force to work on the fort itself. Each nation's army harassed that of the other with petty raids in the Lake George region, but fort-building was the only real order of the day.

Bougainville recorded early in October that the work went very slowly:

The soldier, corrupted by the amount of money he here receives, and by the example set by the Indians and the Canadians, breathes an air impregnated with independence, works with languor. The engineer is almost never at the works, it is to his interest that the fort should not be completed promptly. He has the exclusive privilege of selling wine (it sells at 55 [sous] a bottle [almost three francs]) and all the money of the workmen, even the soldier's pay, go to his canteen. Besides he has built this fort of horizontal wooden timbers, in a region where stone, limestone, and sand are found abundantly, where, in obtaining stone with which to build, the ditch is created at the same time, where there doubtless is timber, but where men are lacking to cut it, square it up, haul it, where there are neither wagons nor horses. [The sand-hauling horses evidently appeared later.] Odd business! This engineer gives the workmen certificates which have the value of money without anyone assigned to control them, and all these certificates come back to him.

A few days later he complained that there was no wine for the regular issue, not even for the hospital; only the canteen had it for sale. Indians and British rangers prowled around, and Bougainville noted a scalping of a soldier and a maid-servant at this time, between the fort and the advance posts.

Since the defenses of Carillon were not yet sufficiently strong, and winter was unpleasantly near, Montcalm decided to erect palisades of vertical logs along the weaker portions, and the soldiers, told this must be done before they could go north to their winter quarters, worked with vigor.

Bougainville recorded that a French regular officer, probably Captain de la Pauze, had succeeded in fixing the sawmill that "the Vauban of Canada could not make work. Unfortunately it is to the interest of this Vauban that the work drag out. The canteen must have its business." All the French regular officers who left us journals seem to have made bitter remarks about de Lotbinière, perhaps because of the contempt of the regular for the colonial, perhaps on account of the character and actions of the young engineer. My own belief is that de Lotbinière was an ambitious young man with little experience but most powerful connections who saw a chance to make a fortune and did, while always keeping within the law as it was then interpreted in New France. His intentions, unlike those of Bigot, were not evil.

In mid-October Montcalm's aide-de-camp had another complaint: "Now we are without candles. For the last fortnight the officers grope their way to bed in the dark, an inconvenience, but a far greater one for the bakery and the hospital. . . . They melt salt pork into tin lamps and use it instead of oil. I admire with what consistency and industry they here take every means of squandering away the King's money. Candles which come from France with much difficulty are fearfully expensive, oil made in [this] country from fish and very little in demand because of the war goes for almost nothing; and so in all the posts they burn candles and send no oil although [Montcalm] often has asked for it."

Bleury at last arrived with his flotilla of bateaux loaded with wine, and all were again happy, released from having to drink spruce beer or even, horrid thought, just water. Spruce beer was made by boiling the tips and small branches of the spruce tree, adding molasses and yeast to the resulting liquid, and letting nature take its course for a very few days. The result is mildly alcoholic and surprisingly enough tastes like beer. (I know, for I have made it.) Bleury had the concession for ferrying supplies to Carillon, and he was paid slightly under a franc a pound for carriage. Each of his great bateaux — he brought fifty-four in this convoy — carried some three tons. Bleury also brought wine, brandy and poultry on his own account for sale to the garrison. It is most evident that here was another Canadian well on his way to making a fortune.

At last, late in October, Montcalm, convinced that there was nothing more that he could accomplish before winter closed in on Fort Carillon, started north to Montreal. The garrison he left in the fort was composed of a hundred and fifty regular troops, one hundred soldiers of La Marine and about fifty workmen. There would be plenty to keep them occupied, for they would have to cut and haul at least three thousand cords of firewood in order to make life endurable in the fort as winter seized the Champlain Valley in its frigid clutches. One hundred skilled woodchoppers would need at least a month to cut this amount of wood, and much more to haul it into the fort. There could be little complaint of lack of exercise at Carillon this winter of 1756-1757.

FIVE

Montcalm Takes Fort William Henry

FORT WILLIAM HENRY was the most advanced post of the British in the Champlain Valley. Sir William Johnson had commenced its construction in the summer of 1755 after his defeat of von Dieskau at the Battle of Lake George. It lay at the southern end of that lake, a fort with four bastions, built of stout wooden cribwork filled with earth. The fort was a fairly formidable structure, but not very large, capable of holding a garrison of only some four hundred men. A competent officer, Major William Eyre, had built it, but its defenses on the west needed further improvement.

In March of 1757 the Marquis de Vaudreuil, governor of Canada, sent his brother, de Rigaud, to assail the fort in a winter raid. Sixteen hundred French regulars, Canadians and Indians plodded their way southward on snowshoes, dragging their supplies on sleds over the ice and snow of Lake Champlain and then on up Lake George. Their hope was to surprise the garrison or at least to scare it into surrender by the size of the expedition, but Major Eyre still was in command, and he was on the alert for trouble. The French took no artillery along and they at once found themselves powerless against the grapeshot and musket fire of the British garrison.

Any stockaded fort, if sufficiently manned and provisioned, and commanded by a wide-awake and capable officer, was

safe against attack by musket fire alone — artillery was needed
to breach the walls. A stout earth-and-timber fort, such as
William Henry, required for its reduction the heaviest of artillery, particularly one or more of the 13-inch mortars which
could toss 200-pound explosive bombs deep into the heart
of the defenses. Without such artillery the French were
helpless. Rigaud's attack was not pushed home and the adventure failed. The assailants succeeded, however, in burning many bateaux and some larger vessels, as well as various
out-buildings, a decided embarrassment to the British.

The Marquis de Montcalm had made a victorious start to
his American campaigns when, shortly after his arrival here
in the early summer of 1756, he had captured and destroyed
Oswego, the important British post on Lake Ontario. Now,
as the campaign of the following year got under way, he prepared to move against the next British encroachment in the
pathway of New France, Fort William Henry.

Montcalm's task was to be made easier, although he probably did not yet know it, by the fact that Lord Loudoun had
taken a great army off on an abortive attempt against Louisbourg, the mighty French fortress on Cape Breton Island. The
depleted forces guarding the New York frontier were left
under the command of General Daniel Webb, a sick and not
overly competent officer. The French assembled at Ticonderoga and there completed the final preparations for the advance up Lake George. Battalions of regulars, La Reine, La
Sarre, Languedoc, Béarn, Guyenne and Royal Roussillon,
covered the flats below the fortress. Along with them there
was a horde of painted Indians, howling, dancing, stealing
and, when occasion offered, boiling captured Englishmen in
their pots. Then there were the Canadians, some men of La
Marine Regiment, but mostly militiamen, along with a few
volunteers, some three and a half thousand in all, not trained
troops, but excellent for the hauling, rowing and digging

which was to be endured. Ticonderoga hummed with activity.

While Montcalm held long and solemn council with staid old Indian chiefs, Ottawas, Chippewas, Menominees and Potawatomis, the young braves, tired of salt pork and eager for fresh meat, ran riot, butchering the draft oxen needed to haul the supplies up the mile-long portage to Lake George. Not even Montcalm's own poultry was safe from pillaging Indians, and there was little the French dared do, lest their touchy Indian allies should quit in a huff. Already a few, satiated with a handful of prisoners, had left for home, warning of what could happen in a much greater way.

Bougainville wrote home about these savage allies, ". . . Indians, naked, black red, howling, bellowing, dancing, singing the war song, getting drunk, yelling for 'broth,' that is to say blood, drawn from 500 leagues away by the smell of fresh human blood and the chance to teach their young men how one carves up a human being destined for the pot. Behold our comrades who, night and day, are our shadows. I shiver at the frightful spectacles which they are preparing for us." Such were the allies that the French were leading against the British defenders of William Henry.

Montcalm brought eighteen hundred Indians on the expedition, some eight hundred Christian redskins from the missions, accompanied by Abbé Piquet and two other priests, and almost a thousand wild Indians from the region of the Great Lakes, with one priest and several partisan leaders and half-breed interpreters in their train. Father Roubaud, the Jesuit missionary at St. Francis, went along with this Indian contingent, and left a graphic account of his experience. "Imagine a great congregation of savages decorated with all those ornaments most capable, to the European eye, of disfiguring one's appearance, vermilion, white, green, yellow, black made with soot or the scrapings of cooking pots; the face of a single

Indian unites all these colors methodically applied, with aid
of a little grease which serves as pomade. Behold the paint
which goes to work on these dress occasions to embellish
not only the face but even the head, almost all close-shaven
except for a little tuft of hair saved on the very top as a point
of attachment for bird feathers or some bits of wampum or
some other such trinket. Each part of the head has a special ornament, the nose has a pendant, there are others for the
ears, which are hung there from childhood and have by their
weight so elongated the earlobes that they reach to the
shoulders . . . a shirt smeared with vermilion, a wampum
collar, silver bracelets, a great knife hung on the chest, a belt
of varied colors, but always burlesquely assorted, shoes of
moose hide, that is the dress of the savage."

A scouting party of French and Indians had paddled up
Lake George and had succeeded in destroying a considerable
body of reconnoitering Englishmen, volunteers from New
Jersey, commanded by Colonel Parker. Many were killed,
but a number of prisoners were brought back to the Indian
camp at Carillon. Father Roubaud wrote home about what
happened to some of these unfortunates. "My tent had been
placed in the middle of the Ottawas. The first object I saw on
arriving there was a great fire, and wooden spits stuck in the
ground, denoting a feast. There was one indeed. But, heav-
ens, what a feast! The remains of the corpse of an Englishman, skinned and the meat half cut off! A moment later I
saw these inhuman beings eating, with famished greed, this
human flesh. . . . What was most sad was that they had
forced a half score of English to be spectators of their infa-
mous meal." Father Roubaud protested without avail, and a
young warrior replied in bad French, "Thou hast a French
taste, I an Indian one, this meat is good for me," and he
offered a choice bit of broiled Englishman to the priest.

Councils with Indians continued as Montcalm outlined to

his savage listeners his plans for taking Fort William Henry. Most of the redskins enthused, but the crafty Iroquois contingent held back, saying that they would have to consult their elders, who were not then present. Suddenly nearby in the forest a great tree fell with a mighty crash, an augury to the savages, but of what, of success or of disaster? The quick-witted Montcalm at once and without hesitation announced that thus would William Henry fall before their victorious advance, and the Indians howled their approval.

The expedition was to advance in two divisions, one by land along the western shore of Lake George, where rugged mountains, thick forests and slimy marshes made progress a constant struggle. The larger party, which Montcalm would lead, was to move by water, a much easier trip, even with the artillery and supplies. The movement was to start on 29 July, but the Indians protested that they were not yet ready, and Montcalm was forced to postpone the advance. Another great powwow was held, and all the Indians, the Christianized of the eastern missions and the heathen of the Far West, promised obedience and unity of action. Now the Iroquois, scenting blood and loot, decided to come along, and immediately claimed the honor of leading the advance, a request it was unwise to deny them. Then each tribe presented Montcalm with bundles of little sticks, each stick representing a warrior in the roster of their contingent. In all there were 1799 of them, 820 mission Indians, the rest untamed savages of the great west.

Somewhat over a third of the army started overland on 30 July, while the remainder in the early morning two days later clambered into their bateaux and canoes, after having spent much of the previous night hauling their cannon and supplies up the steep portage between the lakes. The Indians had left behind in their camp, hanging on a tree, a cloak, a breechclout and leggings as an offering to their manitou.

Three French priests, who had intended to say mass at this very spot, asked Montcalm if it was right to say mass at a place where sacrifice had been made to the devil. Montcalm promptly replied that undoubtedly it was better to say it there than not say it at all.

The vast regatta spread out over Lake Champlain, a majestic sight indeed, but what most impressed young Bougainville, accustomed as he was to the sight of great European armies, were the hundred and fifty birch canoes laden with naked, painted savages. Father Roubaud recorded that when they passed the scene of Colonel Parker's defeat they found many signs of the disaster, stranded whaleboats and a great number of corpses, mutilated and in some cases hacked into pieces. Twenty-four hours later at the appointed place the two parts of the expedition met, the land contingent having arrived the day before, exhausted by endless struggle with steep mountains, pathless forest and fallen tree trunks, and all this through heat as great as armies ever met in Italy. Advance continued both by land and water, and by midday of 2 August the French halted at a point some five miles from the British fort. Reconnaissance was at once pushed forward, while the army went into bivouac and rested. Shortly before daybreak the next morning the troops advanced the remaining distance by land and Fort William Henry was soon surrounded.

There followed the normal routine of besieging a fortress. A trench would be pushed forward from some hillock relatively near the fort, and in a diagonal direction to give cover from enemy fire. At a convenient place a cross-trench would be dug and here the first battery of siege guns and mortars would be placed. Their fire would cover the further advance of the trench as it zigzagged ahead to the next battery position. Batteries might be and often were carried to within two hundred yards of the walls of a fort, because only from such a short range could the cannon of that day develop sufficient accuracy to concentrate their fire on the section of wall it was desired to breach. Such was Montcalm's procedure, and the first battery opened fire early on the morning of 6 August from a range of about four hundred and fifty yards against the west side of the fort.

There actually were two positions defended by the British, for only about four hundred men of the entire army of over two thousand could be accommodated within Fort William Henry itself. The remainder took up a position on a large and rocky knoll nearly half a mile from the fort and separated from it by a marsh and a brook. This place was hurriedly stockaded and barricaded against attack, but it lacked any appreciable artillery and was too far from the fort to be of any real assistance. In effect the body of nearly two thousand men stationed here sat out the entire siege almost solely as spectators, except for one futile sortie. Lieutenant Colonel Monro, a competent officer of British regulars, had now replaced Eyre as commander of William Henry.

Montcalm did not have a force large enough to invest the whole area completely, but this was hardly necessary since relief could come only from one direction, the south, by the road from Fort Edward on the Hudson. The camp of the Indians was placed across this road, thus completely cutting off all British communication to the rear.

The siege proceeded in the usual fashion, the British attempting with their artillery and small arms to delay the digging of the trenches and the emplacement of the enemy guns, the French trying to get their cannon and mortars into sheltered positions from which they could start battering down a wall of the fort. Their fire was concentrated on the weak point about which warning had been given the previous year. All this was normal and conventional in the eyes of a European-trained soldier, even though carried out in the

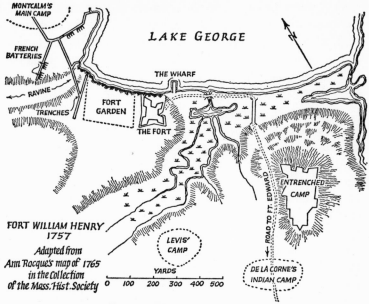

LAKE GEORGE

MONTCALM'S
MAIN CAMP

FRENCH
BATTERIES

THE WHARF

RAVINE

FORT
GARDEN

TRENCHES

THE FORT

ENTRENCHED
CAMP

ROAD TO FT. EDWARD

FORT WILLIAM HENRY
1757

*Adapted from
Ann Rocque's map of 1765
in the Collection
of the Mass. Hist. Society*

LEVIS'
CAMP

YARDS

0   100   200   300   400   500

DE LA CORNE'S
INDIAN CAMP

Fort William Henry, 1757

wilderness against a fort with walls of wood rather than of stone. The Indians, of course, furnished the discordant note. Instead of sending out scouting parties as they had been told, they all trooped into the vicinity of the fort, excitedly watching the French fire their cannon and hiding in the gardens to take potshots at the British. This did little good except to waste powder. Their scouting did, however, produce one prisoner and a dead man, whose waistcoat concealed in its lining a letter from General Webb at Fort Edward to Colonel Monro telling him that he could expect no aid, and that he had better make the best surrender terms he could. This put the game right into Montcalm's hands, but he held the letter for a day or two before sending it to Monro under a red flag of truce, red since the French colors were white.

General Webb had reinforced the fort before the attack, leaving himself only sixteen hundred soldiers at Fort Edward. He has been accused of being a craven for not coming to the rescue. He originally had intended to, then becoming more cautious, felt that he must assemble more militia for the defense of the Hudson corridor before he dared move forward. He had some justification. An advance through that wooded country had grave dangers and there is some question what he could have done once he got near the fort. The final surrender was occasioned to a considerable extent by the bursting of most of the fort's heavy guns and mortars, and only a new supply of artillery or a powerful sortie could have saved the day. The former, Webb could not have gotten to the fort, the latter would have been almost impossible to carry out, so well did the terrain protect the attacking French. Moreover it would seem from reports of the battle that the active defense was left almost entirely to the small garrison in the fort itself, while the very much larger body in the barricaded camp on the high ground did little but watch. Would the presence of another thousand or two English have saved the fort? There seem to be grave doubts. Nevertheless Webb probably should have tried to do something, but he was the man on the ground, and the decision was his. He believed that Montcalm had an army of eleven thousand men, and knew that his own little force at Fort Edward was, save for some scattered regulars and untrained militia levies, the last defense of the Hudson, of Albany, and perhaps even of New York City itself. Had he been able to visualize some of Montcalm's problems, lack of food and supplies, a jealous and carping governor, and militia and Indians both frantic to go home, he might not have been so cautious. One is always prone to think of his own troubles and seldom of those of the other side.

At one time there was a short truce and an Abnaki told a

member of the British party in bad but understandable French: "Ah, no surrender, well! Open fire then, and my Father will then shoot his great cannon, then defend yourself well, for if I capture you, there will be no quarter." Dire warning of what was to come, but Montcalm failed to heed.

The French poured their artillery fire against the cribwork walls of the fort, gradually reducing them to mere piles of dirt, and little by little overpowering the answering fire of the defenders. One by one the British guns burst; and smallpox ran riot through the garrison. Once it was learned that no relief would come morale broke down, and it became obvious that the case was hopeless. After three days and nights of cannonading by the French the fort had shot its bolt, and the white flag of surrender was raised. The terms of capitulation were generous. The French did not want prisoners, for it was difficult enough to feed their own people with the scanty crops of Canada and the modicum of supplies that managed to evade the British navy. So Montcalm decided to parole the troops and send them home. The British were to march out with their arms and baggage and retire south to Fort Edward, leaving to the French the fort and all its supplies, which included food for six thousand men for six weeks, manna for starving Canada. The soldiers retained their muskets, but, according to one who was there, they kept no ammunition.

Before the terms were finally completed Montcalm had a conference with the Indian chieftains, and secured their promise to restrain their young men from any action against the English. It seems hard to believe that after the experience he had had with Indian promises and his knowledge of the inability of the French to control the savages, he was still naïve enough to put trust in this pledge. He must have remembered what happened after the surrender at Oswego the year before. Certainly he should have taken more positive measures to see that the now defenseless British were amply protected. At the start of the siege he had reminded Monro of Indian cruelty in a letter which can be called nothing but threatening. "[I have] all the Indians from the higher parts of this country the cruelty of whom a detachment of your garrison have lately too much experienced. . . . I have it yet in my power to restrain the Indians . . . which will not be in my power . . . if you insist on defending your fort."

Now let Bougainville speak again, this time through a letter to his godmother, Madame Herault, written before the expedition started: "Your son shudders with horror at what he is going to be forced to witness. It is with great difficulty that we can restrain the Indians of the Far West, the most ferocious of all men and cannibals by trade. Listen to what the chiefs came to tell M. de Montcalm three days ago: 'Father, don't expect that we can easily give quarter to the English. We have some young warriors who have not yet drunk of this broth. Raw flesh has led them here from the ends of the earth; they must learn to wield the knife and to bury it in English hearts.' Behold our comrades, dear Mama; what a crew, what a spectacle for civilized man."

The moment the English marched out of the fort and retired to the barricaded camp, the Indians rushed in and tomahawked all the wounded left behind in the barracks and casements. Despite this most pointed warning Montcalm provided out of his force of six thousand regulars and militiamen a detachment of only four hundred to guard two thousand British with empty muskets from eighteen hundred murderous savages. Once the massacre started he undoubtedly did what he could to stop it, but his lack of precautions cannot but make one wonder. It is the one blot on an otherwise stainless reputation.

Some of the French officers had warned the British to make sure that the Indians got no rum or brandy, and strongly advised that they throw away all that they themselves had. Some probably followed this sound advice, but events proved that many did not. All the British had now been concentrated in the barricaded camp on the hillock. Seventeen wounded soldiers had been turned over to the French surgeon, and a guard of French soldiers placed over them, but before dawn on the day the English were to march away to Fort Edward the guard was suddenly withdrawn. The Indians immediately dashed in and finished off the wounded in the presence of the British and in full sight of several Canadian officers and a French guard, but no attempt was made to stop the slaughter.

The escort of four hundred Frenchmen had now arrived, and the column started to leave the camp. The Indians demanded plunder, and the French officers advised that all baggage must be given them, or the consequences would be dire. This was done, but the Indians were not appeased. As the column moved out of the camp they burst into it, snatching guns and clothes and applying the tomahawk to all that resisted, including a number of women and children who had accompanied the troops. Then a Christian Abnaki of the Penobscot Mission shouted the war whoop, and the whole maddened pack, hitherto mainly interested in plunder, turned to butchery. Montcalm and other French officers dashed up and did their utmost to quiet the savages, but only after a hundred or more British had been killed and hundreds carried off as prisoners. Many of the latter were recovered through the efforts of Montcalm, but about two hundred were taken north by the Indians. The remainder, often stripped of everything save their breeches, divided into two groups, one fleeing to the fort for protection by the French, the rest making the best of their way to Fort Edward, either by road or through the woods. The group collected at the fort were given protection at last and several days later were sent to Fort Edward under a heavy escort.

Father Roubaud wrote down in his story of the expedition:

The party of 400 of the French regulars, assigned to protect the retreat of the enemy, arrived and placed themselves in line. The English commenced to file out, misfortune to those who formed the end of the line of march, or to stragglers whom indisposition or some other cause separated by ever so little from the rest of the body. There soon were many dead whose corpses lay scattered on the ground and covered the outside of the entrenchments. This butchery, which at first was the work of only a few Indians, was the signal which turned almost all the rest into ferocious beasts. They let fly right and left with great blows of their hatchets at those who came to their hand. The massacre, however, was not of long duration, nor as great as its fury made one fear; it amounted to scarcely 40 or 50 men. [The best opinion today puts the figure at about three times as many.] The patience of the English, who were content to bow their heads beneath the steel of their executioners, suddenly appeased them, but it did not lead them to sense or to justice. Uttering loud cries, they set about taking prisoners. In the meanwhile I arrived. No, I do not believe that one can be human and remain insensible to such sad circumstances. The son snatched from the arms of the father, the daughter from her mother's bosom, the husband separated from the wife, officers stripped to their shirts, without respect either for rank or decency, a crowd of sufferers who ran hither and yon, some toward the woods, others toward those places that seemed to offer protection; such were the pitiful sights presented to my eyes; the French, however, were not passive and insensible spectators of the catastrophe. The Chevalier de Lévis ran wherever the tumult seemed to appear hottest to try to calm it, with courage animated by a clemency most natural to one of his illustrious blood. He dared death . . . a thousand times. . . . Of what use could [a guard of] 400 men be against some 1500 furious savages, who did not distinguish us from the enemy?

Father Roubaud met a wild Huron Indian from the Far West carrying a very young baby he had picked up somewhere, and he tried to secure the child. The Indian refused. Finally, after much dickering, the savage agreed to exchange the baby for a scalp, and the priest ran to one of the Abnaki and told him his need. The Christian Indian opened his war bag and told the Jesuit to take his pick. He seized a scalp and, followed by a curious crowd of Frenchmen and Indians, he again found his Huron and made the exchange. A little later the good father had the great pleasure of returning the baby to its mother. In later years Father Roubaud led a checkered life, abandoned his faith and married. As late as 1777 he was still trying to collect 6800 francs from the British government for ransom he claimed to have paid out of his own purse to the Indians at William Henry for 103 of their captive Englishmen. One would wonder how a Jesuit priest would have such a sum at hand, but both Montcalm and Colonel Monro seem to have attested to the truth of his claim. Toward the end of his life Roubaud returned to the Roman Catholic Church and died in a monastery in Paris.

Colonel Frye of the Massachusetts Regiment wrote a journal of the siege and its aftermath. He said that after the massacre started, when officers of the French escort were asked for protection, they refused help and advised the English to take to the woods.

Jonathan Carver, whose stories cannot always be trusted, wrote in later years that, when being robbed by the Indians, he sought the aid of a French sentry who called him an English dog and thrust him back into the hands of the Indians.

Montcalm blamed the whole affair on the English for having given rum to the Indians. In a report sent to the French Ministry he wrote: "I cannot conceal from you that the capitulation has unfortunately suffered some infraction on the part of the Indians. But what would be an infraction in Europe cannot be so regarded in America."

Bougainville was sent to Canada to report the capture as

soon as the capitulation was signed, and he missed the massacre. Hence the record in his journal is a hearsay one. Nevertheless he was an honest and very intelligent reporter and we
may be sure that he was certain of his facts. He wrote:

A great misfortune which we dreaded has happened. Apparently
the capitulation is violated and all Europe will oblige us to justify
ourselves. . . . At daybreak the English, who were inconceivably
frightened by the sight of the Indians, wished to leave before our
escort was all assembled and in place. They abandoned their
trunks and other heavy baggage. . . . The Indians had already
butchered a few sick in the tents which served as a hospital. The
Abnakis of Panaomeska [Old Town] . . . commenced the riot.
They shouted the death cry and hurled themselves on the tail of
the column which started to march out.

The English, instead of showing resolution, were seized with
fear and fled in confusion, throwing away their arms, baggage, and
even their coats. Their fear emboldened the Indians of all the nations, who started pillaging, killed some dozen soldiers and took
away 5 or 600 . . . a great number of English soldiers, hoping to
put them in a good humor, had given them rum, which despite all
our warnings they had kept in their flasks. Finally the disorder qui-
eted down and the Marquis de Montcalm at once took away from
the Indians 400 of these unfortunate men and had them clothed.
The French officers divided with the English officers the few spare
clothes they had, and the Indians loaded with booty [and some
200 English prisoners] disappeared that same day.

Would you believe that this abominable action of the Indians
at Fort William Henry had accomplices among those people who
call themselves Frenchmen; that greed and the certainty of getting
all their plunder from the Indians at a low price are the primary
causes of a horror for which England will not fail to reproach us
for a long time? Thank heaven our [French] officers are without
stain in this respect; several risked their lives on this occasion; they
shared all that they had with the unfortunate English, who said
that if they should ever besiege us and capture us, there would be

two terms of surrender, one for the French troops, and the other for the Canadians. These are frightful truths, dear Mama.

Bougainville was in Montreal when the Indians and the miserable party of English captives reached that town.

Meanwhile the Indians arrived [at Montreal] in a crowd with about 200 English. M. de Vaudreuil scolded them for having violated the capitulation. They excused themselves and put the blame on the mission Indians. They were told that they must give up these English, who were captured unfairly, and that they would be paid for them two kegs of brandy apiece. But this ransom was not greeted with enthusiasm. The Canadians bought the English plunder from them.

They did not spare the brandy, and this liquor, the god of the Indians, abounds in their camp. They swill it, and the English [prisoners] die a hundred deaths from fear every day.

At two o'clock in the presence of the entire town they killed one of them, put him in a kettle and forced his unfortunate compatriots to eat him. . . .

Will they in Europe believe that the Indians alone have been guilty of this horrible violation of the capitulation, that desire for the Negroes and other spoils of the English has not caused the people who are at the head of these nations [Canadian leaders of the Indians and the interpreters] to loosen the curb, perhaps to go even further? The more so since one today may see one of these leaders, unworthy of the name of officer and Frenchman, leading in his suite a Negro kidnapped from the English commander under the pretext of appeasing the shades of a dead Indian, giving his family flesh for flesh. That is enough of the horror the memory of which I would hope could be effaced from the minds of men.

The massacre at Fort William Henry was not intentional, but Montcalm failed to take the measures necessary to prevent it. His aide-de-camp Bougainville feared the worst, and in view of the close friendship and understanding existing between the two it is most unlikely that he did not communicate his fears to his general. Why Montcalm did not take the precautions he must have known were necessary is something we shall never learn. The whole affair clearly brings out the inability of the French to control their Indians or to utilize them effectively. You could persuade an Indian to go off to war with you; you armed him and fed him and pampered him. He was flighty and temperamental and gluttonous. When at last you gave him orders to fight, he did what he wanted to, not what he was told. Finally, once you had unleashed him, you lost him, and as soon as he had taken some scalps and plunder his only desire was to go home.

Such were some of the stories of the massacre at Fort William Henry, but one must also look at the event in its broader aspects. As the most advanced post of the British on the great colonial thoroughfare, it was the base for practically all action against the French. Its very existence meant that despite bungling, mismanagement, and inept commanders, the British were at last seriously threatening New France in the Champlain Valley. Some foresighted Frenchmen realized this, and Montcalm was one of them. His attack on the British fort was really a defensive act, an offensive raid aimed at removing a threat, not of occupying ground and advancing farther into the British colonies. The French were much too weak in supplies and transport to be able to move on against Fort Edward, as the Marquis de Vaudreuil expected them to do. The destruction of Fort William Henry, however, set the English back and preserved Canada for at least another year. There was always the hope of peace in Europe, and Montcalm was soon to realize, if he did not already, that only peace could save New France.

There was one final and grisly aftermath that needed a little time to make itself evident. After the massacre some of the Western Indians, still mad for blood and scalps, discovered fresh graves in the English camp. They dug the bodies up and scalped them. It was only later that they learned that they had been resurrecting victims of the smallpox! The disease went home with them and wrought havoc that fall and winter, for smallpox was a disease to which the Indian was most susceptible. Almost the entire Potawatomi nation was wiped out. Thus some of the victims of the campaign at last gained an indirect revenge.

Defeat at the Log Wall

THE BRITISH PLANS for the 1758 campaign called for Jeffrey Amherst to capture Louisbourg, while James Abercromby, the commander-in-chief in North America, seized Ticonderoga and advanced on Canada north down Lake Champlain. Fort Carillon became the major objective on the mainland for 1758, and Abercromby was to lead the attack in person. William Pitt, reinstated as British Prime Minister after a brief eclipse, unfortunately took it upon himself to prescribe many of the details which should have been left to Abercromby, whose hands thus became unjustly tied. He might have done better if granted more latitude, but this seems doubtful. The North American assignment probably was beyond his capabilities.

James Abercromby was a Scot in his early fifties who had seen a considerable amount of active service, and who had the reputation of being a sound, if uninspired, officer. He was made a major general in 1756 and sent to America to serve under Lord Loudoun, from whom he inherited the command when the latter was dismissed by Pitt. Loudoun was a good man who deserved better than he got and whose plans for the attack on Canada were sound, but he became the scapegoat for the failure of the 1757 Louisbourg expedition and for the loss of Fort William Henry.

Loudoun had planned a winter attack on Ticonderoga which was daring and yet sound in concept. It might very well have succeeded but for Captain Robert Rogers's failure to produce the needed snowshoes, which forced abandonment of the attempt. Abercromby assumed command early in the spring of 1758. His health was not of the best, and he had grown somewhat old before his time, slow and unaggressive. He was, however, seconded by a most able assistant. George Augustus, Viscount Howe, a brilliant young man of thirty-four, was approved of by both high and low. Pitt esteemed him highly, and after his death the tight-fisted and unsentimental General Court of Massachusetts Bay thought so well of his memory that they voted the quite material sum of £250 of tax money to build a memorial to him in Westminster Abbey. He was one of the relatively few British regulars — Bradstreet was another — who could break down the barriers and meet provincial officers on a common and friendly level. Lord Howe as brigadier was second in command of the Ticonderoga attack, and it appears that in effect it was intended that he should be the actual combat commander. The two leaders complemented each other not too badly and together formed a high command quite suitable for the purpose at hand.

A great army of British regulars and colonial militia assembled along the upper Hudson and then moved up the river and on to the head of Lake George. It had been planned that the expedition should start early in May, and thus catch Fort Carillon with only its winter garrison. As was usual, however, unexpected delays took place, the militia was late in arriving, and it was not until the end of June that the army had assembled near the ruins of Fort William Henry. There were some 6300 regular troops and 5900 provincials from Massachusetts, Connecticut, New York, and New Jersey. These militiamen of course were mostly raw and untrained soldiers, though some of them had seen service in previous campaigns of the war.

Captain Alexander Monypenny was Abercromby's brigade major, and his sailcloth-covered orderly book lies in front of me as I write. It tells many of the details of preparations for the advance. Equipment was lightened. The officers dispensed with their sashes, and were limited to one portmanteau, blankets and a bearskin, the last useful either as a mattress or as an extra covering. They also were permitted to take a small tent. Instead of being allowed the usual varying number of rations, based upon rank, each officer was restricted to the same ration as the soldier. The colors of the regiments were left behind. All friendly Indians would have a red ribbon tied around the muzzle of their guns for identification. All in all the orderly book shows a very considerable amount of thought and planning, and a reasonable adaptation of standard European practice to forest fighting. Salt pork, flour, dried peas, rice, and butter were to nourish the British soldier, and it is interesting to note that the salt was to be knocked off the pork before it was weighed for issue. Spartan fare indeed! Gambling by soldiers was frowned on most severely; any man caught in the act was to be given three hundred lashes without bothering to hold a court-martial.

The little book prescribed the assignment to the troops of the eight hundred bateaux and the ninety whaleboats. The latter had been bought on Cape Cod and Nantucket the previous fall and sent up the Hudson, and then had been hauled by soldiers on low-wheeled trucks over the portage to Lake George. Various camp activities were ordered while the troops were awaiting word to launch their boats. Some regiments turned out to early-morning target practice, while those who had been issued rifles were told to familiarize themselves with the new weapon. Hitherto the first use of rifles in the British army has always been said to have been in 1800, except for

Patrick Ferguson's private issue of his breech-loader to his own company in the American Revolution. Here in 1758, however, we find the rifle an article of issue, on a small scale to be sure, only ten per regiment, but an official issue to British regulars. The expedition which moved against Fort Duquesne that same summer also received a few. Some open-minded British officer — and he must have been one with powerful friends in the War Office — had evidently been much impressed with the American rifle as used along the Pennsylvania frontier, and had taken one home. A considerable number were made in England, following the American design exactly, and they now appeared in the hands of some of the troops in the campaign of 1758.

Lake George discharged its waters over two hundred feet of falls and rapids in the years before dams and power plants turned them into drab utility. Where they entered Lake Champlain nature had created the high and rocky peninsula the Indians called Ticonderoga. Its point reaches to within a quarter-mile of the Vermont shore, and high above the lake the guns of Fort Carillon decreed that none might pass without permission of the French King. The portage road from Lake George descended to almost the foot of the falls where the French had built a sawmill. Here boats and canoes were launched into Lake Champlain. The road then crossed the outlet on a wooden bridge, climbed the farther slope, and continued for about another two miles along the backbone of the peninsula out to Fort Carillon.

Montcalm's problem was where to make his fight. He had only about thirty-five hundred men, far too few to meet the British in the open field, yet nearly ten times what the little fort could hold. His decision was to take his stand on the Heights of Carillon, the highest part of the ridge, and about half a mile back from the fort. Here the ridge of the peninsula is only a quarter-mile wide. Its southwest slope

[Lord Howe Killed]

SAWMILL

FRENCH CAMP

FRENCH CAMP

ROAD

[the Landing Place]

[the Log Wall]

RAFT WITH CANNON

LAKE GEORGE

Capt. Monypenny's Map of
ABERCROMBY'S DEFEAT
1758

*Copy of the map he sent home with his report
of the battle and of the death of Lord Howe*

LAKE CHAMPLAIN

WOOD CREEK

Ticonderoga

falls steeply into the lake, while the opposite and equally steep northeasterly side runs out into a flat plain almost a third of a mile wide before it reaches the shore of the lake. Across this narrow ridge, from one side to the other, sweating Frenchmen, officers as well as men, hacked down the virgin timber, and set up a wall of great logs, placed horizontally, two and three deep, and pierced with loopholes for musketry. Some of the logs were three feet and more in diameter, remnants of the primeval forest. The top of the wall was crowned with sandbags to a total height of from six to seven feet, so high that only the top of the Frenchmen's hats, and the flags with their golden fleurs-de-lis could be seen above it. The ground plan of the wall formed a great U, its sides crowning the steep slopes on either side of the ridge, and extending well to the rear. In front of the wall all trees and bushes were cleared away for a distance of about one hundred yards and an abatis built of the treetops, which were piled in an almost impassable hedge, the ends of their sharpened branches pointing toward the attacker. It was the predecessor of the barbed-wire entanglement of modern wars, and equally effective.

This great wall, raised in less than two days by the exertions

of perhaps three thousand men, was practically impregnable
to an attacker lacking artillery, but a few cannon could have
knocked much of it down in short order. The line of the
wall zigzagged across the peninsula so as to furnish salients
from which the attackers could be enfiladed. It was hurriedly built, too low in places, and in others exposed to
enemy fire from the flank, but, considering the time and the
manpower available, its construction was a mighty feat. Montcalm placed one battalion in Fort Carillon as a reserve and
to man its guns, while the rest of his force, except for small
detachments sent out to harass and delay the enemy, lined the
wooden wall with their muskets. They did not, however,
have any cannon on the Heights of Carillon.

Abercromby embarked his army on 5 July and proceeded
down Lake George, a great flotilla of almost nine hundred
boats spread in ordered columns across the narrow lake. The
British rowed to the foot of the lake, making a short halt during the night and reaching the outlet of Lake George on the
morning of the sixth. The small French outpost at that point
withdrew without offering any resistance, and the expedition landed on the west side in heavy woods, although the
portage road to Lake Champlain lay on the opposite shore.
The advance party moved downstream through the virgin
forest, not quite sure just where it was going. After advancing
for a mile or so the British floundered into contact with a
French detachment which also had gone astray.

There was a brief interchange of shots, and most of the
French were killed or captured, but a heavy price was paid for
this petty victory. Lord Howe, pushing forward at the head
of the detachment, where a senior officer had no right to be
in such a situation, fell dead almost at the first shot. Everything collapsed into confusion, some of the troops continued to advance, while others returned to the landing
place. Firing broke out toward late afternoon, but there was

no enemy, it was merely British firing at other elements of their own forces.

In short, all was chaos, and night fell upon a scared and disorganized army. Had the French been able to turn a pack of Indians loose upon them in the woods that evening there might have been a fearful slaughter, but Montcalm had less than a score of redskins in his little army. Daylight restored courage, and all the troops were drawn back to the landing place, moved over to the eastern shore, and the expedition advanced down the portage road without meeting any opposition, even at the sawmill where the crossing of the little river offered the French an excellent chance to fight a delaying action. All the advance elements of Montcalm's forces fell back upon their main defenses on the Heights of Carillon, followed by light elements of the British who approached the log wall but remained at a discreet distance from it. Abercromby's main army camped that night on the open ground north of the little river, perhaps a mile and a half from the French defenses.

Up to this point matters had not gone too badly. The British had achieved a major logistical success in bringing so great an army up to the immediate vicinity of their objective, the losses had been small, save for that of Lord Howe, and their enemy was penned up on a peninsula with the lake at his back. Here was opportunity for annihilation of the French, given a proper leader. Such, however, was now lacking, and incompetent command proceeded to bring disaster upon the British.

Lieutenant Colonel Eyre led one of Abercromby's regiments, and he was a most competent engineer officer. Montressor, the senior engineer, was ill, and, instead of sending Eyre to reconnoiter the position and suggest plans for the attack — one of the duties of an engineer officer in those days — the British general, perhaps because of a coolness then apparently existing between the two, bypassed that excellent officer and sent a junior engineer lieutenant instead. This young officer proved his incompetence by reporting that the defenses were weak and could be taken by a frontal infantry attack. Later in the day he was to pay for his poor judgment with his life.

Abercromby had left most of his artillery train on their barges, although nearly forty-eight hours had elapsed, but a few cannon had been advanced to a point within perhaps half a mile of the French defenses. Less than an hour could have had them pounding away at the log wall, and they could have promptly knocked down parts of it. But Abercromby, misled by his engineer's lack of skill, scorned to use his guns and ordered a frontal attack by his infantry. Had he taken the trouble to look at the French defenses himself, he might have chosen another course of action, but there is no evidence whatsoever to show that he at any time went within a mile of the log wall, and considerable reason to believe that he remained in the vicinity of the sawmill throughout the day. His sole leadership throughout the entire action seems to have been merely the ordering of another attack as soon as he learned of the failure of the previous assault.

Montcalm manned his great log wall with seven battalions of French regulars, La Reine, Béarn, Guyenne, Royal Roussillon, 1st Berry, Languedoc, and La Sarre, troops that he knew and in whom he had confidence. On the flat plain on his right he placed his small force of Canadian regulars, soldiers of La Marine Regiment, and his militiamen, expecting little of them, but hoping that they and the guns of Carillon would cover that flank. On his left the slope fell sharply to the water and there was room only for a handful of French volunteers on the narrow strand. The 2nd Berry was held in reserve in the fort along with a small body of gunners to man the cannon on the ramparts. Some three thousand men

armed with muskets stood behind the great wooden wall
and through its loopholes they could fire almost without risk
upon anyone who dared to cross the open ground in their
front. Another five hundred guarded the flanks, but their
defenses were less secure, and they were less apt to be assailed. Provided that the French had sufficient powder and
ball, and that the British failed to use their artillery, the position could be held indefinitely against charging infantry,
however well led.

Governor Vaudreuil had planned to send an expedition in
the early summer of 1758 up the St. Lawrence and on by way
of Oswego to the Mohawk Valley, partly to overawe the
Iroquois, but also to do as much damage as possible to the
English settlements in that region. Late in June, Brigadier
Lévis had led a party of four hundred regulars, four hundred
troops of La Marine, and eight hundred Canadian militia off
on that mission, regardless of Montcalm's warnings of an
English move down the Champlain waterway. At last Vaudreuil appreciated the British threat and recalled the expedition, too late to get most of the troops back. By marching
night and day, however, Lévis managed to get the four hundred regulars to Ticonderoga the evening before the battle,
and this reinforcement was a very material help to Montcalm.

The French actually were in a most precarious condition,
their backs to the lake, only five days provisions on hand, and
a mighty army hemming them in. Of all the possible courses
open to Abercromby he picked the one least likely to succeed.
The correct solution is always easy by hindsight, but even
at that time a little thought would have brought the British
commander to the realization that an immediate infantry attack was not the best course of action to take. He believed
that reinforcements, perhaps six thousand in number, were on
the way. Even so, had he merely advanced to the lake shore
a little north of the fort and put some artillery in position,

he would have secured command of the artery by which the reinforcements must come, and he would at the same time have cut the troops on the peninsula off from their supply base to the north. Starvation would soon have forced their surrender. His other alternative was to bring up artillery and blast the wooden wall to bits. Either of these plans, or even both at once, were perfectly practical to a force as large as his, and the fort would have fallen in a few days almost without bloodshed. Instead, the British leader ordered execution of the worst possible plan, a frontal infantry attack, unsupported by any artillery, against a very strong defensive position. Abercromby must have lost his wits that day. His only possible excuse was fear of an immediate arrival of heavy reinforcements, and hence a belief in the need for speedy action.

Sir William Johnson, His Majesty's Superintendent of Indian Affairs, had promised to bring a considerable body of Iroquois to assist Abercromby as guides and scouts. At that particular time, however, the Five Nations were torn by internal dissensions into pro-French and pro-British groups, and it was with great difficulty that Johnson managed to persuade any Indians to come on the expedition. He at last got some volunteers together at Fort Johnson on the Mohawk River, but, despite his efforts to prevent it, they secured rum from the Dutch traders of Schenectady and proceeded to get completely drunk, as only Indians could. Sir William wrote that "liquor was as plenty among them as ditch water." This carouse further delayed the departure of Johnson's force. They finally joined Abercromby at Ticonderoga on the morning of the battle, some four hundred in number, too late to serve their most useful purpose as scouts during the advance from the landing place, when their presence might well have saved the life of Lord Howe. With Howe alive the chances are excellent that the fort would have fallen, and the whole course of the last of the French wars would have been materially changed. Sir William led his Indians, presumably at Abercromby's order, to the slopes of Mount Defiance, and during the day they delivered a random long-range fire against the extreme left of the French lines. Their total bag, as reported by Montcalm, was one officer wounded. Sir William gained little glory in this year of 1758, but he was to more than make up for it in the campaign of the following year.

Early in the battle the British attempted to send barges armed with cannon down the river flowing out of Lake George, and thus get around the French left flank. The cannon of the fort took them under fire, sank two, and drove the rest away.

The initial British attack was made in the worst possible way, an uncoordinated attack by several regiments in long lines three deep. The only hope of a successful assault on so strong a position as this would have been the carefully co-ordinated simultaneous advance of several columns with narrow fronts and great depth. The slaughter would have been great, but the log wall might have been carried at one place at least. Instead each regiment attacked in a long thin line as soon as it was ready, regardless of the movements of its neighbor. The forces on the right moved forward before the center brigade was formed, and the assault had proceeded for some time before all the troops concerned were up to the line upon which they were supposed to form for the attack. The men at once got snarled in the abatis, some could neither advance nor retreat and merely awaited slaughter, while the Highlanders tried to hack their way through with their broadswords. Eventually a few soldiers would break through the sharpened treetops, then dash toward the wall, shrouded in the smoke of musketry, and fall dead or wounded. The hot July sun had rapidly dried out the leaves and small branches of the felled trees in the abatis, which caught fire at several places. Brave Frenchmen dashed out from behind the wall carrying pails of water brought up from the lake and put the fires out before they became serious.

Almost three-quarters of the Regiment of Berry were young recruits, and their first battle was more than their morale could endure. At one time in the conflict their courage left them and they fled from behind the log wall in utter confusion. Before the British could grasp the initiative, the reserve companies of grenadiers rushed up and plugged the gap, just in time to save the day.

The battle started somewhat after noon and lasted over six hours. The British attacked with the greatest of bravery at various places along the French lines, but never gained their objective. Time and again they tried, as the sun sank lower in the west, throwing their lives away uselessly, but it was all in vain. Perhaps the most gallant assault of all — and all were most gallant — was that of the 42nd Highlanders, the Black Watch, on the right of the French defenses.

Then it was that Duncan Campbell received his death wound and met the fate he had dreamed of many years before. Campbell was the Laird of Castle Inverawe in the western Highlands. Late one night in the 1740s a fugitive knocked at his door and begged asylum, saying that he had killed a man and was pursued. Campbell swore on his dirk to shelter him and hid him in a secret place. Soon the pursuers arrived, and told the laird that it was his own cousin that had been killed. That night and for other nights the murdered cousin came to Campbell in his dreams and begged revenge, but the laird had sworn on his dirk. Finally the ghost appeared for the last time and bade him farewell until they should at last meet at Ticonderoga, a name that meant nothing to Campbell. Later he became a major of the Black Watch and went with it to the wars in North America. Then to his horror he learned that he was to take part in the attack on Ticonderoga, and the night before the battle the ghost again appeared. Such is the legend of Inverawe, immortalized in a poem by Robert Louis Stevenson.

The assault by the Black Watch was the last major effort of the British. Over half of that regiment were lost that day, 499 men in all. When this last attack was made the Canadian militia on the flats were ordered forward to assail the Scots on the flank, but, undependable as militia usually turned out to be, they failed to advance. Two of their officers charged forward alone, unsupported, and one fell wounded. Earlier in the day the French had been forced to fire on a body of their own militia that was running away to the boats. One of the group was wounded and the fugitives returned to their lines, where some hid under their abatis while others cowered behind stumps. The militia earned no glory in this battle, though Montcalm later wrote, "Nevertheless . . . I have considered it for the good of the service to praise them." It was the French regulars and the stout log wall that saved New France on that bloody day.

At last, just as the sun was dropping behind the Adirondacks, the British gave up and retreated back as they had come. Soon the retreat became suspiciously like a flight, so hurriedly did the withdrawal take place. The army reembarked and headed back up the lake, abandoning many provisions, baggage, and burned boats to the exultant French.

Despite his heavy losses Abercromby still vastly outnumbered the French, and he still had all his artillery to use. A renewal of the attack, after cannon had smashed down the wall, would almost certainly have succeeded, but Abercromby was not one of those who could salvage victory out of initial defeat. His losses were very great, 1610 killed, wounded and missing, almost all from the 6367 regular troops, while the

French lost 377 out of their total of about 4000 in their defense of the log wall. From the point of view of numbers engaged and losses sustained this was by far the greatest battle that had yet been fought on American soil. Only the Battle of Long Island in the Revolution was to exceed it until the mighty conflicts of our Civil War set new records in death and suffering.

It is hard to account for Abercromby's actions on this unfortunate day. Although no military genius, Abercromby had the reputation of being a sound and experienced officer. A senior British officer, when he learned of the battle, expressed sorrow for the defeated general, and wrote that he could not understand how it had happened, it was not at all what he would have expected of Abercromby. There is, it would seem, one quite possible solution. A month before the battle, Abercromby was laid up for several days with a violent stomach disorder, and later, two weeks before the battle, he was struck again. Did the general perhaps suffer from some chronic stomach ill that hit him again on the day of battle and rendered him incapable of effective thought or action?

A few days after the battle Montcalm was reinforced by two thousand Canadians and six hundred Indians, but they came too late and succeeded only in consuming precious rations. The British for their part reoccupied their old camp at the head of Lake George and devoted the remainder of the summer to doing nothing, except for firing a *feu de joie* when they learned that Amherst had captured Louisbourg. A most inglorious summer for the British forces on the American soil, but two less-known leaders, both far exceeding Abercromby in competence, were to retrieve the reputation of their country and to deal vital blows to the cause of New France later in that summer of 1758.

Montcalm caused a great wooden cross to be erected at the

center of the lines that his troops defended, and it was blessed by Abbé Piquet. Today a replica of that cross towers above the entrance road to restored Fort Carillon, flanked on either side by posts bearing the arms of France and two commemorative inscriptions written by Bougainville.

SEVEN

Amherst Planned Well

FOR THE CAMPAIGN of 1759 Pitt had planned assaults on Canada from three directions. Wolfe, who had shown his capabilities at Louisbourg the year before, was to move up the St. Lawrence, amply supported by the navy, and assail Quebec. Another expedition, much smaller in size, would reestablish Oswego, abandoned since its destruction by Montcalm in 1756, and, if at all possible, cross Lake Ontario and capture the vital French post of Niagara. Meanwhile Amherst, the commander for North America, would with a very considerable force advance up the Hudson-Champlain Valley, seize Fort Carillon at Ticonderoga and the other French forts in the valley, and reach the St. Lawrence between Montreal and Quebec, thus severing the lifeline of Canada. This last undertaking might well have been accomplished by an energetic and driving commander, but Amherst, competent general though he was, was hardly a driver, and one thing or another delayed his start until late into the summer. Then his natural caution and policy of slow and sure further delayed his advance. The end of the year was to find him still far to the south of the St. Lawrence.

Amherst reached Albany, the assembly point of his army, by mid-May, but the colonial troops did not start coming in for some little time, and it was well into June before the bulk of them had arrived. Then, just to cause further delay, the

Hudson suddenly rose in unexpected freshet and greatly impeded the forwarding of supplies and munitions. Bateaux and barges could usually be poled along the stretches of the Hudson above Albany, but now the high and fast-moving waters prevented this, and the men had to fall back on the slower and more laborious use of oars.

While the regulars are at last marching north toward Lake George and the sweating colonials are manhandling the barrels of provisions, the kegs of powder and the cannon and their shot aboard the boats, we shall leave them for the moment to their toil and go back a few months in time.

In 1758 General Abercromby had bullheadedly sent his great army in a bayonet charge against the strong defensive works on the Heights of Carillon, works which he had never seen. He had acted on the advice of a young and untried engineer who had viewed Montcalm's lines only from a distant hilltop. This year Amherst would take no such risk. Early in March, while the snow still lay heavy in the Adirondacks, Lieutenant Dietrich Brehm of the 60th, the Royal Americans, had been sent from Fort Edward to reconnoiter Carillon and its defenses. He had been asked to find the answer to a number of specific questions, questions which proved Amherst to be a far abler general than Abercromby. Robert Rogers was sent with a party of over three hundred of his rangers to escort Brehm and guard him while he explored the defenses of the place. The engineer lieutenant was a good officer who knew his trade (eventually he would be a colonel of his regiment) and he was able to examine all the works in considerable detail, as fear of the rangers held the fort's small winter garrison within its walls. On snowshoes Brehm prowled the main defensive line by moonlight. He found it much stronger than when he had seen it the year before, and its location was somewhat different, about a hundred and fifty yards farther from the fort, it seemed to him. At its lowest point the great log wall was seven and a half feet high, and the sharpened tree branches of the abatis that had so impeded Abercromby's men in 1758 were now firmly staked to the ground. For a quarter of a mile in advance of the lines, and all the way from the shore of Lake Champlain clear across the peninsula to the outlet of Lake George, every tree and bush had been grubbed away so that there was no cover whatsoever for an attacking enemy.

Brehm climbed Mount Defiance, which the French called Rattlesnake Mountain, and reported that light howitzers and mortars could be gotten to the summit. He said that the main lines of the French looked from this mountaintop like a rail fence surrounding part of a field.

The engineer officer then crossed to the eastern or Vermont shore of Lake Champlain and viewed the fort from the heights that seventeen years later would be christened Mount Independence. Meanwhile Rogers's men took a few prisoners, who gave much detailed information about the structure of the fort, the height and thickness of the walls, the number of the guns. Thus by the end of March Amherst had quite clear and precise knowledge of the condition of the fort and its defenses, and was able to plan well in advance his method of attack.

Now let us return to the army struggling up the Hudson Valley, some fighting the swift waters in bateaux, while others slogged, slipped and splashed up the crude road, made even worse by rains, marching feet and lumbering ox teams. An army such as Amherst led required a vast amount of supplies, barrels of pork and beef and bread and rum, spare clothing, and tents, as well as the heavy cannon and their powder, shot and shell. His eleven thousand men, half regulars, half provincials, would need, for a campaign which would probably last for some four months, nearly thirteen thousand barrels of meat and bread. It would have required one thousand bateaux, eight hundred wagons and a thousand oxcarts, along with at least six weeks of good weather, to move this vast mountain of supplies. But fortunately a considerable portion of these provisions were already at Fort Edward, left over from the unhappy campaign of 1758, and they had only to be hauled over the portage road from the Hudson to Lake George. This was no easy thing, however, for the rough road was also choked with long convoys of wagons carrying part of the vast number of bateaux the army would need to go down the lake. And then there were the Nantucket whaleboats the scouts would use, some carried on men's shoulders, fifteen men to a boat, and others on wheeled trucks dragged along by plodding soldiers. It was indeed a busy road that spring.

Pitt had given Amherst almost complete discretion as to the methods of executing his mission. The general had promised the minister that he "intended to make an eruption into Canada with the utmost vigour and dispatch," but unfortunately he was somewhat lacking in these qualities, particularly the latter. Safe and sure was Amherst's motto, as he would have been the first to admit. The colonial troops slowly draggled in and the general waited, perhaps with more patience than was desirable. There was much to do at Lake George before the army could hope to embark, and there was no real reason why at least some of the essential work should not have been started while the provincials continued to trickle into camp. To be sure, there was some risk from French and Indian raiders, but Amherst could easily have sent ahead to the lake enough of a force to hold the place in safety while the water transport was being readied. Instead he played it safe and accordingly was at least a month late in getting his campaign under way.

Part of the army was started north by early June, and by the twenty-first of that month the British at last had gotten some six thousand men to the southern end of Lake George. A strong stockaded post had also been built at the midpoint of the portage (near the Glens Falls of today), both for security and as a staging point for supplies. There were also two other stockades or blockhouses to guard the road, one four miles north of Fort Edward, the other three miles before Lake George was reached. Patrols from these three posts could maintain constant observation over the road to the lake. Spruce beer was brewed, and troops were given special training suitable to wilderness fighting, while the rest of the boats and supplies were hauled north over the wretched road. To avoid risk of Indian ambush both sides of the roadway were cleared of all trees and bushes for a distance of thirty yards. Four hundred colonial axemen made short work of this job, and must have greatly impressed the British regulars with their skill. Frequent heavy rains kept the road soft and muddy, and there must have been many washouts to repair and miry places to corduroy with logs.

Early in July the British general suddenly realized that he had no way to carry his heavy siege cannon down the lake, and he ordered construction of a radeau, a great slab-sided scow-like vessel. I have found no record of the size of this odd affair, but the radeau Amherst built a little later that year on Lake Champlain was eighty-four feet long by twenty wide and carried six 24-pounders, the same guns he was now transporting, so it is probable that this Lake George radeau was of about the same dimensions. In the fall of 1758 Abercromby's men had built two radeaux at the head of the lake and sunk them for safekeeping. The larger of the two was fifty feet long by nineteen wide and six feet deep. It seems most odd that these were not raised and utilized by Amherst, but they apparently were not, for there is no mention of them in any of the journals of this campaign.

Captain Joshua Loring, a New Englander who held a

commission in the Royal Navy, had been directed by Amherst to raise, rerig and equip the sloop *Halifax,* built the summer before and in the fall sunk in the lake for safekeeping. Only thus could a vessel be held safe from damage by ice or the torch of a party of raiders. And even then there was always a risk that the enemy might locate and destroy the sunken warship. The *Halifax* was a fair-sized vessel armed with fourteen cannon. Amherst used her to carry his artillery ammunition and filled her hold with powder, shot and shell to a total weight of over a hundred tons. The general noted in his journal in mid-July that he had tried out the "flat bottomed English boat," which carried a 3-pound swivel gun at its bow. This almost certainly must have been a craft similar to the ones that we know Wolfe took to Quebec — sectional knockdown "foldboats" which, when assembled, were held together with brass bolts. They were a success both at Quebec and on Lake George, each holding some seventy or more soldiers, yet having a relatively shallow draft. Work meanwhile was continued in bringing the bateaux overland across the low divide between the Hudson and St. Lawrence watersheds, repairing the damage they received in transit, and completing the sloop and the radeau. Amherst seems to have been both patient and somewhat fatalistic, for his journal says on 17 July: "As I can't cross the lake till the whaleboats and the artillery are ready, I may as well keep adoing other things [he was building a new fort at the head of the lake] — as I lose no time by it."

At last on 21 July "at peep of day" the army took to its boats and got under way to the north, a full month after it had first arrived at Lake George.

The defenses of Carillon had, as we learned from Lieutenant Brehm's report, been rebuilt and considerably strengthened since Abercromby's futile attack of the previous year. Brigadier Bourlamaque had a force of about the same size as had Montcalm in 1758, some four thousand in all, but this year Governor Vaudreuil had regretfully realized that the Ticonderoga frontier could no longer be held with the forces that he had available, and he ordered the brigadier to abandon the fort once the enemy had appeared in strength. A delaying force of about four hundred was to be left to stall the British advance for as long as was possible, and then to blow up the fort and make its escape. The French King had failed to furnish enough men and supplies to hold the frontiers of New France, but he was hard pressed in Europe and his troops had to be rationed out to several theaters of war, of which Canada appeared to be of lesser importance. Thus, Fort Carillon was, although Amherst did not know it, ripe to fall to the British once they had landed in force and invested the place.

More than four hundred bateaux and almost half as many whaleboats carried Amherst's men down Lake George accompanied by the little *Halifax,* the radeau *Invincible,* carrying the siege artillery, and the "English flat bottomed boat." Abercromby had left his regimental colors behind, but this year they were taken along, and the narrow waters of the lake must have presented a colorful spectacle. Flag signals had been prescribed for all the necessary maneuvers, and the flotilla advanced in regular columns with military precision. But with nightfall came discomfort, as the boats rested on their oars through the hours of darkness, while high winds and violent waves made keeping position impossible. Many an unhappy man huddled shivering in his drenched regimentals and prayed that daylight would come. Constantine Hardy of Ruggles's Massachusetts regiment noted in his journal: "July the 21. They all imbarct to set out for Tiantaroga and we got with in three or four miles of the landing place and then lay down our ores all night and a teedious night we had." When dawn at last came it must have taken both time and violent language to get the columns re-formed and lined up again in proper order.

At about nine o'clock on that morning of 22 July the army started landing at the foot of Lake George, while an advance party of rangers and light troops was promptly sent forward down the portage road to the sawmill and the bridge. There they made contact with French outposts, which at once fell back after delivering a slight scattering fire. The French had attempted to block the portage road between the two lakes by felling trees, but colonial troops, axes in hand, made short work of these obstructions. The army advanced to the saw-mill, crossed the river, took up position on the higher ground beyond and settled down for the night. Ticonderoga, particularly since Abercromby's defeat, had been a place of ill omen to the colonials — "Boges" they often called it. William Amherst, the general's brother and aide-de-camp, noted in his interesting diary that the provincials were full of spirit and no longer feared the place as being enchanted.

Amherst had promptly pushed his artillery forward and by dark of this first day had several pieces across the river at the sawmill. At daylight next morning, the twenty-third, the British pushed ahead, brushed aside very light resistance and found the enemy's main lines abandoned. This was indeed an unexpected stroke of fortune, for Amherst was thus presented by the enemy with a complete set of lines already built, exactly what was needed as a base from which to commence siege operations against the fort itself. The British general could hardly believe his luck, and it was a complete mystery to him why Bourlamaque had not either tried to destroy the lines or to defend them. The troops at once filed into the long line of log walls and started building new firing platforms on the outer side, while Amherst in his safe, sure, conventional manner started digging saps, establishing advanced trenches and preparing batteries to open fire. His attempt

against Fort Carillon was to be the very antithesis of Abercromby's. He had secured precise knowledge of the fort and
its surroundings, had brought his army safely to it, and practically without any loss at all. Now he was to invest the
place and proceed with formal siege operations, which under
the circumstances could not help but be safe, sure, and certain.

Bourlamaque had planned to delay the British advance by
attacking their forward elements before they reached the log-
wall defensive line, and had designated a force of three hundred mission Indians and some regulars and volunteers to
advance against them before they reached the line. The Indians, however, refused to move forward to the attack, just
as they had so often refused in other battles of the war, and
the soldiers alone accomplished little or nothing. William Amherst was scornful of Bourlamaque's Indians: "The cowardice of these barbarians is so great. . . . Their whole dependence is upon a tree or a bush. You have nothing to do but
advance & they will fly. They never stand an open fire or
an attack." Thus the French brigadier's plan to delay the
British deployment collapsed and he was forced to abandon
all hope of holding his best defensive position for even a day.

Amherst's initial plan, a sound one, had been to get troops
with artillery around the fort and on the shore of Lake
Champlain between Carillon and Crown Point, thus prevent-
ing any relief either of men or of supplies coming from the
north. As soon as it became evident that the French were
starting to withdraw — and this had become apparent by 23
July, the day after the landing — Amherst gave up this plan
and concentrated his forces on the fort alone. This perhaps
was a mistake, for had he adhered to the original plan he
might well have gobbled up all of Bourlamaque's force. Amherst's objective, however, was the fort, not Bourlamaque's
little army, although in the broader strategic sense the latter
was far more to be desired.

The men were kept well under cover while the siege batteries were being prepared. The fire from the French fort was very heavy but the damage was of the slightest except that Roger Townshend, Amherst's close friend and chief staff officer, was cut in two by a cannonball. Work on the trenches and batteries went on for another two days, difficult work because there was little dirt and much ledge in the area around the fort. This required the construction in many places of communication trenches on top of ledges by means of fascines, gabions or sandbags instead of the easier and safer method of digging. By this time the British had with great difficulty hauled up into position a 13-inch mortar, a clumsy, unwieldy weapon of great weight, but possessed of tremendous firepower. In fact, it was almost an axiom in colonial America that if a 13-inch mortar could be gotten within range of a frontier fort, the fort was practically certain to surrender.

Sam Merriman, of Deerfield in Massachusetts, confided to his diary: "July the 25 . . . No firering upon our side, thee enemies fire is very havey. The armi hath entrench within 30 rodes of the French fort our English went to the fort & fired at the sentry upon the wale. Some of our men went into the French garden & fetch a armfull ful of cabbage to Genl. & he gave them tow dollars. . . ."

On this same 25 July the British got whaleboats and the "English flat bottomed boat" into Lake Champlain north of the fort. The next day Rogers and some of his men were to use these craft to make an attempt to cut the log boom which the French had stretched across the lake. There is reason to believe that this boom may also have been intended to serve as a floating footbridge which might have allowed a possible French withdrawal by land along the eastern shore. Merriman's journal continued: "July the 26, 1759 . . . our English never fired one cannon att the enemie till they im bark,

then the fire was vary hot & took 20 prisoners . . . soe
the sege was over a gainst Ticontorogue, with grate rei-
joceing. . . ."

What had happened was that Bourlamaque had withdrawn most of his men once the British had crossed the river
at the sawmill, and had left only four hundred under the able
Captain Hébecourt with orders to hold out as long as they
could, then blow up the fort and get away.

The withdrawal of the major part of the garrison must have
been obvious to Amherst, but he continued his siege preparations in order to make absolutely certain. The batteries of
heavy cannon were almost ready to start smashing down the
walls of the fort when, at nine in the evening of 26 July,
three French deserters came into the British lines and reported that the garrison was leaving. Hébecourt had timed
his actions perfectly. The deserters also reported that a
lighted slow match had been left which shortly would blow
up the powder magazine. Amherst offered one hundred
guineas to any of the three who would guide the British to
the fuse so that it might be extinguished. He found no taker,
however, and two hours later there was a great explosion,
followed by a raging fire, which continued unchecked for
several days, while cannon left loaded for this purpose were
discharged from time to time by the flames. John Hurlburt
was another colonial who kept a journal that has survived.
"July 27, . . . We never fired one gun but they fired canon
and flung bums. When the French marched from the fort,
Rogers fell upon them and killed a great many of them and
took a hundred of them. [This is considerably exaggerated.]
Cabbage is very plenty and all sorts of greens which they
got in the French garden. They had a fine garden large
anuf to give the whole army a mess. We have not lost one
man nor had one man wounded in our regiment. In the
whole loss of men was 16 killed, one colonel, one ensign, be-

longing to the 17th regiment and 50 wounded in the siege of Ticontaroga. They had in the fort a fine stable of horses over the magazine which they blew up and killed about fifty. The[y] burnt up a great many guns and they left 16 canons and six mortar pieces." French soldiers during the last hour or two before they left broached some brandy kegs and drowned their sorrows. Quite a number of drunken Frenchmen were gathered up by the British that night and early morning.

Thus fell the great French fortress against which Abercromby had thrown away the lives of hundreds in a hasty and ill-planned attack. Now Amherst in a slow, almost dilatory campaign, after careful planning and preparation, had seized the place practically without loss. It is true that the French withdrew once the British had landed and started siege operations, but so might Montcalm in 1758 had Abercromby played his cards correctly.

The woodwork of the fort, the barrack floors, the roof timbers and the wooden facings of parts of the outer walls burned merrily for several days, despite the violent activities of bucket brigades of soldiers who passed their water-filled camp kettles up from the lake. The flames did not entirely die down until the end of the month. Examination then showed that the structure on the whole was surprisingly little damaged. The bastion which had held the powder magazine and the unfortunate horses was destroyed, as well as part of the east curtain wall; but the rest of the fort, save for the woodwork of the barracks, had suffered much less than would have been expected. Amherst, who evidently had no high opinion of the engineer officers, wrote: "I will repair the fort upon the same plan as the enemy had built it which will save great expense & give no room for the engineers to exercise their genius."

Early in August the bulk of the British army moved on to Crown Point, where Bourlamaque had also blown up Fort

St. Frédéric as he withdrew to a new position at the northern end of Lake Champlain. Amherst now suddenly realized that the four little French warships on Lake Champlain held unquestioned control of the lake, and that he could not advance until this fleet had been at least neutralized. The commander of these puny warships bore the odd name of Doloboratz, a name so unusual that he must have been the same man who captained a privateer out of Louisbourg in 1744, had been captured by the British and clapped into Boston jail. One of these vessels, *La Vigilante,* was a schooner, but the other three, all bearing names of freshwater fish, were chebecs carrying lateen sails, precursors of the row galleys Benedict Arnold would lead to battle at Valcour Island seventeen years in the future.

Accordingly Amherst settled his army down at Crown Point, started to build his naval force, and meanwhile set his men to work on a new and mighty fortress, one which would cost Britain vast sums and serve no useful purpose. Amherst certainly could exercise patience at least as well as the next man, and he was not to move from Crown Point, save for an abortive advance of about a week, during the remainder of the campaign of 1759. Had he taken a shade more risk and employed a quarter of the dash of a Montcalm, he probably could have cut Quebec off from Montreal and caused the fall of Canada a year earlier. But we must not be too critical, for Amherst planned well, knew what he was doing, and ultimately, if somewhat belatedly, he achieved his purpose with a minimum loss of men.

In the late spring of this year of 1759 Admiral Charles Saunders had found no difficulty in leading a British fleet up the broad St. Lawrence, thus confounding the French, who had long believed that its shoals and swift currents were the best defenses of Quebec. Wolfe, after delays, false attempts and despair, at last gained the Heights of Abraham and the capital of New France fell to Britain. In July Brigadier John Prideaux brought his expedition to the walls of Niagara, catching the French entirely unaware of his approach. He lost his life in the siege, but Sir William Johnson assumed the command and that vital citadel of the French *"pays d'en haut,"* the Far West, hauled down the lilies of France.

Thus the year 1759 ended with two of Pitt's objectives accomplished: the capture of Quebec and of Fort Niagara, the key to the heartland. The third, and in many ways the major, attempt had produced only partial success. On the other hand it was obvious that, barring a miracle, the days of New France were fast approaching their end. On the east the capital city had fallen to the enemy, while in the west the French had lost all hold on the Great Lakes. From the south Amherst, although partially balked in his drive up the Champlain Valley, held all that great waterway with only the minor French defenses on the Richelieu River between him and the St. Lawrence. Next year's campaign would see the fall of Canada, but the tide of war had already passed by Ticonderoga, and the role of this vital key to the Hudson-Champlain Valley had been played out in this year of 1759. The repairs to the fort were completed, and a small housekeeping garrison installed, but it would be many years before Fort Ticonderoga would again appear in history.

EIGHT

"In the Name of the Great Jehovah . . ."

THE WAR MOVED northward, Montreal fell and Canada became part of the British Empire. There was now little if any need for forts on the Champlain waterway, but the King nevertheless decided to maintain Fort Ticonderoga and Crown Point, the great new fort that had occupied Amherst's time in the late summer of 1759 when he might have been pushing on toward the St. Lawrence. Small garrisons were moved into the two forts, and history became silent. Life on the lake, unless one was a keen sportsman, must have been one of deadly monotony, particularly when the heavy snows of a northern winter buried the countryside. The commander at Crown Point ran a farm, as probably did his counterpart at Ticonderoga. The latter certainly kept cows and sheep at one time.

A glimpse of happenings at the fort is given us in the winter of 1764. Private James Cahoon burst one day into the officers' mess at Crown Point, where Colonel Beckwith, the senior officer on the lake, had his headquarters. Cahoon blurted out a plea for justice, stating that he had found the commander at Ticonderoga, Captain Charles Osborne, in bed with Mrs. Cahoon. Imagine the sensation in the officers' mess! The soldier went on to say that, when he told his captain that he really did not think that it was right, he was put in the *"clink"* for ten days. Beckwith at once called on Osborne for an explanation, and received a lengthy letter in reply. This stated that Cahoon was no good and a drunkard as well, and that his wife was Osborne's washerwoman and cowherd. She had slept in the milk room since her husband's bad behavior had forced their ejection from the married quarters and had relegated him to the common barracks. The letter meandered on at a very considerable length, but nowhere at all did it make any denial of Cahoon's charge. There was a further interchange of notes which added but little to the facts and our knowledge of the incident comes to an end. Silence closed in on Fort Ticonderoga for another decade.

The French had left a damaged fortress, its walls partly of great squared timbers and partly of stone. Amherst's men had repaired the destruction resulting from the explosion of the magazine and replaced some if not all of the wooden walls with stone. But these walls were really only thin stone facings covering steep banks of earth and clay, and each bitter winter the frost crept in a little deeper behind the stonework and exerted its destructive forces on the roughly built masonry. Stone walls require maintenance and repair, particularly in our northern climates. Little or no work of this nature was done at Ticonderoga, and the fort gradually but steadily fell into decay. By the early 1770's the walls had collapsed in places, the parapets which sheltered the cannon on the ramparts had disintegrated into a mass of dirt and rotten wood, while the stone barracks that once held a garrison of four hundred men were now in sad repair. Amherst's great fortress at Crown Point had been almost entirely destroyed in the spring of 1773, when a washerwoman's fire got out of control and ignited the tarred wooden facing of its walls. Headquarters had at once been moved to Ticonderoga and a handful of men and a sergeant left behind to keep watch on the ruins.

By the spring of 1775 Captain William Delaplace of the 26th Regiment was in command, with only one officer, Lieutenant Jocelyn Feltham, to assist him. The garrison was composed of forty-two men, and half of these were "old, wore out & unservicable" or otherwise incapacitated. Then there were two dozen women and children. Had Fort Ticonderoga been repaired and restored to battle readiness, it would have required a garrison of at least four hundred. Now with its walls in ruins it had but a score of able-bodied men to hold it safe for Britain.

On 19 April 1775, 120 miles to the eastward, Lord Percy's battered column of British fell back from Concord and Lexington through the Middlesex countryside into Charlestown. They were ferried over to Boston, then a peninsula connected with the Roxbury mainland by an exceedingly narrow neck of land soon to be guarded by ample earthworks. Minute Men from the villages north and west of Boston had harried the steps of the retreating troops, and then, reinforced by eager volunteers from much of eastern New England, they sat themselves down in a tight ring around the town. All was in utter confusion among the provincials; no such development had been foreseen, and there was no effective higher command. No one knew quite what to do. They had the lion by the tail for the moment, but they must watch to keep away from his teeth. A major British eruption from Boston must be prevented at all costs, and eventually General Gage's army must be persuaded to quit the town. The one essential tool which would achieve both of these objectives was to a very large extent lacking to the provincials. This was artillery, and especially heavy artillery. Accordingly every endeavor was soon to be directed toward eliminating this vital deficiency.

Benedict Arnold, captain in the Governor's Footguards of New Haven, led his company to Cambridge five days after the Concord fight. As a boy he had run away to the last of the

French and Indian wars, had deserted after a short period of service, but had enlisted again the following year. Possibly he had been at Ticonderoga after its capture, certainly he had heard much about it. On the road to Boston, Arnold met Colonel Samuel Parsons, who was returning to Connecticut from the encircled town. The colonel must have told the future traitor of the need for cannon and Arnold spoke of the great number of them that were available at Ticonderoga to one who had the courage and energy to take them. Real rebellion such an action would be, an action going well beyond the initial plan of the patriot leaders, who still hoped to avoid war and separation from Britain. Two trains of action were ignited by the chance meeting of these men, and two expeditions against the fort were shortly conceived. Arnold, immediately upon his arrival at Cambridge, contacted the patriot authorities in that town, while Parsons assembled a small but influential group in Hartford.

Concord Fight had exploded some three weeks before the second Continental Congress was due to convene, but the Massachusetts Provincial Congress was actively in session. This latter body initially assumed effective control of the siege of Boston and its accompanying military problems until the Philadelphia congress could organize and take over the reins. Purely military matters were delegated to its Committee of Safety, and it was to this body that Arnold went on 30 April with his story of the great store of ordnance up on Lake Champlain at Ticonderoga, eighty iron cannon and twenty of brass, from 4- to 18-pounders in size, as well as a dozen large mortars. An exaggeration indeed, but actually on the low side when the spoils of Crown Point were later added. The committee showed great interest, and on that same day wrote the New York Committee of Safety that the capture of the fort at Ticonderoga had been proposed to them, but that they hesitated to infringe on the rights of New York. Further thought evidently erased their qualms and fired them to action, for on 3 May the committee gave Arnold a commission to raise a force of four hundred men, appoint his officers and proceed to take the fort. The day before they had anticipated their action by giving him an order for powder, ball, flints and horses, as well as a war chest of £100.

Here we suddenly encounter a fascinating sidelight and a fine example of the might-have-been. Arnold's commission was issued by Dr. Benjamin Church, chairman of the committee, and Church was a spy in General Gage's pay. He had been such for at least a number of weeks before Lord Percy's column was chased back into Boston. Thus on 30 April a British agent knew of the possibility of a raid on Ticonderoga, and two days later he himself authorized it! Why was the commander of the fort not warned? Here was vital information regarding a strategic point about which Gage had recently shown concern. Surely the general would have expected to be informed and, if he had been, would have attempted to alert the fort. The answer probably is that Church's reports to the British general had, in order to maintain the utmost secrecy, to pass through slow and perhaps devious channels. Thus, if information of the impending attack ever reached Gage, it had come too late to allow a warning to be gotten to the lake.

John Brown, a young lawyer of Pittsfield in western Massachusetts, had been sent to Canada in February of 1775 by the Massachusetts authorities to sound out the feelings of the Canadian people. In March he reported on the conditions he had found, conditions not favorable to the American cause. At the same time he strongly urged that the fort at Ticonderoga should be seized the moment that hostilities had broken out. Brown had broached the idea of this seizure to some "people on the N. Hampshire Grants" — the Green Mountain Boys, whose leader was Ethan Allen, originally of Connecticut. It is hard to summarize the character of this man in a few words. For our purpose it perhaps is sufficient to say that he was a born leader, one exceedingly vocal both in word and in print, deeply involved in land speculations in the regions immediately east of Lake Champlain, and a man whose blasphemy approached the majestic. He was boastful, egotistical, abounding in rashness and in energy, and a bitter hater of the Yorkers who claimed the lands of the settlers in the Green Mountains of what later became the state of Vermont. An almost ideal leader for these turbulent folk of the Hampshire Grants.

The Green Mountain Boys were settlers in the southern and western parts of today's Vermont. They held their lands under grants made by New Hampshire, a province which claimed title to all the land within its latitudes as far west as twenty miles east of the Hudson. New York in its turn held that it owned eastward to the Connecticut River. Both provinces issued land grants in the contested region. An appeal to London met with a decision favorable to New York, and this province then attempted to force settlers who held under a New Hampshire grant to pay for their lands a second time. New York's attempts to collect, or in default of payment to evict the settlers, brought on a form of guerrilla warfare between the Green Mountain Boys and agents of the New York grantors which, starting in the mid-1760's, became increasingly violent. Thus these settlers in the Hampshire Grants had to fight the Yorkers at the same time that they were conquering the wilderness. Only the hardy could endure such an existence.

The struggle for the land blew hot and cold, as New York sent surveyors and agents to evict the settlers, who turned out like hornets and thrust the intruders back across the borders. Harsh words, threats, whippings and house-burnings abounded, but practically no blood was shed despite dire threats by both sides. From the point of view of the Green Mountain Boys it was all great fun, in spite of the seriousness underlying the contest.

Eventually two Vermonters lost their lives in a bickering when a Yorker judge tried to open court in the disputed lands, but aside from this unfortunate affair the strife appears to have been carried out, at least by the Vermonters, on very much of a Robin Hood basis. The result, however, was that the Green Mountain Boys, known to the New York authorities as "The Bennington Mob," because that hamlet served as their capital, had little respect for any law, did as they wished and followed only their own leaders. And so we have a few hundred lawless frontiersmen inhabiting the region between Lake Champlain and the Connecticut River, with loyalty only to themselves, experienced in border warfare and ready to take on the devil himself if the spirit moved.

Thus by May Day of 1775 three groups had their eyes on the old French fort, the Massachusetts Committee of Safety, an unofficial but nevertheless powerful group in Connecticut, and the unruly inhabitants of the Hampshire Grants, whose leader was the formidable and energetic Ethan Allen.

The British also appreciated the importance of the forts on the lake, despite the lack of attention they had given them over the years since the Peace of 1763. In 1767 Governor Carleton had declared that the Lake Champlain forts must be kept in repair, but nothing was done. As the troubles with the colonies became increasingly apparent a more positive interest in Ticonderoga developed. Crown Point's destruction had left the fort at the outlet of Lake George the only habitable place and its capacity was most limited. A garrison of only fifty was all that could be sheltered there in winter. In 1774 Captain Montresor, Gage's senior engineer officer, was ordered to the lake to make plans either for repairing one of the two forts or for building an entirely new structure. His report on Ticonderoga was discouraging. "It's ruinous situation is such, that it would require more to repair it than the constructing of a new fort, . . . in many places there are very capitol breaches." Montresor advised building an entirely new fort at Crown Point. The excellent General Haldimand was then in command in America during Gage's temporary absence in England. After receiving the engineer's report he wrote Lord Dartmouth, Secretary for the Colonies, that if it was feared that the New Englanders were heading for trouble, it might be an excellent idea to have a couple of regiments camped in their rear on Lake Champlain, and that they could be sent there under the pretext of their building a new fort. A sound idea, indeed, but one not followed.

In early November of 1774 London at last ordered that the forts should be repaired, but Gage did not receive the instructions until winter had closed in on the Adirondacks, and work would be impossible for months to come. The American commander accordingly took a leisurely approach to the matter, and no action was started. Captain Delaplace at Ticonderoga, however, was warned to be on the lookout for trouble. It was on 19 April that General Gage, having sent the troops off to seize the military stores at Concord, sat down and wrote Carleton in Canada, directing him to send a regiment to Ticonderoga or Crown Point with all dispatch. The letter was a month in reaching the Canadian governor, and it arrived too late.

Colonel Parsons, ruminating on what Arnold had told him of cannon at Ticonderoga, reached Hartford, Connecticut, on 27 April, and the very next day he met with a small group of prominent men, most of them members of the Governor's Council or of the Assembly. This unofficial gathering took upon itself the authorizing of the dispatch of the nucleus of an expedition against the fort, and they withdrew funds of the Province for its use, they themselves going bond for its authorization or repayment. On 28 April, Edward Mott, just appointed captain in the 6th Connecticut Regiment, reached Hartford and was directed by this same group of citizens to push on and catch up with the party dispatched the day before. There is one statement on record which says that this self-constituted committee of citizens had been joined in its deliberations and decisions by "Mr. Hancock and Mr. Adams." This is quite possible, for both John and Sam Adams were in Hartford at least on 30 April, and Hancock had preceded them. None of these men, however, could have known of the action of the Massachusetts Committee of Safety in commissioning Arnold to seize the fort.

On the way northward the Connecticut contingent picked up John Brown and some forty Massachusetts men to add to their initial party of sixteen. Meanwhile the leaders of the Green Mountain Boys were conferring as to their future actions in a meeting at the Catamount Tavern in Bennington, where a stuffed catamount snarled constant defiance at York Province from the top of a tall pole. The Connecticut men dropped in at the ideal moment, and plans were soon under way to make the venture against Ticonderoga. The combined party then went on to Castleton, where they assembled at the farmhouse of Richard Bentley, and completed their dispositions. After the meeting had broken up, and Ethan Allen had gone on ahead to spy out the land, another small party was sent off to Skenesboro to capture Major Philip Skene, the great Tory landholder of the region, and, if possible, to secure boats with which to cross the lake. Then late in that evening of 8 May, Benedict Arnold, colonel by grace of his Massachusetts commission, stormed into the farmhouse, accompanied only by a servant, and demanded command of the expedition. He must in some way have heard of what was afoot in the Hampshire Grants and, abandoning attempts at recruiting his authorized force of four hundred, rushed ahead to get into the adventure before it was too late. His demand was laughed at by the hardy frontiersmen, who would follow leaders of their own choice or none at all. Nevertheless Arnold was allowed to join the force, and, determined to make the best of it, he bided his time and went along. One can easily see how little appeal the brash demand for command by a Massachusetts officer would have to the Bennington boys who formed the major part of the little army, and one might wonder why Arnold was accepted at all. There was a reason, and a good one. Allen had no authority at all for his undertaking, and technically the entire group, both Green Mountain Boys and Connecticut men, was engaged in a highly irregular activity for which, if things went badly, its members might receive the harshest of treatment as bandits and outlaws. Arnold, however, had a proper commission from the Massachusetts Provincial Congress, which, even if most irregular and revolutionary in British eyes, was at the moment the supreme authority in the land, in practice if not in law. He thus had something which might well stave off the gallows if the worst came to the worst. And so Arnold was accepted and granted a certain, if still dubious, standing, although formal command was refused him. Later, when he had caught up with Ethan Allen, his position might be clarified, and we have his statement that it was.

The late hours of 9 May saw waiting at Hand's Cove on the shore of Lake Champlain a motley body of some two hundred, mostly Green Mountain Boys, with some two score from Massachusetts and a handful from Connecticut. The lake was still to be crossed, and the expected boats had failed to appear. Dawn was not many hours away. At last a couple of scows were located and the ferrying of the party commenced. It was almost daylight before some eighty men had been landed on the New York shore, and it was now too late to wait for any more. Just what agreement had been reached between Allen and Arnold we can never know for sure, but after the crossing Arnold made a new demand for command and the right to be first to set foot in the fortress. This was refused, but, according to Arnold's statement, Allen conceded him a joint authority, and the two leaders, marching side by side, led the party onward into our country's history.

It was just turning light as the men, marching in column, three abreast, approached the fort. The provincials passed by the great well and up the slope to the base of the east curtain wall. A small portal and a tunnel here penetrated into the basement of the eastern barrack building, then up a flight of stone steps onto the parade ground. A sentry posted at the entrance snapped his firelock at the leader of the intruders but the gun misfired, and the sentry turned and fled into the shelter of a bombproof on the north side of the parade ground. The Green Mountain Boys poured up the steps and then on up onto the walls and into the barracks, startling the garrison from a sound sleep, overpowering them with ease in their beds, and at once starting their search for plunder.

Allen, Arnold and a few others stormed across the courtyard, where they were accosted by a second sentry who pricked one of the Boys with his bayonet and then was struck down by the flat of Ethan's sword. Allen demanded to be shown the commander's quarters and the cowed sentry pointed out a stairway which led up to the second story of the western barrack. The Vermonter dashed up the steps, closely followed by Arnold. "Come out, you old rat," roared Ethan, mad with excitement. Almost at once the figure of a British officer appeared at the top of the stairs, fully dressed except for the breeches held in his hands. This was Lieutenant Feltham, Captain Delaplace's only officer. The assailants paused for a moment, as Feltham talked and tried to stall for time, hoping that the garrison would come to his aid. But they were already overpowered. Allen became impatient, breathed threats of no quarter, threatened Feltham with his sword, shouted that he had orders from the state of Connecticut to take the fort, and that he exercised a joint command with Benedict Arnold, who had similar orders from Massachusetts. Arnold seems to have remained calmer and attempted to restrain Allen's violence with some little success, but the situation was tense. Vermonters in the courtyard were threatening Feltham with their fowling pieces, when Delaplace, fully dressed at last, appeared in the doorway at the head of the stairs. He asked under what authority the leaders were acting. Allen, now somewhat calmer, cried, "In the name of the Great Jehovah and the Continental Congress." There was nothing that Delaplace could do but surrender, and so the old stone fortress passed into the hands of the Green Mountain Boys without bloodshed.

The question of who really was in command at the fort's capture perhaps deserves a little more consideration, as it has been argued over the years. Arnold wrote to the Massachusetts Committee of Safety just after the capture that he and Allen had agreed to issue orders jointly, while Allen at the same time wrote the Albany Committee that Arnold entered the fort by his side. In a letter to the Massachusetts body, however, Allen made no mention whatsoever of Arnold, while in his *Narrative*, printed in 1779, he made it appear that he and the Green Mountain Boys alone took part in the capture. That left the matter open to argument for many years, Arnold on the whole faring poorly because of the taint of his later career. Thus for a century and a half all credit, practically speaking, was given Allen, and Arnold was portrayed merely as a bystander. Then some thirty years ago a letter was found among the papers of General Gage which brought forth new evidence. This was a complete report of the capture written by Lieutenant Feltham. We cannot be sure to whom it was sent, presumably to General Gage, and it certainly found its way into his hands. The letter was written a month after the capture, but the writer's memory was evidently clear and fresh. Its careful relation of the affair agrees closely in all major points with the tales told by the other reporters. Feltham specifically stated, "I was inform'd by one Ethan Allen and one Benedict Arnold that they held a joint command." This is clear, specific and agrees entirely with Arnold's claim.

Thus we have three stories, two of which agree as to the joint command, one of them by an arrogant, self-seeking and jealous glory-hunter, who soon was to become one of the famous traitors of all time, the other by a British officer who presumably had no reason to distort what he saw and heard. Opposed to them is the story told by Ethan Allen.

Regardless of the technicality of who held the theoretical command, it was Allen alone who held the practical leadership. He had the intent and the men needed to capture the fort without the help of Arnold, while the latter was powerless without Allen's men. The Vermont leader merely made the wise decision to assure his project a better legal status through his concession to Arnold. After the capture Allen secured from Mott, chairman of an informal and self-constituted committee, an ex post facto commission authorizing him to take the fort. Thus it is obvious that he wished as much legal justification as possible for his actions.

And so we should agree with the historians of the past and say that Allen was the commander of the band that captured the old French fortress. But we must also grant Arnold his modicum of credit, for it was his talk with Colonel Parsons on 26 April that started the Connecticut party on its way, and the arrival of these men in the Hampshire Grants was undoubtedly the straw that caused the hitherto hesitant Green Mountain Boys to decide to act.

One final word might well be added. The capture of Fort Ticonderoga was no great military victory. A ruined fort, its ramparts rotted away and its walls already breached, and garrisoned by only some two score men, and only half of these considered effective, was surprised while all were asleep, save dozing sentries, by a rush of a wild crew of at least double their numbers. Even if the commander had shown due vigilance (he had been warned of trouble) there would have been little that he could have done to ward off a determined attack. Allen had more men still on the Vermont shore, with others available on call, while the British could expect no help for many days to come. Allen's seizure of the fort was, however, a most daring and courageous act, the first really overt military act of the Revolution. Lexington and Concord had been defensive measures against a British offensive, but here at Ticonderoga the patriots determinedly and with planned intent seized a possession of the British King. This was revolt.

NINE

Britain Loses the Waterway

BY SUNRISE of that tenth day of May the fort was secure, the garrison disarmed and safely confined. But all
was far from quiet as the Green Mountain Boys dashed
hither and yon after plunder, breaking into the magazines
and storerooms on a wild rampage. The captors were joined
by late arrivals from further ferrying operations who, although they had missed the mad rush into the fort, were
not, if they could help it, to be cheated out of their share of
the loot. At such a time and with such men there could be
no discipline, but Arnold, with experience behind him both
as a soldier and as master of a ship, tried nevertheless to restrain the looting. His attempts were hopeless and achieved
nothing beyond arousing the animosity of the Vermonters.
According to one story a few surreptitious musket shots were
directed at Arnold, but without luck. The future traitor
became for a short period a useless supernumerary, while
Allen styled himself the commander of the fort, as indeed
he was.

A party under Seth Warner, who had been too late for the
capture, at once took off for Crown Point, but contrary
winds held them up, and it was not until the next day that
the ruins of Amherst's great fort and its garrison of eleven
were taken. There were many more cannon here, but little
else. At about the same time another detachment of Allen's

men descended on Fort George at the head of the lake of that name, and it was seized without bloodshed. The British now had no hold on the Hudson-Champlain waterway south of St. Jean on the Richelieu River just north of the outlet of the lake.

Arnold's period of disgruntled inactivity was of short duration, for on the thirteenth Skene's schooner dropped anchor at Ticonderoga. The party that Allen had sent to Skenesboro from Castleton four days previously was on board, but much more important to Arnold were the recruits his officers had raised along the road from Boston. With the addition of these men Arnold now had about a hundred who would follow his orders, as well as a sailing ship, something of no use to the landlubbers of Vermont, but of the utmost value to an energetic man who once had sailed the seas.

Arnold fully appreciated the vital importance of the command of Lake Champlain, and all that stood between him and that command was a single sloop of the British King, then tied up at St. Jean. On 15 May he put some of his men in bateaux and headed north, leaving the schooner behind, presumably to improve its armament. They had the luck to capture a bateau carrying the mail south from Canada, and the catch included not only a British ensign but also a current list of the location of all the troops in Canada, only some seven hundred all told. The next day the schooner — later if not already named the *Liberty* — caught up with the bateaux, and Arnold climbed on board. But before long the wind dropped and the lake became a dead, flat calm, so the bateaux resumed the advance over the last thirty miles. By sunrise of 18 May the party was hidden in a mosquito-infested swamp only half a mile from St. Jean, while one man scouted ahead to spy on the village. There were only fourteen soldiers there, he reported, and the sloop's crew of seven. All quickly surrendered upon the appearance of Ar-

Marquis de Montcalm

Major General Philip Schuyler

Benedict Arnold

Major General St. Clair

Major General Horatio Gates

Major General John Burgoyne

Montcalm's victory

Montcalm congratulating his troops after the victory of 1758

Ethan Allen demands the surrender of Fort Ticonderoga

Air view of Fort Ticonderoga today

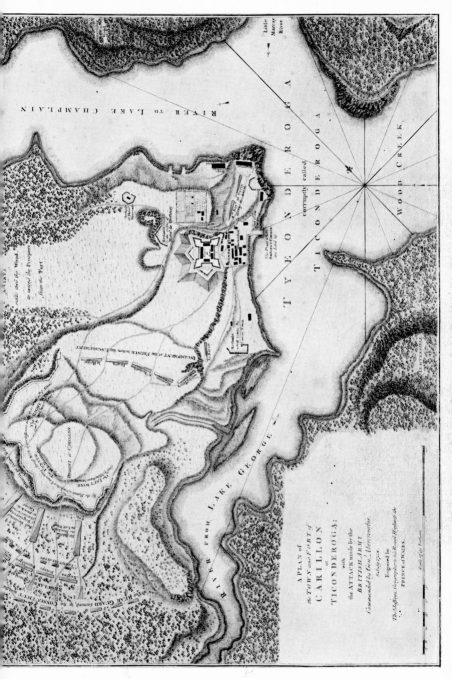

Map Fort Ticonderoga, 1758

Air view showing Lake George

nold's men. The vessel was a real prize, seventy tons in burden, almost sixty feet long, and armed with two brass 6-pounders, quite sizable guns. Within little more than a year this sloop, renamed the *Enterprise* and armed with twelve guns and a crew of fifty men, would take her place in the battle line at Valcour Island.

Arnold promptly loaded his little fleet with his men and his prisoners, taking along four bateaux he found at St. Jean and destroying five others. He put on board all the usable supplies of food and munitions that he could locate and set sail south for Ticonderoga. Not only did Arnold now have absolute command of the lake, but the British did not have a single boat that would float. Until the enemy could build a fleet sufficient to contest the waters of Champlain, it would remain an American lake.

As Arnold was working his way southward he suddenly sighted a fleet of four bateaux carrying Ethan Allen and ninety of his men. The Vermonter, probably not wishing to be outdone by Arnold, had been seized with the idea of occupying and holding St. Jean, a rather useless proceeding now that the Americans controlled the lake. The Green Mountain Boys must have come off in a great hurry, for they were much exhausted, ravenous and without rations. Arnold tried to dissuade Allen, telling him that to hold St. Jean was "a wild impracticable scheme, and provided it could be carried into execution, of no consequence, so long as we are masters of the lake, and of that I make no doubt, as I am determined to arm the sloop and schooner immediately." Allen stuck to his idea, and, after receiving some food from Arnold, continued north.

The Green Mountain Boys and their leader arrived at St. Jean without trouble, learned that a party of British troops was moving toward the village, and set out to ambush it. At the last moment, however, Allen's people lost courage and decamped, crossing the Richelieu River and then bedding down for the night. Next morning they were awakened by a volley of grapeshot from six British cannon, accompanied by musketry. They fled to their bateaux and escaped, leaving behind three of their number.

It is a bit difficult to decide which party should have been the more ashamed of its performance that morning, the Americans for allowing themselves to be caught unawares, or the British for their terrible marksmanship. The river was evidently between the two parties, but even this does not excuse the British artillerymen. Allen, who was loud in proclaiming his successes, had nothing to say about this adventure either in his reports to his various correspondents or in his later pamphlet. He did, however, write the Continental Congress: "Provided I had but five hundred men with me at St. Johns, when we took the King's sloop, I would have advanced to Montreal."

On 22 May, Allen's party was back at Crown Point, while Arnold was at Ticonderoga, but moving to the more northern fort the next day. Arnold now had about a hundred and fifty men under him, whereas Allen's men had been steadily drifting homeward. Within another week all the Green Mountain Boys were gone, and Allen no longer had any command at all.

By the end of May, Arnold was in unquestioned charge of the lake frontier. He had a hundred and fifty men at Crown Point, believing this to be the best place to make a defense against the counterattack he was momentarily expecting from Canada. He seems to have forgotten the enemy had no boats. He had armed his prizes, and with them he would hold the lake until the British should succeed in building a fleet at least as powerful as his. Arnold had moved ten mortars, howitzers and cannon to the head of Lake George for the use of the province of New York. The records do not tell us just what else he was doing the first half of June, but it is safe to assume, knowing his driving energetic personality, that he was furiously busy. Sometime during these spring days he worked up a plan for an attack on Canada. From the dispatches he had captured when on the way to St. Jean he knew the exact strength of the British regulars in Canada — about five hundred and fifty, allowing for those captured during the last few weeks — and he believed that an army of two thousand men could take all Canada. His plan was well thought out, and accompanied by a list of all the supplies needed. Had it been possible to send off an expedition as he specified that spring, it is quite probable that it would have succeeded. But it was neither possible nor considered desirable. Only a mob of undisciplined and untrained soldiers could have been assembled, and supplies of all sorts were practically unavailable. Moreover the patriot leaders were most conscious of the vital need of preserving the friendship of the Canadian people, and they feared that such an expedition might antagonize them.

Connecticut became nervous over its part in dispatching the nucleus of the expedition that took the fort and disclaimed all responsibility for the seizure, stating that it was done solely by private parties acting without authority. New York Province made a similar disclaimer. Late in May the Continental Congress decided to withdraw the guns to the head of Lake George and to abandon the forts, at the same time making a careful inventory of their contents so that all could be accounted for to the King when the present troubles were over. The thought of complete independence was still far from the minds of most men.

Southern New York was quite content with the abandonment of the lake forts, but Albany most certainly was not and protested volubly to the Congress. New England naturally felt the same way with its memories of invasions by French-

men and bloodthirsty Indians less than a score of years before. Connecticut did more than protest, for this province
early in June ordered Hinman's regiment to march to the
lake and reinforce the small garrison of Arnold's men who
still remained.

Meanwhile, Ethan, a leader without followers, went to
Philadelphia early in June to try to persuade Congress to
authorize a regiment of five hundred Green Mountain Boys.
This accomplished, he returned home to get the regiment
recruited, but when the officers were selected by a convention of Vermonters, Allen, to his great chagrin, was left out
entirely. He claimed that this was because the electors were
all older, more staid citizens, and not the younger, rowdy
crew he had led against Ticonderoga. Ethan next undertook
some unofficial scouting into Canada to try to learn the
feelings of the habitants. Finally in the fall, when the American army had moved down the lake and was besieging St.
Jean, he attempted a foolhardy attack on Montreal with a
party of Americans and French Canadians, mostly the latter,
who had been promised pay and plunder. Allen was captured
and taken to England. Later he was released but he never
again took any part in the Revolution.

And so a brilliant actor passes from the scene. His daring
capture of Ticonderoga was an act of great importance, but
one which he could never again approach. Schuyler doubted
his dependability, and after Allen's return from captivity
Washington did not see fit to give him employment. A great
historian of this period wrote of him: "brilliant, versatile and
headstrong [he] lacked steadiness." Perhaps so, but let us
always remember that it was he who first dared to take offensive action against the British King.

Congress gave heed to the pleas for retention of the forts,
and voted to put them under the jurisdiction of New York.
Meanwhile Hinman was marching his Connecticut regiment

northward, arriving at Ticonderoga about 17 June, while the battle of Bunker Hill was being fought at Boston. The problem of command now raised its ugly head again. Arnold had only some two hundred men, while Hinman had a thousand. At about this same time there arrived at the lake a committee from the Massachusetts Congress, charged with examining the situation at the captured forts. Whether or not they actually had the authority, they nevertheless proceeded to order Arnold to serve as second under Hinman, and that violent, egotistical and ambitious man blew up, vowing that he would serve under no man.

The story now becomes somewhat clouded, but of the utmost interest, because it seems to give us the first inkling of Arnold's ultimate treachery. The facts are scanty, perhaps reported with bias, but nevertheless they contain a hint of possible treachery. It is all based on Edward Mott's letter to the governor of Connecticut, written a week or two after the event (and we must remember that Mott was an adherent of Ethan Allen in the contest for command when the fort was taken). Undoubtedly Mott was a hostile witness, and, were it not for Arnold's great treachery at West Point years later, we perhaps should give his story no credence. After hearing the committee's directive Arnold resigned his commission in a rage and retired to the little fleet which was manned by his followers. A bit of a mutiny, or at least a threat of one against Hinman's men, followed. Somebody, we do not know whether it was Arnold, some of his men, or conceivably someone inspired by Arnold — "they" is all the report gives — threatened to sail away and take the boats back to the British. Was this an idle threat, or was the idea in Arnold's mind as a possible course of action? We shall never know, but this hint, intangible as it is, when coupled with the traitor's later action, cannot but make one wonder. In fairness to Arnold it must be noted that as yet there was no

real war with Britain, the provincials at this time were planning to account for all they had taken, and the act of returning the warships was really not treachery to the cause because
that cause was still intangible and in its infancy. Nevertheless the incident offers a fascinating hint as to what may have
been going on in Arnold's mind even at this early date.

The members of the Massachusetts committee attempted
to go on board the vessels, and some of Arnold's men fired off
a few swivels and some muskets at them. They probably fired
over their heads as a threat, for no one was hurt. Eventually
Mott, Judge Duer and two officers climbed into the ships,
and were promptly confined and closely guarded for most of
the day. Arnold apparently was no longer aboard, or perhaps
he was sulking in the cuddy. Anyway Mott tried to argue with
the crews and convince them that they were on the wrong
course. His arguments apparently met with some success, and
the prisoners were released by evening, unharmed.

Arnold now left the lake and headed back to Massachusetts to struggle over the settlement of his accounts, and
then, before many months had passed, to start on his famous
march through the Maine wilderness to Quebec. His men
either joined Hinman's regiment or went home, and all became quiet on the lake. The British had moved some four
hundred regulars to St. Jean and had started to build defenses there to prevent an American advance into Canada.
Neither side, however, chose to take the initiative.

The Continental Congress had at last assembled and gotten down to its work of organizing the rebellion. On 27
June General Philip Schuyler, an Albany patrician, was
ordered to the northern command. The orders given the new
major general were edged with "ifs" and left much to his
judgment. "Resolved, that if General Schuyler finds it practi-
cable, and that it will not be disagreeable to the Canadians,
he do immediately take possession of St. Johns, Montreal, and

any other parts of the country, and pursue any other measures in Canada, which may have a tendency to promote peace and security of these colonies."

A man of the highest character and of considerable ability, Schuyler was no stranger to the military life, for he had seen much service in the last French and Indian war. A captain at General William Johnson's defeat of von Dieskau in 1755, he had been with Bradstreet in the battle of the bateaux near the Oswego portage the next year. He was a staff supply officer with Abercromby in 1758 and with Bradstreet on the Frontenac expedition later that year, and ended the Seven Years War as a supply officer based in Albany. This was more, and more varied, service than many a British regular had seen. Schuyler had a high sense of duty, was free from jealousy and ambition, and was anxious to serve his country; but his health was poor, and he was sometimes leisurely in his actions, certainly in that respect not to be compared with the driving Arnold. His abilities may not have been of the highest, but what he had he gave to his country without stint, and asked for no reward.

At ten o'clock in the evening of 17 July Schuyler reached the head of the portage at the foot of Lake George to find only a single sentry on duty. The soldier left the general and went off to wake the rest of the guard, and Schuyler walked on until he met a second guard who allowed him to approach to close quarters, while the rest of the guard lay deep in slumber. "With a pen knife only I could have cut off both guards," he wrote Washington the next day. The following morning Schuyler received further unpleasant shocks when he found that Hinman's men, although they had been at the fort for a month, had done nothing. "No orders," said Hinman in explanation. Both forts were in ruinous condition, but the Connecticut colonel had not had sufficient initiative to undertake any repair work.

Schuyler was never to be a leader of men in battle. His fate was to remain in the rear as a planner and a provider of necessities for the fighting men. In this last capacity he was most effective, and this he proved once he had reached Lake Champlain. There was much to be done, forts to be repaired, hospitals established, wood to be cut and sawed for the boats that must be provided. Moreover, the relatively few troops on the lake were sick, half starved, without proper clothing and equipment, and almost on the edge of mutiny. Schuyler at once set to work, on the one hand constantly beseeching the authorities at Philadelphia for the essential supplies, and on the other making the most of what he already had on hand. The sawmills were put in shape, and preparations made for building vessels of larger size than bateaux. Tools, however, were in very short supply.

There were also many sick — a hundred men out of the total of five hundred stationed at Ticonderoga. Those who were healthy lacked shirts, shoes, underclothes, blankets, even muskets, but gradually conditions improved as July passed into August. By the middle of the latter month additional troops began to arrive — Waterbury's Connecticut regiment and the first four companies of New York troops. By now Schuyler's letters to the Continental Congress had taken on a more cheerful tone, although there were still great shortages of essentials. Early in August he had launched a sixty-foot flat-bottomed boat said to be capable of carrying nearly three hundred men, and with an armament of five 12-pounders. Soon a second such craft was in the lake, but due to a shortage of carpenter's tools, gun carriages could not be made, and only one of these new boats received its armament. Hospital arrangements were improved, and everyone became more cheerful. It was a real change from the discouraged and almost mutinous condition that had existed when Schuyler took command.

Late in August an unknown officer wrote home: "There is the greatest plenty of salt and fresh provisions here; the men have as much as they can use; a gill of rum and as much spruce beer as they can drink every day; so that they have no occasion to drink the lake water, it being reckoned very unhealthy." By now there were seventeen hundred men at Ticonderoga and another seven hundred at Crown Point. Bateaux were being put together at a great rate. It was time to think of starting the offensive against Canada.

The attitude of the French Canadians, of course, was of the greatest importance. Would they stand by the King, or would they take the American side? That was a question upon which much depended, for if any American advance into Canada should alienate the habitants, it would do great damage to the cause and might be fatal to any invasion. Rumors and reports had drifted south over the border, most of them to the effect that the French Canadian people, except for most of their noblesse and the clergy, favored the cause of the patriots. To seek confirmation, Schuyler shortly after his arrival dispatched John Brown to determine what he could of the military dispositions opposing an advance into Canada, as well as the feelings of the Canadian people. Accompanied by three men, Brown made an arduous journey northward, was discovered, pursued and nearly caught, but made his escape and returned safely to Crown Point, reporting that the Canadian habitants were generally favorable and would furnish supplies to the invaders. Further scouting parties kept Schuyler well informed of the British military preparations at St. Jean.

There was considerable intercourse back and forth over the border and from one source or another Schuyler had a pretty fair idea of the British strength and conditions. Most of the regulars were at St. Jean, probably well over four hundred of them, and they were busying themselves at putting up a stockaded fort and completing two vessels, the frames of which had been made at Chambly, knocked down and carted by the rapids and on to St. Jean for final assembly and planking. One of these would probably be finished before mid-August. It was reported to be fifty-two feet long on the keel and carrying sixteen guns. Then there were about one hundred regulars at Chambly, eighty at Quebec, and, report said, only a score at Montreal. But at the latter city Guy Johnson was believed to have five hundred of his Indians, a dubious factor, perhaps neutral, perhaps pro-British. The true feelings of the French Canadians were yet to be determined. Only an actual invasion could answer this most important question.

The two newly constructed British vessels now being completed at St. Jean, small as they were, could regain the command of Lake Champlain once they sailed into its waters. Schuyler fully realized this. If he could get in position on Isle aux Noix before these little warships could sail south, he could, by placing a boom across the Richelieu and planting cannon to cover it, prevent the British from entering the lake and retain for his own use the vital Champlain waterway. Thus the report of the near completion of the ships at St. Jean was a spur to expedite his advance northward.

Schuyler seems to have been somewhat dilatory in his actions that summer. He perhaps was over-patient with the shortcomings of his subordinates, for he was never the demanding, driving type of commander. His supplies were undoubtedly insufficient for an advance into Canada, and no such move could be made until a backlog of food and supplies had been accumulated. Despite such shortages outposts could easily and without material risk have been advanced farther north toward Canada. It is interesting to inquire why Schuyler did not take up some position farther down the lake than

Crown Point. With his command of the lake he could have safely established himself almost anywhere he wished. Both Ticonderoga and Crown Point were in a ruinous condition, but an excellent stone house, its walls pierced with over two score loopholes, was standing at Pointe au Fer, only thirty miles from British-held St. Jean. A little work of digging trenches or throwing up earthen embankments would have made this place into a strong outpost, one which could have kept closely in touch with both the Canadian habitants and with British activities at St. Jean. Or Schuyler could equally well have occupied Isle aux Noix in the Richelieu River, still closer to the future scene of action.

By the end of August there were enough supplies at the two forts for the seventeen hundred soldiers assembled there, and Schuyler decided to start his move northward. His able second in command, Brigadier General Richard Montgomery, a former officer in the British army, started down the lake with a force of twelve hundred men and four 12-pound cannon to take a temporary station at Isle aux Noix prior to an assault on St. Jean. The island was only about a dozen miles south of the British post. Schuyler followed shortly with the rest of the army, reaching there on 4 September. The Americans made their base at Isle aux Noix, put a boom across the river and placed artillery to cover it. The effective army consisted now of but some one thousand men. On 6 September an advance was made against St. Jean but no attack was undertaken, although a minor skirmish developed, followed by a withdrawal to the island. Soon another seven hundred were added to the invading army, and an unsuccessful attempt was made to cut off the communications of St. Jean with Montreal. Many of the Americans had become sick, including Schuyler, who at last on 16 September was forced to give in, and be carried back to Ticonderoga.

This left Montgomery in command. The short and unsuccessful foray against St. Jean was to be Schuyler's only active military service in the Revolution.

The day after Schuyler's departure Montgomery successfully invested St. Jean, and started a siege which was to continue for six weeks before the post fell. The fort at Chambly, well to the north, surrendered its pitifully small garrison some two weeks earlier. The fall of these two places left the road open to Montreal, and that city surrendered on 13 November, but General Carleton, the Canadian governor, managed to escape just before the capitulation. And so the western assault on Canada succeeded with the fall of one of the only two important cities in the land. The eastern attack, that of Benedict Arnold up the Kennebec and over the mountain chain between Maine and Canada, by this time had stalled in front of Quebec, and was to remain so until Montgomery brought reinforcements to its aid. Then, on the last day of 1775, the Americans attacked the city during a blinding snowstorm, failed and fell back with Montgomery dead and Arnold wounded.

Ticonderoga Becomes the Northern Bastion

LITTLE IS KNOWN of the happenings at Ticonderoga that winter of 1775-1776. The war had moved north from the old French fort, and for the next few months Ticonderoga was to become a backwater, a point on the line of communication to Canada, garrisoned by only a few dozen men at most. Schuyler was there in November, building heavy sleds to move cannon or ship timbers. Homesick soldiers drifted back from Canada, claiming various illnesses and disabilities which would justify their discharge. Schuyler noted that it was amazing how once released from service they perked up; nine times out of ten the invalids at once made a complete recovery and started briskly on the homeward trail.

Late in November all the vessels were assembled at Ticonderoga, two schooners, a row galley and the sloop *Enterprise*, so poorly designed and built that she could never work up to windward and was practically unmanageable. Late in November Congress sent a committee, consisting of Robert Treat Paine, John Langdon and Robert Livingston, up to the lake to look the situation over. They advised the abandonment of Crown Point and concentration of all activities at Ticonderoga.

Meanwhile the Continental Congress had directed Henry

Knox, Washington's artillery officer at Cambridge, to proceed to New York, survey the cannon there and send on to
Boston anything that would be of service. He then was to
continue on to Ticonderoga, assemble as many heavy pieces
of ordnance as possible and take them to Boston — a large
order in view of the existing roads and the time of year. A
contemporary of the former bookseller was reported to have
said that he had never elsewhere seen such an ox of a man —
a few years later he weighed 280 pounds — but he could
move fast and could get things done. Knox quickly accomplished his mission in New York, noting in his journal that
it was a most expensive place to live in, and started north,
reaching Lake George in the first week of December. He
found the Ticonderoga garrison so very small that he was
barely able to sort out the guns and get the best of them
down to the landing on Lake Champlain. There the mortars
and cannon were loaded on barges and bateaux and ferried
the couple of miles around to the foot of the portage. Knox
had selected fourteen mortars, ranging in size from 4½
inches to 13, two 8-inch howitzers and forty-three cannon,
from 3- to 24-pounders. These fifty-nine pieces had a combined weight of sixty tons, perhaps not much in our day of
bulldozers and huge trucks, but a vast weight in those days of
practically no roads, of oxen and manpower.

Knox somehow managed to haul these great pieces of iron
and bronze up the steep portage trail to Lake George and got
them on board various barges, bateaux and a petiauger. The
lake was already partly frozen and they had to cut a channel
about a mile long through the ice. One trip up Lake George
was completed without too much trouble, but a great scow
carrying three mortars and some cannon ran onto a sub-
merged rock and could not be freed. They tried to haul it off,
but the ropes broke. Heavier ones were secured from the fort

and the scow at last came clear. It then sailed on to Sabbath Day Point, where a heavy wind raised waves which swamped the heavily loaded craft. This fortunately occurred in shallow water, and the scow was bailed out, the cargo shifted a little, and the journey resumed. At last all safely arrived at the head of Lake George, where they found a few more guns, sent there by Benedict Arnold in the spring of 1775.

Recourse then had to be made to heavy sleds. Knox proceeded to order these procured, along with yokes of oxen to haul them. Meanwhile he was forced to wait for a snowstorm, for, while the roads were snow-covered as far as Saratoga, beyond that village the ground was nearly bare. The cannon had reached Fort George at the head of the lake on 17 December, a month after Knox had been given his assignment. He had done well, but now the weather would largely determine his further progress. Here we can leave him impatiently waiting for a blizzard, which when it finally came was so heavy that Knox was forced during one part of his journey to struggle on foot through three feet of new-fallen snow. Weeks later, after much toil and struggle, the guns safely arrived in Boston, all except one that was lost through the ice near Half Moon on the Mohawk, endured many vicissitudes and eventually returned to Fort Ticonderoga. There it now lies in company with half of a split 13-inch mortar which also made that winter journey down the Hudson and across the rugged Berkshire hills.

A letter from Schuyler to the Continental Congress tells us that Ticonderoga was almost without troops that Christmas of 1775. What men were there most certainly were devoting almost all their time to cutting the firewood necessary to maintain life in the dilapidated stone barracks, while winter howled outside. Early in February Schuyler was trying to get out timber for repair work at the fort and at the same time he was building bateaux at the head of Lake

George. By spring a hundred had been nailed together but there was a shortage of oakum for caulking, and only thirty-five were finished.

Meanwhile, far to the north in Canada, Arnold, recuperating from the wound he had received in his unsuccessful attack of 31 December 1775, was continuing his siege of Quebec. It was a siege in name only, for at times he had fewer men than had the British defenders; and even more important, he lacked the heavy cannon essential to breaching the defenses of so strongly fortified a city. The Americans had a force of only some seventeen hundred men by the winter's end, as well as nearly eight hundred sick. By late April reinforcements had passed by Ticonderoga and moved down the St. Lawrence to bring Arnold's force up to twenty-five hundred, but he was still woefully short of cannon, powder and shot.

Britain's humane and understanding treatment of conquered Canada was a major achievement. It was the result of the thought and the work of two great soldier-administrators, James Murray, who had been one of Wolfe's brigadiers at Quebec in 1759, and his successor, Guy Carleton, later to be Lord Dorchester. Murray was removed as governor after several years of wise and considerate rule, largely through the maneuvers of a clique of British-born Canadian traders, a class the governor could neither understand nor endure. Carleton carried on the work, and it was he who a few years later largely shaped and pushed through Parliament the Quebec Act, which went far toward conciliating the population of Canada and restraining that province from joining the rebellion.

After the conquest and the Peace of 1763, a large number of Canada's so-called "noblesse" — "gentry" is a better word — returned to France, and all feudal duties formerly owed by the habitant were abolished. Peace reigned, military service was no longer required, a sound currency replaced the fiat card money of the French regime, and taxes became appreciably less. So great was the resulting prosperity and so much greater was the freedom now enjoyed by the Canadian habitant that he became a little spoiled. And so, when he was asked by both the British and the Americans to take up arms for their respective causes, he shied away and preferred to sit the struggle out. What was left of the "noblesse" and the clergy largely favored the cause of Britain, but both these classes had lost their hold on the people and so could accomplish almost nothing. Both sides succeeded in raising a few Canadian troops, but they were of small importance.

Canadian support was essential to any continued occupation of Canada. The habitant was delighted to sell supplies for hard money, but he wisely spurned the colonial paper currency. Two things were needed to secure and hold the Canadian habitant: silver or gold coin and the capture of Quebec. Unless both were forthcoming the Canadian adventure was doomed to failure. The Americans could not produce the hard money, nor could Arnold take Quebec with the facilities at his command. And so Canada was lost.

News of the invasion of Canada must have reached London at least by early October of 1775. That summer and fall the question of the revolt of the American colonies was being argued at length in Parliament, where America was not without friends. King George — and one can hardly blame him — was all for stringent action against the rebels, but he had considerable opposition to overcome, and was forced to reshuffle his Cabinet in order to make it more amenable to his will. Shortly before Christmas he was successful, and the war party was in full control. Early in January of 1776 a relief expedition was being planned for Canada, but due to the ice in the St. Lawrence it could not sail before mid-February at best.

The American army in Canada by early May of 1776 was a little over two thousand strong, with an additional twelve hundred sick, mostly suffering from smallpox. On the sixth of this month the first of the British relief troops reached the Quebec basin, and Arnold immediately raised the siege and fell back to Montreal. It was now quite obvious to all that Canada must be abandoned, the only question was how far the invading army must retreat. An attempt was made to hold Sorel, the town at the mouth of the Richelieu River, the outlet of Lake Champlain. American reinforcements continued to move northward over the border, only to contract smallpox themselves and thus add to the burden of the sick. Early in June the Americans were still trying to hold in the valley of the Richelieu. Their army amounted to 6241 in all, but only 3591 were fit for duty; smallpox and dysentery had claimed most of the rest. A contemporary report stated that some regiments "were all down with the small pox . . . not a single man fit for duty . . . sick, ragged, undisciplined, and unofficered." Three thousand men were reported sick at Chambly in early June. An added problem was that of inoculation. Vaccination for smallpox was still a generation in the future, but years before it had been found that by infecting oneself with matter from someone suffering from smallpox, preferably a mild case, one would catch the disease in a relatively innocuous form and acquire a future immunity. There was almost no risk, merely the inconvenience of being mildly sick for a couple of weeks or so, but the soldier was just as much on the sick list as if he had a real case of the pox.

The army command issued stringent orders against inoculation, but fear of smallpox was more powerful than fear of punishment, and many of the troops engaged in the practice. Whole regiments were out of action at times. And so the natural spread of the disease plus the results of self-inoculation of many of the newly arrived troops rendered the army on the borders of Canada incapable of effective action even on the defensive.

Russell Dewey came from western Massachusetts, and in March he got inoculated. His diary at this time recorded: "Nothing remarcable hapned except hungry men for we being a fixing for the small pox might not eat nor drink anything except bread and water that is we could not get anything else to eat. . . . The snow flu and winds was so high that we was affraid to go out a dore for fear we should be blowed away for our preparation brought us so low that we were almost as light as eagles."

Food was always poor and in short supply. Captain John Lacey of Wayne's Pennsylvania regiment, the son of a man who owned gristmills, wrote that the meal they were given was as coarsely ground as that milled for hogs at home and all the bran was left in it. The salt pork was miserable stuff. The soldiers would slice it up and warm it in a frying pan until all the grease was tried out. Then they threw the pork away, poured their meal into the grease and cooked it for a while. The result, Lacey wrote, was a rich and palatable cake. The only trouble was that there was never enough of it to satisfy the pangs of hunger.

By mid-June all hope of holding any part of the northern province was abandoned, and the retreat southward commenced, first to Isle aux Noix, where sickness spread rapidly in the low, humid, steaming atmosphere of the island, totally lacking in any shelter for the sick. Here, for example, in one so-called regiment of 138 men, 60 came down with smallpox in the course of only two days. In another regiment only five men remained fit for duty.

One must not think that smallpox was necessarily fatal;

on the contrary, the great majority recovered. Captain
Charles Cushing, for instance, took a company of 76 into
Canada and brought them all back again, although 74 had
smallpox while there. During two weeks in July 1497 pa-
tients entered the base hospital on Lake George, but there
were only 51 deaths during the period. The percentage, of
course, would be materially higher at a place like Isle
aux Noix where there were no facilities for caring for the
sick. Even if the fatalities were not too great, the sick were
completely out of action, and the transportation of these
unhappy people to the rear and the provision of reasonably
adequate care for them imposed a heavy burden on the
army. As fast as possible the sick were evacuated south to
Crown Point, and to the large hospital established at the
head of Lake George. The remains of the Canadian expedition reached Crown Point on the first day of July, after
tarrying a bit at Isle La Motte while on the way south. Here
all the sick still remained, and conditions were chaotic.

John Trumbull, son of the governor of Connecticut, was a
most brilliant young man, who as a child of six could read
Greek. He graduated from Harvard at seventeen, and became a painter of considerable merit, famous for his paint-
ings recording the men and the events of the Revolution.
He had, however, a most exalted opinion of his abilities and
certainly made no attempt to hide his virtues. When twenty
years and nine months old he scornfully refused to accept
from the Continental Congress a commission as full colonel
because he did not like the date of rank assigned him. Up
to this time he had given excellent service to the cause but
on account of this quibble he quit the army early in 1777
and went to England to paint. He was, however, a good and
honest reporter of what he saw, and fortunately for history
he wrote his father about the conditions existing at Crown
Point in mid-July of 1776:

At this place I found not an army but a mob, the shattered remains of twelve or fifteen very fine battalions, ruined by sickness, fatigue, and desertion, and void of every idea of discipline or subordination. . . . Last spring there were ten battalions, amounting to about six thousand four hundred men, sent from New York to join this army; there were then here two battalions of Pennsylvanians, three from New England, and one or two from Jersey, all of them strong and amounting to at least four thousand men more, which, joined with the others, make the army upwards of ten thousand strong. We now have three thousand sick, and about the same number well; this leaves near five thousand men to be accounted for. Of these, the enemy has cost us perhaps one, sickness another thousand, and the others, God alone knows in what manner they are disposed of. Among the few we have remaining, there is neither order, subordination, nor harmony; the officers as well as men of one colony, insulting and quarreling with those of another.

There was another reporter of conditions at Crown Point at this time, and a rather bitter and sarcastic one he was. Dr. Lewis Beebe had been a classmate of John Brown at Yale, and he had married Ethan Allen's sister Lucy. Naturally he detested Benedict Arnold, and as early as May of 1776 called him a traitor, probably without any justification beyond hatred. Dr. Beebe wrote that there had been "not the least preparation for fortifying the garrison, which has tumbled to ruin & decay. The generals have their hands full in riding about the camp — prancing their gay horses, the field officers set much of their time upon court martials. The captains & subs may generally be found at the grog shops, the soldiers either sleeping swiming, fishing, or cursing and swearing most generally the latter."

Even so stalwart a soldier as the engineer Lieutenant Colonel Jeduthan Baldwin was thoroughly disgusted with conditions in the army this July. In his journal he recorded that he had had enough of "this retreating, raged, starved, lousey, thievish, pockey army in this unhealthy country." He stuck it out nevertheless and continued as an engineer officer throughout the Revolution.

General Schuyler, acting essentially as a provider of supplies since illness had forced his retirement from the front, had meanwhile been busily building additional watercraft to carry the reinforcements and supplies down Champlain to Canada. He estimated that to feed the Northern Army 120 barrels of pork and flour must move out of Albany each day. This meant that nearly a dozen bateaux must start up the Hudson daily to Half Moon, the Waterford of today, there to transfer their freight to ox teams for the next leg of the long journey north to Canada. Wagoners unfortunately remembered the old trick they had learned in the last of the colonial wars of lightening their load by drilling a hole in the pork barrels, letting the brine drain out to the detriment of the pork. Unless the roads had greatly improved since the fall of Canada in 1760, these provisions would have to be shifted from boat to team and back again until each separate barrel had been manhandled five and possibly six times before it reached the waters of Lake Champlain. Then there was a straight water route to Canada until the rapids of the Richelieu below St. Jean were reached. Here the bateaux could at times pass while still fully loaded.

By the latter part of May, Schuyler, although still diligently forwarding supplies to Canada, realized that it was time to think of defensive measures, and on the last day of the month he sent thirty carpenters, who had been building bateaux on Lake George, to Skenesboro, today's Whitehall, to start work on gondolas. These were flat-bottomed, sharpended craft, not unlike great bateaux, but more heavily built and of relatively shallow depth. Schuyler had built two of these the year before, each sixty feet long. The defenses at Ticonderoga were still in terrible condition, as were those at Crown Point, but shortage of men prevented any attempt at repairs until as late as mid-June, although by then it was quite obvious that the Canadian attempt had failed, and that it was now a matter of resisting an invading British army.

Both Crown Point and Ticonderoga had originally been selected by the French as defenses against attackers advancing from the south. Now conditions were reversed, and the Americans must hold these points against an advance from the opposite direction. Crown Point lies on the tip of a peninusla which extends to the north at a place where Lake Champlain narrows into what almost appears to be a river — in fact the French called it one. Nothing could pass along the lake by the fort without grave risk. The bay on the western side of the peninsula, however, is quite wide and vessels could pass by the fort practically beyond range of its cannon and sail on south to the end of the bay. Troops and guns could be landed in rear of the defenses, thus cutting Crown Point off from communications with its southern base.

Schuyler quickly grasped this most important point, and decided to abandon the more northern fort and make his stand at Ticonderoga. An additional reason for his decision was the terrible condition of the fort. "The ramparts are tumbled down, the casemates are fallen in, the barracks burnt, and the whole a perfect ruin, that it would take five times the men of our army, for several summers, to put it in defensible repair." So General Gates reported once he had visited the place. Although his generals endorsed the position Schuyler had taken, the field officers of the regiments made voluble protest and signed a round robin letter opposing the withdrawal, claiming that it would leave New England open to attack from the Champlain Valley. News of the protest reached Washington, and he wrote Schuyler a rather sharp letter, criticizing his decision to abandon Crown Point. Schuyler had already given proof of his devotion to the cause, of his selfless attention to his duty, of his freedom from jealousy and of his ability in the field of logistics, and his reply to Washington reveals him as a sound military thinker. He wrote of the inherent weakness of the northern fort against a British advance, and then went on to say that he only wished that an invading army would leave Champlain and try to cut through the Green Mountains into the frontiers of New England. Just let them get a score or so of miles into the mountains, he wrote, and then turn light infantry loose after them. From his logistical experience and from his service in the last French war he well knew the practical impossibility of moving men and supplies through the mountains, particularly when harassed and chivied by fast-moving irregular troops.

Schuyler showed his foresight in another way, and time was to prove him right. He realized that eventually it might be necessary to abandon Fort Ticonderoga and to fall back on to some position farther to the south, such as Fort Edward. Then, he wrote, the British advance would be greatly hampered by the difficulty in moving their supplies over the Skenesboro-Fort Edward portage. He included a calculation of just how many two-wheeled carts, the largest he believed that could be brought down from Canada, would be needed to carry the barrels of rations and how long they would take to make the trip between the Champlain and the Hudson waterways.

General Thomas, commander of the invading army, had died from smallpox at Chambly during the retreat from Canada, and the Congress appointed General Horatio Gates to succeed to the command of the Northern Army. Gates's service during the latter part of the Revolution could hardly be called distinguished, but this was more the result of existing conditions than of incapacity on his part. His suspected but unproved involvement in the Conway cabal, which attempted to oust Washington, put another black mark against his name, and the result was that historians have been loath to appreciate his many good qualities. An ex-officer of the British army who had seen considerable colonial service — he had been badly wounded at Braddock's defeat — he was a capable administrator, and as such was what the defeated, disheartened and debilitated soldiers of the Northern Army needed in this summer of 1776.

On the first day of July Gates took over his new command at Crown Point, and he did not like what he saw. Later he wrote Governor Trumbull of Connecticut: "Upon my first joining the troops (or rather the hospital) at Crown Point, all was in the utmost disorder — the pestilence raging, not a cannon mounted, the vessels lumbered with stores, the men dispirited with defeat and fatigue, and, in short, the whole a scene variegated with every distress and disappointment that could conspire to ruin an army." Gates at once got to work, sent all the sick off to the base hospital, and all the vessels then on the lake went back for a refit. Meanwhile the rest of the army moved to Ticonderoga in accordance with Schuyler's orders. The greatest of care was taken to prevent any reintroduction of smallpox.

Despite repeated orders, many of the reinforcements headed for the lake stopped on the way for an inoculation, and in at least one case the senior officers of a regiment stopped off at Williamstown for such treatment, sending the regiment on ahead under the captains. Whenever cases of inoculation were discovered or suspected the men were held in quarantine before they were allowed to join the healthy troops. A large party of desperately needed ship's carpenters stopped on the way north for inoculation. Such men were very hard to come by, and many were needed at Skenesboro to push on the completion of the fleet. Nevertheless, as soon as headquarters learned of this, the carpenters' pay was stopped, and they were ordered to return home at their own expense. By such stringent measures smallpox was at last gotten under control, and one of the greatest threats to the Northern Army practically eliminated.

Another cause of trouble was the question of command. Schuyler in Albany commanded the northern region, while Thomas had been the head of the army in Canada. Gates, as the successor of Thomas, now believed that he was in command of all the Northern Army, while Schuyler, feeling that Gates's command existed only while the army was in Canada, was certain that he was. Although they disagreed, both men were big enough to prevent any damage to the cause, and they worked in relative harmony until the Congress upheld Schuyler, and Gates became his subordinate. Schuyler, however, continued as a commander in the rear; he was, moreover, responsible for the western frontier along the Mohawk, where trouble was brewing. Gates meanwhile was in active command of the troops, where his undoubted administrative ability soon began to produce results. Conditions greatly improved, due, said one who was there, to rest, fresh meat and rum. In mid-July, for instance, Colonel Mathew Ogden's regiment had only eighty men fit for duty, while ten days later convalescents had raised the figure to three times as many.

Despite improved conditions, the camp at Ticonderoga could not have been too pleasant a place, according to reports that have survived. Colonel Anthony Wayne commanded the 4th Pennsylvania that summer and he wrote a friend: "[Ticonderoga] appears to be the last part of the world that God made & I have some ground to believe it was finished in the dark. . . . I believe it to be the ancient Golgotha or place of skulls — they are so plenty here that our people for want of other vessels drink out of them whilst the soldiers make tent pins of the shin and thigh bones of Abercrombies men. . . ."

Ticonderoga and its old French fort could not be considered safe against a determined attack from the north, for, just as was the case at Crown Point, an aggressive enemy could bypass the fort and cut off its rearward communication which was, practically speaking, only by water either to Skenesboro or up Lake George. On the east side of Lake Champlain at Ticonderoga there was, however, a rugged promontory of about the same height as the headland upon which stood the old stone fortress. This point of land, soon to be called Mount Independence, offered many advantages as a strong point to halt a British advance. It commanded the passage through the lake as well or even better than did the old fort, and had a considerable plateau on its top suitable for a campsite. It was surrounded to the west and north by deep water, and to the east by a creek and a swamp of considerable extent. Only at its rear or southern end did a neck of land tie it to the eastern shore and a safe land route to Skenesboro and the villages of the Hampshire Grants. Here then was a place which could be strongly held, but one from which a safe withdrawal could be made if the position had to be abandoned. The decision was made to fortify Mount Independence and to make a stand against the expected British advance on both sides of the lake. Work was commenced on the eastern headland on 11 July 1776.

It was at about this time that Colonel Joseph Wait reported that the Northern Army had "generals without men, and a small artillery without supplies, and commissaries without provisions, pay masters without money, and quartermasters without stores, and physicians without medicines." Gates's competent hands were busily at work remedying these conditions, and even when this was written they had taken a turn for the better. Every morning at beat of drum all stood at their alarm posts until it was daylight; then they were drilled at the manual of arms until breakfast, after which came fatigue, mostly work on the fortifications. A considerable advance guard garrison was still kept at Crown Point, and there were small outposts at Jericho and Colchester Point in the Hampshire Grants, with another at the White House at Pointe au Fer which Schuyler had failed to utilize the previous year. Now it was entrenched and supplied with cannon, and, since a swamp made the place practically an island, it furnished a strong outpost against an enemy advance. Despite all these endeavors on land, it was clearly realized that the British could approach Ticonderoga only by water, and that it was of the utmost importance to continue to hold command of the waters of Lake Champlain.

Britain Wins the Lake, Too Late

T HE GREAT QUESTION to be solved in this summer of 1776 was who was to control the waters of Lake Champlain. A British army was poised on the northern border, but it would not dare advance southward through the wilderness unless its only highway, the waters of the lake, could be made safe for its passage. Far to the south at Skenesboro the Americans were striving to build a fleet, adding to the nucleus on which the farsighted Schuyler had started work in the spring, when he was among the first to realize that the Canadian adventure had failed. The British, on their part, equally well appreciated that they must control the lake if they were to achieve any advance during this campaign. And so the shipbuilding race got under way at opposite ends of Lake Champlain.

The American shipyard was at Skenesboro where Wood Creek enters the southern end of Champlain. Two sawmills in the vicinity were a decided asset, and there was ample wood at hand, even if it must be sawed and spiked in place while still green. Schuyler had sent thirty carpenters there at the end of May, and within some three weeks they had completed one gondola and had a second nearly planked. These craft were flat-bottomed and had relatively low sides, carrying one cannon fixed at the bow. The boat itself was shifted to aim this bow gun, a 12-pounder carrying a ball four and a half inches in diameter. The other two somewhat lighter guns, one on each side, were mounted on the usual naval carriages. A single mast carried a square mainsail and a topsail. These vessels were only expected to sail before the wind, certainly not to beat up against it, and otherwise were rowed by long sweeps. Gondolas were easily and quickly built and carried considerable firepower for their size, with small swivel guns in their bulwarks supplementing the fire of their cannon.

Scouts and spies brought news of British actions at frequent intervals. Early in July it was reported that they were building three sloops and a schooner with a dozen guns. Next came word that Carleton was hauling warships from the St. Lawrence overland by the Chambly rapids. Fortunately this undertaking failed. The British made the attempt with rollers under the vessels, but the soft ground and the round bottoms of the hulls conspired to defeat the operation except in the case of the 30-ton flat-bottomed gondola *Loyal Convert,* captured recently from the Americans at the relief of Quebec. And so it was found necessary to take the three largest vessels, a ship-rigged sloop and two schooners, to pieces, carry the components to St. Jean and then reassemble them there, a time-consuming operation when speed was the essence of the campaign.

Skenesboro became a hive of activity. Ship's carpenters and woodcutters poured into the unhealthy settlement, battled the humid heat and mosquitoes, shouted constantly for more rum, and fell sick with fevers and dysentery. But they built the little warships. By the end of the third week in July four gondolas had been finished and sent away to Ticonderoga for rigging and equipping. The news from the north, however, showed that there was need for more than gondolas if the British ship and the schooners were to be contained. Row galleys, so called, had been built for the defense of Philadelphia, and requisition was made for someone from that region who was familiar with their construction to come to the lake. Such a man, however, was not forthcoming and there apparently was no connection between the Delaware River galleys and those built at Skenesboro. The latter were sizable round-bottomed craft, some seventy feet long, with an ample hold, a gun deck and quarterdeck, armed with eight or ten fairly heavy guns and several swivels, and carrying a crew of eighty men. Their twin masts each carried a triangular lateen sail, a type of sail not usually associated with our waters. This rig had, however, been in some use along our coasts for years, and the French had lateen-sailed chebecs on both Lake Champlain and Lake Ontario during the Seven Years War. The galleys, as their name implies, could also be rowed when necessary, but their hulls had good lines, as can be seen from drawings preserved in the British Admiralty, and they must have been able ships when under sail. The first of them was started by mid-July, and two others rapidly followed. They took considerably longer to build than did the gondolas but were well worth it. They were the battleships of Arnold's fleet. In addition to this new construction the Americans had various sloops and schooners, three of them captured the previous year and one built at Ticonderoga, probably from a keel and ribs abandoned at St. Jean by the British.

The southern end of Lake Champlain was not a pleasant place that summer. High hills shut out any cooling breezes, and the low swampy land harbored untold hosts of hungry mosquitoes. These pests were famous. George Washington, who visited Skenesboro after the Revolution, once told an acquaintance that he had never been so much annoyed by mosquitoes in any part of America as he was in this dismal hamlet. It was, however, a strategic location for the shipyard, on deep water at the northern end of the portage from the Hudson, and it had an iron forge in addition to one of the two sawmills of the neighborhood. These mills had all been built a few years before by Philip Skene, the proprietor of the regional land patent. The other sawmill was about a mile northwest of Fort Anne at a place called Cheshire's. After the American retreat from Ticonderoga in 1777 Lieutenant Anburey of the 29th Regiment made a delightful sketch of the mill and the blockhouse that had been built to guard it. Shortly thereafter American scouts sneaked back and burned both structures. (Various mills followed John Cheshire's sawmill until in modern times a hydroelectric plant was built there. Now even this last undertaking has been scrapped and the waters of that branch of Wood Creek fall free as they cascade over a forty-foot rock precipice, exactly as they did when Anburey made his sketch of the falls 185 years ago.)

The Skenesboro shipyard was fortunate in having the sawmills to rip out the planks for the sides of the vessels and the forge to turn out the necessary ironwork, but there were other serious shortages. Skilled shipwrights were scarce, and most of them were more interested in getting high pay for building privateers along the seacoast. They had little desire for the hardships of the frontier where they must work in the wilderness under primitive conditions for uncertain pay, and that in the depreciated "continentals." Most probably insisted on being paid in hard money. Many of the men that could be persuaded to go to Skenesboro soon went on the sick list. Supplies of all sorts, from food to the blocks and cordage needed for rigging, were short at all times. There was, however, one thing which was readily available and for which there was a constant cry from the workers. That was rum, and anyone sweating out his daily stint in that stinking, humid, mosquito-infested swamp certainly deserved his daily dram. General David Waterbury, the excellent officer in charge at Skenesboro that summer, saw that they got it.

As fast as the vessels were launched they were rowed, riding high and clumsy without their ballast and guns, to Ticonderoga, where the empty hulls were rigged, equipped and armed. Then they were dispatched down the lake to be added to the fleet that was assembling in the vicinity of Crown Point. The New England regiments could produce a considerable number of sailors to form a nucleus for their crews, and soldiers were drafted to complete them.

Meanwhile the British were not idle on the Richelieu. Spies brought back conflicting reports to Ticonderoga, but all agreed that there was great activity at the shipyard at St. Jean. Ten small gunboats had been brought from England in knocked-down form, and they were quickly assembled, while countless bateaux to carry the soldiers and supplies were being built or brought up from the St. Lawrence and hauled by the Chambly rapids on wagons. The ship-rigged *Inflexible*, carrying eighteen 12-pound guns, was the backbone of the British fleet, combining as she did both fire-power and maneuverability. She was far from being a large vessel, only 180 tons in burden, some eighty-five feet long on her deck. There was also the ponderous radeau with even more and heavier guns, some of them great 24-pounders. This strange craft was built like a gigantic scow, ninety-two feet long overall and thirty-three feet wide. She was nearly seven feet deep, keel to deck, and carried massive bulwarks pierced by ports for her guns. There was a small quarterdeck and a cabin. Manned by a crew of nearly three hundred, she was huge, unwieldy and clumsy. Two masts carried her great sails, but in calm weather or when the breeze was light she was kedged along, an anchor being taken a cable's length ahead in a longboat and dropped. Then the radeau was hauled up to the anchor by her windlass, and the process repeated. If there was a good wind in the right direction the craft could make amazing speed under sail (she was once reported to have covered ninety miles in nine hours, but this is somewhat hard to believe). Once this great floating fortress could be brought within close range of an enemy ship, it could wreak tremendous damage with its heavy guns served by its immense crew. The problem was to get it where it was wanted.

Another decided advantage enjoyed by the British was their warships in the St. Lawrence. Supplies, equipment and veteran sailors had only to be brought up the Richelieu as they were needed to equip and man the growing fleet. The *Inflexible* was the last to be completed, but her reassembly was done in record time: twenty-eight days from the laying of her keel she was ready to set sail. In addition to the *Inflexible*, the schooners *Carleton* and *Maria* and the radeau *Thunderer*, the fleet included a score or more of gunboats, each with one good-sized cannon firing over its bow, and with a crew of a dozen gunners, ten sailors, and an artillery officer in command. Early in October all was ready and waiting on a favorable wind from the north.

Meanwhile at Ticonderoga the garrison had been doing its best to repair and to extend the fortifications of the place. But its best was not very good, and the work progressed all too slowly, particularly on Mount Independence. Toward the end of August General Gates had an army of sixty-four hundred men fit for duty with almost two thousand more on sick report. Work had been started on the Vermont shore by mid-July. A battery of about two dozen guns was placed behind an earthen parapet just above the level of the lake on the extreme tip of the peninsula, and a second horseshoe-shaped battery was constructed farther up the hill. Advanced posts were maintained to prevent surprise, one at the White House at Pointe au Fer, another in the vicinity of present-day Burlington, Vermont. Colonel Thomas Hartley's regiment was posted at Crown Point, where the colonel went vigorously to work fortifying the place and planning to make real resistance to any enemy advance. Such action was entirely opposed to the wishes of General Gates, who reiterated instructions to Hartley that he must withdraw when the enemy should appear in force. A company of Stockbridge Indians arrived at Ticonderoga in mid-September, presumably intended for use as scouts. They all wore red and blue caps to distinguish them from the Indians of the British.

Ensign Bayze Wells of Farmington in Connecticut served on board the gondola *Providence* and kept a journal of his activities, a journal more interesting than most, although replete with outlandish spelling and weird grammar. He tells of an accident of a kind all too common in the days of muzzle-loaders. While stationed near Ticonderoga early in August, the gondola was ordered to try out its cannon. One was fired. "[Then] they spunged the bow gun and put in the cartritch one Solomon Dyer who served spung went to ram down the cartritch there being fire in the gun [a spark still smoldering in the bore] it went off while he was standing before the mouth of the cannon which blew both his hands & one nee almost of and likewise the spung rod part or all of it went through the left part of his body at the root of his arm blew him overboard we could not find him until 7th [Aug.] he rose and floted we took him up and buried him decently."

A few days later the fleet's commander, Colonel Jacob Wynkoop, looking north down the lake saw the white sails of a British flotilla approaching. He at once summoned all captains to a council of war, whereupon one of them, enjoying better eyesight than Wynkoop, borrowed a telescope and discovered the sails to be a flock of white seagulls!

The American fleet had been gradually assembling at Crown Point, as each newly built gondola was equipped and sent north from Ticonderoga. Colonel Wynkoop remained in command until mid-August when Benedict Arnold arrived to replace him. Without bothering to notify Wynkoop of the change in command, Arnold at once ordered two of the schooners to sail down the lake to reconnoiter and to furnish protection to a party of men making oars. When the vessels set their sails, Wynkoop at once fired on them and brought them to. Arnold of course was furious and the final result was that poor Wynkoop was put under arrest and sent back to Albany, quite unfair treatment to my way of thinking. He was, however, considered to be incompetent, and was apparently eased back into civil life without a court-martial.

By late August Arnold had eleven warships at his disposal, and he set sail northward, followed a couple of days later by two more vessels. He had a sloop, three schooners and one galley, with a total of forty-six guns, mostly 4-pounders or smaller; the rest of the fleet were gondolas. Four more galleys were under construction, or soon would be, at Skenesboro, but they would not be ready for battle for many weeks to come.

For a month Arnold held his fleet in the northern waters of Lake Champlain, changing station from time to time, waiting for the arrival of the galleys, and constantly writing back for more supplies, food, clothing, ammunition. At one time the fleet was near Willsboro and some of the men seem to have raised havoc at Squire Gilliland's settlement there, destroying crops, smashing windows and stealing everything movable. That at least is what Gilliland reported, but later Arnold denied the charge. In this case my guess is that Gilliland is to be believed rather than Arnold.

Occasionally the fleet engaged in target practice, but powder and ball were precious and usually each cannon was allowed but a single shot. The crews went on shore from time to time, to hunt food or firewood, and sometimes for relaxation. Late in August Arnold invited all the ships' officers on shore for a picnic. They shot at a target for a bit and then ate roast pig (one of Squire Gilliland's?) washed down with wine punch and hard cider. Later there was a similar outing at Valcour Island.

By the second week in September there was report of a twenty-gun ship being put together by the British at St. John, and Arnold talked of building a thirty-six-gun frigate, a delightful but quite impossible dream under the conditions existing on the lake that summer. Arnold was always brimming over with ideas and energy and now was seized with the idea of firing explosive shell from howitzers on the galleys. He did not succeed in this, but it is one of the earliest suggestions of the use of explosive projectiles at sea, a practice that did not become common much before our Civil War. (Such an experiment was successfully carried out at Ticonderoga that summer, when a shell was fired from a howitzer on one of the gondolas.) The British at the other end of the lake had an even more advanced idea, that of firing explosive shells from a cannon. The journal of a British officer recorded that such an experiment was to be made, but there is no further mention of the matter.

Around the middle of September the fleet was holding station a bit south of Pointe au Fer, with two small schooners constantly cruising to the northward by day and guard boats posted every night some two miles toward the enemy. Arnold was not going to be caught napping if precautions could prevent it. Soon spies brought tales of the great radeau, whose armament of heavy guns could quickly pound to pieces anything the Americans had on the lake.

Arnold decided that his best chance for success — or perhaps one had better say survival — lay in taking up a defensive position and forcing the British to attack him while at anchor. After considerable reconnoitering he decided that Valcour Island offered the location best suited to his plan. Accordingly he sailed there in the third week of September and took up position between the island and the New York shore, believing that when the British came up the lake they would pass by before discovering the American fleet. They would then have to beat their way back upwind in order to attack. By this time the three galleys had been launched at Skenesboro, rigged, supplied and armed at Ticonderoga, and early in October they sailed north — a material and most welcome addition.

The weather was getting chilly as September gave way to October, and clothing was scant in the fleet, while the supply of food was never quite enough to satisfy the hungry crews. On 6 October the galleys *Washington* and *Congress* arrived, and were greeted with a salute of five rounds for each. Morale must have enjoyed a real boost when it was learned that the galleys brought a barrel of rum for each vessel of the fleet. The *Trumbull* had reached Valcour a few days earlier.

The British meanwhile were waiting with their army at Isle aux Noix, St. Jean, and Lacolle until the *Inflexible* was ready for action, and then there was further delay pending a favorable wind. So it was not until the morning of 11 October, with snow white on the Adirondacks, that the British fleet cleared Cumberland Head, scudding along before a brisk wind from the north. Arnold had correctly predicted what would happen, and the British, their fleet well stretched out because of the different speeds of the various vessels, overran Valcour Island before they discovered the American vessels concealed in its lee. Commodore Pringle's reconnaissance was certainly much at fault.

The *Inflexible,* technically a sloop-of-war though rigged as a ship, led the armada, along with the two schooners, *Carle-*

ton, and *Maria,* while the gondola *Loyal Convert* and the great radeau wallowed on behind. A floating platform for heavy guns, rather than a real vessel, the radeau served as a supply depot for provisions and ammunition. So slow was its advance that it did not reach the scene until dusk when the battle was over. Well behind the fleet some four hundred bateaux carried the army. They put ashore at Pointe au Fer and the soldiers set up their tents while they waited the outcome of the naval contest.

As the leading British ships cleared the southern end of Valcour and viewed the American line of battle, they turned and beat upwind. Arnold at once sent out the *Royal Savage* and three or four of his more able craft to dispute the advance of the enemy, but he soon recalled them and they scurried back to take up their places in the anchored fleet. *Royal Savage,* however, misjudged the wind, went ashore on the tip of Valcour Island and was out of the fight until, after having been abandoned by her crew, she was boarded by the British, who turned her guns on Arnold's ships. The wind and the lay of the land were such that the British ships had great difficulty in getting up into cannon range of the Americans; in fact *Carleton* was the only one of the larger ships to get to close quarters with Arnold's men. The gunboats had no difficulty in rowing up into position. *Inflexible* and *Maria* never got closer than about the extreme range of their guns, and so had relatively little effect on the battle.

By about noon the gunboats were within cannon shot of the American line and the battle really started, as they hurled solid shot and canister at the anchored vessels. Just how closely the gunboats came is impossible to determine. Captain George Pausch of the Hesse-Hanau artillery company commanded one of these boats. In his journal, one of the few relatively detailed reports we have of the battle, he wrote that about twenty-seven of these gunboats advanced against the American line and that "after getting to close quarters [the attack became] very animated." By "close quarters" one would assume that he meant perhaps one hundred and certainly not over two hundred yards, but another reporter of the battle, Lieutenant James Hadden of the British artillery, a future major general, stated that the range was about seven hundred yards, a distance at which he said that the boats were relatively safe from the American grapeshot. At such a distance the British case shot, or canister, was found to have little effect on the anchored fleet, and only the solid shot did real damage. Naval grapeshot consisted of a bundle of nine iron balls, three in each of three layers, the size of the balls such that three would nicely fit in the bore of the gun from which they were to be fired. The individual balls thus were relatively large. Case shot, on the other hand, consisted of a quantity of much smaller balls, or even musket bullets, soldered up in a tin can of the correct size to fit the cannon's bore. The can burst on discharge and its contents spread like a charge of shot from a giant shotgun, murderously effective at close quarters but doing little damage once the range exceeded some three hundred yards. Arnold in his report of the battle said that the gunboats came up within musket shot (not over a hundred yards), but I doubt this, for if any material part of the battle had been fought at this range, the losses certainly would have been much greater. The schooner *Carleton* came to the closest quarters of all, and for at least part of the battle was in advance of the gunboats. Charles Terrot, a British engineer officer, said that the gunboats lay so low in the water that most of the American cannonballs passed over them without causing damage.

Carleton, commanded by Lieutenant James Dacres, managed, some two hours after the action started, to get up within close range and fired briskly for nearly an hour. Then, seriously damaged by the American fire concentrated upon her, she was forced to drop out of the fight, assisted by two of the gunboats. On board was young Edward Pellew, later to make his name as a great admiral in the Napoleonic wars and to become a British peer, now only a midshipman, but a brave one. He exposed himself recklessly while trying to get the *Carleton's* foresail to fill and so assist her escape. The schooner had two feet of water in her hold and was in a bad way. Dacres was seriously wounded and knocked senseless. His body was about to be thrown overboard when Pellew interposed and so saved another future admiral for the British Navy.

The gunboats continued their fire until late afternoon when they fell back to a distance of nearly half a mile, too far for effective gunnery. At one time during the action Lieutenant Longcroft of the gondola *Loyal Convert,* unable to beat his vessel upwind into the fight, rowed over with some of his crew to the stranded *Royal Savage,* abandoned by her men, and turned her guns on Arnold's fleet. American fire was concentrated on the schooner, and Longcroft was forced to withdraw. At dusk the British returned and set the *Royal Savage* on fire. Her magazine blew up in a splendid explosion, and the hull burned briskly throughout the night. By dark the action was over, and Pringle had formed a line across the westerly part of the lake to prevent an American retreat.

All in all, it had been a rather bloodless battle, and the casualties both in men and vessels were surprisingly small. The American gondola *Philadelphia* sank just before dark, "hulled in so many places," reported Arnold. In recent years this gondola, in amazingly good condition, was raised from the bottom of the lake and is now in the Smithsonian Institution, a unique relic of the Revolution. Examination shows that the hull was penetrated by only a single cannonball, and a rather small one at that, but it was sufficient to cause the craft to sink.

On the British side one gunboat was lost, its magazine exploded by a lucky shot. This particular boat had been manned by a crew of about two dozen, largely Germans, and yet despite the explosion, the casualties were only one killed, one wounded and two badly burned. The gunboat was in charge of Lieutenant Dufais, one of Pausch's officers, and the captain went to his rescue, taking her crew on board his own vessel just before the damaged craft sank. Pausch's gunboat was nearly swamped by the weight of the extra men.

The total British losses were not over forty killed and wounded, and fourteen of these were suffered by the crew of the hard-fought *Carleton*. The Americans lost about sixty in all. When one considers that the action lasted all of five hours, it is rather amazing how little damage was done. But if Hadden's statement of the range during the battle being about seven hundred yards is correct, this would easily explain the relatively ineffective fire. Accuracy at such a range was almost impossible to obtain with the smooth-bore cannon of those days. It was nearly the extreme range at which cannon would then have been fired, and a range of not over some two hundred yards was sought when accuracy was desired — and that from a stable platform on dry land against a fixed target.

The American casualties were something less than ten per cent of the force engaged. For a land battle this would have been considered high, but it would not have been for a hard-fought naval engagement when ships met in close action. John Paul Jones lost a little less than half his crew in his famous action with the *Serapis,* and in our War of 1812, fought with similar weapons, Perry had more than half his crew on the *Lawrence* out of action before he shifted his flag to another vessel. *Carleton,* alone of the British ships, came to close grips with the American battle line, and her casualties were nearly half of the crew, about what would be expected in a desperately fought close-range encounter. In addition to naval gunfire, the Americans were peppered by musket fire from Indians on both the island and the New York shore, but this did little if any harm. Arnold reported that he personally had pointed most of the guns fired from the galley *Congress* that day, and one might infer that he was not a very good shot with a cannon.

By dark three-quarters of the American ammunition was gone and many of the vessels were badly battered, Arnold later reported. A conference of captains advised a retreat during the night. One by one the vessels worked their way south, hugging close to the New York shore, with all lights extinguished save a carefully screened guiding lantern in each boat's stern. The record does not tell us whether there was sufficient wind or whether they had to row with muffled oars, but by daylight the wind had died away to nothing.

When one considers the great preponderance of the British fleet over that of the Americans, this was an inconclusive fight. One would have expected a greater British success. Inability to bring his major ships to action was one reason for Pringle's failing to gain an overwhelming victory this day. Another was Arnold's correct reasoning of what would happen and to his happy choice of position. The unweatherliness of the radeau, and to a lesser extent of the gondola *Loyal Convert* can be understood, but since *Carleton* got up into the thick of the fight, it is hard to account for the failure of the *Inflexible* and *Maria* to do the same. Months after the battle Lieutenant John Schank, commander of *Inflexible* and the inventor of the centerboard, and the captains of *Maria* and *Loyal Convert* wrote a scathing letter to Pringle, stating that he had made a most unfair report of the battle, accusing him of handling the attack very badly and even hinting at personal cowardice. They wrote that the reason the American fleet escaped the night after the battle was because Pringle so arranged his line of blockade that there was a gap of a mile between its western extremity and the New York shore. They also stated that he knew of the disposition of Arnold's fleet the night before the battle. Despite its bitterness the letter apparently did not result in any trouble for either Pringle or Schank from the Admiralty, and both men had successful careers and died admirals. It is rather remarkable that the battle of Valcour Island, so petty an engagement when measured by the standards of the British Navy, should have had four future admirals among its officers.

All that night and the next morning the battered American fleet struggled southward, stopping awhile at Schuyler's Island, some eight or more miles south of Valcour. Here two damaged gondolas were sunk, and many leaks repaired, while Arnold wrote his report of the previous day's engagement. Then they struggled on up the lake under oars and torn canvas. At first there was a fresh wind, but that died away by nightfall, and the exhausted crews toiled all night at the oars, seeking to put additional miles of safety between themselves and the pursuing British.

When dawn broke on the morning of 12 October, Carleton realized that the Americans had escaped, and he at once set off in chase, but the wind soon turned against him. Moreover, the army was still at Cumberland Head, and it was advisable to move it farther south before the fleet continued its pursuit of Arnold's fleeing vessels. Lieutenant John Enys was on board the radeau, and in his journal he told how that huge, unwieldy craft ran into trouble that morning. While trying to work her way upwind, her lee boards broke, her head fell off, and the wind, coming abeam, heeled her over so that, despite her great width, water poured in her lower gun ports. This was her only venture as a fighting ship, and her future was to be that of a transporter of supplies.

It was in vain that Arnold's battered fleet struggled south, for on the morning of 13 October the rising sun shone on the sails of the advancing fleet of the enemy. The chase continued, the *Inflexible* and the two schooners far outdistancing Carleton's other vessels. By noon these three were close enough for the action to begin, and it did not last very long, perhaps some two hours at most. The galley *Washington*, commanded by General Waterbury, who had supervised her building, somehow lagged behind the other American vessels, came under the guns of all three of the British warships, and was forced to surrender. Arnold ran the galley *Congress* and five gondolas on to the Vermont shore, and set them on fire, retreating overland to Crown Point with his crews. Only a row galley, the sloop *Enterprise,* the schooner *Revenge,* and one gondola out of Arnold's fleet of fifteen escaped south to safety at Ticonderoga. All the rest were burned, sunk, or captured. In this last battle the Americans lost perhaps another twenty men, while the British did not suffer a single casualty.

And so the American fleet was utterly routed and driven from the waters of Lake Champlain. Yet it had already achieved a most notable victory, and gained the struggling United States another year of life. For its mere existence had presented to the British a threat too great to be risked. Carleton could not hazard an advance over Lake Champlain, the only route to the south and to Albany, until he had assembled a fleet sufficient in size to neutralize, at the very least, Arnold's motley warships. Meanwhile the American naval power was not remaining static, but was steadily increasing as more ships were launched and equipped. The delay entailed by the building of these two fleets was so great that when battle was ultimately joined it would not matter who won, for the season was so far advanced that the British, even if victorious, could do nothing but retire to winter quarters in Canada.

Valcour has always been considered one of our country's

decisive battles, but incorrectly so, I believe, for this really is true only if we realize that the building of the fleet was far more important than the actual fight itself. Although the battle was lost, and our fleet was destroyed, the main objective actually had been achieved before the battle was fought. The British advance was stalled, and many months of respite had been gained for the struggling American states. And so the battle really was unnecessary, for it had in effect been already fought and won by the men who sweated and sickened at the malaria-ridden Skenesboro shipyard as they launched their crude and makeshift craft into the waters of the lake.

TWELVE

The Fort Awaits Assault

W HILE ARNOLD'S FLEET was cruising the northern waters of the lake, finally taking station at Valcour
Island, preparations to receive the enemy were continued at
the fort. The White House at Pointe au Fer had been burned
in late June and its troops withdrawn, but an outpost, occupied by some of Warner's regiment of Green Mountain
Boys, on the Onion River, near today's Burlington, Vermont,
was held until the end of September, when the garrison
mutinied and marched south, leaving its officers no other
course but to follow. A fortnight later a court-martial cashiered the unfortunate officers.

Scouting parties were sent out from time to time to report
on the actions of the enemy, while the fleet maintained its
screen and made such observations of enemy movements as
it could. Work continued on the defenses at Ticonderoga,
largely on the western shore, where redoubts were built to
reinforce the old French fort. According to one who was
there, however, everything went with shameful slowness.

On 11 October the sound of violent cannonading to the
north caused great excitement at Ticonderoga, but it was not
until noon two days later that the result of the battle was
known. The enemy was now expected at any moment and
activity redoubled. Work was pushed on an abatis of sharpened treetops. Dr. Lewis Beebe recorded in his journal that

the approach of the British reanimated all and put new life and vigor into the entire garrison. On the night of 16 October an unfortunate ox discovered this new vigilance when, failing to answer a challenge, it was promptly slain by the simultaneous shots of half a dozen sentries. A week later all the troops were issued a quarter-pound of buckshot apiece to supplement their regular ball cartridges. Another defensive measure was the provision of twelve-foot-long spears for use in defending the breastworks — an anachronism perhaps, but more effective than bayoneted muskets in such a situation.

Within little over a week after the Valcour fight some of Carleton's Indians were prowling around the sawmill and the portage, killing or capturing an occasional straying American. The main army was slower in its advance; although the British now had entire command of Champlain, it took time to row the soldiers' bateaux on up the lake.

And so it was not until nearly the end of October that Carleton had his troops assembled at Crown Point, awaiting reconnaissance of the defenses of Ticonderoga. On 28 October enemy vessels came within sight of the fort, after landing British and Hessian regulars some three miles north of the narrows. The ships were taken under fire by the more northern works of the defenders, but no damage was done and by nightfall the enemy had retired.

That was the limit of the British advance for this year of 1776, and soon it was learned that Carleton had started to move back toward winter quarters in Canada. He had been forced to the conclusion that the fort could be captured only through formal siege and he knew that the rapidly approaching Adirondack winter made such an undertaking quite out of the question. By 4 November, Crown Point was abandoned. There was one last alarm early in December, when a ship was sighted heading for Ticonderoga. As it came closer all were alerted for battle, cannon hurriedly loaded, muskets freshly primed and slow matches lighted. Then it was seen that the vessel was only a bateau from Onion River with sails made of three blankets and a bed tick, come to sell potatoes and corn to the garrison!

On 17 November, General Gates learned from a flag of truce, who was returning after delivering to Carleton a note (which was received with utter contempt and burned unread), that the British fleet had been laid up and that the army had gone into winter quarters. Before the end of the month the lake had frozen solidly for several miles north of the narrows, sure sign that no major thrust could be made against the fort before spring. The evacuation of the major portion of the garrison started at once. Gates selected as the winter commander of the fort Colonel Anthony Wayne of Pennsylvania — "Mad Anthony," he would later be called. The general wrote Congress that Wayne had "health and strength fit to encounter the inclemency of that cold, inhospitable region."

The troops that were left at the fort bedded themselves down for the winter, determined to make themselves as comfortable as possible in the old stone barracks and the surrounding huts. By December there were only some seventeen hundred of them, and it was reported that at least a third were without shoes. This seems a bit hard to believe, for moccasins of a sort could certainly have been extemporized from the hides of slaughtered cattle. There is no question, however, but that food and other essentials were in extremely short supply, and that living conditions were deplorable. Cutting and hauling of firewood must have engaged much of the time of the healthy members of the garrison.

Early in December Wayne wrote: "I paid a visit to the sick yesterday, in a small house, called a hospital. The first object presented my eyes, one man laying dead at the door, the inside two more laying dead, two living lying between them; the living with the dead had so laid for four and twenty hours."

This was a shocking state of affairs, but it was one for which the commanding officer, Wayne himself, was responsible, and it certainly is a reflection upon the kind of discipline maintained. On the other hand, one must remember that a healthy, well-fed garrison and a sick, discouraged and partly starved one offer quite different problems in management. At this same time Wayne reported not a single pair of shoes nor even one blanket was in store. He wrote the Pennsylvania Committee of Safety, "We have neither beds nor bedding for our sick to lay on or under, other than their own clothing; no medicine or regimen suitable for them; the dead & dying laying mingled together in our hospital, or rather house of carnage, is no uncommon sight."

It very possibly was on the same day this was written that Wayne received from Schuyler a letter sent a week or so before, a letter that must have caused the fort's commander to utter caustic and blasphemous remarks. The general said nothing about supplies on the way or of improving the defenses of the place, but he was quite specific in his injunctions as to cleanliness of both men and their quarters, and decreed that barrack chimneys must be swept out every fortnight. He did, however, remind Wayne to keep scouting parties out to the north.

Perhaps it was because of Schuyler's letter that an order was issued three days before Christmas directing that all meat must be boiled and never under any circumstances fried. It was also recommended that dumplings be prepared to thicken the soldier's stew. Tar was to be burned periodically in every tent (tents in December in northern New York!) and barrack room in order to remove and purify the "putrid" air. It is apparent from Wayne's orderly book that some women were wintering at Ticonderoga, washing clothes and perhaps caring for the sick.

Christmas Day was a lively one at the old stone fort in that year of 1776. Old Colonel Asa Whitcomb of the Massachusetts troops had a son who was a shoemaker before the army took him from home. The son set up his bench in his father's quarters and patched up the worn shoes of the soldiers. This gave offense to some of the officers of the Pennsylvania troops, who, believing themselves of finer clay, looked down their noses at the New Englanders. Late that day, Lieutenant Colonel Craig of Wayne's regiment, his spirits over-elevated by the day's libations, decided that action was in order. He burst into Whitcomb's quarters, smashed the cobbler's bench, and then proceeded to beat the elderly colonel, bruising him rather badly. The noise at once attracted a crowd, and a near-riot developed as Pennsylvanian and Yankee came to the aid of the two principals. The former went so far as to take up their muskets and fire some two score rounds at the unfortunate New Englanders, several of whom were badly wounded. Despite Craig's inexcusable assault Wayne took no action to punish anyone, and the affair ended in a farce when the Pennsylvanians produced a fat deer and offered Colonel Whitcomb a feast of venison. The kind old man, never really cut out to be a soldier, forgave Craig, and that ended the affair — except for those unlucky Yankees whose wounds would be weeks in healing.

New England winters unquestionably are harsh but they nevertheless are interspersed with periods when outdoor work is both possible and pleasant. Granted that cutting of firewood must have taken much of the time of the men at Ticonderoga that winter, it does seem that an energetic and capable commander could have done much to improve the defenses of the place, even if Schuyler did not order the work. Such labor, moreover, would have kept idle troops out of mischief. Posts for stockades could certainly have been cut and prepared, as well as logs for redoubts, while planks could have been sawed for the little ships that might be built in the spring. This last was a matter that Schuyler had in mind, for in mid-January of 1777 he sent Captain Frederick Chapple off to salt water to recruit a company of seamen, presumbly for the vessels he planned to build on Lake George when the snows and ice of winter had thawed into April mud.

Even when making full allowance for all the difficulties arising from inclement weather, bitter cold, lack of food and supplies, illness and expiring enlistments, I cannot help but feel that Wayne could have accomplished more. Winters at Ticonderoga really are not too much different from those, say, at Boston or Albany, and that of 1776-1777 was not a particularly cold one. The lake froze across quite early, but that was all to the good, as the weather then ceased to be damp and became a healthy and pleasant dry cold. Dr. James Thatcher, who had been a medical student at Barnstable on Cape Cod at the outbreak of the Revolution, spent that winter at the fort, and his journal reported on 30 January 1777 that it had been mild, with the snow not as deep nor the weather as cold as he had feared. Nevertheless it would not have had to be very cold to make like miserable for scantily clothed men living in tents and crude huts with hardly enough to eat.

Schuyler in Albany was devoting himself to logistical planning and administration, and he was excellent in this field of activity. His directives were carefully prepared, clear and explicit, but there were, to my mind at least, two great points of weakness. Almost all thought or action was devoted to next spring, little or nothing to the present. Boats were to be built, a vegetable garden started at Ticonderoga, this and that to be done, but it was all for the future, not for now. I also cannot but wonder if Schuyler's carefully thought-out orders for securing supplies were followed up to make sure of their execution, or even if they were capable of being met in view of the scarcity of all necessities save perhaps of rum. When one studies Schuyler's letters of this period and examines his actions, one is forced to the belief that while the general undoubtedly was a supply officer of high caliber, nature had never intended him to lead an army. For one thing he was too considerate and too patient.

Enlistments were gradually expiring, and it became increasingly hard to hold the discouraged, homesick men. Late in January of the new year seven hundred reinforcements reached the fort, and this allowed the release of some of the Pennsylvania troops. At this time such fatigue duty as could be carried on was directed to building an abatis around the fort, and to work on two new blockhouses. Despite the arrival of the welcome reinforcements the garrison continued to suffer attrition from one cause or another, and by late February there were less than one thousand effectives. At this period an advance post was being maintained at the "Red House," five miles north of Crown Point, and Schuyler directed that a pair of fast horses be kept there so that prompt warning of an enemy approach could be rushed south. Once the ice broke up they would be of little use, however, since there were no roads along either side of the lake north of Crown Point.

Discontent flared into open mutiny in mid-February, when a company of Pennsylvania riflemen decided that their time was up and that they were going home come hell or high water. Wayne quelled this outbreak with drawn pistol, and the men remained. He also handled another attempt to incite mutiny, in the same spirited way and with equal success.

Winter at last drew to a close, brightened for Wayne by news that he had been made a brigadier general. Toward the end of March, as the ice in Champlain was starting to break up, Ticonderoga was held by only twelve hundred men, both sick and well, one-third of them militia whose enlistments would expire in ten days. The following month Wayne left to join Washington's army, to share the rigors of Valley

Forge, less harsh perhaps than those he had just endured, and to achieve fame at the storming of Stony Point.

On almost the last day of November 1776, Congress had decided upon the construction of a fort on Mount Independence on the Vermont shore. Schuyler was directed to execute the work that winter, but nothing would happen until, in mid-February, Colonel Jeduthan Baldwin was sent north to get the project under way. Work was started the first day of March on a bridge across the lake. Holes were cut in the ice and log crib piers sunk and filled with rocks. There had already been an earlier footbridge across the lake, but this one was much more of an undertaking. The piers were built about fifty feet apart, and chained against them were floating sections consisting of great logs covered with a plank deck, making a roadway twelve feet wide.

General Gates had gone south in mid-November to cultivate the good will of Congress, which, because of Washington's retreat from the lower reaches of the Hudson and on through New Jersey, had quit Philadelphia for the greater safety of Baltimore. At the same time Gates apparently was attempting to undermine Schuyler's standing with that body. Fortune played into his hands, for the Albany aristocrat wrote Congress a letter which gave offense to some of the members, and resulted in a resolution which stung the New Yorker's feelings.

In late March Schuyler set out for Philadelphia, to which city Congress had recently returned, to attempt to clear up what was only a misunderstanding, blown up by his enemies in Congress — the New Englanders — into undue proportions. While on the way he learned that he had apparently been superseded by Gates, and that General St. Clair had been ordered to the command at Ticonderoga. New York at once appointed Schuyler a delegate to Congress, and Pennsylvania put him in charge of military affairs in that state. In this latter capacity, during the course of only a scant two months, he accomplished a much-needed reorganization of the commissary. His request for an inquiry into his conduct was approved by Congress in mid-April, and a committee appointed.

The hearings of this group of congressmen resulted in a complete vindication and the resolution that the Champlain and Mohawk approaches should constitute the Northern Command under Major General Schuyler. Gates, hearing the news upon Schuyler's arrival at Albany, refused to serve under him, and started south to lay his woes before Congress.

Thus Schuyler was once again in command of the northern frontier — and it was he who would be responsible for meeting the British advance in 1777. We have, however, gotten a little ahead of our story, and it would seem best to go back a few months and pick up a few threads hitherto not examined.

THIRTEEN

A New Year Opens

THE HUDSON RIVER formed not only the southern portion of that great north-south throughway that was the only practical route from Canada to the American colonies, but also acted as an effective barrier between New England, where the spirit of rebellion was rampant, and the middle colonies, where Tories were much more in evidence. This was particularly so in the New York province, where at least half of the population favored the King. Since there were no bridges over the river, armed vessels patrolling its length could easily prevent transit either along it or across it, at least of a force of any size.

In the summer of 1776, Fort Washington had been built to close the lower Hudson. It stood near the New York end of today's George Washington Bridge, and Fort Lee supported it from the Jersey shore. In mid-November the British in a spirited attack seized Fort Washington, and its companion fort was promptly evacuated.

Near Bear Mountain great cliffs border the river and form the Hudson Highlands, and here in the fall of the same year work was started on Fort Montgomery on the western shore. By early November the works were well under way and they were further strengthened by a nearby redoubt named Fort Clinton. Thus, although Fort Washington and Fort Lee had fallen to the British, by the start of the year 1777 the great

Hudson Valley was guarded by Fort Montgomery at the south and Fort Ticonderoga to the north. West Point was yet to be built, but work would soon start on Fort Constitution just across the river. For the moment General Howe had no interest in sailing up the Hudson toward Albany and testing the mettle of Fort Montgomery, and it would not be until Burgoyne was in trouble near Saratoga that such a move would be attempted.

The British plans for the campaign of 1777 were for General Burgoyne — "Gentleman Johnny," some called him, a sound and experienced but pleasure-loving officer who had replaced Governor Carleton as commander of the invading army — to advance south up the Champlain Valley and on to the Hudson. Meanwhile Lieutenant Colonel Barry St. Leger, with a mixed force of regulars, Indians and Tories, was to lead a diversion down the Mohawk Valley from the west. Burgoyne was expected to reach Albany without any particular trouble, and he was then to cooperate with General Howe, commander of the main British army in New York, as the latter should direct.

There has long been a pretty story about Lord George Germain. Lord Sackville he had been when at Minden in the Seven Years War he disobeyed orders, possibly through cowardice, but more probably through pique, and was cashiered by court-martial, condemned never again to hold the King's commission. But memories are short and the power of political families was great and now he was Secretary of State for the colonies, the cabinet officer most directly concerned with the conduct of the British armies attempting to quell the Revolution. The tale was that in this campaign Germain had planned for Howe to move up the Hudson toward a junction with Burgoyne as the latter approached Albany. Orders for Burgoyne and Carleton had been prepared, the story went, but those for Howe were not yet finished when

Germain went to his office just before starting on a long British weekend in the country. Not wishing to waste a minute of his time, the cabinet officer signed the two orders that were ready, but those for Howe were left unfinished, unsigned, and unsent. Thus Howe remained in ignorance of the fact that he was supposed to advance to Albany and join Burgoyne there. The truth is that it apparently was never intended that Howe should move up the Hudson, that Burgoyne was entirely confident of reaching and holding Albany without assistance, and that Howe was sent and duly received a copy of the instructions sent the commander of the invading army. And so it is not at all fair to say, as many have, that Germain's hurry to get out of town that day was responsible in the final analysis for the surrender at Saratoga.

Burgoyne's occupation of Albany and Britain's continued hold on New York City would divide the colonies quite effectively, as only the forts at the Highlands would then prevent free access between the two cities. The forts could be captured if and when the time came, so it was hardly necessary for British planning to advance much if any beyond the proposed seizure of Albany. Further developments could be met as they occurred. The immediate objective for the campaign of 1777 was the overcoming of the defenses of the colonials at the narrows of Lake Champlain.

The American failure to hold Burgoyne or at least delay him at Ticonderoga in 1777 has always seemed difficult to explain, since Carleton had been effectively blocked the year before. But that had been largely due to the threat of Arnold's navy, and this year the Americans had only a few survivors of the Valcour fight. No attempts were made to put an effective naval force on the lake, and the reinforcements and supplies sent to the fort were on the scanty side. Journals kept at Ticonderoga that spring seem to indicate somewhat leisurely attempts at improving the defenses, and the exertions of the previous fall were apparently lacking. The reason behind this undoubtedly was the fact that nobody believed that a real attack on the fort would be forthcoming this year, and that Burgoyne's threat from the north was merely a feint to draw American troops away from farther south, thus allowing General Howe to take more decisive and less hindered action.

On 12 March George Washington wrote Schuyler that he believed that the British would bring most or all of their troops from Canada around by water to reinforce the army in the New Jersey and New York City areas, and that their naval command of Lake Champlain gave them complete confidence in their security against any possible American attempt on Canada. Washington then went on to say that accordingly he believed that "much too large a part of our force is directed to Ticonderoga," and that "I cannot help thinking [it] is against all probability" that the British should "attempt to penetrate the country by way of the lakes" so that a large force at Ticonderoga "wou'd be an useless body of troops . . . [which] the service here [in the Jersey region] might suffer an irreparable injury for want of."

Washington had ordered all the Massachusetts Continentals to Ticonderoga, but on 13 March he wrote the legislature of that state that he believed that the British would not attack the fort and that he was at once sending a major part of these troops to the lower Hudson instead. The forts at the Highlands as yet were far from strong, and a raid by the British on Peekskill made late in March led to fear that they might be about to make a serious attempt at opening the Hudson, and consequently cutting off Ticonderoga's line of supply by ascending the river to Albany.

Ticonderoga, large as it loomed in the thoughts of its defenders, was only one of many places for which General Washington must provide the defense. Fortunately for the student of history the general's orders and letters clearly reveal his constantly varying thoughts that spring of 1777.

By the end of March British actions made Washington continue to fear an attack on the forts on the Hudson, which if successful, would force the evacuation of Ticonderoga for want of provisions and munitions.

Two weeks later in mid-April he still was worrying about the chance of the British cutting off Ticonderoga's line of supply. The rest of the month produced no alarms or change of thoughts, but early in May reports arrived that the British were on Lake Champlain. These were soon shown to be false, and Anthony Wayne had cheerfully written from Ticonderoga that all was well and that "the post could never be carried, without much loss of blood."

Washington had now come around to the belief that Howe would assault the Hudson defenses, rather than move against Philadelphia, and he sent reinforcements to Peekskill. Soon he was practically convinced of an attack northward, but by the end of May had thought better of it and was anticipating a move south to the Delaware. Before long he felt certain of it. Early in June, he learned that British forces which had been on Lake Champlain at Split Rock near today's Essex, New York, had returned toward Canada, and he felt that the alarm of a British move against Ticonderoga was groundless. On 16 June, Washington wrote Schuyler that he remained strong in his belief that the Canadian troops were being moved by water around to New York to reinforce Howe. Nevertheless he ordered that four regiments should be held at Peekskill, alerted for a prompt move to Ticonderoga, if it should prove necessary. He had by this time received Schuyler's letter giving information secured from a prisoner named Amsbury, information which later proved to be amazingly correct. St. Clair at Ticonderoga was confident that this man was a spy, sent to spread false information, and the commander-in-chief, even if he did not accept this view, felt that the plans outlined by Amsbury were entirely beyond the capabilities of the British. Moreover, he believed that the garrison then at Ticonderoga was sufficient to hold it against an attack.

Congress evidently shared Washington's beliefs, for at St. Clair's court-martial in 1778 General Poor testified that General Gates had "had the strongest assurances from Congress that the King's troops were all ordered round to New York [from Canada]." This was early in June while Gates was still in command.

By now mid-June had been reached, and by hindsight we know that unless reinforcements and supplies were sent to the north within a day or two, they would have arrived too late. Under the best of conditions it would have taken practically a week to move the first of the provisions from Albany to Ticonderoga, and then several days more for a good supply to accumulate. This, moreover, assumes an ample supply of bateaux and ox teams, a situation that almost certainly did not exist. Actually it probably did take considerably longer than a week for supplies to reach the fort. Schuyler ordered some sent on 6 June, but did not expect them to arrive at Ticonderoga for over two weeks. Soldiers could have been forwarded a little, but not much, faster. And so this critical date passed with Washington confident that there were sufficient men and supplies at the northern post to foil anything the British might do on Lake Champlain. By the first day of July he had come around to the belief that Ticonderoga would be attacked, but still felt that there was a possibility that the British "fleet and a small force of Indians and light troops . . . were amusing us." He now, instead of a move against Philadelphia, expected one against the Hudson forts, a return to his earlier thinking.

Washington's mind had been in a state of confusion that

spring of 1777 when his headquarters were in Morristown. Would Howe move south against Philadelphia? By land or by sea? Or would he move north against the forts at the Hudson Highlands? A decision as to the enemy's intentions here in the New York region was difficult enough, but what about the British forces in Canada? Until almost the fall of Ticonderoga, Washington was convinced that there would be no real attack up Champlain from Canada, and he believed that the forces at the fort could easily defeat any attempt that the British would be able to make. This belief was passed on down to his subordinates. They for their part were only too willing to accept it, developed too much of a spirit of complacency and failed to reach out for enemy intelligence, fighting to get it if necessary, since intelligence often can be obtained only in that way. Furthermore, so imbued were they with confidence in the correctness of Washington's belief that they entirely refused to believe or to give any weight whatsoever to contrary evidence. Thus Washington was, in effect, constantly reassured by his subordinates in the north that all was well on that frontier. And so, with everything confirming his own conclusions, he was able to devote himself to the more imminent problem of what Howe was going to do. Ticonderoga was left with an insufficient garrison and was still short of essential supplies. Moreover, those in command had really adopted a defeatist attitude, despite their brave words.

And so the campaign of 1777 opened with everyone confident that Ticonderoga would not suffer any serious attack, men and supplies were diverted elsewhere, and improvement of the fort's defenses continued at but a leisurely rate. More attention was devoted to building the great floating bridge than to improving and adding to the more essential redoubts and earthworks. Actually, the defenses, instead of benefiting from fatigue work during the course of the winter, had deteriorated, particularly on the Vermont shore, where the abatis had been burned for firewood, and now would have to be entirely replaced. The scanty survivors of the Valcour battlefleet had received no additions and, confined in rear of the new bridge into the narrow waters of the lake, they would be unable to maneuver, and could be utilized only as floating batteries anchored in place to await destruction from the heavy guns of the British fleet. The great bastion of the northern frontier was in desperate shape.

Colonel Baldwin's daily journal for late winter and spring of 1777 shows no sense of urgency or need for haste. He was prompt in his return trip to Ticonderoga, taking about a week for the difficult winter journey from his home in Brookfield, near Worcester, Massachusetts, although he spent several days at Albany while on the way. Soon after his arrival at the fort he tried to persuade Wayne to get some of his men at work sawing out boards and cutting timber for the great new bridge to which project the engineer officer seems to have devoted almost all his time for the next fortnight. Then he drew up plans for a new hospital, and at last in the middle of March started planning the fort on the Vermont shore that Congress, long before winter had locked Ticonderoga in ice and snow, had ordered built. Undoubtedly Baldwin was badly handicapped by lack of men, but there is nothing in his journal to show that he felt any need for haste or any worry over the slow progress achieved. He was a good man, and apparently a reasonably competent engineer officer, but he certainly lacked the drive of an Arnold, a Sheridan or a Patton. It was not until the first of April that plans for the proposed fort on the Mount at last went off to Schuyler in Albany for approval.

While our story is that of the old French fortress of Carillon at Ticonderoga, we must not lose sight of the other events of the Revolution. The Champlain Valley was only one of several places where the war was being fought. The capture of Fort Washington on the upper end of Manhattan Island in mid-November of 1776 had been followed by the retreat of the main American army into New Jersey, closely followed by the British. A small force had been left at Peekskill under General Heath as a cover for the Hudson Highlands.

Conditions became well-nigh desperate for the American cause as the year of 1776 drew to an end. Washington's army was fast wasting away through sickness, desertions and expiration of enlistments. Food and clothing were scarce and morale was approaching its lowest ebb. It is true that Carleton's invasion from the north had stalled in front of Ticonderoga and recoiled back into Canada, but the enemy held New York City and much of New Jersey, and could occupy Philadelphia at will, outnumbering Washington's unhappy army by more than two to one. Newport, then a place of much greater importance than today, was also in British hands and constituted a threat to New England. On 12 December Congress fled Philadelphia for the greater safety of Baltimore, but a day later General Howe decided to suspend operations for the year and to retire into winter quarters. It was a grave question whether there would be any American army left by spring.

Then on the night of Christmas Day in a blinding storm, half rain, half sleet, Washington crossed the Delaware and overwhelmed the German troops garrisoning Trenton. He followed up this startling victory eight days later by defeating the British force in Princeton and driving it headlong in retreat. The enemy now abandoned all of New Jersey save for Amboy and New Brunswick, while Washington fell back into the hill country at Morristown to wait the coming of spring. The long campaign of 1776, which had commenced with the British evacuation of Boston, at last was over. Washington's prestige, which had sadly declined after the Battle of Long Island and the loss of Fort Washington, rebounded to a new high through Trenton and Princeton, and Congress gave him practically a free hand as the military commander-in-chief.

When spring at last brought dry roads to New Jersey, the two armies shadow-boxed for a few weeks without material result. By the end of June, however, the British had pulled all their troops into the close vicinity of New York City, abandoning all of Jersey. It was obvious that some new move was afoot. What would it be? A move up the Hudson toward Albany? Possible but most unlikely, thought Washington. He had learned of Burgoyne's return to Canada and was practically convinced that part, at least, of the troops in Canada would sail down the St. Lawrence and on around by water to reinforce Howe in New York. Then, he feared, a descent would be made on Philadelphia.

In the first week of June Major General Arthur St. Clair had been ordered north to take over command at Ticonderoga from the newly promoted General Wayne. St. Clair was a former British regular officer who had seen much service in the last French war before resigning to seek his fortune on this side of the Atlantic. He at least partially achieved this through marriage with a niece of James Bowdoin of Massachusetts, a lady who brought him a fortune of fourteen thousand pounds, a great sum in those simpler days. He invested in western Pennsylvania lands and was a prominent citizen of those parts when the Revolution broke out, and he again took up his sword, this time against his king. St. Clair was directed to concentrate a major part of his forces on Mount Independence, and Schuyler furthermore gave him careful instructions for maintaining the health of his troops, including making certain that their food was properly cooked.

Schuyler believed that three thousand men could hold Mount Independence, while the navy on Lake George would be able to block that avenue of advance even if the old French fort on the New York side should be lost. Then, if the British invested the Mount, as it was usually called, the militia could be called out to march to its relief.

Unfortunately, there was no Lake George navy. Schuyler had planned to build row galleys on that lake, and a 14-gun schooner had actually been launched in June, but there were not guns and rigging to equip her completely. A second smaller schooner, almost certainly unarmed, was in commission and two other craft were still on the stocks. Even if these last could be hurried into the lake, there was no equipment to complete them. Thus the Lake George navy upon which Schuyler was depending to cover the western passage from Champlain to the Hudson never came into existence, save in his plans and hopes.

Baldwin's journal for the spring of 1777 contains almost as much about dining, wining and tea-drinking with the wives of some of the officers and local inhabitants as it does about more serious matters, but on 6 June he notes the arrival of Kosciuszko, the Polish engineer officer, and on the twelfth General St. Clair reached the post. The new commander must have been somewhat unhappy over the conditions that he found. Only a fortnight before, Lieutenant Colonel James Wilkinson wrote General Gates that no dispositions had been made for defense against an attack and no alarm posts assigned. Quite an indictment of Mad Anthony as a commander! But Wilkinson was a toady and an intriguer, so perhaps his accusations lacked justification. A particular protégé of Gates, he would a few months later be promoted brigadier general by Congress for bringing the most welcome news of Saratoga, although he slowed his trip considerably by stopping for two or three days while on the way in order to visit his fiancée. One sharp-tongued congressman had suggested that perhaps a pair of spurs would have been a more suitable reward than the brigadier's star. But this is a digression, and we must return to Ticonderoga, where on the same day that Wilkinson wrote his letter a gale broke both the new bridge and the great log boom just north of it, just as a scouting party returned, chased away by the enemy before they had learned anything of value.

American information about the enemy was most faulty this spring, particularly as to what was brewing north of the Canadian border. The British counter-reconnaissance screen was effective, and little information passed to the south. Their fleet closed the waters of the lake, while Indians prowled the woods. By mid-June these redskin allies hovered around Ticonderoga, making an occasional kill of a straying colonial. At this time a prisoner was brought in who reported that the enemy was ten thousand in number and would attack the fort in force, at the same time sending an expedition driving up the Mohawk Valley, and all this before the end of the month. The minds of the Americans were closed, blissfully trusting in the belief of a feint, and it was decided that the prisoner was really an enemy agent, sent to spread false information.

A few days later the report of a scout seeped back from Willsboro, some forty miles north of the fort, that a great body of men had landed there, but St. Clair refused to believe it. Only when Burgoyne's army had actually invested the fort would it be appreciated that this really was a major assault. Nevertheless there was a slight realization that the feint theory might after all possibly be wrong, and should it prove so it was planned to hold the old French fort for as long as possible and then to fall back on to Mount Independence, there to continue the fight. All this, however, was really

KEY

A Old fort in very bad condition, wanting repair; could not be defended with less than 500 men.

B Stone redoubt, about 200 men would defend it, overlooks the line Y, opposite the Lake, in Fort Independence.

C Blockhouse for 100 men.

D French redoubt upon the low ground for about 200 men, commanded by the opposite side.

E New breastwork for 200 men.

F New fleche for 100 men.

G New redoubt for 150 men.

H New redoubt for 100 men.

I Redoubt upon the low ground for 250 men, commanded by the opposite side.

K Jersey redoubt upon the low ground for 300 men, commanded by the opposite side.

L Redoubt upon the low ground for 100 men.

M Redoubt upon the low ground for 100 men.

N French lines upon the high ground, overlooks all the works on Ticonderoga side, for 2000 men, and not less, considering the great length and importance of the place.

O P Q R New works, in addition to the French lines.

S High ground, occupied by the enemy, and overlooks the French lines.

T Mount Hope, overlooks ground S, occupied by the enemy.

U Blockhouse, burnt by the enemy.

V V High hill, overlooks Ticonderoga and Mount Independence.

X The bridge.

MOUNT INDEPENDENCE

Y Line upon the low ground, commanded by the opposite side B, for 800 men.

Z Barbet battery.

2 Line only marked upon the ground.

3 Picket fort for 600 men.

4 Blockhouse for 100 men.

5-6 Line, with three new made batteries, for 1500 men, and not less.

7 Blockhouse for 100 men.

8 Battery made by the enemy.

9 Road made by the enemy to cut off the communication from Mount Independence to Skenesboro.

Scale of a Mile

only in the land of dreams, and, if any detailed dispositions had been planned for a defense of the fort, no attempt was ever made to implement them. In view of what little evidence we have it seems that no plans were ever made for any real attempt at resisting a British advance.

The end of June, then, saw an American force of about twenty-five hundred men attempting to hold works on two sides of the lake which required at least four times that many. The old stone fort itself could only hold a garrison of some four hundred and could quickly be battered into submission by Burgoyne's heavy cannon. The French lines, now a series of trenches following the trace of the great log wall against which Abercromby's men had dashed in vain, offered a good defense if properly manned. But they were over six hundred yards long and to be effective would require more than the entire force available for use on both sides of the lake.

There were, moreover, on the New York side several re- doubts and water batteries, as well as the outworks on Mount Hope Hill which covered the road to Lake George. The pick- eted fort on top of Mount Independence was intended to hold one thousand men, while the various blockhouses, bat- teries and trenches on that height of land required many more. Early in June St. Clair had been ordered to concen- trate on Mount Independence, but it does not appear that he made any real attempt to obey these directions. It was most obvious that Ticonderoga could not hold out against a determined attack. All that could be hoped for would be to delay the enemy for as long as possible.

On 19 June General Schuyler reached the fort, and next day he held a council of war with the general officers, St. Clair, Poor, Patterson and the worthless French adventurer Roche de Fermoy. The council decided (1) that both sides of the lake could not be held with the forces available, but that it should be attempted if possible; (2) that the New York side should be the first to be abandoned, and that all cannon and stores not essentially needed should at once be transported across to the Vermont shore; (3) that the Vermont defenses were insufficient and should be improved, as should the obstructions placed in the lake; (4) that it would take at least six weeks to do all this; and finally (5) that it was prudent to provide for a retreat, and steps should be taken to do this. While it is barely conceivable that it was the intent of the council to do all possible to provide for the making of a vigorous defense on the Vermont shore at least, to my mind what their various resolutions really meant was that they had decided upon retreat, a decision clothed in ifs and whens and other such qualifying words and phrases, but an admission, none the less, that retreat was inevitable. In this they were entirely right, barring a sudden and quite impossible influx of many more troops and supplies, and they could, when facing the actual facts, have arrived at no other decision. What was lacking, however, was a determination to fight, and to delay the enemy and make him fight hard before a retreat from the Mount could be forced on the defending troops. The abject and shameful surrender of Fort Ticonderoga a fortnight later was the direct result of this weak and equivocal decision of Schuyler's council.

FOURTEEN

The Last Surrender

GENERAL JOHN BURGOYNE was a professional soldier of experience and ability, yet at the same time a member of Parliament, a courtier and a man about town. Later in life he would write plays, one or two of which were quite successful. He was one of three generals sent to Boston in 1775 to assist General Gage, and he witnessed the Battle of Bunker Hill, although he took no active part. Burgoyne returned to England early that winter and next year, 1776, he was sent to Canada as second in command to Governor Guy Carleton in the latter's attempt to drive the invading Americans from Canada and pursue them to the south.

The arrival of British reinforcements in Canada, greatly assisted by the ravages of smallpox in the American army, quickly achieved the first of these objectives, but, as we have already seen, the failure to secure naval control of Lake Champlain stalled further British advance and the army retired to winter quarters in Canada. Burgoyne then returned to England, matured his thoughts on the American campaign and presented the King with a plan for a new invasion from the north. The result was that he was put in command of the 1777 expedition. It has been said that while in England he had endeavored to supplant Carleton in the command, but this does not seem correct, nor was it necessary, for in August of 1776 orders were sent the Canadian governor —

orders he did not receive until the following spring — to restrict his active command to Canada.

Early in May, Burgoyne returned to America, and his dilatory nature was soon made evident, for it was not until a full month later that he requisitioned the carts and horses needed to haul his guns and supplies across the land carries he must pass. Moreover he did this only when his artillery officer, the competent General Phillips, reminded him of the omission. Thus a month was already lost, a month that might well have allowed the expedition to reach Albany. Whatever were his other capabilities, and they were numerous, Burgoyne lacked drive.

The plan the general had offered the War Office for an advance from Canada had called for 8000 regular troops plus artillery, 2000 Canadians and 1000 Indians, over 11,000 men in all. When the expedition at last assembled at Cumberland Head on 20 June, it numbered but 7213, mostly regulars, 3724 of these British and 3016 German troops, while the Canadians were represented by less than a tenth of the number originally required.

Although Burgoyne had failed to think of the overland haulage of his artillery until reminded of the omission, he planned to carry a great train of cannon along with his army. After the surrender at Saratoga he was severely criticized for providing so much artillery. In this, however, he was entirely right. Only through the battering down of its walls could one expect to seize a well-defended fortress in those days. Stockaded forts protected only by palisades of logs could be overcome by relatively light guns, but a masonry structure such as Ticonderoga and its earthen outworks and redoubts required much heavier weapons: 18- and 24-pounder guns and great mortars up to 13 inches in bore. The artillery train consisted of 128 cannon in all.

The uniforms the troops had worn the year before were in

bad shape, and no replacements had come from home. Now, partly in order to secure patching material, but also because it was appreciated that a short jacket would be more suitable in the woods, the tails of the uniform coats were cut off. At the same time the three-cornered felt hats were trimmed down into caps probably much like those already worn by the light infantry, and tufts of colored hair designated the various regiments and lent a jaunty touch. Some British soldiers got into difficulties with the habitants when caught cutting off the tips of the tails of Canadian cows in order to secure white hair that would take a brightly colored dye effectively. Many, eventually all, of the German troops were issued long overalls striped blue and white, probably not unlike modern bed ticking. They apparently had buttons on the legs which in effect made them both breeches and leggings in a single piece of apparel. Even the horseless dragoons were given these, and let us hope that their huge, clumsy boots were then replaced by some lighter form of footgear. Each British soldier carried a knapsack, blanket, haversack of provisions, canteen, hatchet, one fifth of the equipage for a tent, a musket and sixty rounds. The total weight was about sixty pounds.

A new frigate, the *Royal George*, this year had been added to the 1776 fleet, but most or all the other vessels, save the *Invincible*, had been disarmed and were used as transports. The five American survivors of the Valcour fight, safely ensconced behind the bridge at Ticonderoga, presented no threat to the British possession of the waters of Lake Champlain. The enemy moved south by water, but it was planned that the herd of fifteen hundred horses would go overland through the woods to Crown Point. How would the five hundred two-wheeled carts move south? Horses could be led through forest paths, but carts required construction of a road. Eventually both horses and carts reached the southern end of

Champlain, but we do not know by what means the latter got there.

Burgoyne's army reached Crown Point late in June and on the thirtieth of that month advanced elements were only four miles from Ticonderoga; British troops on the west shore of the lake, Germans on the east. Next day Indians were prowling all around the outskirts of the fort, and the two frigates had moved up almost within gunshot of the narrows.

At this time, when only Indians were in contact with the fort's defenses, and while it was still believed that no real attack was coming, St. Clair ordered the abandonment of the Lake George landing, after removal of such stores as could be gotten away, and the destruction of the defenses at that place. The signal for setting the torch would be smoke from the burning sawmills at the lower falls on the creek flowing from Lake George into Champlain. This latter destruction was decreed the next day, 2 July, and all the American defensive works, provisions and watercraft on Lake George and the creek went up in flames. The little garrison on Mount Hope fell back to the old French lines, thus abandoning to the British all access to Lake George and possible retreat by that route of escape. The enemy promptly moved in, occupied the deserted outpost on Mount Hope and brought up light artillery. They soon extended their lines down to the sawmills, where the bridge over the creek had been burned by the retreating Americans. Although cannon fire from the fort's outworks forced a British withdrawal from the mills to a somewhat less exposed position, the investment of Ticonderoga was complete. Only Mount Independence was as yet left unassailed.

On this day, the second, British skirmishers approached the French lines, now held by a considerable force of colonists. General St. Clair ordered the Americans to hold their fire and to make certain that they complied he directed them to sit down in their trenches with their backs to the enemy, and to remain so until further orders. Wilkinson, who tells the story in his memoirs, noticed a Britisher skulking behind a stump just a good musket shot away. He pointed the man out to a sergeant, whom he told to try a shot. The sergeant fired one shot, the man dropped, and every soul in the American trenches jumped to his feet and started firing at nothing as rapidly as he could pull trigger and reload. The artillery joined in, and at least three volleys of musketry and cannon fire ripped out before the men could be controlled. The British scampered away apparently unhurt. A party was sent out to bring in for burial the man the sergeant had knocked down, but as soon as it approached the redcoat jumped to his feet untouched. Wilkinson remarked that there were some five hundred British along the front, and that about a thousand Americans and eight cannon opened fire. No one was killed and only one British lieutenant wounded! Such was the discipline and marksmanship of the fort's defenders.

Up until this time St. Clair had persisted in his wishful thinking that the British were only feinting with a small force, screened by many Indians, but the prisoner taken in this ridiculous affair at last disillusioned him. This man, a sulky Irishman, at first refused to talk. He was put in a cell, and a compatriot, an American officer disguised as another prisoner, was introduced, along with a flask of rum. The man soon talked, revealing what St. Clair should have grasped much earlier, that the British were really in force.

By 3 July, Burgoyne's men had moved up more closely to surround the place, but little action occurred, although the Americans delivered a vigorous artillery fire on their abandoned post on Mount Hope and on any exposed enemy troops that they could see. The next day, the first anniversary of the birth of our country, the great radeau at last arrived and started unloading the heavy siege artillery. Engineer

Twiss, who was still only a lieutenant at thirty-two, but who would live to command the Royal Engineers and die fifty years later a full general, was sent on 5 July to look over Mount Defiance, also sometimes called Sugar Loaf. British forces had already occupied the mountain, probably around noon of the previous day. Twiss reported that cannon could be gotten up to the top and that they would be able to fire effectively on both the old French fort and the works on the Vermont shore. The range would normally have been considered excessive, some fourteen hundred yards, but the added elevation given by the mountain made fire just practical in his estimation. Burgoyne acted promptly on this report and two light 24-pounders were ordered up to the top of Defiance.

In the summer of 1776 young Colonel John Trumbull had become disturbed when he noticed how Mount Defiance overlooked the defenses of Ticonderoga. His fear was that if any enemy should get artillery onto the mountain, the fort would become untenable. He was laughed at — everyone knew the place was inaccessible, and besides the range was too great for artillery fire, almost a mile. Trumbull nevertheless persisted and pulled his rank sufficiently to have a heavy French gun on Mount Independence double-shotted and pointed at the crest. The balls were seen to strike halfway up the mountain side. Trumbull then crossed over to the western shore and, with General Gates and others looking on, had a 6-pounder on the ramparts of the fort pointed at Defiance. The three-and-a-half-inch cannonball struck near the top. Trumbull had proved his point as to range, but so what? The place was inaccessible, was it not, so cannon could never be gotten up there. The future artist, accompanied by the lame Benedict Arnold and Anthony Wayne, among others, then climbed the rocky hillside and looked down on the fort, lying apparently almost at their feet. Where men could go they certainly could drag cannon —

with the utmost difficulty perhaps and only through the hardest of labor, but still it could be done. Trumbull's discovery was nothing extraordinary, for Lieutenant Brehm back in 1759 had told Amherst that cannon could be gotten to the crest of Mount Defiance. No one else, however, until Trumbull came along, had given thought to the matter and his concern, although he had proved his point, was evidently pooh-poohed by Gates and the other senior officers. Nothing was done and Sugar Loaf was left neglected and forgotten. Trumbull wrote a memorandum advocating the abandonment of all the existing defenses at the narrows and the substitution of a small five-hundred-man fort on the top of Defiance, claiming that this at infinitely less cost of men and supplies would effectively block the lake. He was overoptimistic in this, for the range was too great for accurate fire and a waterborne expedition could easily have passed the narrows during the hours of darkness. On the other hand hindsight tells us that the mountaintop should have been covered by some sort of defense to prevent the British from occupying it. But again we must remember that not only was everyone certain that no serious attack would be made, but vastly more important was the fact that there were not even enough men to man the main defenses, let alone scatter themselves around elsewhere on mountaintops.

A large British working party started to hack out a road toward the summit on 4 July and all would have been ready for the battery to open fire on the sixth. By some mischance, however, the British activity on Mount Defiance was noticed by observant Americans. There is a story that some thoughtless person, very likely one of the Indians, lighted a fire, or it is possible that Twiss's scarlet jacket might have been noted against the background of green pine trees on the summit and inference drawn of what portended. Whatever might have been the case, St. Clair soon learned that the enemy was there, and he at once called a council of war, apparently quite early in the morning of 5 July. The council, consistent in the defeatist philosophy which permeated the place, decided upon immediate abandonment of Ticonderoga as soon as darkness fell; and the members furthermore recorded their perturbation by adding that they felt it would be great good fortune if a successful retreat could be accomplished. No one apparently had the slightest stomach for battle in that summer of 1777.

The decision to give up the fortress without any fight was privately announced to various senior officers — the quartermaster learned of it at three P.M. — but it was to be kept secret until dark as far as all others were concerned. The story has often been told that cannon fire from Mount Defiance first gave the Americans knowledge of the British feat, but this apparently is not correct, according to Burgoyne's own statement, and he certainly should have known. Moreover, there do not appear to have been any cannon in position until well after the American retreat had gotten under way. Lieutenant William Digby of the 53rd Regiment noted in his journal that at about midnight of 5 July he met a gunner captain taking the two guns up the mountain in great secrecy. The American retreat had then been going on for hours.

Shortly after sunset on 5 July the great floating bridge to the Vermont shore started to become a bedlam as men poured across the lake, and frantic but largely unsuccessful attempts were made to move cannon and supplies to the comparative safety of the eastern shore. Utter confusion reigned everywhere, and discipline, dubious and tenuous under the best of conditions, collapsed, while men and supplies struggled up the rough road over Mount Independence which led to the boat landings and the escape road to Castleton. The sick and some supplies were put on board the five survivors of the Valcour fleet, two galleys, two schooners and a sloop, and into the great number of bateaux lined up along the shore. The

retreat, despite its confusion, was apparently not disclosed
to British eyes until the French adventurer Roche de Fermoy,
contrary to specific orders, set fire to his hut high up on the
Mount. It burned brightly and like a great torch illuminated
all the surroundings. The retreat was now most evident, yet
Burgoyne, sleeping soundly on one of the frigates, did not
learn of it until daylight, when Brigadier Fraser had already
taken it upon himself to start a pursuit. Light infantry
poured over the bridge, left usable although somewhat
damaged by the fleeing garrison. It was covered by the fire
of several cannon on the Vermont abutment, tended by a
crew of four gunners — but all were dead drunk from a keg
of Madeira they had somewhere filched. Redcoats got up
on to the Mount just as the last of the Americans scurried
away toward the hamlets of the Hampshire Grants. Fraser
sent his light infantry on to bark at their heels, meanwhile
preparing his brigade for a vigorous pursuit.

The fleet and the nearly two hundred bateaux had been
loaded with sick, but also, it is feared, with many able-bodied
men who should have taken the Castleton road. Thus most
of the provisions and essential supplies had to be abandoned. St. Clair afterward claimed to have carried much of
these safely away, but Burgoyne reported their capture, save
for three hundred barrels of powder, soon to be seized or
blown up when Skenesboro fell. A high wind was blowing,
making the embarkation difficult, but by daylight all were
safely away and headed up the narrow lake toward the security of the defenses at Skenesboro.

Once the vessels were a few miles to the south of the narrows all sense of haste vanished and progress became leisurely.
The great bridge and the boom with its huge logs bound together with chains whose links had been forged from inch-
and-a-half-square iron bars would surely hold the British
fleet up for many hours if not for days. Why hurry? By early

afternoon they had at last reached Skenesboro. Hardly had they started to land when they were thunderstruck to learn that the British also were almost there, and that this place must also be abandoned, and in the greatest of haste. Bateaux were started south up Wood Creek, loaded with women and the sick, while the torch was put to the stockade, buildings, baggage and all remaining supplies. It was a mighty bonfire.

The British had moved at daylight and they had moved fast. The great bridge had been set on fire by the Americans, but the damage was speedily repaired. Troops rushed across it, while the navy prepared to break it and secure passage up the lake. Only a scant half-hour and a few well-directed cannon shot were needed to break this obstruction which had caused the colonials so much work, work which could have been utilized more effectively elsewhere. By eight in the morning the two frigates and some gunboats had pushed through the gap in the boom and bridge, and by midafternoon they were within a couple of miles of Skenesboro. Infantry was rushed ashore to struggle up over the intervening mountain chain in an attempt to cut off the American retreat up Wood Creek. Meanwhile the warships continued up the east branch of Champlain, met the five American vessels in a sharp skirmish, and destroyed them. Two struck their colors, while the remaining three went up in smoke and flames. The Americans fled, abandoning the raging furnace of Skenesboro to the victors. Their hold on the Champlain waterway, first grasped by Ethan Allen over two years before, was gone, and Champlain had become a British lake.

From almost every point of view the defense of Ticonderoga in 1777 was shameful. The high command was certain that no serious attack would be made; intelligence of the enemy was almost entirely lacking during the critical weeks; the decision to make the defense on the Vermont shore was not implemented; no attempt at a delaying action was undertaken; and finally the craven abandonment and retreat were decided on hurriedly and without any intelligent plans made for their execution. It was indeed fortunate for the American cause this summer of 1777 that time, space and the wilderness were to combine to slow the further progress of the British. There was little that the Americans did in the Champlain Valley this year that would have prevented an aggressive commander from occupying Albany. How he would have maintained his army once there is, however, another question. Perhaps he could have, or, more likely, the British New York force could have broken through the forts on the Hudson and opened water communication for the supply line.

It is always easy to be wise after the event, particularly in war; still, I cannot but feel that the attempt to hold Ticonderoga was wrong. With the forces and supplies then available it was hopeless, since it was well appreciated that a garrison of about ten thousand was needed to man all the works. But even if there was a full complement, an energetic enemy could still have bypassed the defenses and secured access to Lake George. Then, unless the Americans came out of their lines into the open field, the British could have contained them while forces moving up Lake George crossed the mountains, as had Rogers almost a generation before, and cut off Lake Champlain in their rear. A defense only on the Vermont shore was more logical, but it could have held only up to the time that troops had crossed East Creek and reached the eastern shore of Champlain in rear of the Mount.

The most logical point to hold would have been Fort Edward on the Hudson. True, considerable land would have thus been abandoned to the enemy, but it was mostly wilderness, and the few inhabitants were largely Quakers or Loyalists. The American supply problem would have been far more simple, that of the invaders more difficult. Here at

Fort Edward the two routes from Ticonderoga met, that by the upper end of Champlain and the alternate route across Lake George. A single strong fort at this point would block all access from the north, while at the same time possessing excellent communication to sources of supply in its rear. It is, of course, easy to say this today, but anyone who then had dared suggest giving up so famous a fortress without a fight would have sounded his own political death knell. Nevertheless, that was just what did happen in effect — a craven and frantic abandonment of the place before the British had even commenced their attack.

FIFTEEN

Surrender at Saratoga

THE MAIN American army, demoralized and disheartened as it was by the sudden loss of Fort Ticonderoga, nevertheless covered its retreat by effective rearguard action and got safely away. St. Clair led it to Castleton, Vermont, a march of some thirty miles, that first day. He planned to move westward to Skenesboro, not then realizing that the British had anticipated him. Despite St. Clair's orders Colonel Seth Warner, a former Green Mountain Boy in command of the rear elements, decided to stop for the night at Hubbardton rather than continue on to Castleton, a few miles farther. He had about a thousand men in all, but he did not take the trouble to establish any outposts. During the night some of Burgoyne's Indians, for once at least performing their intended function, scouted the American position. At daybreak Fraser struck the bivouac while the men were preparing breakfast. Many of Warner's men ran, but others, falling back into the woods, put up a brave defense. Eventually the British outflanked them and drove them from the field. It was a hardfought skirmish that produced considerable casualties. St. Clair learned of the action at about the same time that a messenger arrived with the news from Skenesboro, and the American army fell back eastward to Rutland that night. Two days later it was at Manchester. St. Clair then continued south and west, joining Schuyler at Fort Miller on the Hudson on the twelfth, nearly a week after the fall of Ticonderoga. Here had also been collected those of the army who had escaped by way of Skenesboro. On this same day Fraser's troops, after their victory at Hubbardton, rejoined Burgoyne's main force at Skenesboro. The two opposing armies, one thoroughly disorganized and demoralized, the other exhausted by the vigorous action of the preceding week and outrunning its supplies, sat down to catch their breath. They were a little over a score of miles apart, some six thousand British and German regulars and over one thousand Canadians and Indians on one side, about twenty-eight hundred continentals and sixteen hundred militia on the other.

On 8 July a small British force advancing south from Skenesboro along Wood Creek had run into a considerable party of Americans at Fort Anne, and a brisk little battle took place. The British advance was checked, but the Americans fell back and abandoned the field to the invaders. A party of Indians, sent forward to aid the British, balked at the last minute and refused to enter the battle, an action quite in keeping with Indian behavior throughout the colonial wars. The Indian wanted to loot, to kill and scalp the helpless, not to do battle with those who could defend themselves. It seems probable that it was at this affair that the Stars and Stripes was first flown in battle, for Lieutenant Hadden of the 53rd Regiment describes a captured American flag as having thirteen red and white stripes with a "constellation."

Ticonderoga was lightly garrisoned by the victors and the war moved southward into a temporary stalemate as Burgoyne tarried at Skenesboro. The British general had procrastinated in getting the expedition started from Canada that spring and had wasted a good month in commencing his advance. On the other hand, his investment of Ticonderoga, once he had arrived there, was prompt and effective. He believed the American garrison to be twice what it actually was, yet he proceeded with dash and even perhaps a touch of rashness. Had the Americans been much greater in number than the twenty-five hundred they actually were, there was little they could have done against Burgoyne's double envelopment which, avoiding a direct attack, threatened their rearward communications on both flanks. Only a determined sortie by the defenders could have forestalled Burgoyne's well-planned actions. The American abandonment of the Mount Hope position made easier the British seizure of the Lake George landing and the disruption of that avenue of supply and of possible retreat, but such a small detached post could easily have been bypassed had the Americans made a serious attempt to hold it. Meanwhile, the German troops advancing on the east bank of Champlain would soon have cut the rearward communications of Mount Independence. All in all, Burgoyne's assault on Fort Ticonderoga was a well-planned and well-executed affair. Moreover, the pursuit of the retreating Americans to Skenesboro and Hubbardton could hardly have been bettered. Yet Burgoyne reached Skenesboro on 6 July and it was not until over three weeks later that he reached the Hudson, only some twenty-three miles away.

It is customary to explain this apparently extraordinary delay by saying that men sent north by Schuyler from Fort Edward had so damaged the road by destroying bridges and felling great pine trees that it took the British a month to open it again. Actually, the road was made usable from Skenesboro to Fort Anne in only six or seven days, and the road onward to Fort Edward through "the pitch pine plains" had only a few felled trees and was cleared in a matter of hours. Others hint or state outright that Burgoyne was paying more attention to his bottle and his mistress, the wife of an unnamed commissary officer, than to carrying on the war. Neither explanation is correct. What delayed the British advance was the logistics of colonial warfare. Men must be fed and cannon and ammunition carried forward. By hindsight it became easy to say that Burgoyne took too much artillery onward after the fall of Ticonderoga, and this probably was true. At the time, however, the British general had no way of knowing it. He had to be prepared for all contingencies, and heavy artillery was the ace in the game of colonial frontier warfare.

As far as Skenesboro the invading army possessed perfect water transport all the way south from St. Jean on the Richelieu, but the moment it advanced farther, either from Skenesboro or from the foot of Lake George, it faced the problem of overland transport. Burgoyne of course had appreciated this, but not to a sufficient extent. He had requisitioned five hundred small Canadian carts, each capable of carrying eight hundred pounds, or one day's rations for 267 men. Fifteen hundred horses had been called for to be driven south through the woods along the shores of Lake Champlain, certainly a difficult operation. Lieutenant Hadden in his journal wrote that the horses were shipped up the lake in flatboats, a simpler procedure, one would think, than attempting to herd them through an empty and roadless wilderness. Probably both methods were used. A few ox teams were picked up from the settlers south of Skenesboro, but there never was enough wheeled transport.

Burgoyne has been subjected to criticism for not drawing his troops back to Ticonderoga and ferrying them across Lake George, but the cold facts of logistics clearly show that this would not have solved the problem. He wisely realized that if he were to advance to Albany he must build up a reserve of provisions as well as move his artillery forward. Moreover, his army now numbered a bit over seven thousand and every day ate up ten tons of food, which must be moved forward every twenty-four hours before anything could be added to the reserve. If Burgoyne moved his troops over Lake

George, he could not also move his supplies, for there were
not enough boats. Accordingly he determined to move the
troops, the light artillery and some provisions overland from
Skenesboro, while the heavy artillery and most of the supplies went by Lake George, thus utilizing both avenues at the
same time. Three or four hundred bateaux would have been
needed to carry the army, and it would have taken nearly
two weeks to get these boats from Champlain up into Lake
George. Hadden recorded that the portage road was not
too bad, and that two hundred American prisoners kept it in
repair. He wrote that it took eleven days to move up enough
boats into Lake George to carry the heavy artillery and the
supplies. All this would have to be repeated at the much
longer carry from Lake George to the Hudson, where, it was
later found, the bateaux were so racked in transit that they
required much recaulking.

The British commander had an unusual, and by the standards of his day an almost unthinkable plan in mind. Nearly
a century later Ulysses Grant achieved fame and victory at
Vicksburg by abandoning his lines of communication and
plunging into enemy territory without any way of replenishing his supplies save off the country. Burgoyne in 1777 dared
the same plan, but he realized that he could not live off a most
sparsely inhabited country and would have to accumulate a
reserve of provisions before he could risk cutting his ties with
Canada. Much of the apparent delay in the advance to the
defeat at Saratoga was an intentional action requisite to the
accumulation of a month's provisions for his army, at least
twenty-five hundred barrels of pork, beef, peas and hard
bread.

The plan for an advance by two routes was sound and
correct. Whatever action he took, the army would have to kill
time at some location until the supplies had been advanced.
They could do this quite as well along the Skenesboro–Fort

Anne road as they could by waiting at Ticonderoga or at the head of Lake George. Moreover, their presence on the more easterly route continued to offer a threat of an advance against New England that the Lake George route did not present. The mistake that Burgoyne made was the failure to push a light force farther south at the earliest possible moment. He certainly could have occupied and held Fort Anne without waiting to clear the road, and this could have been done within a day or two after the skirmish of 8 July, instead of waiting until 23 July, the day after the road was finally cleared of the felled trees, all of which had been cut down after the 8 July affair.

Burgoyne had assembled the component parts of his army at Skenesboro by 12 July, but it was not until two weeks later that he moved on to Fort Anne, occupied two or three days before by Fraser's advance troops. Two days later Fraser was within a mile or two of Fort Edward, where on 27 July there occurred an incident which was to have great effect on the American cause. That was the death of Jane McCrea, an event too well known to describe in detail. Jane was visiting in the near vicinity of Fort Edward a Widow McNeil who, oddly enough, was a cousin of Brigadier Fraser. The house was raided by some of Burgoyne's Indians and Jane was carried off on horseback. The current story, one of great propaganda value to the American cause, was that she was killed by the Indians, either wantonly or in the course of an argument between two of her captors, each of whom claimed her as his prize. Later research has made it appear that she probably was accidentally shot by American pickets firing at the Indians. It is certain anyway that she was killed and scalped, and her scalp was taken into the British camp, where it was recognized by her fiancé, a Tory officer. Jane at once became the occasion for widespread propaganda throughout the northern colonies, and her death was the cause of a great increase in the turnout of militia against the British invasion. Burgoyne was shocked by the incident and tried further to curb the excesses of his Indians, with the result that almost all of them quit the expedition in disgust and went home. Soon only about fifty of his original five hundred Indians remained. Actually, they were a small loss, having on the whole done more harm than good, particularly when they slaughtered the horses they found, horses so necessary to the army. Burgoyne had intended that his Indians should "spread terror without barbarity," and he had so directed them in a rather fatuous speech made in the early days of the expedition. On the whole his endeavor was to a considerable extent successful; certainly the actions of his Indians were more restrained than they had been in previous wars.

While at Fort Edward, Burgoyne expressed much concern over what he considered the excess baggage carried by his officers. He issued orders begging that this baggage be reduced to a minimum, saying that an officer could, if he wished, carry all that he needed in a knapsack. The general himself seems to have been the major offender in this direction, if the story is true that some thirty of the Canadian carts were loaded with his wine, his equipment and the baggage of his light of love. Although tradition puts the number at thirty, I have as yet been unable to find an authoritative contemporary source for this report and it may be unfair to the general, whom the more I study, the more I like. Even if he did fill up thirty carts and take a lady along with him on his expedition, he only acted in conformity with the spirit of his times, when much more than now rank had its privileges and took advantage of them.

After almost two weeks spent at Fort Edward the army moved forward a few miles to Fort Miller, a place name but no longer a fort, and here Burgoyne made probably the greatest of his mistakes, the dispatch of a force of Germans to

Bennington. From the very beginning he had wished to penetrate eastward to the Connecticut River and thus threaten
New England, but this operation had been forbidden him.
His orders were clear and specific — "Get to Albany." Burgoyne maintained faith in his plan and endeavored to continue to feint a threat toward New England so far as was
possible within the bounds of his mission. A great store of
wagons, provisions and horses was said to have been formed
by the Americans at Bennington, and the general determined
to seize the place, securing both provisions and horses for his
hitherto foot-slogging cavalry detachment, until now forced to
act as infantry. The extent of this store was probably much
exaggerated in the reports received at headquarters, since the
region was still sparsely settled and of no great productivity,
but there evidently was some sort of a cache of supplies held
in this hamlet. There was a guard of some four hundred
men, soon to be greatly augmented for a day or two by New
Hampshire militia marching westward under General Stark.

Instead of sending British light infantry, Burgoyne picked,
for reasons not entirely clear to us, the slow-marching Germans and the dismounted cavalrymen. He gave them the
broad mission of penetrating eastward as far as the Connecticut River, gathering all the horses they could, learning the
feelings of the inhabitants (Baum, the commanding officer,
could speak no English!) and then returning to the main
army by the way of Brattleboro. It was a most foolish move.
Burgoyne changed his written orders to verbal ones at the
last minute and directed Baum to march directly to Bennington, but we do not know whether he made any change in the
Connecticut River mission. Baum led his men eastward and,
nearly at Bennington, met the American militia, spread his
force of about eight hundred out into overly dispersed units,
and suffered utter defeat and death. The battle of Bennington, contrary to popular belief, was actually fought on New

York soil by a force largely of New Hampshiremen. Baum
had soon realized the difficulties in which he was becoming
involved and had sent a plea for help. An additional body of
Germans plodded to his aid, delayed by heavy rain and
atrocious roads, but it arrived near the scene of battle too late,
and itself was badly mauled during its retreat to the Hudson. This unsuccessful foray to the eastward cost Burgoyne
over eight hundred men.

On 3 August, over a week before Baum's expedition left
Fort Miller, Burgoyne heard from General Howe in New
York that the latter was moving against Philadelphia and
planned no action up the Hudson unless Washington moved
in that direction. Sir Henry Clinton would be left to hold New
York with a force too small to take offensive action up the
river. Reinforcements, however, were expected from England. This may have given Burgoyne something to worry
about, but at this period he seems still to have been confident of reaching Albany through his own exertions alone.
For a month, 14 August until 13 September, the army waited
at Fort Miller while supplies were being pushed forward.
Meanwhile, the tale of Jane McCrea, soon followed by the
wondrous news of how Stark's militia had attacked and annihilated the German regulars at Bennington, was a marvel-
ous incitement to new enlistments and the turnout of militia
forces. The roads became thick with men moving north and
west "agin Burgine," and soon Gates, who had replaced
Schuyler early in August, had a sizable army at his disposal.
On 22 July the American army had fallen back from Fort
Edward for a few miles, and a week later it continued on
south to Stillwater, where it entrenched and soon began to
grow daily in strength.

The month-long wait at Fort Miller would be fatal to the
British invasion, yet there was nothing else that Burgoyne
could do until he had advanced the supplies necessary to

further forward movement. The campaign, basically sound in its essentials, failed because the high command did not sufficiently appreciate the logistical problems of colonial warfare, and grossly inadequate provision was made for moving the supplies, once the waters of Champlain had been left behind. Burgoyne had wasted a month before he thought of ordering horses, and then through one cause or another he never received more than a third of the fifteen hundred for which he had contracted. Had the difficulties of wilderness transport been properly appreciated and sufficient provision made to overcome them, Burgoyne might have been in Albany by late July or early August, well before any effective American army could have assembled to oppose him. Later, when he had returned to England, Burgoyne wrote: "In such an undertaking as mine . . . for one hour he [the commander] can find to contemplate how he shall fight his army, he must allot twenty to contrive how to feed it."

There were many women with the expedition, just how many it is hard to say, but orders allowed three to march south with each company to act as nurses and laundresses in accordance with the custom of the times. This would produce a total of probably between three and four hundred. In addition there were a very few wives of officers, and of course Burgoyne's lady love, the wife of the complaisant but nameless commissary. On 14 August the army received a most notable addition, Baroness von Riedesel, wife of the general commanding the German troops, and her three little girls. She was a lively and cheerful person who at once was in everyone's good graces, but, and more important to us, she wrote home many letters that give us further insight into the life of the expedition. She had come to Canada early in the year while the army was still north of Lake Champlain, but had been sent back to safety at Trois Rivières. She recorded many observations and happenings in her letters, such as

what she said was the common scandal of many of the
Canadian priests having pretty young housekeepers. She
visited with the nuns of the Trois Rivières convent who,
made merry with wine, disguised themselves and did a Cos-
sack dance for her benefit. Then they dressed the baroness
up as a nun, which badly scared the little daughters, who
feared their mother was really entering the convent. Wherever she went and whomever she was with, she enjoyed
life and made others happy to the best of her ability. One description of her says that she was small and rather too plump,
another that she was Amazonian in figure.

By midsummer von Riedesel relented and allowed the
baroness to join him at Fort Edward. From her we learn
that Burgoyne, although he spoke highly of Riedesel, snubbed
him, a major general, by excluding him from the councils of
war, which various British officers, much junior in rank to
the baron, attended as a matter of course. Despite this obvious unfairness the Briton and the German got on together
pleasantly, and Burgoyne had only favorable reports to make
of Riedesel, who spoke fluent English. The baron had seen
the fallacy of the Bennington expedition, but his earnest pro-
tests fell on deaf ears, recorded Baroness von Riedesel.

Bennington must have been a shock to Burgoyne's complacency, although his letters written at the time show no
sign of it. Despite his early belief of his ability to reach Albany unaided he must have begun to have doubts. Regardless of any such possible qualms he intended to carry out his
orders. He attempted to be cheerful in a letter to Germain,
written from Fort Miller on 20 August, but it is obvious that
he had started to worry, as he wrote: "Wherever the King's
forces point, militia, to the amount of three or four thousand,
assemble in twenty four hours; they bring with them their
subsistence, &, the alarm over, they return to their farms. The
Hampshire Grants in particular . . . now abounds in the

most active and the most rebellious race of the continent, and hangs like a gathering storm upon my left." There is little of Burgoyne's former confidence remaining. On 3 September he learned of St. Leger's retreat from the siege of Fort Stanwix, and at last realized that no immediate help was forthcoming. By this time, however, he had nearly accumulated the reserve of provisions he had determined upon, and on 13 September in conformity with his instructions, he bravely crossed the Hudson, knowing that he was thus voluntarily abandoning his communications with Canada. He believed that the American forces between him and Albany numbered at least fourteen thousand, but in obedience to his orders he advanced to attempt to execute his mission.

A scant ten miles below Saratoga, today's Schuylerville, a height of land looms above the Hudson. The place is very close to halfway between Fort Edward and Albany. Here Gates took his stand and dug his defenses. By mid-September he had between six and seven thousand men, perhaps a thousand more than had Burgoyne. Woods masked the American position so that effective reconnaissance was almost impossible. Burgoyne knew that Gates was in force and that, in order to reach Albany, he must drive him from his chosen position.

There is little need here to tell of the ensuing battle in detail; it has been amply covered by many writers. On 19 September the British army advanced, spread out over a wide front. Gates at once moved forward from his defenses against the British right, which was perhaps a mile and a half inland from the Hudson, and the two forces joined in furious battle over a wooded area, interspersed with a few open fields. The fight was intensely sustained on both sides for three or four hours. The Americans, attacking from woods against troops lined up in open fields, perhaps enjoyed a slight advantage, but this was balanced by the artillery of the British.

Finally Burgoyne became hard pressed, with heavy losses and little ammunition remaining. Riedesel, who had been moving the Germans along the river road, heard the noise of battle and marched part of his forces to the sound of the guns, arriving just in time to save the day. Soon it was dusk and Gates withdrew his men, leaving the field to the sadly battered British.

Technically, perhaps, the victory went to Burgoyne, but his losses were nearly six hundred, while the Americans suffered only about half as many casualties. The battle did much to raise the spirits and strengthen the morale of Gates's army. They had attacked and for half a day held their own against British and German regulars. As the news spread through the colonies more volunteers rushed toward Stillwater to swell Gates's forces, which meanwhile were strengthening their defenses, replenishing their ammunition, and preparing for another battle.

Burgoyne now fully realized the difficulty of his situation. On 21 September, two days after the battle, a message was at last received from New York. In it Clinton said that he would attack Fort Montgomery in the Hudson Highlands on about 22 September. Burgoyne replied that he badly needed a diversion to the south, and that he would remain where he was until about the end of the second week in October. He feared that any retreat on his part would free Gates to march against Howe, and he believed that he would best do his duty by continuing to threaten Gates, even if he could not longer hope to advance without aid from Clinton or Howe. And so he settled his command down in close vicinity to the scene of the recent battle, and dug his defenses, determined to play a waiting game. There he remained for seventeen days, consuming his sadly reduced supply of provisions, and hoping that a diversion on the lower Hudson would cause Gates to fall back to the south.

No help came. The two armies were in close contact and

outpost and scouting actions were constant, actions in which the British usually suffered more than did their enemies. Burgoyne's provisions were running low despite a reduction in the daily ration. Clinton did move up the Hudson and seize Fort Montgomery, but this did not loosen Gates's hold. At last the British realized that lack of action was fatal, and that something must be done or the army would succumb to starvation. Accordingly on the morning of 7 October Burgoyne in a desperate attempt sent out about a third of his force to feel out the enemy defenses. Such procedure was called making a reconnaissance in force, and its purpose was to brush aside pickets and outposts so that the true strength of a position might be determined. Burgoyne promptly learned the answer as the American army poured out from its defenses like a swarm of angry bees and drove the British back to their starting point. Then, urged on by Benedict Arnold, who, now without a command, had ridden madly to the sound of musketry, they broke the British and drove them into their defenses. A further advance, again led by the indomitable Arnold, seized the western redoubt held by Breymann's Germans and burst the British defenses wide open. Night came at last. Both forces were exhausted and disorganized, but the battle was over and the fate of the campaign of 1777 decided. Burgoyne realized that he could advance no farther, and that he must choose between starvation and retreat. Two days after this second battle the British army turned its face northward and sadly plodded through heavy rain over roads deep in mud toward its ultimate surrender at Saratoga.

Help was on the way but it was too little and it came just too late. Clinton, as he had promised, moved up the Hudson against the Highland forts, but not until 3 October. He had received reinforcements from England a week or so before, and thus felt able to make a diversion to aid Burgoyne. Clinton, an able general, took three thousand men up the Hudson

in frigates and transports. Soon he received another message
from Burgoyne telling of the latter's troubles, but still giving
no hint of approaching disaster. Meanwhile preparations for
attack on Fort Montgomery proceeded, and shortly through
clever maneuver and a determined attack with the bayonet
the British overcame the fort's defenders. But sad to say, the
spirited defense of the Americans and the blood lust of battle
caused the victorious British to massacre many of the captured
garrison. The supporting Fort Clinton soon gave up. That
night the Americans burned their river defense vessels, and,
save for a boom across the Hudson, the river was open to a
further British advance.

Clinton wrote a brief note to Burgoyne telling of his success, and it was concealed inside a hollow silver bullet; Sergeant Daniel Taylor put this in the pocket of his civilian
clothes and rode off northward. Unfortunately, the sergeant
fell into American hands, and he swallowed the bullet, but
his action was observed. An emetic produced the bullet, which
today, still enclosing its original message, is in the museum at
Fort Ticonderoga. Needless to say, the unlucky sergeant was
promptly hanged.

A British force under General Vaughn was now dispatched
on up the river. It reached Esopus, today's Kingston, New
York, by about 15 October, and promptly burned the town.
Vaughn was now only about forty miles from Albany, and
that city was practically defenseless since all available troops
had marched against Burgoyne. For some unknown reason
Vaughn failed to advance any farther, although he could well
have reached Albany in a day. It was no matter, for it was now
too late. On 16 October Burgoyne had surrendered his army.

SIXTEEN

The Fort Holds Fast

WHEN BURGOYNE MOVED on across the Hudson toward surrender at Saratoga he left as a garrison at Ticonderoga the Prince Frederick Regiment of German troops and the 53rd British, supported by the frigates *Maria* and *Carleton* and a few gunboats. Brigadier Powell held the command, his headquarters in the Vermont defenses, and his troops were deployed on both sides of the lake. At the Lake George landing there was a detachment of a dozen seamen and their two officers, and a few hundred yards away a camp of about a company of the 53rd. Between the two stood a large barn used at night to hold American prisoners, who by day loaded stores and provisions at the landing for transport up Lake George. A small armed sloop was moored by the wharf. Near the bridge over the creek at the lower end of the portage and in the vicinity of the sawmill there was a blockhouse, while another British detachment, probably about a company in size, camped along the road to the old French fort, near another barn which held additional American prisoners. The fort itself was occupied by some one hundred men, about three companies, and finally on top of Mount Defiance a blockhouse was under construction. Here were seventy-two artificers, a sergeant's guard, and a 12-pounder brass gun with ample ammunition. Except for those in the fort itself, all the troops on the western shore of the lake were highly vulnerable to a surprise attack.

On the eastern bank of the lake the rugged southern end of Mount Independence rises high above the neck of land, between Champlain and East Creek, which connects the Mount with the mainland and the road to the Vermont settlements and Skenesboro. The German troops and about a half of the British held the Mount, the southern crest of which was rimmed by an abatis, a defensive line with three batteries and as many blockhouses, none of them as yet finished. The entire garrison was perhaps five hundred in all, far from enough to defend the whole Mount against a real attack, but ample to cover the rugged southern extremity against an attack not of major proportions, particularly one that brought no artillery. Additional security was furnished by the two frigates, anchored bow and stern so that their broadsides could sweep the flat approach to the Mount, and some gunboats covered the same avenue from East Creek on the other side of the low-lying neck. Thus by mid-September the narrows at Ticonderoga were strongly held on the Vermont shore, while across the lake in New York, except for the men in the old stone fortress, the troops were widely dispersed and in no condition to meet even a minor raid.

General Benjamin Lincoln was one of Washington's tried and trusty generals, one of the few on whom he could rely. On 2 August Lincoln arrived at Manchester in the Hampshire Grants as commander of the troops assembled in that region. His mission was "to divide and distract the enemy" and of course to offer such protection as he could against any British threat against New England. He moved from time to time in the area between Bennington, Manchester, and Pawlet, keeping constant reconnaissance on the two roads to the north, one to Rutland and the other toward Skenesboro and Fairhaven. Meanwhile he sought opportunity "to amuse the enemy," as he expressed it. A raid on Ticonderoga seemed to fit the need, particularly since it was reported to be lightly held at the moment. There were known to be American prisoners there who might be released and stores which could be destroyed. Any threat to his rear would certainly give Burgoyne cause for thought.

On 13 September, Lincoln ordered the dispatch of three expeditions, each of about five hundred men. One, sent against Skenesboro, found the place abandoned by the British, while the other two groups marched to attack the British at Ticonderoga. Colonel John Brown, whom we first met in 1775 when the Green Mountain Boys kept Vermont in ferment, led the force which was to attack the old stone fort, while a Colonel Johnson was to test the defenses of Mount Independence with the other five hundred militiamen. Brown approached the head of the portage along the western slope of the mountains which separate Lake George from Lake Champlain, and reached the vicinity undiscovered on 17 September. He concealed his men in the woods on the western side of Mount Defiance and proceeded to spy out the British dispositions.

Brown's basic mission was to release the American prisoners, to destroy the provisions at the Lake George landing and to make as much general trouble as he could. Should he find it feasible he was to attack the fort itself, but this was not at all the main objective of his mission. Hitherto it has been believed that this expedition constituted a serious attack on Ticonderoga, but a recently discovered letter of General Lincoln to General Gates has brought out the interesting fact that a real attack on the fort itself was planned only "if an opportunity should offer without risking too much."

The action which followed was a relatively minor one, and one actually of little importance, for Burgoyne's fate was already sealed; but it is of interest on two counts. During it there occurred the only attack in its history on the old stone fort itself, for Allen's sudden seizure never developed into what could be called a real attack, and the whole action of some four days is well documented by reports by members of both of the opposing forces. Too often we have only the story of one of the opponents. Lieutenant John Starke commanded the frigate *Maria* and he left a fine map and a story of the affair, while Brown's reports to Lincoln give excellent coverage from the American side. Brigadier Powell sent several reports to Carleton, and the chief of the artificers on Mount Defiance wrote a long letter telling of the engagement. And so for once in a Revolutionary affray we know quite well the thoughts and actions of both parties.

At daybreak on 18 September Brown assaulted the camp near the Lake George landing, capturing all the British and releasing the rejoicing American prisoners from their barn. Meanwhile forty Vermont Rangers under Captain Ebenezer Allen (apparently no near kin of Ethan), after working their silent way up the western face of Mount Defiance in the dark, pounced on the partly finished blockhouse. All the artificers, and perhaps even the sergeant's men, were soundly asleep, and all but nine were killed or captured. Brown's men moved on to the landing, where without difficulty they seized the sailors and the sloop. Then they went, a wild and exultant mob, down the portage road to the bridge over the creek and its nearby blockhouse. The noise of the waterfall over the ledges at the sawmill had drowned out all sounds of the actions which had already taken place farther to the west. The British again were completely surprised and the blockhouse was soon surrendered.

The detachment guarding the prisoners at the second barn on the road to the old fort was also overcome without difficulty. It certainly would appear that all the people on the

New York shore were sound asleep that September morning and no sentries out at all. Brown then moved on and without opposition occupied the French lines, thus gaining possession of all the British posts on the western shore save for the old stone fortress itself. His total losses were three or four killed and five wounded, while those of the British were even less. In all he secured 293 prisoners and released 118 Americans. Altogether a most satisfactory action up to this point. The British in the fort had been alerted by the last skirmish, and Brown's men made no further advance, but brought up to the lines two 6-pounder guns they had found near the bridge, guns intended for the top of Mount Defiance. These took the fort under fire, while Captain Allen's men on Defiance started action with the 12-pounder they had found there.

The Vermont defenses appear to have first realized that an attack was being made at about six o'clock, an hour after the action had started, and it was the gunfire from Mount Defiance that gave notice. Johnson's attack against the southern end of Mount Independence, supposed to start at daybreak, had been delayed. Just as it was about to start, the frigates, roused by the cannon fire of Allen's men, started to pound the edge of the woods with grapeshot. Johnson's men held themselves within the woods, shouting Indian war cries and discharging their muskets, but never showing themselves. The attack failed to take place then or later. Thus by early morning there was a stalemate, the Americans fired their captured guns from the French lines and from Mount Defiance, while Johnson's men on the Vermont side did nothing.

At this point it is of interest to note that here was nearly duplicated, in a small way to be sure, the situation which St. Clair had so feared: the old fortress assailed by a force five times its number, and with cannon firing at it from Mount

Defiance. Yet the attackers accomplished nothing, fearing the losses which would result from a final assault, and the fort was held. All of which goes to show in what a panic St. Clair must have been two months before, and how unnecessary was the mad haste in which he evacuated Ticonderoga.

Cannon fire continued the next day, the nineteenth, "without doing much damage," Powell reported. The British brigadier may have been almost criminally careless in his lack of security on the New York shore, but he proved stubborn in his defense and could not be bluffed into surrender. General Warner apparently took over command from Johnson on this day, but Brown was left free to act as he thought best. Gunfire and stalemate continued on for another day, but the twenty-first was enlivened by two events. A welcome reinforcement of one hundred Germans arrived to give cheer to Powell. They almost certainly were brought by St. Leger, who, after his march down the Mohawk Valley had stalled in front of Fort Schuyler, at today's Rome, New York, and had returned by way of Oswego to Montreal, where he received orders to join Burgoyne. He got as far as Ticonderoga, but there were no carts and animals to get him over either portage to the Hudson, and he never gained Burgoyne's unfortunate army. By nightfall of the twenty-first a heavy fog set in. Again a cow, this time temporarily more fortunate than the ox that had wandered into the lines in the fall of 1776, strayed into the German lines. Here were highly trained, regular troops, yet they evidently acted like the rawest militia. A general alarm rang out and "a most thunderous cannonade" from all over the Mount and from all the warships burst forth to wake the echoes. This continued until almost daylight, although the offending cow was soon captured and taken into the lines, where she was probably converted into beefsteaks.

Lieutenant Starke had some interesting remarks to make about the action on the Vermont shore:

The defence of Mount Independence is mentioned in the same letter [Powell to Burgoyne] as a gallant and spirited service! It certainly was so if men are to judge from the quantity of ammunition fired; but it is an undenyable truth that the Mount was never attacked by the rebels otherwise than by paper [i.e., letter demanding surrender]. The only living creature (except paper messengers) who approached it after September 18th, was a poor stayed [strayed?] cow. . . . A most thundering cannonade from all quarters of the Mount and from the vessels ensued. . . . Indeed it must be confessed the cannon were fired every night, from the several batteries, and also from the vessels, as a preventative, and to scour the woods if the rebels should chance to be there, and so great was the ardor of the garrison that when the fire of the vessels seemed to slack at any time, they were hailed and told it was the brigadier's orders to renew it. It must have been a pure and noble flame for military glory which burnt so much powder, and not the effect of f——r, as some have insinuated; for every person of truth and candor must allow that nothing had been done in the repair of the fences [defenses?] of the Mount or of Ticonderoga, from the time the Rebels had destroyed and abandoned them July 7th, till they come back to attack them Sept. 18th. The guns on the French lines at Ticonderoga, and the round and grape shot, everywhere very numerous, were nearly in the same state they were left. And so secure were the garrison in their own prowess, that no scouts were ever sent out to gain intelligence, but all strangers were allowed to come and go where they thought proper.

Brigadier Powell expected the enemy to storm either the fort or the Mount, perhaps even both at once, the next morning before the low-lying fog had cleared away, but nothing happened. The appearance of the southern end of Mount Independence, the steep bluff crowned with its batteries and blockhouses, was enough to chill the stoutest heart, even without the crossed fire of the naval cannon which covered the low approaches over which the troops would have to advance. Nor did anything take place on the other shore, where the stone walls of the French fort scowled across the barren landscape that stretched to the old French lines. The sporadic fire of the two 6-pounders produced little result, and the 12-pounder on Mount Defiance was but a threat which accomplished little or nothing. It perhaps was this day that a flag of truce approaching the fort was fired on by the defenders, and three of its party of five killed. Such treatment of a white flag by British troops seems most unlikely, yet the story was reported by one of that nation who was there, and he wrote that it was Powell himself who ordered the fire. Brown realized that his artillery was useless against the walls of Ticonderoga. He felt confident that he could take the fort by assault, but believed that the resulting losses would be high and would not at all justify the capture, particularly since there seemed no chance that Mount Independence would fall to the Americans during the current engagement.

Brown accordingly destroyed the hundred and fifty bateaux he had seized in Lake Champlain below the sawmill falls, as well as all but a score of the fifty he had found on Lake George. His force, reported now to be about 420 — the remainder were probably conducting the prisoners south by land — climbed aboard the three-gun sloop, two British gunboats and the bateaux. They set forth up Lake George to see what could be done to annoy the British at the southern end. Burgoyne had marched his men and his two-wheeled carts over the Skenesboro–Fort Edward road, but his artillery and heavy supplies had moved by water over Lake George, his main line of communication since Skenesboro had been abandoned. Old Fort George at the southern end of the lake was the unloading point, but the fort was of little use, small and commanded by neighboring heights. This latter objection had just been shown by Brown's attack to be a dubious one, but in colonial days it was a military fetish that a fort commanded by higher ground in the vicinity would be untenable.

And so Diamond Island, a few miles to the north, was made the bastion of the lake head; at the moment it was garrisoned by Captain Aubrey and two companies of the 47th.

The expedition got under way late in the afternoon of 22 September, expecting to surprise the British on Diamond Island the next morning at dawn; but a heavy storm churned up the waters of Lake George, forcing the boats ashore by midnight while only halfway to their objective. A former American sutler, now apparently serving the British, had been picked up that day while coming north down the lake from Diamond Island. Brown put him on parole, but he made his escape that stormy night and managed to reach Captain Aubrey with warning of the coming attack.

It was not until nine in the morning of 24 September that the attack was made on an alerted garrison, who had several cannon emplaced behind ample earthworks. Brown advanced his armed ships directly against the front of the island, while the men in the bateaux, divided into two parties, were to attempt a landing on the two flanks. The island defenses were taken under fire for nearly two hours, but without material result. The British cannonading, however, disabled the sloop and one of the gunboats, while the landing parties were able to accomplish nothing. Brown had lost four men and several others were wounded before he was forced to realize that his attempt must fail. Reluctantly he abandoned the assault, withdrew his boats, then ran them ashore and burned them, along with everything that he could not carry away. Then his men, well loaded down with plunder, most of it clothing, took to the woods and marched east to Fort Anne. Among the spoils was a Continental standard abandoned at the hurried evacuation of Ticonderoga the previous July. Brown forwarded it to its former owners with the sarcastic request: "Please present my compliments to those gentlemen who in their hurry slipt off and forgot them [the colors],

— hope never to have the like occasion to present them . . . with our own colours."

All in all, Brown did well in this raid on Ticonderoga and the British communications northward. He was energetic, did considerable damage to the enemy, and yet showed discretion in avoiding a pointless assault on strongly held defenses, although urged on by overzealous subordinates. He had served his country well as a delegate to the first Continental Congress; he had traveled to Canada early in 1775 to determine the feelings of the habitants and the British merchants to the cause of revolution. Yet there evidently was a side to his character that does not ring so true. He hated Benedict Arnold with a fervent hate, and showed it in every way. That is quite understandable and no reflection on Brown, though some of his accusations and vituperations today sound a little too shrill. Largely on account of his feud with Arnold, Brown had resigned his commission in a Connecticut regiment early in 1777, and he led this attack on Powell's men as a militia colonel. Upon its completion he returned to civil life in Pittsfield. In the summer of 1780, when Brant and Sir John Johnson were raiding the Mohawk Valley, he again turned out with the militia levies, and was killed at Stone Arabia, a little west of Johnstown, New York.

SEVENTEEN

Two Centuries of Peace

IN 1888 a boy of eight was playing with his brother on the grass-covered mounds that hid the old walls of Fort Ticonderoga. A stone in a partly exposed bit of masonry was dislodged and a little bronze tinder box dropped into sight. Stephen Pell first saw and seized the treasure, only to fall into immediate argument and perhaps a scuffle for its possession, for Howland Pell claimed that since his was the foot that had loosened the stone, the tinder box should be his. Stephen, however, held fast to his find, and today it forms the prize exhibit in the case in the Fort Ticonderoga museum devoted to the memory of the late Stephen Pell.

We are, however, getting far ahead of our story of the fort, and we must retrace our steps over a century and again pick up the thread of history. General Powell had burned and abandoned Ticonderoga when he learned of Burgoyne's surrender at Saratoga. The fort was never again occupied by a garrison, although from time to time raiding parties of British made it their headquarters for a day or a week. Many cannon still remained in the various defensive works, too heavy to be removed except by water. The British had no present need for these guns, while the Americans most certainly did. Britain, thanks to her ships, commanded Lake Champlain, and periodically they were sent cruising up the lake to Ticonderoga to keep an eye on the fort and make certain that the Americans did not get any cannon loaded on bateau or barge. One or two of the raiding parties who harried the upper Hudson and the Mohawk camped for a bit at the fort, and emissaries of Haldimand and Ethan Allen met there to discuss the possible reunion of Vermont with Britain, secret schemings of which even today we do not know the whole story. Beyond such happenings, minor in view of what had gone before, the stone fortress remained empty and abandoned. Nothing was left but the walls and these soon started to collapse.

The Revolution ended and settlers surged into the valley of Lake Champlain. Naturally they needed stone for their cellars, or, in the case of the more ambitious, for the walls of their new homes. Why go to the trouble of quarrying when all the stonework of the fort lay free for the taking? And so they took it away, rolling it down to the lakeside or carrying it away in ox-drawn wagons. No one tried to stop them, for no one cared. The fort was no longer of any military value and its new owners made no objection. The fort lands had been either Crown property or a part of a land grant to some now exiled loyalist who no longer was there to attempt to reclaim them. The state of New York assumed ownership, and in 1790 its regents donated the land to Columbia and Union Colleges as grants to aid them in their activities. Such action in aid of education was quite customary at that period.

William Ferris Pell (1779-1840) was a New York merchant dealing largely in the import of marble and rare woods. He often had occasion to make the trip between New York and Montreal, using the only route then, the Hudson-Champlain waterway. Steam had come to Champlain in 1808; in fact, the second successful steamboat in the world, the *Vermont*, had followed closely on Fulton's *Clermont* and was puffing her way back and forth over the waters of Lake Champlain well before the War of 1812 broke forth and slowed the advance of steam propulsion on the lake. One of MacDonough's fleet that was victorious at the Plattsburgh naval fight had been started as a steamer before military necessity had changed her construction to that of sail. Once the war was over, steamers (or to be more correct, perhaps, small steam-driven vessels) ran regularly on schedule on Lake Champlain.

For several years Mr. Pell moved up and down the lake admiring the scenery of the Champlain Basin. The ruins of the fort on the Ticonderoga headland caught his eye and soon he arranged to lease the fort lands from their scholarly owners. Then in 1820 he bought them and built a summer dwelling. Within a very few years this burned to the ground, and in 1826 he built the Pavilion to replace it, a summer residence that has lasted down to our day. The Pavilion is almost unique in America, the summer dwelling-place of a family which has maintained possession for 138 years.

In 1839 Archibald Pell, who customarily preceded his father north from New York each year, was killed when his usual salute to the arriving family blew up the cannon. William Ferris Pell at once lost his interest in Ticonderoga. By this time steamboating on Lake George and Lake Champlain had become one of the most favored ways of passing a summer vacation. Steamers ran up the Hudson from New York, and others the length of beautiful Lake George. At the northern end of the latter lake one took a stage coach for the short ride down to the Pavilion, now operated as a hotel for the fashionable trade, where, after a pleasant lunch, one could tarry a bit and climb over the ruins before taking the steamer for Burlington and the north. And so for many years, as long as the northern tour remained fashionable, the Pavilion continued as a hotel. Members of the Pell family, who still retained ownership, often visited the place in summer, and so it was that Stephen Pell found his tinder box and before many years had passed made his promise to himself to restore the old French fort.

By 1908 the fort lands were divided in ownership among seventeen descendents of the original owner and there were a number of squatters who had never been evicted. The hotel had ceased operation, and was now a farmhouse with a horse stabled in one of the bedrooms. Stephen Pell had grown up to serve on board the *Yankee* in the Spanish-American War, and in 1901 he married Sarah, daughter of Colonel Robert M. Thompson, a man who had done much to develop the International Nickel Company. Sarah Pell shared in Stephen's dream of restoring the fort, and at last in 1908 a start became possible through the financial aid of Colonel Thompson. A young English architect was engaged to supervise the work. (Years later he returned home and entered Parliament. Today he is Lord Bossom of Maidstone in Kent.)

Fifty and more years ago little was known about colonial and military archaeology. The study of the early days of Egypt, Persia, the American Indian, all these were being carried on, but our colonial and Revolutionary periods had received almost no attention. There were no real experts to turn to for help in restoring the fort, and so Stephen Pell and Alfred Bossom had to rely almost entirely upon their own knowledge and common sense. Despite continued depredations over many years, as well as gradual natural erosion of the ruins, a considerable part of the fort remained. One of the three original barracks within the fort still stood, badly damaged indeed, but with more than enough of its walls remaining to show clearly the height, window spacing and many details of construction. Of the other two stone buildings surrounding the courtyard little remained but their foundations.

The walls of the fort were grass-covered mounds over which wandered grazing cows, but when workmen dug into their sides they at once encountered the original walls of the fort. These walls had not really been built of stone — they were of earth, covered by a rather thin stone facing, too thin for the frigid winters of the region where frost can wreak havoc in only a single winter. Time and frost loosened many of the stones composing the walls during the years after the Revolution when there was no garrison to make repairs. The post-Revolutionary settlers quickly took away the stone facing from the upper half or two-thirds of the walls. The earth, hitherto held in place by the facing, collapsed and covered the base of the walls that remained, giving almost complete protection over the years.

The first year's work was devoted to restoring the West Barracks, and Fort Ticonderoga was officially opened to the public, with President Taft in attendance, in the summer of 1909. The ambassadors of Great Britain and France, as well as the governors of New York and Vermont, were also present at the opening ceremonies.

The work of restoration continued over the years, progressing as rapidly as funds became available, for it is a costly business rebuilding an old fort, particularly when all the money is raised among one's family and friends, with no assistance whatever received from state or federal government. Digging out around the old walls produced many relics of all sorts, far too many and too varied to itemize. The best of them are now displayed in the museum in the fort, a military museum which also contains a great many other exhibits procured from varied sources both here and abroad. Stephen Pell was foresighted in acquiring land to protect the fort from unfortunate real estate developments, and today some thousand acres are owned on the New York shore. John Pell, Stephen's son, some years ago gave the fort a great many more acres on the Vermont side, land which includes most of the Revolutionary defenses on Mount Independence, as well as an ample shore frontage that guarantees that the view to the east from the old stone fortress shall not be defaced.

In 1931 Stephen and Sarah Pell, sole owners of the fort since acquiring the rights of the other Pell heirs, established the Fort Ticonderoga Association, a nonprofit educational corporation, and gave to it the fort, the museum and all the lands. Stephen Pell lived until 1950 to see the reconstruction of the fort complete save only for the East Barracks, and he was succeeded as president of the association by John Pell, his son. And so the old colonial and Revolutionary fort, once scene of actions of such vast importance in the history of our country, today during the summer season is host to a throng of visitors from all over our country, who learn the story of the old stone fortress and enjoy the glorious view of Lake Champlain and the Vermont shore, with the Green Mountains forming the backdrop. They go away again a little richer in their knowledge of those men who some two centuries ago served their countries so well.

Bibliography

ALLEN, ETHAN. *Narrative of Colonel Ethan Allen's Captivity*, Walpole, N. H., 1807.

AMHERST, JEFFREY. *The Journal of Jeffrey Amherst*, ed. J. C. Webster, Toronto, 1931.

AMHERST, WILLIAM. *Journal*, ed. J. C. Webster, London, 1927.

ANDERSON, T. S. *The Command of Howe Brothers*, New York, 1936.

ANON. Journal of Campaign in Canada . . . in 1776 . . . & 1777, MS. at U. S. Military Academy, West Point, N.Y.

BALDWIN, COL. JEDUTHAN. *Revolutionary Journal*, Bangor, 1906.

BALLANTINE, JOHN. MS. Diary, American Antiquarian Society.

BAXTER, JAMES P. *The Journal of Lieut. William Digby*, Albany, 1887.

BEEBE, DR. LEWIS. "Journal," *Penn. Magazine History*, Vol. 59.

BLOOMFIELD, MAJ. JOSEPH. MS. Journal, Morristown Nat. Park Library.

BOUGAINVILLE, L. A. "Journal," *Quebec Archives*, 1923-1924.

BREHM, LT. DIETRICH. MS. Report in Gage Papers, Univ. of Michigan Clements Library.

BRODHEAD, J. R. *Documents . . . Colonial History of New York*, Albany, 1856——.

BROWN, COL. JOHN. "Letters," *N. E. Hist. Gen. Reg.*, Vol. 74.

BURGOYNE, LT. GEN. JOHN. *Orderly Book*, Albany, 1860.

——. *A State of the Expedition from Canada*, London, 1780.

CARROLL, CHARLES. *Journal*, Maryland Hist. Society, Baltimore, 1876.

CARVER, JONATHAN. *Travels*, London, 1778.

CASGRAIN, ABBÉ HENRI. *Levis Papers*, Quebec, 1889-1895.

——. *Montcalm and Levis*, Tours, 1899.

CHAGNY, ANDRÉ. *François Piquet,* Montreal, 1913.

CHAMPLAIN, SAMUEL DE. *Voyages of Champlain,* New York, 1907.

CHITTENDEN, L. E. *The Capture of Ticonderoga,* Vermont Hist. Society, Rutland, 1872.

CLARKE, T. WOODE. *Bloody Mohawk,* New York, 1940.

DE KERALLAIN, RENÉ. *La Jeunesse de Bougainville,* Paris, 1896.

DE LERY, CHASSEGROS. "Journal," *Fort Ticonderoga Bulletin,* July, 1942.

DU CREUX, FATHER FRANÇOIS. *History of Canada,* Champlain Society, Toronto, 1951.

ENYS, LT. JOHN. MS. Journal, Dominion Archives, Canada.

EPPING, CHARLOTTE S. J. *Journal of du Roi the Elder,* Univ. of Penn., 1911.

FLICK, ALEX. C. "Gen. Henry Knox's Ticonderoga Expedition," New York State Historical Assoc., XXVI, p. 119.

FORBES, ELI. *A Family Book,* Salem, 1801.

FORCE, PETER. *American Archives,* 4th and 5th Series, Washington, 1837-1853.

FREEMAN, DOUGLAS. *George Washington,* New York, 1948, II & III.

FRENCH, ALLEN. *The Taking of Ticonderoga,* Cambridge, 1928.

GAGE Papers, Clements Library, Univ. of Michigan.

GIPSON, L. H. *Lewis Evans,* Philadelphia, 1939.

———. *Great War for British Empire,* Vols. I-IX, Caldwell, 1936, New York, 1939-1956.

GORDON, WILLIAM. *History of Rise of . . . United States,* London, 1788.

HADDEN, L. JAMES. *A Journal . . . Burgoyne's Campaign,* Albany, 1884.

HALL, HILAND. *The Capture of Ticonderoga,* Vermont Hist. Society, 1869.

HAMILTON, EDWARD P. *The French and Indian Wars,* New York, 1962.

HARDY, CONSTANTINE. "Diary," *N.E. Hist. Gen. Register,* Vol. 60, 1906.

HAWKS, MAJ. JOHN. *Journal,* N.Y. Soc. of Colonial Wars, New York, 1911.

HITCHCOCK, DR. ENOS. "Diary," *R.I. Hist. Soc. Pub.,* 1899.

HOLBROOK, STEWART. *Ethan Allen,* New York, 1940.

HURLBURT, JOHN. "Diary," *Magazine of Am. Hist.,* 1893, p. 395.

JESUIT RELATIONS. *Lettres Edifiantes et Curieuses,* Toulouse, 1810.

KNOLLENBERG, BERNHARD. *Washington and the Revolution*, New York, 1940.

KNOX, CAPT. JOHN. *An Historical Journal of the Campaigns in North America*, London, 1769.

KNOX, GEN. HENRY. Papers, Mass. Hist. Society.

LACEY, JOHN. "Memoirs," *Penn. Mag. Hist.*, Vol. 25.

LINCOLN, GEN. BENJAMIN. Papers, Mass. Hist. Society.

LOCKWOOD, JOHN H. *Westfield and Its History*, Springfield, 1922.

London Gazette, 1777.

LOSSING, B. J. *Life and Times of Philip Schuyler*, New York, 1860.

MAHAN, A. T. *The Major Operations of the Navies in the War of American Independence*, Boston, 1913.

MERRIMAN, SAMUEL. "Diary," in George Sheldon, *History of Deerfield*, Deerfield, 1895, I, 661.

MONYPENNY, CAPT. ALEXANDER. MS. Orderly Book, Fort Ticonderoga Library.

NEW YORK STATE ARCHIVES. *The American Revolution*, Albany, 1926.

NICKERSON, HOFFMAN. *The Turning Point of the Revolution*, Boston, 1928.

O'CALLAGHAN, E. B. *Documentary History of the State of New York*, Albany, 1849-1851.

PARGELLIS, STANLEY. *Military Affairs in North America*, New York, 1936.

PARKMAN, FRANCIS. *The Jesuits in North America*, Boston, 1867.

———. Papers, Mass. Hist. Society.

PELL, JOHN H. G. *Ethan Allen*, Boston, 1929.

PORTER, COL. ELISHA. MS. Journal, Fort Ticonderoga Library.

POWELL, BRIG. H. W. "Letter to Sir Guy Carleton," *Fort Ticonderoga Bulletin*, July, 1945.

RIEDESEL, BARONESS FREDERIKA VON. *Letters and Memoirs*, New York, 1827.

ROGERS, MAJ. ROBERT. *Journal*, Dublin, 1769.

ST. CLAIR, MAJ. GEN. ARTHUR. "Trial of," *New-York Hist. Soc. Collections*, 1880.

SALTONSTALL Papers, Mass. Hist. Society.

SCHANCK, LT. JOHN. "Letter to Captain Pringle," *Fort Ticonderoga Bulletin*, July, 1928.

SCHUYLER, GEN. PHILIP. "Court Martial of," *New-York Hist. Soc. Collections*, 1879.

SEWALL, HENRY. Diary and Letters, Mass. Hist. Society.

SMITH, J. E. A. *History of Pittsfield,* Boston, 1869.

SMITH, JUSTIN H. *Our Struggle for the Fourteenth Colony,* New York, 1907.

SMITH, WILLIAM HENRY. *The St. Clair Papers,* Cincinnati, 1882.

STARKE, LT. JOHN. MS. map and description of Brown's 1777 attack, Fort Ticonderoga Library.

STILLE, CHARLES J. *Major General Anthony Wayne,* Philadelphia, 1893.

STONE, WILLIAM S. *The Campaign of . . . Burgoyne and . . . St. Leger,* Albany, 1877.

———. *Journal of Captain Pausch,* Albany, 1886.

———. *Memoirs . . . of Baron Riedesel,* Albany, 1868.

THATCHER, DR. JAMES. *A Military Journal,* Boston, 1823.

TILGHMAN, LT. COL. TENCH. *Memoir,* Albany, 1876.

TRUMBULL, JOHN. *Autobiography,* New York, 1841.

WALLACE, WILLARD M. *Traitorous Hero,* New York, 1954.

Index